A Good Thinking Approach to the NCLEX® and other Nursing Exams (2nd Edition)

BECOME A SUPER TEST TAKER!

by

Susan G. Poorman, Ph.D., A. P.R.N., B.C.
Melissa L. Mastorovich, M.S.N., R.N., B.C.
Karen L. Molcan, Ph.D., A.P.R.N., B.C.

ISBN# 978-0-9640556-3-6
Printed in the United States of America

First Printing

A Good Thinking Approach
to the **NCLEX**® and other
Nursing Exams
(2nd Edition)

Susan G. Poorman, Ph.D., A.P.R.N., B.C.
Professor
Department of Nursing and Allied Health Professions
Indiana University of Pennsylvania
Indiana, PA
President
STAT Nursing Consultants, Inc.

Melissa L. Mastorovich, M.S.N., R.N., B.C.
Senior Clinician
STAT Nursing Consultants, Inc.
Pittsburgh, PA

Karen L. Molcan, Ph.D., A.P.R.N., B.C.
Clinical Director
Synergy Behavioral Healthcare Enterprises, LLC
Beaver Falls, PA
Vice President
STAT Nursing Consultants, Inc.

The authors have made every effort to ensure that drug selections and dosage ranges appearing within this text are based on current practice and recommendations at the time of publication. Due to on-going research in the area of drug therapy and reactions, when questions arise in this area, the reader is urged to check package inserts and current research literature.

All of the questions utilized in this book were tested on samples of associate, baccalaureate and diploma nursing students and revised to meet acceptable testing standards.

PLEASE VISIT OUR WEBSITE AT
WWW.STATNURSING.ORG

CONTRIBUTORS

(provided some of the practice questions and rationales used in this textbook)

Susan E. Miller, MSN, MBA, RN, BC
Instructor
Nursing Department
Edinboro University of
Pennsylvania

Annette M. Kostelnik, MSN, RN
Assistant Professor
Department of Nursing and Allied
Health Professions
Indiana University of Pennsylvania
Indiana, PA

Michele S. Rega, MSN, RN
Instructor
Citizens School of Nursing
New Kensington, PA

Kathleen Waller, RN, MS, FNP
Professor
Department of Biology and Health
Professions
Westmoreland County Community
College
Youngwood, PA

Traci Zorak, RN
Murrysville, PA

Contributors from a previous STAT publications provided questions for A new approach to the NCLEX-RN (1989).
Anita Marie Allender, Karen Baldwin, Angeline Bushy, Robert Campbell, Verna Carson, Nedra Dixon, Amy Gresh, Helen Halstead, Barbara Hicks, Linda W. Higgins, Sandra Hollen, Jane D. Jacob, Doris Jaeger, Mary Lou Keller, Jane Carolyn Kinyon, Marty Kuhns, Mary Lentz, Regina Markovich, Magaret L. Muntz, Paula Reams, Linda Robertson, Christine Sebulsky, Jeanne M. Thompson, Sandra Underwood, Karen Wedge, Rhonda M. Weller.

Contributors from a previous STAT publications provided questions for A good thinking approach to the NCLEX and other nursing exams. (1999).
Eveline Edwards, Marietta Hupert, Jeanne M. Messick, Viola A. Smith

A special acknowledgment is extended to Dr. Cheryl Webb who has been an author on all of our previous textbooks. We thank her for her many years of service.

TABLE OF CONTENTS

ACKNOWLEDGEMENTS

Our sincere appreciation is expressed to all the people who proofread and gave their valuable suggestions and revisions for this text. They include: Elsie H. Mastorovich, BSN, RN and Jean Gentry Smith, MSN, APRN, BC. **We extend a special thank you to Mary Jane Geier who meticulously proofread the entire manuscript.** We would also like to thank all of the artists who contributed their creative talents to enhance this textbook. They are: Silvia Lemus who created the cartoon character, NATALIE, seen throughout this text; Destiny Wall who created the cartoon character, NATHAN has also added several new NATALIES and NATHANS in the text and the cover; and Jerry Sweeney, for his portrayal of the three authors.

REVIEWERS

Elsie H. Mastorovich, BSN, RN
Murrysville, PA

Melissa J. McIntyre, BSN, RN
Clinical Administrator
Children's Hospital of Pittsburgh
Pittsburgh, PA

Elizabeth A. Palmer, PhD, RN
Associate Professor
Department of Nursing and Allied
Health Professions
Indiana University of Pennsylvania
Indiana, PA

Bonita Shearer, RN. MSEd, CCDP, LPC
Case Worker
Comprehensive Counseling Center
Excela Health
Westmoreland Hospital
Greensburg, PA

Jean Gentry Smith MSN, APRN, BC
Private Practice
Lower Burrell, PA.

Deborah M. Strickland, MSN, RN
Director of Clinical Services
Community LIFE
Pittsburgh, PA

Marie E. Twal, DrPH, CPNP
Assistant Professor
Department of Nursing and Allied
Health Professions
Indiana University of Pennsylvania
Indiana, PA

ABOUT THE TEXTBOOK

This textbook is written for all nursing students who want to become better students and test takers. It includes a focus on NCLEX-RN preparation. The purpose of this book is to enhance your "good thinking" skills. By good thinking we mean "clear, uncontaminated thinking that helps you understand the information you are learning and most importantly, use it effectively in your nursing practice. It is the ability to think beyond the basics of learning copious amounts of factual knowledge, to having the ability to understand and apply concepts and principles that guide nursing practice" (Poorman, Mastorovich, Webb & Molcan, 2003; p. 1).

The first ten chapters include a section on self assessment to help you determine your strengths and weaknesses as a test taker. It also includes cognitive, behavioral and test taking strategies to enhance your strengths and diminish your weaknesses. The cognitive element includes cognitive restructuring which allows you to examine how thought processes affect feelings and behaviors. The behavioral element includes learning a combination of behavioral techniques; such as thought stopping, relaxation exercises and visual imagery which when mastered, decrease the test taker's anxiety and increase critical thinking. The test taking strategies section focuses on analyzing the test questions thereby aiding you to choose the appropriate nursing response. This section of the text also includes chapters on metacognitive strategies and games to enhance your test preparation skills and make preparing for a test more efficient and enjoyable. The NOW WHAT game was specifically designed to help you think through a client problem and apply nursing knowledge to a simulated clinical situation.

The second half of the text includes over one thousand questions and extensive rationales. They will provide you with the opportunity for repeated practice of the thinking and problem solving skills necessary for success on nursing exams and the NCLEX-RN. The rationales were written in a comprehensive manner to help you understand what the question was asking and whether your thinking about the question was clear and correct. Many times students miss a question and do not know why their answers were wrong. Reading the rationales will help you not only see why the correct answer is right but also why the incorrect options were wrong. We believe this will help you improve your thinking and reasoning skills.

ABOUT THE AUTHORS

This book contains the elements of a treatment program that was developed by the authors after working with thousands of nursing students preparing for nursing exams and the NCLEX-RN.

Over the past 25 years we have learned several important things that we want to pass on to you, our reader, in the hope that they will help you develop a "Good Thinking" approach to your nursing exams and the NCLEX. First we learned that our students were not failing exams only because of lack of knowledge but because they were also having difficulty with their reasoning. Simply memorizing or learning factual information is not enough to help you do well on nursing exams.

Secondly, we have learned that practicing nursing questions, although not a favorite strategy among our students, is one of the very best ways to increase problem solving abilities necessary for improving test taking skills, especially when preparing for the NCLEX.

Thirdly we have learned that our treatment program for test taking which includes cognitive, behavioral and test taking strategies has been very successful in improving test scores. Finally we have learned that developing confidence in your abilities to think critically and problem solve accurately is an extremely important part of the entire process. Believing that you have the ability to be a good test taker is as important as practicing the questions and cognitive and behavioral skills.

We believe that reading this text, actively participating in the exercises and completing the practice questions will not only enhance your skills as a test taker but will help you develop that important self confidence necessary for "Good Thinking" and test taking success.

Susan G. Poorman
Melissa L. Mastorovich
Karen L. Molcan

STAT SOAPBOX

Through out the first 9 chapters in this book you will see a section called the STAT SOAPBOX. It will be Natalie and Nathan nurses, our cartoon characters, asking you an important question or giving you a piece of important advice.
We try not to preach to you or stand on our soapbox but sometimes we just can't help ourselves. We have been doing this work for such a long time that we have learned that there are several major issues that students who are preparing for the NCLEX need to pay close attention. The purpose of the soapbox question or comment is to help you increase your awareness of some point that will help you prepare more effectively for this very important test.

1

WHAT'S YOUR STORY?

For centuries teachers have used story telling as a way to teach an important concept, illustrate a point, give an example of something that is difficult to understand, or to help us make a connection (Cangelosi & Whitt, 2006). Recently, in nursing, there has been increased interest in using storytelling for educational purposes. Listening to other people's stories and telling our own stories to others can really help us make meaning out of our life experiences. We believe that listening to and reading other students' stories can be a powerful learning experience.

Throughout this text we will share with you common stories from students and teachers with whom we have worked. We think that they will be helpful to you in your journey through nursing education and as you prepare to take the NCLEX. It is our hope that you will sometimes identify with them, learn from them, be comforted by them, and at times be inspired by them.

GETTING STARTED: SELF-ASSESSMENT

All nursing educational programs include tests from start to finish. From your first nursing exam in fundamentals of nursing until the NCLEX (the licensure exam when you graduate), learning to be successful with these exams is an essential part of your nursing education. No matter where you are in that process, it is time to take a look at yourself as a test taker. The sooner you master the skill of test taking, the more enjoyable your education will become.

It is important to ask yourself, what kind of test taker are you?

In an attempt to get started, we suggest you conduct a self-assessment. By self-assessment we mean taking a good, hard, honest look at yourself to identify your strengths and weaknesses as a test taker. The first step is to take an accurate testing history. The self-help questionnaire presented in this chapter on Worksheet 1 will help you to examine your test taking history. Take a minute now to complete Worksheet 1. Remember to be honest with yourself.

WORKSHEET 1
TESTING HISTORY QUESTIONNAIRE

1. What is your general reaction to tests? In other words, when the teacher says that you are going to have a test on Tuesday, how do you feel and what do you think?

_____

_____

2. Do you consider yourself to be a good test taker? Explain.

_____

_____

3. If test taking has been a problem for you, when did it start (nursing school, high school, grade school)?

_____

_____

4. Do you believe your test grades reflect the amount of time and effort you put into studying? Explain.

_____

_____

5. Are most of your test grades consistent? Are your scores within a 5% range of each other? Please explain (i.e., Are nursing exams harder than non-nursing exams? Does your grade on a comprehensive final decrease significantly?).

_____

_____

6. Are the questions on most nursing exams what you expected and about what you studied?

_____

_____

Your answers on this worksheet can be the first step in helping you identify what your thoughts and feelings are about tests. As you review your responses to Worksheet 1, ask yourself two questions, **"What did I already know about my self in relation to tests?"** and **"What did I learn about myself as a test taker?"**

Let's look at the following student story...

Leslie tells of how filling out the worksheet made her think about herself as a test taker, something that she had not done much thinking about before.

> "Filling this out reminded me of when I went on a diet and the nutritionist asked me to keep a food diary. Well, at first I thought it was a real waste of time to write down everything I ate and what I was feeling at the time but I really learned a lot about myself that I didn't know. Things that you think you would know about yourself but you don't. Like I eat the same stuff every day for months at a time. I was really surprised. I hope that writing about my habits and behaviors about test taking will help me in the same way. One thing for sure, it already has me thinking about how long I have been having trouble taking tests. I am trying to remember when I didn't have trouble with tests."

It is not uncommon to see vast differences in people's responses to test taking situations. For some individuals, taking exams is a stressful event, which creates a great deal of anxiety.

Jim recounts a time when he learned about an upcoming exam.

> "As I walk across campus to my next class, I keep hearing the teacher's last words to us as we filed out of class. Those words just keep circling in my brain; those dreaded words that I have come to hate hearing...there would be a test next week. I am trying not to let the dreaded words ruin the rest of my day but I am having trouble focusing. Will there ever be a time when I don't have to worry about taking a test? I can break out into a sweat just thinking about the test and it is a week away. It is not like I am worrying for no reason. I have never been what you would call a good test taker. I make silly mistakes, I run out of time, and I can never figure out what the teacher is going to ask."

For others, tests are viewed as a fact of life and something that must be endured. They are able to tolerate any anxiety that they feel and then make plans to attack the test head on as in the following narrative.

> "I guess I am going to have to change my work schedule for this weekend and cut back some hours since I am having a nursing test on Tuesday. I could have used the money but I will need to spend some extra time studying, this material we are learning is tough. It is kind of interesting though. I want to do well on this test and I think if I put in some extra time I can get it. I wonder if Doug is going to put a study group together. Last time, that was really helpful, I think I'll call him tonight and suggest it. Maybe he and I can review our notes together before the group meets."

ASSESSMENT OF SIMULATED TEST PERFORMANCE

One of the best ways to actually find out what kind of a test taker you are, (including your general reaction to tests, strengths, weaknesses, and test taking patterns) is to be mindful of your performance as you complete the practice sessions in this book. We suggest that you use the answer sheets that we have provided as a model. It will be helpful to keep them in a book so you can see your patterns over time. Throughout the book, we will add test taking principles and other test taking patterns for you to assess. For now, let's start with looking for some basic test taking patterns that can be problematic.

One of the first patterns that occur with some students is **first question freeze**. For example, people see the first one or two questions on an exam and think, "Oh no, I don't know the answer to this question!" When they have this thought, it makes it harder to get started and they freeze. Like starting an old car in freezing weather, some people have trouble getting their brain started. They need to warm up first. Ask yourself, "Do I often miss the first one or more questions on an exam?" Problems with first question freeze usually occur because you are anxious or nervous at the beginning of a test and it takes you a while to calm yourself down. Learning progressive relaxation discussed in chapter 4 may help with this problem.

Another problem is **missing several questions in a row.** When you miss 2, 3 or 4 questions in a row, we have identified this as "clumping." This generally indicates a problem with the first question missed in a series. Generally, when you do not know the answer to the first question in a series, this can result in feelings of anxiety or panic. Your thinking at this time may become distorted and may ultimately result in choosing an incorrect answer. Unfortunately, these distorted thoughts continue through several of the following questions resulting in a series or "clumping" of incorrect answers.

An example of this might be a student who sees a question on Addison's disease. The student might think, "Oh no, I don't know anything about Addison's disease. I'm going to miss this question. I don't remember learning this. I don't remember learning anything. I must not have learned anything in school." Thoughts such as these can rapidly produce anxiety and consequently more negative thoughts. When completing the questions, the student is plagued with negative disruptive thoughts, which compete with the rational thoughts in trying to answer the questions. The self-fulfilling prophecy occurs when you miss the next four questions even though they were not on Addison's disease. Your thoughts were so distorted; you were not able to think through the questions. This obviously is a pattern you need to avoid. This pattern is easily identified when you look at your practice test answer sheet. When you find yourself missing several questions in a row or "clumping," ask yourself what you were thinking and feeling when you read the question or what occurred to you when you were reading the first question of the clump. Sometimes it is easier for you to identify your feelings than your thoughts. Chapter 5 will help you identify the feelings and the negative disruptive thoughts that contribute to clumping and help you realistically evaluate and restructure the thoughts for more positive results. Many of our students and clients also report that the thought distraction technique that is presented in chapter 6 is helpful in halting the pattern of missing several questions in a row.

Some people have difficulty with maintaining their concentration. It is like the engine **losing steam** as it chugs up the hill. These people are able to start out the test with good thinking and good concentration but as the test continues they find it more and more difficult to maintain their concentration and stay focused. This pattern is evidenced by seeing the majority of missed questions toward the end of the test. Increasing your concentration during an exam can be enhanced by consistently practicing more and more test questions.

Another pattern that you can sometimes see when you look at your answer sheet is evidence of **changing answers** on the test, including frequent erasure marks and scratching out answers. This indicates indecision and difficulty selecting and trusting what is believed to be the correct answer. One of the best ways to begin trusting your original answer is to keep track of how often your original answer is correct. Many people start out with the right answer but quickly talk themselves out of it. This can be a dangerous pattern and if done repeatedly during an exam, can significantly change your score. Look over your last several nursing exams. How many answers did you change? Did it affect your score? Seeing this destructive pattern is often the impetus for developing an increased reluctance to change your original answer. If, however, your pattern is to change from wrong answers to right answers, you need to cautiously continue to change them. The key here is to know your pattern.

Now we are going to show you how you can best assess these patterns by using the daily practice sheet found at the end of the chapter. By placing the answers on this answer sheet, it will be easier to determine your visual patterns. We call them visual patterns because you can see them develop on the answer sheet. It is imperative for students to identify their test taking patterns because the treatment to decrease these destructive patterns is specific to each pattern. We have included several students' practice session answer sheets. See if you can identify their visual testing patterns.

HOW TO ASSESS YOUR VISUAL PATTERNS

Let's take a look at Traci's answer sheet. We suggest that you use a brightly colored pencil or pen to correct the practice session so that the patterns practically jump out at you. What pattern can you see as you look at four days of Traci's practice questions?

DAILY PRACTICE SHEET

DATE: 5/4	DATE: 5/6	DATE: 5/7	DATE: 5/9
1. _A_ **X**	1. B	1. _D_ **X**	1. C
2. _A_ **X**	2. _D_ **X**	2. _C_ **X**	2. B
3. _C_ **X**	3. _C_ **X**	3. A	3. _B_ **X**
4. D	4. A	4. B	4. _C_ **X**
5. _B_ **X**	5. A	5. _C_ **X**	5. _D_ **X**
6. C	6. _D_ **X**	6. D	6. A
7. _C_ **X**	7. D	7. _D_ **X**	7. _B_ **X**
8. _D_ **X**	8. _B_ **X**	8. D	8. _C_ **X**
9. B	9. A	9. A	9. C
10. B	10. _C_ **X**	10. _A_ **X**	10. _D_ **X**
11. _A_ **X**	11. D	11. C	11. B
12. A	12. _A_ **X**	12. _B_ **X**	12. D
13. _D_ **X**	13. A	13. C	13. B
14. _D_ **X**	14. _C_ **X**	14. A	14. _B_ **X**
15. _C_ **X**	15. _B_ **X**	15. _A_ **X**	15. _D_ **X**
16. A	16. D	16. B	16. _C_ **X**
17. B	17. A	17. B	17. C
18. C	18. D	18. B	18. A
19. D	19. _A_ **X**	19. A	19. _C_ **X**
20. _C_ **X**	20. C	20. _A_ **X**	20. B
21. B	21. C	21. C	21. A
22. A	22. _B_ **X**	22. D	22. C
23. A	23. A	23. A	23. _C_ **X**
24. _D_ **X**	24. B	24. B	24. A
25. A	25. C	25. _B_ **X**	25. D
26. D	26. A	26. D	26. C
27. _B_ **X**	27. _A_ **X**	27. C	27. D
28. B	28. A	28. _C_ **X**	28. D
29. C	29. D	29. C	29. A
30. A	30. C	30. A	30. _B_ **X**

AR = 57%	AR = 63%	AR = 67%	AR = 60%
TIME=27Min	TIME=29Min	TIME=29Min	TIME=31Min

If you saw that Traci had the pattern of first question freeze, you were correct. Notice that Traci misses most of her questions in the first half of the test. First question freeze is often caused by feeling nervous at the beginning of tests and having difficulty calming yourself down. Progressive relaxation, as discussed in chapter 4, is a specific intervention for first question freeze patterns.

Now let's look at Zackary's daily practice sheet. What patterns can you see?

DAILY PRACTICE SHEET

DATE: 4/5	DATE: 4/7	DATE: 4/8	DATE: 4/9
1. B	1. A	1. C	1. A
2. A	2. D X	2. B	2. C
3. D	3. A X	3. A	3. A
4. D	4. A X	4. A X	4. D
5. C X	5. B	5. B	5. B
6. A X	6. B	6. D	6. C
7. B X	7. A	7. A	7. A
8. C	8. D X	8. A	8. B
9. C	9. A X	9. D	9. B
10. D	10. C	10. C X	10. C
11. D X	11. D	11. B X	11. A X
12. B X	12. C	12. D X	12. C X
13. C X	13. D	13. A	13. A
14. C X	14. B X	14. D	14. C
15. C	15. A X	15. A	15. A
16. D	16. C X	16. C	16. B
17. D	17. A X	17. A	17. D X
18. A	18. B	18. D	18. B
19. B	19. C	19. B	19. D X
20. A	20. A	20. D X	20. C X
21. D X	21. D	21. B X	21. C X
22. C X	22. A	22. C X	22. A
23. A X	23. C	23. D X	23. B
24. B	24. D	24. A	24. C X
25. C X	25. B	25. A X	25. D X
26. B	26. C	26. C X	26. D X
27. D	27. C X	27. C	27. B
28. C X	28. B X	28. D	28. C
29. A X	29. C X	29. B	29. B
30. C X	30. A X	30. C	30. C
AR = 53%	AR = 57%	AR = 67%	AR = 70%
TIME=25Min	TIME=31Min	TIME=29Min	TIME=30Min

If you identified Zackary as a clumper, you were right. Notice that Zackary rarely misses one question at a time. Most of the time, Zackary misses a minimum of two questions in a row. Sometimes his clumps can be as large as five and six questions. As you can see, clumping is a dangerous pattern that would definitely decrease your overall testing performance.

Now let's look at Ginny's daily practice sheets. What pattern do you see?

DAILY PRACTICE SHEET

DATE: 6/10	DATE: 6/11	DATE: 6/12	DATE: 6/13
1. C	1. B	1. A	1. D
2. B	2. C	2. C	2. C
3. A	3. D X	3. D	3. D
4. A X	4. C	4. B	4. B X
5. D	5. A	5. B	5. A
6. C	6. D X	6. C X	6. C
7. A	7. B	7. B	7. B
8. B	8. C	8. C	8. C
9. D X	9. D	9. C	9. D
10. A	10. A	10. D X	10. B X
11. A	11. B X	11. A	11. D
12. C	12. B	12. B	12. A
13. D X	13. A	13. A	13. B
14. A	14. C X	14. C	14. A
15. C	15. D X	15. A X	15. C
16. B X	16. B	16. B X	16. C X
17. A	17. A	17. D	17. C
18. A X	18. C X	18. A	18. B
19. B	19. D	19. C X	19. A
20. C X	20. A	20. B	20. A X
21. B	21. B X	21. B	21. B X
22. D	22. D	22. A X	22. D
23. C X	23. B X	23. B	23. C X
24. B	24. A X	24. D X	24. B X
25. C X	25. A X	25. B	25. A
26. A X	26. B	26. C X	26. C X
27. C	27. A	27. B X	27. C X
28. B X	28. D X	28. D X	28. D
29. C	29. D X	29. A X	29. D
30. A X	30. C	30. A	30. C X

AR = 57%	AR = 60%	AR = 63%	AR = 67%
TIME=29Min	TIME=26Min	TIME=29Min	TIME=28Min

If you identified Ginny's test taking pattern as losing steam you were right. Notice that for the first half to two thirds of the practice test Ginny rarely misses a question. Most of Ginny's questions are missed during the last section of the test. One of the best ways to assess for losing steam and first question freeze is to take another piece of paper and cover the second half of the test. How many questions are missed? Now cover the first half of the test. How many questions are missed here? Are there significantly more questions missed on one half versus the other? Not everyone's patterns will be so easily identifiable at first nor will they occur everyday. Some people may have a combination of two patterns or may show all three patterns at one time such as Donna. Look at Donna's practice tests to see the patterns.

DAILY PRACTICE SHEET

DATE: 5/26	DATE: 5/27	DATE: 5/28	DATE: 5/30
1. A	1. D X	1. B	1. C
2. C	2. B X	2. A	2. B
3. D	3. C X	3. C X	3. D X
4. B X	4. D	4. B X	4. B X
5. D X	5. A	5. A X	5. A X
6. C X	6. C X	6. D X	6. C
7. A X	7. C X	7. D	7. B
8. C	8. D	8. B	8. B X
9. D	9. B X	9. A	9. A X
10. A	10. B X	10. D X	10. C X
11. B	11. D X	11. C X	11. B
12. D	12. C	12. D	12. D
13. B X	13. A	13. B	13. A
14. A	14. B X	14. A	14. B
15. C	15. D X	15. B	15. D
16. A	16. C	16. A	16. C X
17. A	17. B	17. D	17. B
18. C X	18. A	18. C X	18. A
19. D	19. A	19. D	19. B
20. B	20. D	20. B X	20. C
21. D	21. C X	21. A	21. A X
22. A X	22. C	22. B X	22. D
23. C X	23. B	23. A	23. D
24. C	24. D X	24. D X	24. B
25. B	25. A	25. D	25. C
26. B	26. B	26. A X	26. A
27. A	27. D	27. B X	27. B X
28. D X	28. C	28. C X	28. C
29. D	29. B	29. A X	29. B
30. A	30. A	30. B X	30. D
AR = 67%	AR = 60%	AR = 50%	AR = 70%
TIME=26Min	TIME=28Min	TIME=25Min	TIME=28Min

10

Identifying Donna's pattern is more difficult because she demonstrates more than one. Let's first identify which one she does most frequently. In reviewing her answers, the pattern of clumping seems to occur in every practice session. The majority of the clumping happens in the first half of the exam. These two problems can be interrelated in that Donna has both difficulty getting started and difficulty controlling her negative thoughts at the beginning of the test. Notice that one day Donna has difficulty with losing steam at the end of the test. According to the practice sheets this is not a usual pattern for Donna. She needs to ask herself, "What was unique about this day's practice questions?" After reviewing that day's practice questions, Donna remembers feeling tired and rushed while doing her questions. This could explain that day's loss of concentration.

The important issue here is assessment of your existing test taking patterns. One thing that we have learned in our years of working with test takers is that students tend to repeat the same test patterns. Before any interventions can be implemented, students must become aware of the test taking patterns they repeatedly demonstrate.

On the following pages we have included blank daily practice sheets for you to use in conducting your own visual pattern assessments. Please feel free to make copies of these daily practice sheets to help you identify your test taking patterns.

SELF EVALUATION OF TESTING PERFORMANCE

Each time you complete a practice session in this book, it is important for you to conduct a self-evaluation of your testing performance. The self-evaluation process can enhance your test taking ability in a variety of ways. First, it will help you determine the rate at which you answer questions correctly. We call this an accuracy rate. Second, the self-evaluation process will help you identify and correct common problems in the way you "reason out" or answer questions.

ACCURACY RATES

At the end of each practice session, you will notice a place to calculate your accuracy rate. The first thing to do is correct your answers and see how many questions you have missed. **An accuracy rate is the percentage of questions you answered correctly in a one minute per question time frame.** For example, if you are completing a practice session of 30 questions, allow yourself 30 minutes. After the 30 minutes are up, determine how many questions you have answered correctly. If you got 20 correct out of 30 questions, divide 20 by 30 for an accuracy rate of 67%. This should be calculated each time you answer questions. Then go to the rationale section and read the rationales for the practice test.

Ideally, you should read the rationale for every question you have completed. This helps you see if you understood what the question was asking and that your thinking on the matter was clear and correct. This is especially important for the questions that you missed or were unsure of during the practice session. It will help you discover where your problem solving skills were incorrect. It will also help you identify areas of weakness. This is not a time to agree or disagree with the question or rationale but a time to understand the concept or principle that is being tested

In our experience of working with clients preparing to take the NCLEX, the lower their accuracy rate is, the more they need to practice questions. We also suggest you continue to practice until your accuracy rate is consistently high. In this textbook, we like to see consistent accuracy rates of greater than 75%. Consistently means most of the time. Do not be discouraged if your accuracy rate is not always high. Naturally most people have days when their accuracy rate drops. The key is consistency or what happens most of the time. This means that whether you complete 30, 60 or 90 questions you maintain a high accuracy rate.

SUMMARY

This chapter focused on the self-assessment process in relation to testing history and study habits. Case examples of how several nursing students and graduate nurses responded to the questions raised throughout the chapter were presented to aid you with your own self-assessment process. Taking an honest look at your testing history and study habits is the first step in successfully preparing for the NCLEX or any other test in a cost efficient manner.

The self-assessment process described in this chapter is an important first step in increasing your effectiveness as a test taker. Some individuals do not take a good, hard, honest look at their testing behaviors and, therefore, continue the same ineffective study habits and test taking behaviors they have always used. If you have been able to identify your weaknesses in testing and study behaviors, then you are ready to change them. Do not just jump into preparing for the NCLEX or any other nursing exam in a haphazard manner. You will soon find yourself sinking to the bottom and feeling utterly discouraged because nothing seems to work. It is important to determine what suits you best by identifying an appropriate approach to your particular situation. The following chapters will give more specific information to aid you in effective test preparation.

Name: _____

DAILY PRACTICE SHEET

DATE:_____	DATE:_____	DATE:_____	DATE:_____
1. _____	1. _____	1. _____	1. _____
2. _____	2. _____	2. _____	2. _____
3. _____	3. _____	3. _____	3. _____
4. _____	4. _____	4. _____	4. _____
5. _____	5. _____	5. _____	5. _____
6. _____	6. _____	6. _____	6. _____
7. _____	7. _____	7. _____	7. _____
8. _____	8. _____	8. _____	8. _____
9. _____	9. _____	9. _____	9. _____
10. _____	10. _____	10. _____	10. _____
11. _____	11. _____	11. _____	11. _____
12. _____	12. _____	12. _____	12. _____
13. _____	13. _____	13. _____	13. _____
14. _____	14. _____	14. _____	14. _____
15. _____	15. _____	15. _____	15. _____
16. _____	16. _____	16. _____	16. _____
17. _____	17. _____	17. _____	17. _____
18. _____	18. _____	18. _____	18. _____
19. _____	19. _____	19. _____	19. _____
20. _____	20. _____	20. _____	20. _____
21. _____	21. _____	21. _____	21. _____
22. _____	22. _____	22. _____	22. _____
23. _____	23. _____	23. _____	23. _____
24. _____	24. _____	24. _____	24. _____
25. _____	25. _____	25. _____	25. _____
26. _____	26. _____	26. _____	26. _____
27. _____	27. _____	27. _____	27. _____
28. _____	28. _____	28. _____	28. _____
29. _____	29. _____	29. _____	29. _____
30. _____	30. _____	30. _____	30. _____

AR = _____   AR = _____   AR = _____   AR = _____

TIME = _____   TIME = _____   TIME = _____   TIME= _____

2

TEST TAKING ROADBLOCKS

Now that you have conducted a visual assessment of your test-taking errors, let's go on to examine some of the other errors, or test-taking roadblocks that can occur as you prepare for or take a nursing exam. On the highway of life in nursing school, there can be several roadblocks. For many students test taking can be the most formidable.

What are the major reasons that nursing students have difficulty with tests? What are the major test-taking roadblocks that students encounter? We believe that most of the roadblocks fall into two broad categories: content and reasoning errors and test anxiety.

CONTENT AND REASONING ERRORS

The first type of error is the one that occurs because of content deficit. By this we mean you just do not have the knowledge that is required for that particular test question. We call this roadblock a content error because the problem is in lack of recall or knowledge to answer these questions. Content errors usually occur because you either do not know the information or you have forgotten the information. A common reason you may have content errors relates to ineffective study habits. Over the years, in working with numerous people preparing to take nursing exams and the licensure exam, we have seen a direct correlation between the way people study and their test performance. There are several common errors in studying that can create or enhance content weaknesses.

One of the first problems that can occur is when students do not complete their assigned required readings before class. They expound numerous excuses why they do not have time to read before class. Examples may include; "I have to go to work. I have to pick my kids up at school. I have a care plan to do. The textbook is confusing. It doesn't help me anyway." However, as good as the excuses might seem at the time, reading the textbook before going to class helps to reinforce the knowledge when you hear it in class the next day. With all of these excuses, be honest with yourself. Ask yourself, "Is it really true that I don't have time to read before I go to class?" If the answer honestly is that you do not have time, then take a few minutes before class to skim or look over the reading material. We realize that the idea of reading before you go to class seems like too much work. However, that time is really well spent and will cut down on your studying later.

Another problem related to ineffective study habits is that students do not take class time seriously. They may sporadically attend class or take skimpy notes always promising to fill them in or check them with a classmate later.

Consider Kirsten's story:
> "When I was a freshman, a senior told me to never miss a nursing class. She said that going to every class and taking good notes really helped her. I thought she was trying to help me so I politely nodded and thanked her for the advice. I remember thinking later as I walked away that it might have helped her to go to class but I wasn't going to go to every class. I was going to be able to read the textbook and get by. Well, now I am a senior and I did get by, but sometimes just barely. Now as I get ready to take the NCLEX and look for a job as a nurse I am starting to think differently. I wish I had gone to class more regularly. I think there are big holes in my nursing knowledge and it is going to be a lot of work on my part to fill in those holes."

Never underestimate the importance of attending class. No matter what you do, you can never make up for the missed class time. Learn to take good notes. Check with classmates who are good note takers to find where your notes are inadequate, and then work on your note taking skills.

Another type of error related to content is a reasoning error. This type of error occurs when you do not know what to do with, or how to think about, the content or nursing information once you have studied it. An example of this reasoning error is not being able to determine what is really important to study. Students report they are often so overwhelmed by the vast amount of information they are expected to learn, they have a difficult time focusing on what is important. They cannot sift through all of the information to come up with the most important information or what information will be on the test. Students frequently ask faculty "What's going to be on the test?" Faculty often turn that question around and ask them what do they think is going to be on the test or what do they think should be on the test and why?

This type of question forces students to use their reasoning skills to think about what is important and what the teacher will expect of them. We encourage students to try to think, "What information will I need to practice nursing safely?" It is important to keep in mind that even though this is your teacher, she is also an experienced nurse and knows what is important in order to practice nursing effectively. Being able to identify the main ideas that are tested indicates that you understand what the nurse really needs to know.

Another reasoning error occurs when you memorize your class notes. You fool yourself into believing that you have a good grasp of your nursing content. However, you are shocked when nursing exam questions ask you not for memorization of facts but for an understanding of the information and the ability to apply the information in clinical situations. For example, you memorize the normal levels of all the serum electrolytes but the question asks what to do for a client who has a serum sodium level of 125. It is not enough to know that this level is below the normal level of 135-145. You must also be able to know how this would affect the care of this client. Knowing that low serum sodium levels can cause seizures, you would want to place the client on seizure precautions until his sodium level returned to normal.

Reasoning errors can occur not only when you study but also when you are taking a test. One example of a common and deadly thinking error is when you misunderstand what the question is asking. You select an incorrect answer because you did not appropriately interpret the question. Your reasoning in this question was faulty. It was an error in your thinking. A second example of this thinking error is called the **"what if."** In this situation, your thinking is disturbed because you bring extraneous information into the question that has no relevance and is not needed to answer the question. In other words, as lawyers say, you assume facts not in evidence. Your thinking has not followed the clear logical pathway necessary to go from problem to solution. Often students who have this problem will believe that the right answer is not even among the options. These reasoning errors are discussed in greater detail in the test-taking strategy section in chapter 3.

There are several strategies that can decrease these errors. The first strategy is to write your own test. Get together with several classmates and each writes five questions you think might be asked on the exam. Write them on index cards. Share your questions with each other and then give the answers. Give each other feedback about why you think this information is important and will be tested. The second technique is to use the practice questions in various test taking and NCLEX preparation textbooks related to the content that you are learning. For example, if you are studying information in pediatrics, look through the questions in this textbook and answer several pediatric questions. See if you can get the correct answer. Try answering several questions in a row without looking at the answers. Then look at the answers in the rationale section of the book. If you selected the incorrect answer, read the rationales carefully to see where your thinking went wrong.

TEST ANXIETY

A student's test anxiety story...

> "When I find out that there is going to be a test I get the feeling that my body and mind have abandoned me. My head starts to spin, my stomach churns and my whole body gets hot. The teachers voice goes into a slow garbled tone like she is speaking into a tape recorder at the wrong speed. "There... is... going... to... be...a... test... on... this...material... next... Friday." As long as I can remember my reaction has always been the same. I am just terrified of tests. I can't remember when I wasn't afraid. From the time I hear those fateful words it seems like I feel more panic every day. Then the actual day of the test I feel like I am going to jump out of my skin. I remember during one test I got so nervous that my vision got blurry. I couldn't read the words on the test. I really started to panic. I can remember thinking what will I do now? I just started randomly filling in the dots on the answer sheet. I kept thinking I am going to fail this test and I did. Now every time I take a test I worry that my vision will get blurry again."

Some individuals do not experience content errors during an exam. However, they still perform poorly. This roadblock is often related to an uneasiness or nervousness when even thinking about taking a test. We call these roadblocks anxiety errors, or those testing mistakes created by anxiety. Test anxiety is a situation specific personality trait with worry and emotionality as its major components (Spielberger & Vagg, 1995).

Three components of test anxiety can be identified: physical, emotional and cognitive. The physical component involves autonomic reactivity such as sweating, increased heart rate, stomach butterflies and headaches. Emotionality involves the test taker's mood and feelings associated with the situation. The cognitive components or worry involves thoughts such as: "Why are tests so hard for me? I wish I could calm down like everybody else." (Casbarro, 2003).

In other words, test anxiety is not just the diffuse feeling of dread that someone experiences prior to or during a test, it also includes thoughts the person has prior to or during the test. Unfortunately, many people are more aware of the emotionality aspect of test anxiety and less aware of their thoughts prior to or during a test. However, upon more careful examination, they are able to understand that not only did they feel anxious, but they often experienced anxiety-related thoughts such as "Oh no, I don't know the answers to these questions." "This test is too hard, I'm going to flunk." "I remember reading that in my notes but I can't remember it now." Very often these negative thoughts center on the person's negative self-appraisal and doubting his or her ability such as " I'm too dumb to get these questions right. I don't know anything, why is everything so hard for me?" These types of thoughts are detrimental during an exam in that they clutter the person's mind and keep the individual from focusing on the task at hand, which is correctly answering the questions. Negative thoughts also interfere with the person's ability to problem solve.

Pay attention to not just how you feel but what you think during a test.

For example, Melissa reads a question that states:

A 66-year-old female client has just been admitted to the hospital with a diagnosis of right-sided congestive heart failure. Which of the following symptoms would you expect her to display?

Melissa reads the question and her feelings of anxiety increase. She is able to recognize her thoughts that interfere with problem solving such as: "Oh no, a cardiac question, I'm not good at cardiac questions. I didn't review my notes on congestive heart failure. I'm going to fail this test, I don't know anything!"

While Melissa is experiencing these thoughts she cannot possibly concentrate on the task at hand, which, in this case is determining the signs and symptoms of congestive heart failure. Her thoughts are negative, debilitating and interfere with the task of correctly answering the questions on the test.

Anxiety relating to testing situations can be crippling and frustrating for the student. However, test anxiety, if recognized, can be treated. Over the years, we have learned that students experience and demonstrate their test related anxiety in a variety of ways. The following are examples of some of the most commonly expressed symptoms of test anxiety. As you read the next section, ask yourself if you experience any of these symptoms on a regular basis. Do you experience any of these symptoms to the degree that they impair your test-taking performance? The key here is finding out if the symptoms get in the way of showing the teacher what you know. Everyone will occasionally have one or two symptoms of test anxiety. However, it is the pattern and the repetition of symptoms and how they impact your performance that you need to examine.

SIGNS AND SYMPTOMS OF TEST ANXIETY

Students who have test anxiety report many different symptoms. Here are the symptoms or signs that they most commonly report to us.

PHYSICAL SYMPTOMS. These symptoms can occur prior to or during a test and can range from butterflies in the stomach to extreme nausea and diarrhea. "I always get a headache right before a test and it gets worse as the test continues."

DECREASED ABILITY TO CONCENTRATE. Students sometimes have difficulty focusing or concentrating on the test and are easily distracted by noises or other students during the exam. "During a test I hear everything. If someone taps their foot or chews their gum too loud it really bothers me." Sometimes students have distracting thoughts during the test, which can interfere with concentration. They have thoughts that are totally unrelated to the test like, "What am I going to cook for dinner tonight? I wonder if I can skip my English class tomorrow. Do the kids have soccer practice after school?"

COMPETITIVE WORRIES. Some people worry that others are doing better than they are. "I know I'm the dumbest one in this class."

DIFFICULTY RECALLING INFORMATION. Individuals may have difficulty remembering what they have studied. "When I start the test I just go blank. I can't remember anything."

HISTORY OF TEST ANXIETY. Some students repeatedly display the pattern of poor test performance related to anxiety. "I've never been a good test taker. What's the use; it is a waste of time to study."

MISREADING. It is not uncommon for test takers to misread questions or skip important key words in the question.

MISSING QUESTIONS IN A ROW. In reviewing tests students can miss "clumps" of questions. For example you miss numbers 17, 18, 19 and 20 on a test.

CATASTROPHIC FANTASY. Very often students worry about the consequences of failing. "If I fail this test my life is over. This probably means I'll fail the course. I'll never be a nurse."

PRESSURE TO BE PERFECT. Doing well is not good enough; it must be perfect. "I have to get an A."

AVOIDANCE. One of the most dangerous aspects of test anxiety is that it can occur days or weeks before the test. Some students start to feel nervous and fearful as soon as the test date is announced. Their minds quickly become contaminated with negative self-appraisal. These thoughts can be even more damaging and can lead to procrastination. The thoughts create feelings of increased anxiety; students want to avoid these unpleasant feelings of anxiety so they avoid the studying which they perceive as causing the uncomfortable feelings. "I'm too nervous to study now, so I'll do it later."

Many experts have written about test anxiety, its diagnosis and treatment. Worksheet 2 provides a self-assessment questionnaire to help you explore the degree to which you might experience anxiety in testing situations. Before you continue reading, take a minute to complete Worksheet 2.

WORKSHEET 2
TEST ANXIETY SELF ASSESSMENT
QUESTIONNAIRE

1. Do you ever get **physical symptoms** before or during a test (e.g., butterflies in the stomach, sweaty palms, palpitations, etc.)? What are they?

_____

_____

2. Do you find yourself **easily distracted** during an exam (e.g., are you aware of what others are doing around you, shuffling papers, tapping pencils, etc.)? What distracts you most often?

_____

_____

3. During a test do you **worry** that others are scoring higher than you?

_____

4. During the test do you have a **hard time recalling the material** you previously studied?

_____

5. When reviewing tests do you find that you have **missed several questions in a row?**

_____

6. During a test, do you frequently **misread questions or skip an important key word** in the question?

_____

7. Do you worry about **what will happen if you fail?** What specifically do you worry about?

_____

_____

8. Do you **feel pressured** to get above average grades?

_____

9. Do you, your parents or significant others feel that **winning isn't everything, it's the only thing?**

_____

_____

10. Do you find yourself always making excuses to **avoid studying?**

_____

_____

SUMMARY

Treatment of test anxiety focuses on both the feeling or emotional aspect of anxiety and the negative thinking or worry component. Cognitive restructuring, progressive relaxation, visual imagery and thought stopping have all been successful in treating test anxiety and are discussed in chapters four through seven.

3

TEST TAKING PREPARATION AND PRINCIPLES

Preparing For the Test

Pre-study Tactics

How often have you had the experience of trying to put off or avoid studying for a test? Unfortunately, it is a common experience for many students. They will engage in a behavior, (do something) just so that they can avoid studying. You know what we mean. It is time to study but instead, you find yourself calling a friend, watching TV, even cleaning your room. You know, all of those things you do to not study. You are engaging in study avoidant behaviors when you hear yourself saying, "I'll study after I ..." or "I'll study as soon as..." You fill in the blank. At the time you are involved in the avoidance behavior you tell yourself that you are really easing into studying, that you will get to it soon.

Many of us think the activity that we engage in will make us feel better but often our students tell us that the entire time they are not studying they are actually becoming increasingly worried about needing to study. They repeatedly think "I should be studying; I should be studying..."

According to Jensen (2003) other activities may appear much less boring than sitting down to study. He suggests that we must learn to avoid what he calls **prestudy tactics** such as watching TV, talking on the phone or even staring at the ceiling. These pre-study tactics are done out of habit rather than a need to do them. He suggests that students think about whether or not they really need to complete these rituals before they begin to study.

Many students have talked with us about their study avoidant behaviors and have shared their stories. Often students sheepishly admit that for them the reason that they avoid studying or put it off as much as possible is that when they begin to study it creates anxiety and recurrent thoughts such as "I am so dumb, I will never learn all of this. I am getting mixed up. This is too hard for me I don't understand this. I am going to flunk this test. Everybody understands this material but me."

Jacob relates the following story:
> "I know that I am really avoiding studying when I start thinking about
> doing my laundry. Not just thinking about it but actually wanting to do it.
> That is really strange for me because I have to admit that there has been
> many times in my college career that I have worn dirty clothes rather than

do my laundry. I hate doing laundry and no matter how hard I try I always mess it up. Once I died a load of shirts pink because I put a red towel in with a load of light clothes. I hate doing laundry and will do almost anything to avoid it, anything except studying. For me, the only time that I have a full closet of clean clothes is during midterm and finals week. One time I was so nervous about my senior med-surg final exam that I not only did all of my laundry to avoid studying I did my roommate's as well."

It is important for you to identify any pre-study tactic or rituals that you have. Take a few minutes to think about what you tell yourself you are going to do before you begin to study. Here are some common examples:

I'm going to study after I:
    watch my soap opera.
    walk the dog.
    do the dishes.
    put the kids to bed.

List your pre-study tactics.
I'm going to study after I:

_____
_____
_____
_____

After you have thought about what your pre-study tactics are, ask yourself how much time they take and how far they delay the actual time that you begin to study. Ask yourself a question, "Why do I do this?" Often when we first ask people why they engage in these avoidance behaviors they will report, "This other activity is more fun than studying. If I get this out of the way, then I can concentrate on studying. It makes me feel better to do this first before I study." Now ask yourself, "Is this really true?" Are you really having fun while you are walking the dog to avoid studying? If you are honest, you will admit that while you are walking the dog, you are probably having one or two recurrent thoughts such as; "I should be studying, I'm never going to pass, and I don't know enough." So when you reexamine this situation, do your pre-study tactics actually help you prepare for studying? Do they help you get organized or feel better? In all probability, they do not. Although most people may, at first, believe that pre-study tactics decrease anxiety; for most of us, nothing could be further from the truth. While engaged in our avoidance behaviors we generally find our minds wandering and worrying about studying. So why not consider taking control and just begin to study.

Pre-study tactics or rituals can be especially dangerous when people combine them to the point that they take hours to complete and, as a result, there is very little time left for studying. The rule of thumb here is to contain your pre-study tactics to five minutes or less; therefore, it cannot become detrimental to your study time.

One of the most important aspects in preparing for any nursing exam, is to set reasonable and realistic study goals. When you reach each goal, reward yourself. Many students devise elaborate study sessions in their heads where they are going to sit down for three to four hours every night for at least a week to study for a nursing final. They take out numerous books from the library. They start recopying forty pages of notes. They reread (or read for the first time) their required books. Then when they sit down to actually begin their elaborate study plan, they are dismayed when they become frustrated and overwhelmed at the immensity of the task they have set for themselves. They become immobilized and have thoughts such as, "What's the use? This is too much for me to learn, I'll never get this all done." Some even give up and do nothing. The problem here is that the goal was unrealistic. Interestingly, most nurses have spent years learning about goals and helping their clients set and reach goals. However, we are often remiss in setting appropriate goals for ourselves.

Keep your prestudy tactics to 5 minutes or less.

DEPRIVATION SYNDROME

One of the main reasons to set goals for ourselves is that student nurses and graduate nurses alike are at high risk for feeling deprived or, as we call it, having the deprivation syndrome. For example, students often find themselves deprived. They are short of money, time and opportunities to be nice to themselves. Often the longer students are in nursing school, the more deprived they feel. Students can become increasingly angry or resentful with every new testing opportunity because they begin to see it as another form of deprivation. They believe there is no time for fun and feeling good. This can also occur to new graduates as they prepare for the NCLEX. Many students feel so deprived that by the time they graduate, the last thing they want to think about is the NCLEX. Now that the NCLEX is self-scheduled, students find reasons to continue to put off taking the exam. We hear such things as, "I'll take the exam after I take the kids on vacation," or "After I rest for several months and recover from school," or "After I get a job and make a little money," or "After the next holiday," or "After the end of summer." It is important to note that, often with new graduates, continuing to put off taking the NCLEX gives the same result as the **study avoidance behaviors** (SAB). Even though you believe putting off the test will make you feel better, it becomes an ever-present nagging worry that never completely leaves you alone. In our experience, if people continue to repeatedly put off the NCLEX, they have an increasingly difficult time passing the exam.

The treatment for the deprivation syndrome is learning how to become a cost effective student. When students think about studying they often think, "The more the better." They think that the more you study, the more you learn, the better prepared you are, and the better grade you get. The truth is, no matter what nursing exam you are studying for, more is not necessarily better. Do not allow any test to become an albatross around your neck so that you feel resentful for every minute you must spend in preparation. It is important to think about and plan for an upcoming exam. However, it is equally important not to allow thinking about and preparing for the exam to control your life. Believe it or not, you can prepare adequately for any exam and still enjoy your life. The trick is to be a cost effective student. By this we mean you want the most effective learning for the least amount of time. In simple terms, you want the most for your money. Instead of planning long and arduous study sessions, use short, frequent ones with small rewards every time you complete one study session. This will get you the most in the long run.

The first thing you need to do is to establish a realistic plan. For example, look at the material you need to learn. What information do you want to spend the most time reviewing? Be judicious as you select your weaknesses, and then study them first. Once you develop mastery over these, you will feel a tremendous sense of accomplishment. Let's say you are having an exam on all of endocrine nursing. You find Addison's and Cushing's diseases to be the most difficult. Plan a short study session where you will review those two diseases until you understand them, then take a break and give yourself a small reward such as watching your favorite soap opera or calling a friend. Later, you will feel so accomplished; you will feel ready to tackle another content area. For example, Molly is getting ready to take a final exam on cardiac disorders. Congestive heart failure is something that she finds to be extremely difficult. When she develops her study plan, she finds herself coming up with several excuses for not reviewing her notes or reading the textbook on that information. She may have thoughts like, "I'll get all the other cardiac problems out of the way and then I'll have time to tackle congestive heart failure." When she begins to study other content areas, her thought process is continually interrupted with worrisome thoughts about her inability to understand congestive heart failure. She finds by the end of her study session that she has not effectively utilized her time. It is now 2:00AM and she still has not studied congestive heart failure. By this time she is tired, frustrated and becoming increasingly anxious. She starts to read the textbook and her symptoms get worse. She is plagued with thoughts of, "Why can't I understand this? I can't get the difference between left-sided and right-sided failure. This is too hard for me. The whole test is probably going to be on congestive heart failure and it's the one thing I don't understand." Molly finally gives up and goes to bed feeling discouraged that she wasted her whole evening and is no better off than before. The next day when she shares her frustration with a friend, her friend says that she did not understand congestive heart failure either. Her friend suggests that they each plan to spend an hour that evening looking over the information on congestive heart failure, then maybe the two of them can get together to review that disorder and other information for the test. Afterwards, Molly feels more prepared and in control. She definitely feels she has control over the information and has spent less time preparing the second day and knows more than she did with her method of studying. She tells her friend, "I can't believe I've been studying hours every night getting nowhere, avoiding what was making me so upset. I should have just studied this in the beginning."

It has been our experience that, with a little organization and some simple realistic goals, nursing students can achieve success on nursing exams without letting it ruin their lives. In the above example, it's easy to see why setting and keeping realistic goals help decrease anxiety. They also keep the task at hand manageable and most importantly, keep you from feeling deprived of fun and good times. Again, keeping yourself from feeling deprived is the most important task. When people feel the deprivation syndrome, they become angry and resentful. When goals are unrealistic, people tend to become immobilized and totally give up. These feelings and behaviors are extremely debilitating and totally unnecessary as you prepare for tests.

STUDY GROUPS

Throughout nursing school and when preparing for the NCLEX, people often form study groups. Study groups can be extremely helpful or detrimental, depending on how they are used and the compatibility of the members. Make a decision about joining a study group carefully. Ask yourself if being in a study group has helped in the past. If you are someone who has benefited from study groups, then this can be a help to you. In forming study groups, choose the members carefully. This may seem like a silly study tip but it is also a very important one. Often the members of the study group determine the success of that group. Do not choose to study with people who you know are exceedingly competitive or who get great pleasure in making a major point of everything you may not know. Choose people for your study companions who will be supportive of you and conscientious within the group. Do not agree to study with people because you may hurt their feelings if you refuse. If you do decide to be in a study group and find it is not helping you, you need to reexamine your purpose for attending the group. If it is not meeting your needs, you need to seek alternative methods. Now that you have the tools to decide how best to study, you are ready to learn some test taking strategies.

Test Taking Strategies

The following strategies will help you learn to more skillfully answer multiple-choice questions. In working with people preparing for nursing exams and the NCLEX, we have found that often they have missed questions not because they lack the knowledge to get the questions correct but because they do not understand the basic strategies important to test taking. Utilizing these strategies will minimize your chances of missing questions for reasons other than lack of knowledge. The only reason you should miss questions on a test is because you really do not know the content. Read over these strategies carefully. Use them when you complete your practice questions. Students often report that after they learn and consistently implement these strategies, their performance improves on their nursing exams.

1. WHAT ARE THEY ASKING ME?

After you read the question, ask yourself, "What are they asking me?" Sometimes trying to put the question into your own words (i.e. rephrasing) is helpful. In our opinion, this is the most useful of all the test taking strategies, yet one of the most commonly overlooked by most students. Failing to implement this strategy can become very problematic. Let's see how this strategy might work on the following question.

A client is placed on a low-sodium diet. What client selection would indicate an understanding of the dietary regime?
a.   Cheeseburger, frozen mixed vegetables, gelatin, glass of whole milk.
b.   Canned beef vegetable soup, rye bread, fruit salad, cola.
c.   Chicken salad, tomato wedges, fresh brussel sprouts, coffee.
d.   Pork roast, sauerkraut, scalloped potatoes, iced tea.

When reading this question, the first thing you need to do is ask yourself, "What is this question asking me?" Try to put the question into your own words. In this case, it might be: "What foods would be appropriate for a low-sodium diet?" Then examine each option individually.

Option a: Cheeseburger, frozen mixed vegetables, gelatin, glass of whole milk.
You know this would be an incorrect response because cheese and processed foods such as frozen vegetables are high in sodium.

Option b: Canned beef vegetable soup, rye bread, fruit salad, cola.
You know this should be an incorrect response because canned soups and cola are both high in sodium.

Option c: Chicken salad, tomato wedges, fresh brussel sprouts, coffee.
              You know that this could be a possible correct response since these foods
              contain small amounts of sodium.

Option d: Pork roast, sauerkraut, scalloped potatoes, iced tea.
              You know this should be an incorrect response because sauerkraut and
              scalloped potatoes would be high in sodium.

Since the question is asking you to pick the foods lowest in sodium, **option (c) is the
correct answer**. Of the options available, option (c) has the lowest sodium content.

2. ELIMINATE OPTIONS

Eliminate options you immediately know are wrong. This makes deciding on the correct
answer somewhat easier. Read the next question and rationale to see how to eliminate
options.

A client is admitted to the hospital in delirium tremens secondary to alcohol abuse.
Based on the nurse's understanding of delirium tremens, which medication would the
nurse expect to be prescribed?

a.   Disulfiram (Antabuse).
b.   Chlordiazepoxide hydrochloride (Librium).
c.   Olanzapine (Zyprexa).
d.   Benztropine mesylate (Cogentin).

The question is asking what drug is usually prescribed for a client in delirium tremens. In
this question you can immediately eliminate option (a) because Antabuse is a drug, which
causes severe reactions such as nausea and vomiting when alcohol is in the system. This
drug would not be prescribed for the client since some alcohol still remains in the system.
This leaves you with three options and a greater chance of choosing the correct response.
Of the three remaining options, you remember that Cogentin is used for side effects of
antipsychotic medications. Therefore, you can eliminate option (d). Now your choices
are down to two options. You now have a 50-50 chance of choosing the correct answer,
so even if you do not know which of the two options is correct, you have increased your
chances from one in four, to one in two. You may be asking yourself, "What is the
difference if I choose the wrong answer in the end?" Many people make the mistake of
taking a wild guess when they do not know an answer. Most people can at least eliminate
one or two of the options, which increases your chances of getting the question correct.
Eventually, the more you practice eliminating incorrect options, the better you will
become at this skill and you will choose the correct response the majority of the time.

Now you are down to the last two options, Zyprexa and Librium. Zyprexa (option c) is a
neuroleptic drug used for psychoses such as schizophrenia. Librium is the drug of choice
for alcohol withdrawal. It is a sedative that will help prevent seizures, decrease acute
anxiety, tremors and tension that often occur as a result of alcohol withdrawal, so **option**

(b) is correct. This technique of eliminating options is especially important because you may frequently come across questions where you do not know the answer. No one walks into the NCLEX, or any nursing test for that matter, knowing everything there is to know about nursing. Therefore, it is unrealistic to believe you will immediately choose the correct answer to all of the questions. However, this technique provides you with some control over the situation so that you can eliminate some options and give yourself a higher probability of choosing the correct response.

Even after using this technique to eliminate the options you know are wrong, you may still be unsure of the correct answer. In these instances **trust your glimmer**. By this we mean your first instinct or hunch, the answer that comes to you as the first "glimmer." Often this is your best bet because it is the option you thought of before your thoughts became contaminated with self-doubt.

3. DON'T "WHAT IF..."

When answering multiple-choice questions it is very important not to add extraneous data or information to the situation at hand. Do not to read into or "what if" the question. For example, while answering questions, avoid asking yourself, "What if the client is on intake and output?", "What if he's short of breath and can't climb the stairs?", "But what if that intervention wouldn't work?" A golden rule we suggest you apply is: if it is not written down or is not information that would always be true for this situation, do not add it to the question. Simply read the question and choose the option that specifically answers the question that is asked. The following question illustrates this strategy.

A client with a history of type 1 diabetes is admitted because of ketoacidosis (DKA). This is the third admission in the past month. The client also has an infected foot ulcer that will not heal and amputation is being considered. The nurse realizes that the most probable cause of the DKA is:

a.   lack of knowledge of sick day rules.
b.   decreased need for insulin due to foot infection.
c.   noncompliance with treatment regimen due to suicidal ideation regarding
      amputation.
d.   inability to see the lines on the insulin syringe for accurate measurement.

The question is asking for the usual cause of DKA. **The correct answer is a.** The most common causes of DKA are: illness or infection; decreased or missed dose of insulin; and initial onset of type 1 diabetes. This client has an infected foot that will not heal. When a diabetic client has an infection, it is important to follow specific sick day rules because the infection often raises the blood glucose levels, which may require an increased, not a decreased amount of insulin (option b). If these levels are not monitored and treated, the client can become hyperglycemic and develop DKA. There is no evidence to support that this client is suicidal (option c). Although, many clients with type 1 diabetes have visual changes due to retinopathy, there are no data in this situation to support that assumption (option d).

4. IDENTIFY PRIORITIES

It is important to identify priorities in questions requiring an intervention, in other words, "What should the nurse do first?" For example, maintaining a patent airway is more important than encouraging the client to express his feelings. That is because airway problems can be life threatening whereas unexpressed feelings are not fatal. This principle is demonstrated in the following example.

You are the first person to arrive at an automobile accident. You find a person lying on the side of the road unconscious. You notice a deep laceration on his forehead and a large pool of blood under his left leg. The initial response of the nurse should be to:

a.   apply pressure to the leg wound.
b.   assess for a patent airway.
c.   check pupil response to light.
d.   flag down another car for assistance.

This question is asking what the nurse should do first. This also means more than one of the options may be correct but only one would be done first. In this question, **option (b) is the correct answer** because it would be the priority response from the nurse. All of the options presented are proper responses at the scene of an accident. However, if the client does not have a patent airway, the other options would be futile because the client would probably die.

5. SCOPE OF PRACTICE

Keep in mind the scope of nursing practice when answering questions. For example, an option that required the nurse to give pain medication would be an incorrect answer because giving medications without a physician's prescription is not within the scope of nursing practice. The following sample question illustrates this point.

A client is admitted to the hospital with pneumonia. During the admission assessment she states that she has been coughing up greenish sputum but is having difficulty expectorating it. To assist this client with expectoration, the best nursing measure would be to:

a.   increase fluid intake.
b.   administer acetaminophen (Tylenol) as needed.
c.   administer the antibiotic as prescribed.
d.   obtain a sputum specimen.

The question is asking for a nursing measure to assist a client in bringing up sputum. You immediately know that options (b) and (d) are incorrect since they need a physician's prescription and are outside the scope of nursing practice. Option (c) is incorrect because antibiotics are not related to expectoration. **Option (a) is the correct response** since increasing fluids will decrease the viscosity of secretions so that they can be more easily expectorated.

6. DON'T ANSWER QUESTIONS ACCORDING TO YOUR HOSPITAL'S POLICIES

Be careful not to answer clinical questions according to specific policies and procedures at your hospital unless specifically requested to do so. Individual hospital policies are not to be considered. Most test questions relate to your textbook or classroom notes. It is not unusual for two students in the same class to have a clinical rotation on different units or even different hospitals. Therefore, the test could not be specific to any one hospital. Also, the NCLEX is a national test and is not specific to any one-hospital policy. The following example illustrates this point.

After a spontaneous abortion, a woman is to receive Rh immune globulin (RhoGAM). Before administering the injection, the nurse would:
a.   ask the client to sign a consent form.
b.   ask the physician to get a consent signed.
c.   determine if the client is allergic to blood products.
d.   clean the ventrogluteal site.

The correct answer is c. The question is asking how to prepare for an Rh immune globulin (RhoGAM) injection. Rh immune globulin (RhoGAM) is prepared from the blood's plasma so clients allergic to blood products would be unable to receive the injection. A consent form needs to be signed only if the hospital requires one. This is not standard to all hospitals but is dependent upon the individual hospital's policy (options a & b). The medication is generally given in the deltoid muscle of the arm, not the ventrogluteal site (option d).

7. AGE AND DEVELOPMENT

Keep in mind the age and developmental stage of your client when answering questions. For example, the doses of many medications would differ significantly between adults and children. Consider the following example:

A 4-year-old girl is admitted to the pediatric unit with dehydration and fever of unknown origin. She complains that she has nothing to do and asks the nurse for something to play with. The nurse knows that the most appropriate toy for this client is a:

a.   computer video game.
b.   coloring book and crayons.
c.   pegboard and toy hammer.
d.   deck of cards.

The question is asking for an age appropriate toy for a 4-year-old girl who is ill. In any question where a developmental need of a child or adult is addressed, always check the age of the client. Try not to personalize your responses by remembering what your own children, nieces and nephews or younger brothers and sisters were doing at those ages. Instead, base your response on the principle of developmental norms. Since many people are slightly ahead or behind these norms, thinking of specific people may confuse you. In this example, **the correct answer is b** (coloring book and crayons). In option (a), a 4-

year-old lacks the fine psychomotor skills necessary to play most computer video games and she would become easily frustrated. In option (c), a pegboard and toy hammers are usually more suitable for a toddler. Option (d), a card game, would probably be too advanced for the cognitive level of a 4-year-old child.

8. ANSWER OBJECTIVELY

Try to read and answer each question objectively. Do not react to the question emotionally. For example, in questions that ask what you would say to the client, try to stay away from thoughts such as, "These are all dumb! I wouldn't say any of these things to a client." Remain calm and try to pick an option that demonstrates a key concept or principle of communication theory or therapeutic relationships. The following question demonstrates this principle.

A client is admitted to the intensive care unit with a diagnosis of pheochromocytoma. The evening prior to surgery the nurse attempts to review the client's preoperative regime. He appears to be preoccupied and inattentive while the nurse speaks. The appropriate intervention by the nurse would be to:

a.   continue with the preoperative review since this will most likely decrease his anxiety.
b.   stop and come back at a later time so that the client has time to compose himself.
c.   explain to the client the need for his cooperation to minimize postoperative complications.
d.   comment to the client that he seems to be preoccupied and ask him what he is thinking.

In questions such as this, some people have a tendency to respond emotionally to the question, e.g., "Oh no, pheochromocytoma, I don't know what that is. Why didn't they teach me that in nursing school? I'm going to get this question wrong." These statements can be a self-fulfilling prophecy. If you believe you know nothing and cannot answer the questions, then you probably will not answer the questions correctly. Instead of this negative thinking, go back to the basics.

The first strategy tells you to rephrase the question. When you rephrase the question you find that the question is about learning principles related to client teaching and not about pheochromocytoma. You now can reexamine your negative thoughts (listed above) since the subject of the question is different from what you originally thought. You realize that the **correct answer is d** because it responds to the client's anxiety regarding the upcoming surgery. Any attempts to teach at this time would be ineffective because the client may not be ready to hear it and would be unable to listen to what the nurse is saying (option a). Stopping and coming back later (option b) may create more anxiety and does not assist the client to become calm enough or voice fears. Option (c) may create guilt in the client and focusing on postoperative complications may increase anxiety.

9. IDENTIFY KEY WORDS

Look for key words that will help you more specifically understand the question, for example: **initial** action, **early** sign, **characteristic** symptom. The next sample question illustrates this point.

The nurse assesses a client for early signs of alcohol withdrawal which include:

a.   tactile hallucinations, agitation.
b.   visual hallucinations, convulsions.
c.   disorientation, anxiety.
d.   diaphoresis, tremors.

The question is asking for early signs of alcohol withdrawal. **The correct answer is d,** diaphoresis and tremors are early signs of alcohol withdrawal. Anxiety may also be an early sign but all of the other responses are late signs of alcohol withdrawal. The key word in this question is **early**. All of the responses (options a, b & c) are signs of alcohol withdrawal but only option (d) contains two early signs.

10. REHEARSE

The last strategy that we will discuss in this section is that of rehearsal. By this we mean practicing NCLEX questions in this and other test taking and NCLEX preparation books. Remember you are trying to develop your thinking and problem solving ability. The best way to do this is to practice doing sample questions, as many and as often as possible. Not only will practicing questions enhance your thinking and reasoning skills, it will also help you with timing, in that you want to be able to complete each multiple choice question in approximately one minute. Often without practice, students are unaware of timing difficulties. They are too slow or too fast in answering the questions. When you answer questions too quickly, you can often misread or misunderstand what the question is asking you. When you answer questions too slowly, you can easily read into or add information to the question that you should not. The best rehearsal involves answering test questions using the same conditions, as you will experience in the exam situation. First, number a separate piece of paper with the amount of questions you will be expected to answer on the "real" test. This practice especially helps students who have to transfer their answers to another paper or to a computer sheet rather than answering on the test paper. Now, take the practice test as you would at school or for the NCLEX. For example, take all materials (notes, books, food and drink) off your practice area; sit at a table rather than curling up on the sofa. Make sure you do not look up the answers to the questions as you go through the test. Wait until you complete the practice test before correcting it. Answering a question after you know you got the last one wrong can often start worrisome thinking such as: "If I got the last one wrong and I thought it was easy, how can I move on?" You also cannot check your answers on a real test, so it is better not to get into the habit while completing practice tests. You can become frustrated and anxious when you are unsure of how well (or poorly) you are performing. Often this becomes distracting as you think of a previous question or go back to change answers. After correcting the practice test, read all of the rationales. This means reading rationales to questions you answered correctly as well as those you missed. Sometimes you get the questions right for the wrong reasons and you want to be aware of it. This also means to review all of the options and not just the one right or wrong option you chose. This helps with the reasoning process to see why the right answer is right and the wrong options are wrong. Finally, keep your practice tests in a notebook to review over time. Keeping the practice tests helps you to identify those patterns that may be destructive for you and makes them easier to correct. Good rehearsal practices will really facilitate your thinking, reasoning and consequently your performance.

SUMMARY

This chapter offered students options to effectively and comprehensively prepare for testing situations. Self-examination of prestudy tactics or rituals, setting realistic study goals and usefulness of study groups were described. Further, ten test taking strategies with examples of sample test questions to illustrate each strategy were provided. Practicing these strategies will enable test takers to gain confidence, control and improve scores on exams.

4

HOW TO RELAX AND ENJOY TESTS

Consider this student story:

> "When I take an important test the muscles in my body seem to turn to
> wooden boards. They are stiff and rigid and when I try to bend them it
> feels like they are cracking in half. By the time I am half way through the
> test my neck hurts so bad it feels like I can't bend it to read the questions.
> Then my head starts to pound. It is like a ritual with stages. It always
> happens the same way and by the time I am done with the test I feel so stiff
> I can hardly get out of my chair without limping. I am embarrassed for
> any of my classmates to see me. I know that this is all anxiety; that my
> muscles tense up like this, but telling myself not to get nervous just
> doesn't work."

A progressive muscle relaxation exercise is the first behavioral technique to incorporate
into your test preparation program. The majority of relaxation programs focus on
managing stressful situations. There are a variety of programs available on the market in
the form of "how to" books and audiocassettes. Later in this chapter, one form of
relaxation exercise is presented. We believe it is easy to learn and an effective
component to stress management. This exercise will help you differentiate between the
sensations of tension and relaxation. Muscle tension can be caused by a variety of
factors. During our day-to-day activities we pay little attention to which muscles are
tensed or relaxed until the tension begins to cause strain or discomfort. At this point, our
attention is drawn to the discomfort, which may interfere with the activity we are
performing. A simple example of this is "walking." Most of us, during a leisurely walk
through a shopping mall, may feel quite relaxed. We are never thinking about which
muscle groups are "working" or tense in order to keep our bodies erect and moving. We
are not consciously aware of the work performed by our legs and back muscles.
However, after shopping for several hours and carrying a shopping bag of packages on
each arm, we begin to notice a tightness and strain in the shoulder and arm muscles. This
type of strain begins to draw our attention toward the discomfort, alerting us to seek some
sort of relief (or relaxation). At this point, many of us may take a short shopping break,
rest over a cup of coffee, take our packages to the car or stop shopping for the day.

Most of us have experienced a situation similar to the above example. The key point to
remember is that discomfort associated with tension can draw our attention away from an
enjoyable activity such as shopping, or an activity that demands concentration, such as
taking a test, forcing us to pay attention to that discomfort. We have found that practicing
a progressive muscle relaxation exercise has been helpful for many people to reduce their
tension and anxiety, therefore, enabling test taking to be a much more tolerable
experience. When this experience becomes more tolerable and less stress ridden,

students' thinking becomes clearer and their test scores improve.

STRESS RESPONSE

Stress affects everyone in a variety of ways. Your response to stressful situations and circumstances depends on your ability to cope and combat the stress. In a perceived emergency situation our bodies become more alert and energized. For example, in response to witnessing a serious car accident, your heart may start to beat faster, you may begin to perspire, and your breathing may become shallow and rapid. This emergency situation triggers an arousal response of the sympathetic nervous system, which sends messages to virtually all organs of the body to energize them into action. This energized state is often called a generalized arousal response or "fight or flight"(Stuart & Lairia, 2005). This reaction calls your body into action against a perceived threat.

The stress response can also be triggered by less extreme circumstances than provided in the above example. Day to day pressures, deadlines to meet, term papers to complete, etc., can all trigger an arousal response that is needed and helpful "to get things done." However, viewing the response to stress as a physical component alone is only half of the story. Reaction to stress, in addition to the physical component, can affect our cognitions (e.g., the way we think and what we think) and our emotions (e.g., our feelings related to a particular situation). The stress arousal response is most likely to be triggered when we perceive a threat to our well being and/or believe that we have little control over resolving a particular situation (Bourne, Brownstein & Garano, 2004).

Take a few minutes to think about how you respond to stressful situations. Try to recall an anxiety-producing situation, for example, your first day at a new job, a final examination, an argument with a friend or family member, a job interview. How do you respond physically, cognitively and emotionally to these situations? Is your attention drawn toward the physical discomfort, disturbing or unproductive thoughts and emotions rather than the task at hand? It is equally important to consider and evaluate other events occurring simultaneously in your life. What other types of events are occurring in your life that may add to the stress you are experiencing (e.g., moving to a new apartment, buying your first new car, planning your wedding)? Remember, positive life events as well as negative events can be equally stressful.

WHY RELAXATION?

We are often puzzled by the resistance we get to this strategy from our students. When we mention it, our students often roll their eyes in disgust and offer the following retorts:
"It puts me to sleep."
"I think it is funny and then I start to laugh."
"I don't have time for this."
"I'd rather ride my bike to relax."
"These silly self help tricks don't work for me."
We have to ask ourselves, "Why is trying relaxation such a hard sell? Why do people find it so avoidable?"

Basically, there could be a myriad of reasons why many are hesitant to try a relaxation exercise. Some people are not used to relaxing. Others may be afraid something bad will happen if they relax. Maybe we don't want to believe that we have the power to control our bodies to that extent or that practicing relaxation might make us totally lose control.

Our busy lives put us into a constant battle to get the most done in the least amount of time. Our clients often tell us that when they think about listening to their relaxation tape they immediately think of all of the tasks or errands that they should be doing that seem much more important. We struggle to make time for ourselves. However, there is more to this than just the time issue when we avoid this helpful technique. Could it be that we have difficulty doing something that is truly in our best interest? Why do we avoid what we know will be helpful to us? So when you are thinking of all of the excuses to not practice your relaxation technique, ask yourself why? "Why am I avoiding this? How will I know if it will work if I don't practice? What is the worst thing that can happen by spending a few minutes a day learning this?"

When our students ask us directly why they should practice relaxation techniques, our answer is simply that stress, tension and a sense of well being and relaxation cannot occur at the same time. Progressive muscle relaxation decreases stress and tension and cannot coexist with the feeling of anxiety (Davis, Eshelman & McKay, 2000). Think about weight training where you strengthen arm and leg muscles to counteract a weak lower back. The reason you do this is to learn how to use proper body mechanics to compensate for your weak back. Over time, as you "build up" your relaxation response, it becomes strong enough to quell the anxiety in a stressful situation. That is why the most effective results are felt when you practice the progressive relaxation on a daily basis. Keep your expectations of the relaxation exercises realistic. People often believe that relaxation should work immediately and they should never feel the anxiety once they do the relaxation. In reality, relaxation exercises are effective when they decrease your anxiety to a manageable level. By this we mean that you are able to work effectively with a level of anxiety that does not interfere with your activity, whether we are talking about tests, swim meets, speeches or anything else. Remember, a little bit of anxiety (mild anxiety) is necessary because it makes you more alert and enhances your performance.

WHAT TO EXPECT

It is important for you to remember that relaxation is a skill that requires consistent practice in order to master and gain maximum benefits. The exercises will take approximately 15 to 20 minutes to complete and ideally should be practiced twice each day. The effect of relaxation is a gradual one. In general, relaxation exercises can be mastered in one to two weeks. Initially, you may not experience any difference at all. Do not be discouraged, this is a common occurrence...just remember practice makes perfect!

As you practice, you will become increasingly aware of many sensations. Progressive muscle relaxation will teach you, which muscles in your body tend to be tenser than others. Some people may feel tension in their shoulders and the back of their necks while other people experience the tension in their abdominal muscles. Those areas where your body tends to store tension are areas you can focus on while doing your relaxation exercises. Progressive muscle relaxation will also teach you what tension actually feels like. Many people do not realize how tense they are until they do the exercises. Most people tend to focus on their thoughts and not the physical sensations of their bodies. As you become increasingly aware of the sensation of muscle tenseness, you will start to become aware of when those muscles are in the beginning stages of tenseness and you can then begin to relax those specific tense muscles before your anxiety level grows. You will also notice that sensations of your body are temporary and a muscle may feel tense but you can learn to relax it in a matter of minutes as you become proficient in your use of relaxation. Of equal importance, is the fact that feelings such as anger and fear are also temporary and can be changed just as easily and quickly (Johnson, 2000).

PREPARATION FOR RELAXATION EXERCISES

Common Distractions

As you begin your relaxation exercise program, it is important that you also become aware of three common problems related to relaxation exercises, including:

MUSCLE CRAMPS. If this occurs, it is generally the result of tensing muscle groups too tightly, and usually affects the calf muscles of the legs.

FALLING ASLEEP. This is probably the most common problem associated with the exercises. For the purposes of decreasing anxiety, falling asleep during the exercises reduces any potential benefits to be gained by the exercises. If you find that you are starting to fall asleep, the exercises should be stopped. Remember, our goal is to reduce and control anxiety, not eliminate insomnia.

INTRUSIVE THOUGHTS. Sometimes people may find it difficult to concentrate on the exercises and they begin thinking of, for example, things they should be doing instead of these exercises or thoughts about taking or retaking the NCLEX or any nursing exam. If this happens, try to focus your thoughts on something more positive or pleasant. For example, think of a pleasant scene (e.g., the beach, leaves changing during Fall, etc.). If "things to do" is the problem, try changing the time of day that you practice the exercises to a less demanding time.

WHEN TO SAY "NO" TO RELAXATION

For most people, relaxation exercises produce a sense of well being and comfort; being virtually free from harmful side effects. However it is advisable to seek medical clearance before beginning any new treatment modality. It is important to determine that the root of your anxiety is not caused by a physical disease (Mayer, 2005). Many disorders have been linked to stress and anxiety. These include but are not limited to: cardiovascular disease, cancer, gastrointestinal disorders, eating disorders, diabetes, eating disorders, pain, sexual dysfunction, allergies, skin disorders and hair loss. Although progressive relaxation has been used as an adjunctive therapy for many problems, it is important for your doctor to approve it as part of your treatment. Progressive relaxation is effective in treating anxiety, insomnia, chronic pain and migraines (Mayer, 2005).

TIME TO GET STARTED

Students frequently ask us when they should do the relaxation exercises. As a general rule, we suggest that students should experiment different times of the day. You might try the relaxation exercises after work or before you begin to do some practice questions. You will discover when the relaxation exercises are the most beneficial for you.

To gain maximum benefits from relaxation exercises, you must create the appropriate atmosphere. Find a place where you can be alone and uninterrupted. Wear loose comfortable clothing. If something is tight, loosen or unzip it. Get into a comfortable position with your entire body supported. We recommend that, for at least the first three weeks, you practice the exercises in a reclining or semi-reclining position, with your legs and arms relaxed at your sides. This type of position should help you create not only an atmosphere conducive to relaxation but also assist you in the beginning of the program to differentiate between relaxation and tension.

After approximately three weeks, as you continue to learn to differentiate the sensations of relaxation and tension, change your position to a seated upright position, resting your hands on your lap and feet flat on the floor. The main reason for this change in position is that you will be seated when you are taking a test. Again, remember our goal is anxiety reduction and control while preparing to take the NCLEX and other nursing exams. The exercises, however, will remain the same regardless of the practice position.

To help you master this technique, it is important that you practice the exercises twice daily. Remember, practice makes perfect. As mentioned previously, the relaxation program will take approximately 15 to 20 minutes to complete. In our experience, as soon as we mention practicing these exercises twice a day to students and graduate nurses, we usually hear moaning and statements like, "I don't have time to do this every day." We are recommending that you find a total of 30 to 40 minutes in a day. Honestly ask yourself if this is an unreasonable request. If it really is unreasonable, plan to practice the exercises once a day with the understanding that it will take longer to master the technique.

GUIDELINES FOR USING PROGRESSIVE RELAXATION

1. As a general safety rule, you may want to check with your physician prior to starting a program of progressive relaxation.

2. Take caution when tensing neck and back muscles. Excessive tightening can result in muscle or spinal damage. Over tightening the toes and feet can result in muscle cramping (Davis, Eshelman & McKay, 2000).

3. **Do not try to do your relaxation exercises or listen to your relaxation tape while driving a car or operating any equipment.** The purpose of the tape is to make you very relaxed. This can be dangerous if you are driving. It is similar to falling asleep at the wheel. Instead, find a quiet place where you can close your eyes and relax.

4. To achieve success with progressive muscle relaxation, practice is required. Listen to your relaxation tape at least once a day, twice if possible. As you gain skill many people find they are able to use a shortened version of the exercise.

DIRECTIONS FOR MAKING A TAPE

Many people find it very helpful to have a tape recording of their progressive relaxation exercise. For this reason we have included a script that you can talk into a recorder and use on a regular basis. Some people like to record their own voice because they can individualize the script to meet their own needs (Davis, Eshelman & McKay, 2000). However, many of our clients have said that it is disconcerting to them to listen to their own voice on their relaxation tape. They believe that listening to their own voice hampers their ability to relax. For these individuals, we suggest that they ask a friend or family member to make the recording for them. There are many relaxation tapes that can be purchased at local book stores, if the above options do not work for you.

When you read the relaxation script into the tape recorder, remember to read slowly. It is important to remember that when the tape instructs you to tense a muscle group you need to leave time (approximately 5 to 10 seconds) to tense the muscle and hold it in a tensed state.
Pay attention to the pauses that are placed judiciously throughout the script. They allow you to take time to notice the relaxation responses that are occurring. When you are recording your tape, wait several seconds at each (PAUSE) before proceeding.

The relaxation script is adapted from the works of: Bernstein, Borkovec and Hazlett-Smith (2000); Bourne (2000); and Davis, Eshelman and McKay (2000).

RELAXATION SCRIPT

Make sure that you are in a quiet setting and get into a comfortable position. You may want to lie on a sofa or bed, or sit in a reclining chair. Your entire body including your head should be supported. Take a few minutes to focus on your breathing. Take a few slow deep breaths to begin the relaxation process. (PAUSE) Starting with your hands, clench both of your fists, hold for 10 seconds. Feel the tension in your fists and forearms. Now relax, let go of the tension. Note the difference between tension and relaxation in your hands and forearms. (PAUSE) Now bend your elbows by drawing your forearms toward your shoulders. Tense them as hard as you can. Feel the tension. And relax, noticing what it feels like as the muscles become more and more relaxed. (PAUSE) Turn your attention to your head and wrinkle your forehead as tightly as you can. Notice the tension. Now relax, let the muscles of your forehead become more and more deeply relaxed. Imagine your forehead muscles becoming smooth as they relax, deeper and deeper. (PAUSE) Next tense the muscles around your eyes by clenching your eyelids tightly shut. Hold. Relax your eyes. Allow your eyes to remain gently closed. Noticing the pleasant feelings of relaxation; just let go of all the tension. (PAUSE) Next, tighten your jaw by opening your mouth widely and holding it open. Feel the tension in your jaw. Now let go, feel your jaw relax. Let your lips part and allow your jaw to hang loose. Notice what it feels like as your muscles become more completely relaxed. More and more deeply relaxed. (PAUSE) Focus all of your attention on the feelings associated with relaxation. (PAUSE) Next, press your tongue against the roof your mouth, experience the tightness in the back of your mouth. Relax. Let go…more and more. (PAUSE) Feel yourself becoming more completely relaxed. (PAUSE) Now turn your attention to your shoulders, shrug your shoulders, keep the tension as you hunch your head down between your shoulders. Relax. Feel the relaxation spreading to your neck, throat and shoulders. Notice the difference between tension and relaxation. Enjoy the feeling of deeper and deeper relaxation. Notice how good your neck feels as it becomes more and more relaxed. Feel the comfort and the heaviness of your relaxed body. Take a deep breath and fill your lungs completely. Hold your breath, and feel the tension. Now exhale. Letting go of all of the tension; feel the tension draining out of your body. Continue relaxing, allowing your breathing to become more and more relaxed and effortless. (PAUSE) Now tighten your stomach muscles by sucking your stomach in. Hold. Let go. As your stomach muscles relax, imagine waves of relaxation spreading through your abdomen. Notice what it is like as your muscles loosen up and unwind. Allow yourself to experience the sensations of complete relaxation. Feel the relaxation flowing into your muscles. (PAUSE) Now turn your attention to your back, tighten these muscles in whatever way feels best. You can arch your back or simply squeeze your back muscles together. Gently hold the tension. And now let go. Let go of all the tension. Thinking about nothing but the very pleasant feelings of relaxation. Notice how those muscles feel as they become more and more completely relaxed. (PAUSE) Now tighten your buttocks by pulling them together. Hold. And relax. Feel the muscles in your hips getting loose and relaxed. Take a moment and really feel the relaxation, deeper and deeper relaxation. (PAUSE) Squeeze the muscles in your thighs all the way down to your knees. And relax. Again noticing the difference between tension and relaxation. Feel the relaxation spreading through your body. Feel the comfort and the calm. Your body is becoming more and more completely and deeply relaxed. Pay attention only to the sensation of relaxation. Allowing your muscles to let go of all the tension and become more deeply relaxed. Allow the waves of relaxation to wash over your body as you become more and more relaxed. (PAUSE) Next, tighten your calf muscles by carefully pulling your toes toward you. Now, let go, feel the tension leave your body. Let go more and more. Enjoy the feeling of total relaxation as your muscles become more relaxed. Notice what it feels like as your muscles become more and more completely relaxed. Feel the comfort and heaviness as the warmth of deep relaxation moves throughout your body. (PAUSE) Now tighten your feet by curling your toes downward. Hold. Now relax and feel the difference. Let go. Feel yourself let go of all the tension remaining in your body. Let go more and more. Let all of the tension dissolve away. Feel your body relaxing. Deeper and deeper. (PAUSE) Take a moment to mentally scan your body checking for any residual tension. (PAUSE) If any part of your body remains tense, repeat the tension-relaxation cycle for those muscles. Take a moment and do that now. (PAUSE) Now let that wave of relaxation spread throughout your entire body. Start at your head; slowly move down your body allowing the relaxation to penetrate every muscle group down to your toes. (PAUSE) Feel the deep relaxation throughout your entire body as you continue to relax deeply. Letting go of that last bit of tension in your body. (PAUSE) Relax your head and your scalp. Notice the feeling of relaxation in your face and neck. Feel the relaxation deepening in your shoulders, and your arms, now to your hands. Feel the relaxation, deeper and more completely relaxed. Let the relaxation spread to your stomach, to your lower back and to your chest. Relax your buttocks, your thighs. Relax your knees, your calves, relax your ankles. Feel the relaxation as you relax your feet. Relax your entire body, deeper and deeper. (PAUSE) Sit quietly for a moment and enjoy total and complete relaxation. Feel the calmness and pleasure as all of your tension is replaced with the feeling of relaxation.

PLAN OF ACTION

The following guidelines summarize the step by step procedure to start you on the road to controlling anxiety and tension associated with preparing for the NCLEX or other nursing exams.

STEP 1: Do you have any medical conditions that would inhibit you from beginning a program of relaxation? Have you received medical clearance from your doctor to begin your relaxation program?

STEP 2: Make a recording of the relaxation exercise outlined in this chapter.

STEP 3: When beginning the relaxation program, have you created a relaxing environment?
For example: Is it relatively quiet?
Are your phone and TV turned off?
Are you wearing comfortable clothing?
Do not forget about timing.
For example: Are you pressed for time?

STEP 4: Begin the exercises in a reclining or semi-reclining position.

STEP 5: Do not be discouraged if you do not feel any difference during the first few days of practice. Remember, practice makes perfect!

STEP 6: After three weeks, change your position from reclining or semi-reclining to a sitting position.

SUMMARY

The first behavioral technique to incorporate into your NCLEX and test-taking preparation program was presented in the form of relaxation exercises. Before continuing with chapter 5, take time now to make your recorded version of the relaxation script. We often suggest you choose someone who has a calming voice or someone who helps calm you to record the script for you.

5

NURSES' COGNITIVE SELF ASSESSMENT MODEL

We have already demonstrated that your cognitions, the way you think, can affect test performance. Negative or distorted cognitions ("Oh no, I'm going to miss every question; I'm too stupid; I'll never pass this test; I'll never be a nurse") can be debilitating to your problem solving ability and test performance. Substituting more realistic thoughts ("I'm going to take one question at a time; I'm prepared for this test") are more believable and can have a lasting positive impact on your feelings and your behavior (Lam, 2005). Realistic thoughts can facilitate your problem solving ability and, therefore, test performance. This chapter contains the Nurses' Cognitive Self Assessment Model (NCSAM), which is designed to assist graduate nurses in identifying, evaluating and restructuring cognitive distortions related to test taking. The NCSAM was based on the theory of cognitive behavioral therapy developed by Aaron T. Beck (1976). Although Beck (1976) developed his approach for use with depressed and anxious clients, it is easy to see how a cognitive approach would be helpful in aiding student and graduate nurses to improve their problem solving skills and test taking behaviors. In the broadest sense, cognitive therapy is based on the concept that cognitions have an enormous impact on feelings or "you feel the way you think" (Burns, 2006). More specifically, what a person is thinking affects his feelings, which can then affect his behavior. A cognitive approach to treatment consists of alleviating psychological distress through the medium of correcting unhealthy irrational thoughts. Frequently, students and new graduates experience anxiety as they are preparing to take exams and the NCLEX. Although they may be aware that they feel anxious or uncomfortable, they are often unaware of the irrational cognitions that accompany these feelings. Unfortunately, these negative thoughts influence feelings, which can influence the person's behavior during the test. If test takers have negative thoughts about performance on their tests, they will also experience negative feelings and negative test taking behaviors. The NCSAM helps test takers to identify the connection among their behavior, the feelings that accompany their behavior and their associated thoughts. Identifying thoughts is often the most difficult because thoughts occur so quickly that it is difficult to identify them as being separate from feelings.

Sandy's story illustrates this point:
> "Yesterday I was taking a final exam. I was feeling more and more nervous. I kept telling myself calm down, don't be nervous but it never seems to work. So I tried to say it to myself with more emphasis, still nothing. I kept getting more nervous. I just don't understand why I get so nervous during a test. I tell myself to calm down over and over again but it never seems to work. I look around and I see everyone else taking the

test they seem so calm. But not me, I feel like I am going crazy!"
As nursing students we are taught to get in touch with our own feelings. However, this is often much easier said than done. Nurses may be able to identify their feelings in a vague and uncertain way, but this does not provide much insight into understanding the connections among thoughts, feelings and behaviors. Table 1 provides a sample situation demonstrating this relationship. In this situation, Kasey looks at her responses on the NCSAM and is able to see the connection among her negative thoughts, negative feelings and negative behaviors.

TABLE 1
Connection among Behavior, Feelings and Thoughts

Situation:
Kasey, a new graduate, is preparing to take the NCLEX in several months. She finds it difficult to sit down for any period of time to study. She finds herself discovering many small household tasks that "must" be done around her apartment every time she gathers her materials to study. In helping Kasey look more closely at her negative behavior, the NCSAM can assist her to identify the connection among behavior, feelings and thoughts.

BEHAVIOR	FEELINGS	THOUGHTS
Kasey avoids studying for the NCLEX by engaging in household chores; every time Kasey has time to study, she does the dishes, vacuums the living room, etc.	Kasey identifies that she feels anxious and scared every time she begins to study.	Kasey is able to discover several negative thoughts that accompany her feelings of anxiety and fear: "I should be studying for this test but what's the use, I'm never going to learn enough to pass the test. There isn't enough time...I'm too stupid to learn all of this. I'm going to fail."

The following exercise, Worksheet 3, will help you to identify thoughts, feelings and behaviors in a variety of situations. To increase your self-awareness, take a few minutes now to think of a situation that was troublesome or confusing to you, or a situation in which you imagine having difficulty. Using Worksheet 3, write your situation and try to identify all three parts (behavior, feelings, thoughts) of the NCSAM.

WORKSHEET 3
Situation:

BEHAVIOR	FEELINGS	THOUGHTS

Completion of Worksheet 3 provides you with a beginning understanding of the way your behavior, feelings and thoughts relate to each other. Since the goal is to change negative behavior, we must evaluate how realistic the thoughts are. The next step is to critically evaluate the basis of the thoughts. By this we mean to look at these thoughts and determine how true they are. Ask yourself "Is this thought true? What evidence do I have to support my thought? What is the worst thing that can happen if this thought is true?"

Let's go back to Kasey's situation and add a fourth column to the NCSAM. Table 2 illustrates Kasey's evaluation of her thoughts.

TABLE 2
Evaluation of Thoughts

BEHAVIOR	FEELINGS	THOUGHTS	EVALUATION OF THOUGHTS
Kasey avoids studying for the NCLEX by engaging in household chores; every time Kasey has time to study, she does the dishes, vacuums the living room, etc.	Kasey identifies that she feels <u>anxious</u> and <u>scared</u> every time she begins to study.	Kasey is able to discover several negative thoughts that accompany her feelings of anxiety and fear: "I should be studying for this test but what's the use, I'm never going to learn enough to pass the test. There isn't enough time...I'm too stupid to learn all of this. I'm going to fail."	"Is it really true that I'll never be able to learn enough to pass the test? I was able to learn enough to pass nursing school. I learned enough to work successfully and haven't been fired yet. I don't have to know or learn everything to pass the test." "What evidence do I have to support my thought? I really don't have any evidence to support it. I've always been a relatively good student. I passed all of my nursing courses. I graduated from nursing school." "What is the worst thing that can happen if this is true? I would have to take the test again. In reality, how many tests did I have to take over because I failed them? And even if the worst thing would happen and I would have to take the test again, I'll do it systematically; I'll find out what my weaknesses are and study those areas to prepare for the test."

From the above example, you can see that only when Kasey was able to write down her thoughts was she able to truly examine and evaluate them. When she (on paper) asks herself several thought provoking questions, she can then begin to see how negative and even unrealistic her thoughts are. This is the beginning process for looking at the basis of her thoughts. Then she found evidence to counteract or dispute the negative thoughts and replace them with more positive ones. You may find that your thought column has numerous thoughts for one behavior and that thoughts tend to run on. Take one thought at a time and evaluate it as we have done in the evaluation column on Table 2.

Students and clients frequently ask us when they should do the 4-column log. The best time is whenever you find thoughts becoming negative or distracting. In this sample situation, Jean's negative thoughts occurred while she was on a clinical area. Jean and another student are discussing their upcoming final exam.

Kristine: "Hey Jean, did you start studying for the final exam?"

Jean: "No. We have so many other things to do, care plans and health promotion projects. I haven't had time to get started."

Kristine: "Really? I've been studying all week. There's so much to learn. The students from last semester said the test was a real killer!"

Jean: "Really! Do you think it will really be that bad?"

Kristine: "Yeah, I sure do. You'd better start studying for it!"

Jean walks away from the conversation feeling somewhat uneasy. As she continues her day, thoughts of the conversation with her classmate begin to haunt her. On the way home from school, Jean promises herself that she's really going to buckle down and study. When Jean gets home and begins to study, she finds it increasingly difficult to concentrate and again finds the classmate's conversation racing repeatedly through her mind. She keeps reading the same paragraph over and over, finding herself repeating the same thought: "What's the use? This test is too hard, it probably is the hardest test in the world and I'll never pass it." Jean looks at the clock and finds she has been sitting at her desk for two hours and she's still on the same page. She feels exhausted and even more exasperated. She closes her book and decides to go to bed. If Jean had used the NCSAM to examine her thoughts and feelings and their impact on her behavior, she would have been able to decrease the negative effect of the conversation with her classmate.

Now let's examine the same situation, but this time Jean uses a different approach. After the conversation with her classmate, Jean begins to feel anxious and has difficulty keeping her mind on her work. On her lunch break Jean decides to use the NCSAM to evaluate her feelings and thoughts. Table 3 illustrates the NCSAM in action.

TABLE 3
NCSAM in Action

BEHAVIOR	FEELINGS	THOUGHTS	EVALUATION OF THOUGHTS
After a conversation with her classmate, Jean has difficulty concentrating at clinical. She becomes forgetful and is easily distracted.	<u>Discomfort</u> and <u>uneasiness</u>, which increase as the day continues.	"My classmate says this is the worst test I'll ever take; it's really hard; she says there is so much material, how could anyone ever learn it; this is so unfair; I'll never pass!"	"Is it really true that this test is the worst test I'll ever take? What evidence do I have? Our instructors reviewed the major points on the test. It doesn't make sense that this test would be unfair." "The worst thing that could happen is that I'd flunk the test, but that's never happened before. Besides, if the test is so hard, how did the other students pass it?"

Through the above example it is easy to see that negative thoughts and perceptions about events can create negative feelings and thus negative behaviors. When Jean is able to examine her thoughts immediately after the situation occurs, she halts the negative process rather than allowing it to escalate to the point that she feels overwhelmed and cannot study.

After completing the evaluation of thoughts column, there is a perfect opportunity for problem solving and developing a revised plan of action. This helps create new and more useful behavior. In both examples about Jean, she had negative thoughts related to not being able to pass the test. She encounters difficulty in studying because of these thoughts. Thoughts of not passing the test or not preparing sufficiently to take the NCLEX can become very overwhelming. Once you evaluate your thoughts to see how realistic they are, you can congratulate yourself for combating your negative thinking. However, you still need to prepare for the test. The longer you wait to take action on the situation, the more likely the negative thinking will return. After you evaluate the negative thoughts, take a few minutes to do some problem solving. First, define the problem. If you had negative thoughts about passing the test, then what can you do about the situation? What alternatives do you have? Which is the best and most workable alternative for you to try? Set up an actual timetable to carry out your newly devised plan. Make sure the alternatives are realistic and can be put into practice. See Table 4 for an example of this five-step process.

TABLE 4
NCSAM: A Five-Step Process

BEHAVIOR	FEELINGS	THOUGHTS	EVALUATION OF THOUGHTS	SOLVING THE PROBLEM: A PLAN OF ACTION
After a conversation with her classmate, Jean has difficulty in concentrating at clinical. She becomes forgetful and is easily distracted.	<u>Discomfort and uneasiness,</u> which increase as the day continues.	"My classmate says this is the worst test I'll ever take; it's really hard; she says there is so much material, how could anyone ever learn it; this is so unfair; I'll never pass!"	"Is it really true that this test is the worst test I'll ever take? What evidence do I have? Our instructors reviewed the major points on the test. It doesn't make sense that this test would be unfair." "The worst thing that could happen is that I'd flunk the test, but that's never happened before. Besides, if the test is so hard, how did the other students pass it?"	"A lot of what I am thinking is not really true. I'm letting one person's opinion influence my thoughts and my behavior. What are some things I can do to stop this? I need a new plan of action. I am going to develop a plan of study for brief periods of time every night. This is not an overwhelming task. I can break it down into manageable parts and do the best I can. I will practice questions and review my answers for one hour every night. I'll begin my studying within 1/2 hour of getting home from school and if I start feeling anxious, I will reexamine my thoughts."

Now from Worksheet 3, take the situation in which you have identified behavior, feelings and thoughts. Add the last two columns of the NCSAM. On Worksheet 4 fill in the first three columns from the situation you wrote in the previous exercise. Now evaluate your thoughts using the questions: "Is it really true?, What evidence do I have to support this?, What is the worst thing that could happen to me?" In the last column, formulate a plan of action to solve the problem. As you develop your plan of action, keep it realistic and attainable.

One helpful technique in keeping track of one's thoughts, feelings and consequent behaviors is to write a daily journal that can be kept with you at all times. Divide the pages of the log into five (5) columns and complete the NCSAM during times when your thoughts become troublesome. By doing this on a daily basis, you will increase awareness of your negative thoughts and begin to see their influence on your feelings and behaviors. It will become increasingly easy for you to evaluate and restructure your thoughts and thereby develop a useful plan of action. As you continue to restructure your thoughts, you will notice an increase in positive mood and control over the task at hand. You will also be able to use your study time more effectively.

WORRY LOG

After the NCSAM has been done for several days, some people like to switch to a shortened version of this called the worry log. Choose a time every day to write the events, feelings and thoughts, which have occurred during that day. Give yourself at least 15 minutes to think and write. Write the log in a narrative form as though you are talking to someone. This is less structured and does not need to be written in the five columns. Make sure you write the day and date before you begin the log. You should do this every day and keep them in a notebook to see your progress. See the example below of a typical worry log.

WORRY LOG

Day: Monday   Date: 5/10

Today while I was driving to school, I kept thinking about the final exam next week. Every time I think of it, I get sick in my stomach. When will I study? I don't have any free time between work and school. I'm always busy. If I do find time to study, how will I ever learn it all? It's too much for me. I'm not smart enough. What if I fail this course, I'll flunk out of school. I'll be so embarrassed I'll just die. I've got to stop worrying about this. I'm driving myself crazy. All this worry isn't helping me. I need to redirect my energy to preparing for the test. I'll write a plan of study so I can do a little bit every night that will make me feel better.

Another helpful technique is to list your negative cognitions or thoughts on a piece of paper and try to restructure them to neutral or positive cognitions. The example below demonstrates this technique using negative cognitions a student might experience during a major nursing exam.

51

NEGATIVE COGNITIONS COGNITIONS	RESTRUCTURED
"I should have studied more."	"I don't need to spend more time studying. Maybe I need to change the way I study."
"I'm so stupid, even when I really study, I still fail the test."	"I'm not stupid but I must be doing something wrong. Maybe I need to get some help."
"Oh no, here's another question I don't know. That's seven in a row...I'm dead."	"If I just sit back and think, I can get this. I know this material."
"Where did they get these questions?"	"Everyone must be having a hard time. Relax..."
"They're trying to trick me."	"That's not true, they are testing a principle. I need to figure out what they're asking in this question."

SUMMARY

The five step process of the Nurses' Cognitive Self-Assessment Model (NCSAM), the worry log and the two column restructure list were presented in this chapter to demonstrate the effects of feelings and thoughts on behavior and your ability to restructure them for the better. Examples of each of the techniques were presented to help you see how these ideas can be put into practice. Worksheets 3 and 4 provide you the opportunity to put this model into action using your personal situations.

52

WORKSHEET 4

NCSAM

BEHAVIOR	FEELINGS	THOUGHTS	EVALUATION OF THOUGHTS	SOLVING THE PROBLEM: A PLAN OF ACTION

6

STOP SELF-DEFEATING THOUGHTS

In this chapter the technique, thought stopping, will be discussed as a way of decreasing negative thoughts that can occur prior to or during a test. Thought stopping can also be very effective in eliminating negative thoughts that occur when preparing or studying for a test.

Thought stopping is a behavioral technique that can be very effective in reducing negative thoughts (Peden, Rayens, Hall & Grant, 2005; Peden, Rayens, Hall, 2005; Bourne, 2005). It can be described as the practice of noticing negative or destructive thoughts then teaching yourself to stop them and then redirecting them to more realistic or positive ones (Adamson, 2002).

Thought stopping has been used for individuals who experience many types of anxiety, depression, and low self-esteem. This technique should be used if repetitive or intrusive thoughts exist that are unrealistic, unproductive and often anxiety provoking. Examples may include: "I will never be able to do this job right." or "I am going to have a hard time getting through this interview." At this point in the program, you most likely are working toward mastery in identifying and evaluating your nonproductive, self-defeating thoughts by understanding and practicing the concepts underlying the Nurses' Cognitive Self Assessment Model (NCSAM) discussed in Chapter 5.

Consider this teachers story about a student with troubling thoughts.
> "Tom was a good student. He worked hard and always came to class prepared. That's why I was so surprised when he didn't do well on the first test. When I asked him what he thought happened he told me that it was hard for him to stay focused on the test because he kept having thoughts that he called thoughts of doom and gloom. He further explained that on major nursing exams he would always think about how he just couldn't measure up. 'I just start thinking, I can't do it. I am not smart enough. I don't know the answer to this question. This is the third one in a

row I just don't know.' He then told me that when we review the test he couldn't even remember many of the questions or what he selected as the correct answer. I also noticed that Tom would miss clumps of questions such as numbers 5, 7, 8, and 9. He did this again with numbers 29, 30 and 31."

The technique of thought stopping can be taught in a variety of ways. In our experience, we have found using a rubber band to be easier to learn and implement. A rubber band is also practical, in that you can wear it in public, into the classroom or the testing center.

The underlying concept of the thought stopping technique is that a stimulus (e.g., snapping a rubber band) can help you suppress and/or eliminate self-defeating thoughts. For example, imagine you are in your home or apartment reading a magazine or talking to a friend; suddenly you hear a loud crack of thunder, or a car screeches to a halt. The noise from the thunder or car (stimulus) generally startles people enough to momentarily stop what they are doing. When the stimulus occurs, by nature, a person's thoughts are directed toward that stimulus. The same is true for the technique of thought stopping. When self-defeating and nonproductive thoughts occur, the snap of a rubber band on your wrist is the stimulus that will suppress and/or eliminate those thoughts.

GUIDELINES TO THOUGHT STOPPING

The following guidelines are provided in order to implement the thought stopping procedure:

1. Place a rubber band on your wrist. This should be worn at all times. Common sense should be used here; obviously wearing a rubber band with formal attire may be a bit odd! However, in most situations, the rubber band can be worn without drawing attention to it.

2. The rubber band should be snapped (used as a stimulus) for each occurrence of self-defeating thoughts. The important thing here is that you stop the thoughts immediately. As soon as you determine the thoughts to be self-defeating, snap the rubber band.

3. Initially, you may experience feelings of awkwardness or self-consciousness in anticipation of implementing this technique. These are natural feelings, but remember that the first time is the worst. The feelings will fade with practice.

4. Do not be too hard on yourself when snapping the rubber band. The goal is to produce a stimulus that is distracting, not one that produces bruises!

5. After producing the stimulus (snapping the rubber band) tell yourself to STOP. At first you may want to say the word STOP out loud. Try to empty your mind of the distressing thought for a few seconds. If the thought comes back, say STOP again. As you get better at this technique you can move to saying the word STOP silently to yourself.

As with other behavioral techniques identified throughout this program, practice makes perfect. According to Davis, Eshelman & McKay (2000) thought stopping requires that you be consistently motivated. They recommend working on one stressful thought at a time. "For effective mastery, thought stopping must be practiced conscientiously throughout the day for three days to one week" (Davis, Eshelman & McKay, 2000). During the early learning stages of this technique, you may find that after snapping the rubber band, self-defeating thoughts may reappear in a relatively short period of time...this is normal. In the initial stages, you may find the need to produce the stimulus several times in order to STOP the thought. With practice, however, the number of times that the stimulus is initiated will drastically reduce. In time and with enough practice, some people are able to tell themselves to STOP without the use of the rubber band as a stimulus.

The identification and evaluation of thoughts as self-defeating or a "dead end" way of thinking is an important first step to successfully implement the thought stopping procedure. The following example may be helpful in clarifying this point.

Carla, a graduate nurse preparing to take the NCLEX, is aware in general, that psychiatric nursing is an area of content weakness. It has been over a year since she has had class and clinical experience in psychiatric nursing. She never really had any interest in this area of nursing and had always hoped that she would work on an intensive care unit. Although her grades in psychiatric nursing were average to above average, she really had not thought about "psych" in a long time. From reviewing practice questions, she was able to narrow down her areas of content weakness within psychiatric nursing to communication theory and setting limits in caring for the manipulative client. In developing her plan of study, Carla identifies communication theory and limit setting as a first priority. She plans to reward herself by having dinner and a movie with friends on Saturday night. On day one of her study plan she is able to keep her prestudy tactics to less than five minutes...success... she's pleased with herself. She begins reading about therapeutic and nontherapeutic communication theory; she finds at the end of the first page of reading she has no idea what she read. She takes a minute to try and figure out what she was thinking while she was reading. Carla discovers that her thoughts; "I'm never going to remember all this stuff...These examples of nontherapeutic and therapeutic statements are stupid, I'd never say this to a client. I hate psych." led her to the feelings of being overwhelmed and anxious.

Carla had been practicing the Nurses' Cognitive Self Assessment Model and was quickly able to identify her thoughts as self-defeating, which in turn led to feeling overwhelmed and anxious. The cognitive and emotional components combined led to Carla's inability to concentrate. Carla starts with her first negative thought, "I am never going to remember all of this stuff." She recognizes this thought as negative, nonproductive and a dead end way of thinking. With each occurrence of this thought, Carla implements the thought stopping procedure (snaps the rubber band, tells herself to STOP and shifts her thoughts to a more positive, appropriate thought such as; "I can remember the basic concepts. If I keep at them, I will learn them." With consistent practice, Carla is able to suppress the self-defeating thoughts and effectively study the psychiatric nursing content outlined on her study plan.

SUMMARY

This chapter presented the behavioral technique of thought stopping to incorporate into your test preparation program. This technique is easy to implement and, when mastered, is an effective way to suppress self-defeating thoughts or dead end type of thinking.

7

VISUALIZE CHANGE

Guided visualization is a technique using mental imagery to modify your behavior, your feelings and even your internal physiological state (Bourne & Garano, 2004). Essentially, we are talking about your ability to form mental pictures of making positive changes in yourself. The ability to create vivid images in your mind can be a powerful technique in preparing for exams. When we practice creating positive images, any type of performance can be enhanced (Bourne, 2005).

There are a variety of uses for visualization. In particular the technique is effective in treating many stress related and physical illnesses such as headaches, chronic pain and general or situation-specific anxiety (Davis, Eshelman & McKay, 2000). For our purposes, we have included this technique to combat situation-specific anxiety, i.e., what you experience in preparing for a nursing exam or the NCLEX.

PREPARATION FOR VISUALIZATION

For best effectiveness it is important to be relaxed when using visualization exercises. When you are relaxed you are able to develop the mental images more vividly and enhance the effectiveness of the visualization. After any visualization exercise, it is important to return to a full state of alertness. This is why all of our visualization scripts end with a counting statement to help you return to a fully alert state. When you have completed your visualization exercise make sure you stand up and walk around for several minutes to increase your alertness. **Wait 10 minutes** before driving or getting involved with any activity that requires intense concentration or coordination (Bourne, Brownstein & Garano, 2004).

Get into a comfortable position with you head and neck supported. Your clothing should be comfortable; the environment should be quiet and free from distractions. Remove eyeglasses or contact lenses and shoes. Close your eyes and take a few minutes to relax before the visualization. You may want to use abdominal breathing or progressive muscle relaxation for several minutes before you begin.

As with any behavioral technique, it is important to practice the visualization exercise at least twice a day. The more you practice, the more powerful the visualization becomes.

TIME TO GET STARTED

The following visual imagery script can be recorded on the opposite side of your relaxation tape or as a second track if you are using a digital recorder. You may choose to record the script yourself or have someone else whose voice you find soothing record it for you. When making a recording, make every attempt to create a quiet environment during the recording session. The first script is written for any nursing exam and the second script is specific to the NCLEX preparation.

REMEMBER!!! DO NOT DRIVE OR OPERATE MACHINERY WHILE LISTENING TO YOUR VISUAL IMAGERY TAPE OR WHILE PRACTICING ANY VISUALIZATION TECHNIQUES

SCRIPT 1: NURSING EXAMS

Get into a comfortable position and close your eyes. Visualize your body relaxing. Start with the muscles of your head and neck; gradually move down your body relaxing each muscle while feeling the tension leaving your body. (PAUSE) Take a deep breath. Hold it for five seconds (PAUSE) and slowly exhale. (PAUSE) Repeat this again. Take a deep breath and hold it for five seconds (PAUSE) and again slowly exhale. Let go of all the tension in your body. As you experience this feeling of relaxation, form a mental picture in your mind. Imagine yourself on the day of your next test. Imagine getting up the morning of the test and getting dressed. Visualize what you will be wearing. Imagine that picture in vivid clear detail. (PAUSE) Picture yourself getting into your car and driving to school. You feel good. You know that you have studied well and are prepared to take the test. See yourself parking the car in the parking lot. Visualize this in your mind. See this clearly in your mind. See your self getting out of the car and walking to the entrance of the school. You know you will be successful. Imagine yourself walking into the classroom and seeing your classmates who are all anxiously talking about the test. Imagine yourself in a protective suit of armor that repels all your anxiety. Visualize yourself walking into the room and taking your seat calmly and quietly. See how you can block out all of the noise. You feel confident. You are able to block the anxiety of the other students because you are prepared and calm. You feel good. You feel successful. You know you will do well. Picture the classroom and the teacher in front of the class. As you visualize this scene you may want to use the following positive statements or affirmations:

"I am prepared and ready to take this test."

"I will protect myself from anxiety by controlling my negative thinking during this test."

"I am in control in this situation."

"I know that I have the ability to do well on this test."

"I am confident that I will do well."

As the test is being handed out, you feel calm, you feel good, and you can anticipate your success. (PAUSE) You now have the test in your hand and you turn to the first page. If you feel yourself getting anxious, use your techniques to stop the anxiety. You are in control. See yourself taking control and relaxing. See yourself changing the feelings of anxiety into calm and confident feelings. Imagine yourself taking the test calmly with a feeling of confidence. You feel good. You feel successful. Get that image of yourself firmly and vividly in your mind. (PAUSE) Picture yourself moving through the test, answering the questions one at a time, moving through the exam at an even pace and in a

calm manner. See that exact picture now. Remember, if you are feeling anxious as you are taking the test, visualize yourself using your techniques to gain control to decrease your anxiety and feel calm and relaxed. You have gained control of the situation. You feel good. See yourself feeling good as you take the test. See yourself doing well. Get that image in your mind clearly and specifically. You are taking the test. You are doing well. You are able to block out all of your classmates noises. Nothing can bother you. It's as if you are in a clear glass bubble where nothing can bother you. No one can interfere with your successful test performance. Your attention and energy are on the test. No one can distract you from your task. You are focused. You feel good. You are completing the task of taking the test. Experience how good you feel, how successful you feel. Take a moment and feel those good feelings now. (PAUSE) You are finishing the test and getting ready to turn your paper in; visualize the scene of putting your pencil down and picking up your test paper to hand to your teacher. (PAUSE) You feel good because you know you've been successful. You know you have passed the test. You were prepared. You were calm. You know that you have done well. Picture yourself walking out of the test room, handing the test to the teacher. Picture yourself feeling successful as you leave the classroom. Sit quietly for a few moments and enjoy these good feelings. (PAUSE) Now you are ready to return to a state of alertness. Now count backwards from five to one. With each progressive number begin to slowly return to that state of alertness. Five, open your eyes and slowly look around the room. Four, slowly move your hands and feet. Three, move your arms and legs. Two, sit up and one, stand up. You have now finished the visualization exercise.

SCRIPT 2: NCLEX

Get into a comfortable position and close your eyes. Visualize your body relaxing. Start with the muscles of your head and neck; gradually move down your body relaxing each muscle while feeling the tension leaving your body. (PAUSE) Take a deep breath. Hold it for five seconds (PAUSE) and slowly exhale. (PAUSE) Repeat this again. Take a deep breath and hold it for five seconds (PAUSE) and again slowly exhale. Let go of all the tension in your body. As you experience this feeling of relaxation, form a mental picture in your mind. Imagine yourself on the day of the NCLEX. Imagine yourself getting up the morning of the exam and getting dressed. Imagine what you will be wearing. Visualize yourself getting ready for the exam. Get that picture in your mind as clearly as you can. Picture yourself eating breakfast...getting in your car...and driving to the testing center. While driving to the testing center, you feel good. You feel successful. You know that you are prepared and ready to take the test. Imagine yourself driving to the testing center, feeling good, feeling prepared, knowing that you will do well. (PAUSE) Imagine yourself parking your car. Visualize this in your mind. You are now getting out of your car and walking into the testing center with the feeling of positive anticipation. You are ready to take this test. You know that you are going to do well. You know that you are in control. Picture yourself walking into the building and having that good feeling; feeling successful. You walk into the room where you will be taking the test. Picture this scene in your mind. Picture yourself walking into the room and taking your seat. Block out all of the other noises. You are sitting down, waiting with positive anticipation. You are feeling confident and successful knowing that you are prepared. Picture that scene as clearly and concisely as you can. Picture yourself sitting at the computer terminal. You feel good. You feel successful. You know that you are prepared. Picture yourself in that scene now. As you visualize this scene you may want to use the following positive statements or affirmations:

"I am prepared and ready to take the NCLEX."

"I will be able to control my negative thinking during the NCLEX."

"I am letting go of my anxiety."

"I know that I can pass the NCLEX."

"I am confident that I will do well."

Picture yourself at the computer getting ready to begin. Picture yourself feeling good. You are now seeing the first question on the computer screen. You feel good. You feel successful. (PAUSE) If you get anxious, use your techniques to stop the anxiety. Picture your relaxation scene that you did earlier. Change you irrational thoughts. Picture yourself feeling good, feeling successful, knowing that you will do well and can control your anxiety. Change the anxiety into a calm and confident feeling. Imagine yourself taking the test; get a visual image of yourself taking the test. Picture yourself answering the questions, one at a time...moving through the exam calmly. Now imagine that you have come to a question that you are unsure of the answer. If you are feeling anxious in this scene, visualize yourself using your techniques to decrease your anxiety and gain control of the situation. You are in control. You feel good. You feel successful taking the test. You know that you will do well. You know that you will pass. Get that image in your mind as clearly as you can. You are taking the test. Imagine the room, the proctors, and the other test takers. Get that picture very clearly in your mind. Experience how good you feel, (PAUSE) how successful you feel. Put yourself into the picture and feel those good and positive feelings. You are taking the test. You feel good, you feel successful. (PAUSE) Now you have finished the test. Visualize the scene of leaving the room smiling, feeling confident. You feel good because you know that you have been successful. You passed the test. You were prepared. You knew the information. You have controlled your anxiety. You know that you have done well on the test as you walk out of the room. You feel successful and good. You know that you were well prepared, and you have passed the test. Sit quietly for a few minutes and enjoy these good feelings. (PAUSE) Now you are ready to return to a state of alertness. Now count backwards from five to one. With each progressive number begin to slowly return to that state of alertness. Five, open your eyes and slowly look around the room. Four, slowly move your hands and feet. Three, move your arms and legs. Two, sit up and one, stand up. You have now finished the visualization exercise.

SUMMARY

The visualization exercises described in this chapter are the final behavioral techniques to incorporate into your test preparation program. As mentioned in chapter 4 with the relaxation exercises, consider asking someone who has a calming voice to record the script for you. **With adequate practice (minimum two times per day),** visualization can be a powerful tool toward changing your behavior and outlook related to nursing exams or the NCLEX. As with the other behavioral techniques described in this book, practice is the key to success and mastery.

8

METACOGNITIVE TECHNIQUES TO ENHANCE LEARNING

As psychiatric nurses and nurse educators, we have always been interested in the way people think, how they make decisions and solve problems. The more experiences we have, the more we realize that learning how our clients and students think and helping them to become aware of their thinking processes is paramount to being successful as a nurse. Metacognition is often simply defined as thinking about thinking. It refers to higher order thinking and involves our having control over the thinking processes that we use in our learning (Livingston 2003). Martinez (2006) defines metacognition as the monitoring and control of thought. It is your ability to think about what you are learning or being taught. Metacognitive skill helps you focus on what you need to know and how to go about learning it. It is asking yourself reflective questions while you are attempting to learn, such as "Am I understanding what I am studying? What can I do if this study strategy isn't working for me? How will learning this help me be a better nurse?" It helps you problem solve and connect information that you already have to the new information that you are learning.

Learning metacognitive techniques helps students see the interconnectedness between old and new information and group data in an organized, coherent fashion. Learning and using metacognitive skills are also important in learning effective clinical reasoning skills (Kupier & Pesut, 2004). Research has demonstrated that instruction in metacognitive strategies is an effective teaching method and is useful in enhancing students' reading comprehension and test scores (Eilers & Pinkley, 2006; Applegate, Quinn & Applegate, 1994; Nolan, 1991; Jacobowitz, 1990; Worrell, 1990). It is these skills that are necessary to be successful on nursing exams and the NCLEX.

Certain metacognitive strategies have been helpful to our clients so we have described them for you below. It is our hope that one or several of them may be beneficial to you in your quest to enhance your thinking.

MNEMONICS

A mnemonic is a device that provides an easy way to memorize and access those memories because of its familiarity (Beitz, 1997). Although learning facts and memorizing data are not enough to develop the high level thinking that one needs to practice nursing competently, you must first have the basic facts or information to be able to move on to higher level concepts and principles. Mnemonic devices help us store and retrieve information in an easier fashion. We can organize information, create memorable images, and even facilitate comprehension in a novel way.

Basically, there are two categories of mnemonic devices; verbal and visual. Mnemonics organize material into either a specific written pattern (verbal) or pictures created to help you remember. Examples of verbal mnemonics are included below.

ACROSTICS

Acrostics are an arrangement of words into a phrase that is familiar to you and can help you recall other information that you now associate with it. Two examples are:

> <u>O</u>n <u>O</u>ld <u>O</u>lympus <u>T</u>owering <u>T</u>ops <u>A</u> <u>F</u>inn and <u>G</u>erman <u>V</u>iewed <u>S</u>ome <u>H</u>ops
> These are the twelve cranial nerves: **O**lfactory, **O**ptic, **O**culomotor, **T**rochlear, **T**rigeminal, **A**bducens, **F**acial, **A**coustic, **G**lossopharyngeal, **V**agus, **S**pinal accessory, **H**ypoglossal.

> <u>C</u>onk, <u>R</u>apidly, <u>P</u>lease <u>O</u>ld <u>M</u>an
> This is how to evaluate coma: **C**onsciousness, **R**espiratory pattern, **P**upillary size and reflexes, **O**culocephalogyric reflex, **M**otor response to pain.

ACRONYMS

An acronym is a word made up to remind you of other words, lists, people or dates. Most often acronyms are the first letters of several words you want to remember. For example, the name of our nursing consultation firm is **STAT** Nursing Consultants, Inc. In our company **STAT** stands for: **S**trategies for **T**est **A**nxiety **T**reatment. Some other examples include:

> **PEARL** is **P**upils **E**qual **A**nd **R**eactive to **L**ight

> **UNLOAD ME** (treating congestive heart failure) is **U**pright position, **N**itrates, **L**asix, **O**xygen, **A**lbuterol (or Alupent), **D**obutamine, **M**orphine, **E**xtremities (dependent position)

DRAW YOURSELF A PICTURE

Draw yourself a picture is almost self explanatory study technique. Basically we want you to draw pictures of disease processes and important nursing concepts to help you remember them. The pictures you draw help you use visual images and create a memory tool for you.

Memory tools help you make connections between ideas and use pictures to help you pull together concepts (Gaglione, Zerwekh, Claborne & Miller, 2005; Zerwekh, Claborne & Miller, 2004). This technique is often helpful because it allows you to visualize several pieces of information and get the whole picture. It often makes it easier to remember information that you are trying to understand. In a study by Trausch (2003) nursing students who actually drew their clients' pathology rather than just reading about it felt they had greater comprehension. Drawing helped them put all the pieces together which resulted in a better understanding of the whole.

We have included an example for a memory tool for pheochromocytoma. Tremendous artistic talent is not required to use this technique of drawing. As you can see in the

PHEOCHROMOCYTOMA

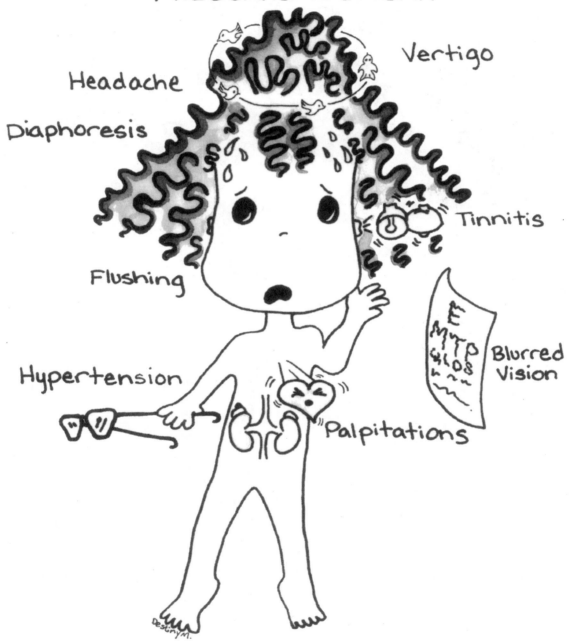

Headache

Diaphoresis

Vertigo

Tinnitis

Flushing

Hypertension

Blurred Vision

Palpitations

picture of Natalie, the signs and symptoms are illustrated for you and will help you remember and comprehend the data.

We have also included a nonillustrated picture of Natalie. Feel free to copy her so you can draw in your own signs and symptoms and make your own notes. You can be creative as you develop your own memory tools for what ever information you are trying to learn. You can add the medications or basic nursing interventions to your picture. Excellent examples of this technique can be found in the <u>Memory Notebook of Nursing</u> Volumes, I and II by Zerwekh, Claborn and Miller (2003, 2004). and <u>Memory Notebook of Nursing: Pharmacology & Diagnostics</u> (2005) by Gaglione, Zerwekh, Claborn and Miller.

TALK TO THE TEXTBOOK

In chapter 2 we have hopefully convinced you to read your textbook assignments before you go to class. We now want to caution you about another problem that can occur. This, we have labeled as "**highlighter hyperplasia.**" When we are working with students who are having trouble in nursing school with exams, we ask the students if we can review their class notes with them. At that time we also look at their textbook reading assignments with them. What we often see is that the student has highlighted every word of every page of the reading assignment. In fact, they admit that they highlight as they read. When we ask the student why they have highlighted the whole page, they state it is because they believed every word on every page was important. This response is very puzzling to us because how do you decide what is important if you highlight most of the words on every page. This indiscriminate highlighting can be symptomatic of several potential problems. Often students do not know how to identify what is important and, therefore, deem everything as important. The students also are not interacting while they are reading; they are just passively taking in the words without actually thinking about or participating in the assignment. Often students do not understand the purpose of the reading assignment so they see no need to become actively involved. The treatment of highlighter hyperplasia is a technique called **talk to the textbook**, developed from the Author's Intended Message (AIM) technique (Jacbowitz, 1990). In talk to the textbook, we ask you to pretend that the highlighter you have now is the only highlighter you will ever get in nursing school, so you must use it sparingly. Only what is extremely important should be highlighted. As a rule of thumb, no more than five lines on a page should be highlighted. Limiting highlighter abuse forces you to really think while you read and interact with the reading material. You must ask yourself questions like, "What is really important? What is the priority? What is the author trying to say here? What is the main point? What is it that the nurse needs to know?" Another way to talk to the textbook is to actually write questions to the author in the margin of the page. Pretend that you are actually having a conversation with the author and that you have the opportunity to ask questions, tell the author when something does not make sense to you or paraphrase the main point in your own words. It is also a good idea to put a marker on that page with a question to ask a classmate the next day, five minutes before class. When you talk to the textbook, reading your required assignment takes on a new meaning. You go from a passive to an active participant in your educational experience.

Often students complain that the reading assignments are so long that they are overwhelmed by them and have thoughts such as, "What's the use, I'll never read all of this," so they give up before they even get started. A good strategy here is to break your reading assignment up into small segments. Read a few pages when you get home, a few more after dinner, and finish up the next morning before class.

RECIPROCAL TEACHING

In reciprocal teaching, the student and teacher take turns being the teacher (Reeve & Brown, 1985). One of the best ways to really learn something is to teach it to someone else. As you are preparing for a nursing exam, divide information you want to review with one or several of your friends. Learn one of the divided sections of information and teach it to a friend. Then try to think of several questions in multiple choice format on that information. Have your friends do the same for you with the other divided sections. Remember, teaching someone a subject makes you think about how to help someone else make sense of the information and understand it. To do this, you must understand it. It also forces you to think out loud so that you can hear yourself think and correct any reasoning errors.

THINK OUT LOUD

Think out loud is another metacognitive technique (Beitz, 1995). When you think out loud you can see that the material can be approached in a number of different ways. It is also a great way to hear your thought processes and reasoning errors or faulty thinking. We have developed a game using the think out loud process. This game is called **DEFEND YOUR ANSWER** and is played with NCLEX questions or other multiple choice nursing test questions. Get a couple of your friends together with some practice questions. You can have two teams and a moderator. Have the moderator read the question and have one team answer the question. The team that answers the question must think out loud to defend their answer. More specifically, defending your answer means that you provide not only a rationale for your chosen answer but why it answers the question. For example:

A client is receiving lanoxin (Digoxin). What therapeutic effect from the lanoxin (Digoxin) will the nurse expect?
a.   Decreased pulse rate, decreased weight, increased urinary output.
b.   Decreased pulse rate, increased weight, increased urinary output.
c.   Decreased pulse pressure, increased blood pressure, reduced heart murmur.
d.   Increased pulse rate, decreased blood pressure, stable fluid balance.

"I chose option (a) as the correct answer because the question asked the expected effects of Digoxin. I know that the purpose of Digoxin therapy is to increase the force of the cardiac contraction. It makes the heart beat stronger which slows it down so it increases cardiac output, and decreases edema. The client would have a slower pulse, less edema and more urinary output." If the moderator decided that you have defended your answer appropriately, your team gets one point. If you miss the question, the opposing team can defend an answer from the remaining options. If correct, they get one-half point because it is easier when you only have to select from three options. If you get the question right but your reasoning is wrong, you get no points. This game will really help you understand the thinking necessary to get nursing multiple choice test questions correct. Listening to yourself and others think through a clinical nursing question will really help identify problems with reasoning and how to correct them. Get creative with this game, have fun. Have the moderator use an egg timer for how long the team has to answer a question. Give each team a bell to ring when they know an answer. Give silly prizes. Make the losing team buy the winners pizza. Chapter 9 will provide you with several other games that will enhance your thinking, promote learning and hopefully, make that learning more enjoyable.

SUMMARY

This chapter stressed the importance of students being able to identify what they "know they know": i.e., metacognitive awareness. Learning tips on how to memorize information (mnemonics), determining which material has the most importance (reciprocal teaching and talking to the textbook) and being able to identify your thought processes and reasoning errors (think out loud) are described.

9

MAKE A GAME OF IT

Sometimes no matter how much you realize that you need to prepare or study for an exam, it is just plain hard to do and you find yourself putting it off. Making a game of it or developing games can make learning more enjoyable especially for dry and somewhat boring material. The literature supports the use of games as a teaching strategy to enhance learning in nursing education (Cowen & Tesh, 2002). Games help students acquire knowledge, facilitate problem solving and sometimes foster critical thinking skills (Kuhn, 1995). Games are fun. They help take some of the drudgery out of studying and test preparation. Another major advantage to games is that they promote active involvement for the learner (Henderson, 2005). Over the years we have noticed that students often seem to experience a decrease in anxiety when they are involved in playing an educational game. After all, it is hard to focus on your anxiety when you are having fun.

We have included several games we use to help our students and clients overcome the hurdle of learning difficult or dry material for a test in nursing school, in NCLEX preparation or just to "jump start" someone who procrastinates. First, think about what games you like and how you like to study. For example, do you like to study in groups?

If you like to work in groups, you can write NCLEX practice questions on index cards and play one of the popular trivia board games, substituting the clinical areas (pediatrics, medical-surgical, obstetrics and psychiatric nursing) for the traditional game categories. If you prefer to study alone maybe crossword puzzles are for you. If you having difficulty with a particular content area, we suggest you might develop a crossword puzzle from that content. This forces you to study the material that is difficult for you but makes it less frightening because it is a game. Another suggestion is to make a deal with a classmate and exchange crossword puzzles and complete each other's puzzle so that now you have reviewed content in several different areas. Crossword puzzles on eye disorders, arthritis and connective tissues diseases can be found on the following pages. For those of you who are artistically inclined, you might consider mnemonics (see chapter 8) to help you remember difficult concepts. Think about a specific pathological condition that is difficult for you to understand. Sometimes if you draw a picture of it, the visual connection will help you tie it all together.

EYE DISORDER PUZZLE

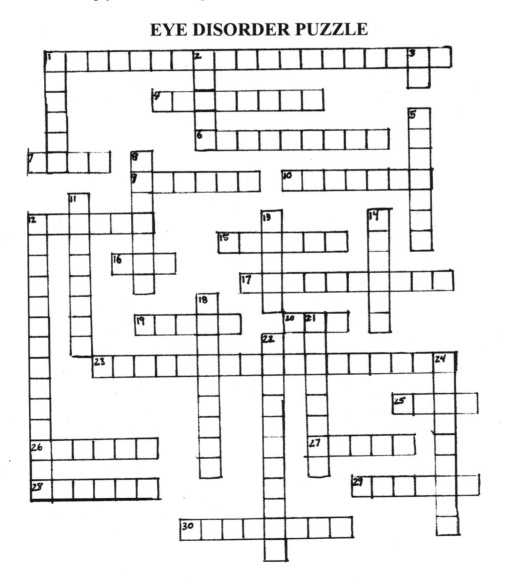

EYE DISORDER PUZZLE
CLUES

ACROSS

1. _____ _____ is one of the leading causes of visual loss in the elderly.

4. The medical term for double vision is _____.

6. Better visual acuity at a distance is known as _____.

7. Seeing a _____ around a light may indicate glaucoma.

9. When instilling ophthalmic drops or ointment, instruct the client to _____ _____.

10. The _____ is the angle at either end of the slit between the eyelids.

12. The _____ is the clear structure that covers the iris and pupil.

15. Often wounds of the eye, such as burns, can result in corneal _____.

16. A _____ may be one of the presenting symptoms in a client with a detached retina.

17. Deviation of the position of the eye is known as _____.

19. _____ are retinal cells that are receptive to colors in bright environments.

20. _____ is one of the distinctive criteria when considering diagnosis of the eyes.

23. A client complaint of a "curtain coming over the eye" is an indication of a _____ _____.

25. The _____ of the eye bends the light rays and allows them to fall on the retina.

26. An enucleation is often necessary for the treatment of _____.

27. To avoid eye infections, eye cosmetics should be changed every _____.

28. The _____ is the white collagen fibrous body covering the "white" of the eye.

29. The distance to place the client from the chart when doing an eye test is _____ feet.

30. The letters, O. D. indicate: _____ _____.

DOWN

1. _____ is the medical term for a person who is nearsighted.

2. _____ perception is lost without binocular vision.

3. Left eye is indicated in medical terminology by the letters __ __.

5. _____ of the tear duct is the first line of treatment for an infant whose tear duct is clogged.

8. Spots that drift into the line of vision are really vitreous humor debris and are known as _____.

11. The initial care for the chemical splash to the eye is to _____ the affected eye.

12. _____ may be caused by an allergen or a bacterial infection.

13. Immediate care by an ophthalmologist is needed for _____ glaucoma.

14. A "droopy eyelid" is known as _____.

18. _____ is inflammation of the cornea.

21. Elevated intraocular pressure causes _____.

22. _____ _____ is a clinical manifestation of cataract formation.

24. A _____ is the instrument used to measure the pressure in the anterior chamber of the eye.

ARTHITIS AND CONNECTIVE TISSUE DISORDER PUZZLE

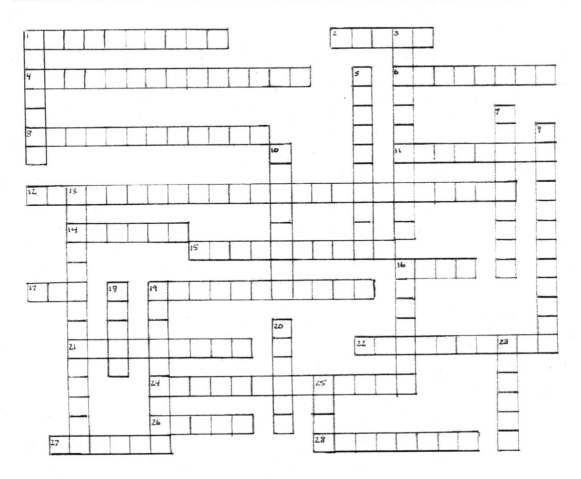

ARTHITIS AND CONNECTIVE TISSUE DISORDER PUZZLE
CLUES

ACROSS

1. _____ is a drug that may be used in the treatment of gouty arthritis.

2. The _____ may be affected in systemic lupus erythematosus causing confusion and memory loss.

4. When a client has had joint replacement, _____ is one of the most important factors for a successful outcome.

6. Loss of _____ is a characteristic of all kinds of arthritic diseases.

8. _____ of the great toe is the most common early manifestation of gouty arthritis.

11. An _____ _____ is a diagnostic serum test used to detect rheumatoid arthritis and/ or systemic lupus erythematosus (SLE).

12. _____ _____ _____ was once the name given to osteoarthritis.

14. Peptic _____ can result from the pharmacologic treatment of arthritis.

15. Clients who are prescribed aspirin must be monitored for the development of _____

_____ _____ .

73

16. A _____ high in purines is often a large factor in gouty arthritis.

17. Aspirin is also known as: _ _ _.

19. _____ _____ is transmitted by the bite of a tick of found on deer.

21. _____ _____ on stairs and around the tubs in the bathrooms are changes that would help the client with arthritis.

22. After joint replacement surgery the client must be carefully observed for the possible formation of _____.

24. Most joint replacements are done for people with _____ to relieve pain and restore loss of function.

26. A major goal in treating a client with SLE is to preserve _____ function.

27. _ _ _ _ _ _ is the acronym for nonsteroidal anti-inflammatory drugs.

28. _____ lupus erythematosus involves clinical manifestations in many systems of the body.

DOWN

1. Rheumatoid arthritis is _____, systemic disease involving the connective tissue in the joints.

3. The client with arthritis will do better when given adequate _____ about the disease.

5. One of the diagnostic tests for sepsis is _____ of the affected joint.

7. Clinical manifestation that may be seen in the client with SLE is a _____ rash on the face.

9. _ _ _ _____ in osteoarthritis show narrowing of the joint spaces.

10. _____ syndrome is the lessening of lacrimal and salivary gland secretions.

13. _____ _____ is a metabolic disease of the bone where purine metabolism is changed which results in increased uric acid.

15. _____ is the acronym for immunosuppressive drugs used in rheumatoid arthritis.

18. SLE is more common in the _____ adult.

19. When constructing steps to aid the client with arthritis, it is important to install _____ _____.

20. _____ arthritis most often occurs in the large joints.

23. Excess _____ may be placed on other joints when joint replacement surgery is delayed.

25. The arthritic client should be taught to lift loose _____ from the floor to avoid trips and falls.

Puzzles were developed by Elsie H. Mastorovich, BSN, RN

BINGO

Another suggestion is developing a bingo game for hard to remember facts such as fluid and electrolyte lab values and blood gases. We have included a bingo game on the following pages that can be used to learn different lab values. To play the game cut out the bingo cards provided and give each player one. The corresponding lab values can also be cut out of this book and taped on index cards. The cards are then shuffled. A moderator then selects an index card and reads the lab value presented. The players must then remember the corresponding lab test. After identifying the appropriate test, the player places a marker on that space. When a player has a complete vertical, horizontal or diagonal row of markers, that player yells BINGO to win the game. The game can be made easier by having the moderator announce both the test as well as the lab value (e.g., K+ = 3.8-5.0 meq/L). This may be helpful when first learning the values and the more difficult way may be used to actually test what you know.

BINGO LAB VALUES

Albumin = 3.5-5.0gm/dl

Alanine aminotransferase (SGPT) = 10-40u/ml

Ammonia (NH_4) = 40-80mcg/dl

Amylase = 60-160 u/dl

Arterial pH = 7.35-7.45

Aspartate aminotransferase (SGOT) =7-40u/ml

Blood Urea Nitrogen (BUN) = 10-20 mg/dl

Calcium (Ca+) = 8.5-10.5mg/dl

Carbon Dioxide ($PaCO_2$) = 35-45mmHg

Chloride (Cl^-) = 95-105meq/L

Creatinine = 0.7-1.4 mg/dl

Fasting Blood Glucose (FBG) = 60-110mg/dl

Hemoglobin for men (Hgb m) = 13-18gm/dl

Hemoglobin for women (Hgb w) = 12-15gm/dl

Hematocrit for men (Hct m) = 42-50%

Hematocrit for women (Hct w) = 40-48 %

International Normalized Ratio (INR) = 1-1.3

Lipase = 0.2-1.5u/ml

Magnesium (Mg) = 1.3-2.4 meq/l

Oxygen saturation (SaO_2) = 94-100%

Partial thromboplastin time (PTT) = 20-45 sec

Platelets (Plts) = 100,000-400,000/mm^3

Potassium (K+) = 3.8-5meq/dl

Prothrombin time (PT) = 9.5-12 seconds

Red Blood Cells for men (RBC m) = 4.6-$6.2x10^{12}$/L

Red Blood Cells for women (RBC w) =4.2-5.4 x 10^{12}/L

Sodium (Na+) = 135-145meq/L

Thyroxine (T_4) = 4.5-11.5mcg/dl

White Blood Cells (WBC) = 5,000-10,000

B	I	N	G	O
PTT	PT	Hct (m)	Hgb (f)	WBC
Plts	pH	$PaCO_2$	Ca ++	SaO_2
FBG	K+	Na +	SGOT	INR
BUN	RBC (w)	NH_4	Amylase	Lipase
Cl^-	Mg	Albumin	Creatinine	T_4

B	I	N	G	O
Cl⁻	Na +	Mg	Amylase	PTT
Albumin	T_4	RBC (m)	BUN	$PaCO_2$
Lipase	FBG	PT	Creatinine	K+
Ca ++	SaO_2	WBC	Hgb (f)	Plts
NH_4	Hct (m)	SGPT	SGOT	pH

B	I	N	G	O
SaO_2	Amylase	FBG	Albumin	K+
SGOT	Lipase	Creatinine	Plts	SGPT
Na +	Mg	Hct (m)	Ca ++	T_4
pH	INR	BUN	$PaCO_2$	RBC (w)
PT	WBC	Hgb (f)	PTT	Cl⁻

B	I	N	G	O
Cl^-	Creatinine	Hct (m)	Hgb (f)	Albumin
Plts	pH	FBG	SGPT	Ca ++
SaO_2	SGOT	RBC (m)	K+	$PaCO_2$
BUN	Na +	NH_4	Mg	INR
PTT	Amylase	WBC	T_4	PT

NOW WHAT

NOW WHAT is a game we developed to help students take the information from their class notes and discussions and attempt to apply that information into a hypothetical clinical situation format. In other words, it is our intention to help the student make the connection between theory and practice. The work of nurses is to make good decisions using the information that they have. This means that they know when they need more information and how to use the information that they have to understand what is happening with their clients and what they can do about it. It also helps them to determine if what they are doing is safe, in the best interest of their clients and if it will work toward helping the clients meet treatment goals. On a frequent basis, a problem that nursing students report is that even though they can recite their notes forwards and backwards for the test, when they take the test, they find the questions shock and surprise them and they do not do as well as expected. Often the reason for this is that students study the facts but test questions often ask them to apply facts to a simulated clinical situation. It is our hope that this game will aid you in making this necessary transition in thinking. Below we have given you numerous examples of the **NOW WHAT** game. Read these examples and try to understand the nurse's thinking process. Look and see what the nurse is thinking, how the thinking progresses and how to clinically use the information. What you are looking for is not just the fact but why a nurse needs to know it and how it will be used in a clinical situation. The NOW WHAT game takes a basic clinical situation and shows you how to think through the information so that you can see how to use and apply the data to help in caring for the client.

To play the game with a group, have one student be the moderator and read aloud the situation. The moderator then asks, NOW WHAT? You can then either brainstorm together as a group or each take turns trying to think like the nurse who would be caring for this client. The moderator can stimulate your thinking by reading the bolded questions in each scenario. A point can be given each time a student is able to think like the nurse caring for this client. This game can also be played alone. Read the background information and bolded questions to see if you can think like the nurse who is caring for this client. After using the situations in this book, be creative and make up your own clinical situations using the NOW WHAT format.

NOW WHAT - ANXIETY

A 33-year-old recently married female requested an appointment at a mental health outpatient center. Over the past two months she has been having "spells" every time she goes to the basement to do laundry.

NOW WHAT? **What assessment data do you need?** The first thing you would want to explore is: **What does the client mean by spell?** The client tells you, "The spells started with thoughts that I was getting sick. My heart started pounding real fast and I felt like I couldn't breathe. Sometimes I get a terrible headache and start to shake. Lately they've been getting worse and I feel like I'm going to pass out."

NOW WHAT? **Where would you go from here?** Look at what the client just told you. **What do you notice about what she just said?** That's right; during a spell she has a lot of physical symptoms. You would want to ask her if she has been checked by a medical doctor. **How did she decide to come to the mental health center?** The client reports, "I was afraid I had a serious illness so I went to my doctor for a complete checkup. My doctor told me there is nothing physically wrong with me. He suggested that I come to the mental health center."

NOW WHAT? **What further assessment data do you want to explore?** As you remember the spells only started two months ago. You might ask the client, **"What has been going on in your life recently? What changes have you experienced?"** The client states, "I got married three months ago. My husband and I are very happy. But I do notice that I sometimes get very nervous."

NOW WHAT? Look at what the client has just told you. You would want to clarify what she means by getting nervous. **You could ask the client, "Tell me more about these nervous feelings you have."** The client tells you, "My husband works a lot of evening shifts and when I'm home alone is when I notice the nervous feelings. Most of the time, it's when I'm working in the basement. Sometimes the thought of going to the basement makes me feel nervous. I'm scared I'm going crazy. Nothing like this has ever happened to me before."

NOW WHAT? Let's review. **What do you know about this client?** We know that she is 33-years-old, recently married, and states she is very happy. She has physical symptoms without medical cause: heart pounding, sensation of difficulty breathing, headache, shakes, feels like she's going to pass out, feelings of nervousness especially when she's alone and thinks about going to the basement.

NOW WHAT? **What does all this information mean?** The physical symptoms that the client is experiencing have no physical basis and can occur with people who experience anxiety. This client seems fearful and unclear as to why she is afraid (which is the definition of anxiety). Obviously these symptoms are severe enough and they significantly concern the client enough that she went to her doctor and now to the mental health clinic. We need to find out how much these symptoms are impairing our client's ability to function. **"How do these symptoms affect your life? Do they interfere with you ability to carry out daily activities?"** The client tells you, "Recently, when I felt really scared, I asked my husband to stay home from work. Several times we have gotten into arguments when he has refused my pleading attempts for him to stay home with me. This past week, when he wouldn't stay with me, I called friends and begged them to come over. During the day I have problems focusing at work because I keep thinking about how my husband won't be home and I'll be there by myself."

NOW WHAT? Perhaps the nurse would want to share her observations with the client. The nurse might ask, **"I noticed that the nervousness happens when you're alone and start thinking about going to the basement. What scares you about the basement?"** The client says, "It's interesting that you would ask me that. It seems strange to me too. I'm not really sure. All I know is I just get this overwhelming feeling that something bad is going to happen in the basement. But I could never figure out what it is. And that's when the symptoms start."

NOW WHAT? Obviously the client is unaware of her thoughts that precede her negative feelings about going to the basement. She is unable to determine what that is at this time. In planning care for this client, you would explore with the client possible ways to allow her to feel safe in her own home and gently explore as the client is able to discuss the possible reasons for her overwhelming fear. This client obviously needs ongoing sessions with the psychiatric nurse, a psychiatric evaluation, and possible medication if her symptoms do not subside, so that she can function. The goals of nursing care would be to: provide a safe environment for the client, have her be able to stay by herself and get back to a functional level.

NOW WHAT - MAJOR DEPRESSION

A 35-year-old female who is an attorney comes to the mental health clinic. She reports having difficulty focusing at work and sometimes forgetting appointments. She tells a co-worker that recently she even has problems getting out of bed to get to work. Although she is well dressed her appearance has deteriorated in the past month. She spends most of her time at work in her office, rarely interacting with co-workers.

NOW WHAT? **What would you look at first? What is the important**

information in the above situation? The client has difficulty concentrating, problems focusing at work and forgets appointments. She is experiencing social withdrawal; she spends most of her time at work in her office. She has anergia (losing energy), she has great difficulty getting out of bed and her appearance is deteriorating.

NOW WHAT? **What would you do next? Based on this information, what further assessment data would you gather?** You might suspect that the client is suffering from a major depressive episode. **If so, what do you know about major depression? What else would you ask?** She told you about work, what does she do at home?

NOW WHAT? You might ask, "**Tell me what a typical day is like for you at home?**" The client states, "After I go to work, I come home. I feel totally exhausted. Half the time I'm too tired to make myself dinner. I lie around and think about all the things I have to do but I just don't feel like doing anything. What's the use? Sometimes I just start to cry for no reason. Then I just go to bed. But I have problems because I keep waking up and in the morning I don't want to get up because I haven't gotten any rest at night."

NOW WHAT? **How does this information compare to what you know about depression?** You might remember that the signs and symptoms of depression are: sad mood, change in appetite, lack of energy, change in sleep patterns, decreased concentration, feelings of worthlessness and hopelessness, social withdrawal, psychomotor retardation, recurrent thoughts of death and suicidal ideation.

NOW WHAT? **How do the client's data compare to these symptoms?**

Sad mood	Client reports that she cries often for no reason.
Change in appetite	She does not feel like eating or making herself dinner.
Lack of energy	Just lies around after work; she has so much she wants to do but does not have the energy.
Change in sleep patterns	She goes to bed early, has difficulty in continuing sleep and does not feel rested in the morning.
Decreased concentration	Problems focusing at work, forgets appointments.
Feelings of worthlessness and hopelessness	Says "What's the use?"
Social withdrawal	Spends most of her time at work in office.
Psychomotor retardation	She is too tired to do anything.

You know that suicidal ideation and thoughts of death are symptoms but the client has not mentioned experiencing them.

NOW WHAT? In order to be safe, you have to assess whether or not she is suicidal. What questions would you ask to elicit that information from the client? You know that you need to ask the client directly if she is suicidal and can do that with a question such as: **"Have you ever had thoughts of harming yourself?"** The client reveals, "Recently I have had scary thoughts about death and wonder if it wouldn't be better just to end it all."

NOW WHAT? At this point you may be frightened by her admission of suicidal thoughts. But you do not let your fear keep you from continuing. You would focus on your client. **So now what do you ask? "You have said these thoughts are scary to you. What else do you think about when you have these thoughts?"** The client says, "I started having these thoughts occasionally three months ago, since I lost that big case... Lately, I think about it all the time. I don't think I'll ever be the same person any more. I've really lost confidence in myself. I think the other people at work see me the same way. I think about that a lot and wonder if I'll still have my job next week." You know this client is having suicidal thoughts of increasing frequency, feelings of self doubt, has lost her confidence, and fears she is going to lose her job.

NOW WHAT? You need to find out more about the suicidal thoughts. You might ask, **"Tell me more about your suicidal thoughts. Do you have a plan for ending it all?"** The client replies, "It seems funny to talk about it. I actually have had fantasies about taking a lot of pills. But when I think of that, it really scares me and I don't think I'd ever do it."

NOW WHAT? Your client has admitted thoughts of suicide and a plan of how she would do it. Even though she has serious doubts about making an attempt, you know this needs further assessment and attention. **Now what do you do with this information?** Again with the principle of safety in mind, you know this information needs to be communicated to other members of the mental health treatment team, especially the physician. You also know that you must inform the client that you are going to do this and suggest that they schedule an appointment for her to see the physician. Also, the client must remain safe until seen by the physician so you make an agreement with her to call the crisis line or go to the emergency room if she is thinking about acting suicidal thoughts.

After the client sees the physician, she is placed on antidepressants and given an appointment the next day to see the nurse therapist.

NOW WHAT - MYELOMENINGOCELE

A newborn is admitted with a myelomeningocele. He was born by cesarean section. Due to alpha feta protein testing and ultrasound, the parents and physicians were aware of the defect prior to his birth. The baby is placed on a bed warmer, an IV was started in the delivery room and the infant is receiving an infusion of D10 in water.

NOW WHAT? **What would you assess first? What do you know about myelomeningocele?** It is a spinal defect in which there is a sac-like protrusion of the spinal cord, meninges, spinal fluid and nerves. Knowing that it involves the spinal cord, **what further formation do we need?** Safety is a big factor. You know that the spinal cord has come outside the body and is being protected by an intact thin layer of a transparent membrane. You can see the meninges and the spinal cord. Knowing the baby is on a bed warmer, **what would you think about?** You would need to protect the spinal cord so nothing would happen to it. **How could you do that?** First, you have to think about how to position the baby. You would not want the baby to lie on the spinal cord or something could happen to it. So you need to lay the baby prone (on the stomach). Second, the lights from the bed warmer are shining on the baby and can dry the sac out. Then it could tear, lose fluid or could get infected. **How can you stop this from happening?** You would have to keep it from drying out. **How can you do that?** You might place sterile saline soaked gauze over the sac to keep it moist and intact until surgery. Third, you do not want anything to get into the sac or it could get infected. **So how could it get infected?** Since the baby's in a prone position, when the baby has a bowel movement, the stool can get on the sac causing infection. So you might want to tape a piece of plastic over the baby's buttocks so the stool cannot reach the sac.

NOW WHAT? **What else do you need to assess? Where is the location of the lesion?** The nurse finds that the lesion is located at T_6. **How would the location of the lesion affect the child?** To a certain degree this will give you starting data.

NOW WHAT? Because of the location of the lesion, you would expect the legs to be affected. **How would you determine how affected they are?** You might conduct a neurovascular assessment. Using a sharp pin as a stimulus to the extremities, you might see that the legs are flaccid and the upper extremities withdraw to a pinprick stimulus. Since the lesion is at T_6 you would expect that bowel and bladder function would be impaired. **How would you assess this?** You note that the baby's diaper is dry even though he has been getting an intravenous infusion and it has been six hours since birth. He should have had his first voiding by now.

NOW WHAT? **So what should you do about it?** You know that it could be harmful for the baby not to void because having all that urine in the bladder could cause a bladder spasm, damage to the bladder tissue from the pressure or might even make the bladder rupture. It can also lead to an infection in the urinary tract. This means it is important to empty the bladder. **So how would you do that?** First you could try to credé the baby by applying firm gentle pressure over the bladder area. If the baby still does not void, you might let the doctor know what is going on and ask for a prescription for catheterization. The doctor agrees that the baby needs to be catheterized and prescribes it to be done every three hours if the baby does not void on his own.

NOW WHAT? **What other neurological assessment would you want to do knowing the baby has a myelomeningocele? What else do you know?** You know from reading your book in preparation for clinical that often babies with myelomeningocele also have hydrocephalus. **How can you tell if this baby has it? What does hydrocephalus mean?** It means excessive fluid in and around the brain. **How would you know if there is too much fluid in and around the brain? Where would it go?** Because the central nervous system is a closed system, you realize that it has nowhere to go, so the head would get bigger. **How could you assess this?** The best way to assess this is to measure the head. You note that it is 40cm which is above the 95th percentile for a newborn's head circumference. It is too big. Because the fluid has nowhere to go you also see that the fontanels are bulging and when you touch them, they are tense.

NOW WHAT? You would expect that the baby is going to have surgery to repair the problems by closing the wound and placing a ventriculoperitoneal shunt within the first 18 hours of life. Closure of the spinal column will help prevent infection and trauma. The shunt is placed to drain excess fluid from the brain into the peritoneal cavity via a one way valve.

NOW WHAT - PREGNANCY INDUCED HYPERTENSION

A 27-year-old primipara in her third trimester is at the doctor's office for a check up. Her blood pressure today is 144/94. Her pre-pregnancy baseline blood pressure was 110/78. The doctor prescribes a home health nurse to visit her to monitor her condition.

NOW WHAT? On the first visit **what assessment data would the nurse gather?** If the blood pressure was elevated you could suspect PIH. **What are the signs of PIH? What other assessment variables would you look for?** You know that preeclampsia (a type of PIH) may include high blood pressure, proteinuria and edema which developed after 20 weeks gestation. Now you should assess for those things. You take the client's blood pressure, weigh the client and check the urine for protein. Results are as follows: BP 148/94, 1+ protein in the urine, and the client has gained 2 pounds (0.8 kg) since her doctor's visit last week.

NOW WHAT? **What are other symptoms of preeclampsia and eclampsia?** You can check for edema of the legs, hands and face. You can check for headache unrelieved by rest and for visual changes. **What else would you want to check?** You could test her reflexes because you know that hyperreflexia is a symptom. You could monitor her blood for an increase in creatinine. You could also ask if she has been having any heartburn or diminished amount of urinary output lately because epigastric pain and oliguria are also symptoms of preeclampsia and eclampsia. You would teach the client to tell the doctor immediately if these occur. The client says, "The doctor told me I have to stay off my feet and I have to take a medical leave from work. Is this serious? I can't stay in bed all day. I feel fine."

NOW WHAT? You need to teach her about mild PIH and why precautions now would keep this problem from becoming serious. She needs to follow instructions and alert the nurse and physician to any changes. "You could put your baby and yourself at risk." She agrees to try to stay in bed as instructed. The client states "You mean the only thing I can do for this is to stay in bed?"

NOW WHAT? **What else could you teach her besides staying in bed?** Well, if her blood pressure gets too high it could be dangerous for her and the baby, so you would want to teach her how to take her own blood pressure. **What else would you want her to know?** Proteinuria and edema are signs of preeclampsia, so you could teach her to dipstick her urine for protein and weigh herself daily using the same scale. You would then tell her to call her obstetrician if she noticed any changes in her weight, blood pressure or urine. You would also want her to be evaluated by her obstetrician regularly to make sure that everything is alright, so you would encourage her to keep all of her prenatal appointments. The client then states "All of these things will tell me if I have a problem, but how can I prevent it besides bed rest?"

NOW WHAT? **What else would keep her blood pressure down?** You could teach her some relaxation exercises that she could do regularly each day. You could also teach her to do range-of-motion exercises. The client agrees to try everything that she was taught. You give the client the agency telephone number and schedule a visit for tomorrow.

NOW WHAT? On the second visit, you have made an appointment when the husband is available, to teach him about his wife's condition. **As you prepare to do the teaching, you first ask what he knows.** He says, "Well, she's pregnant." The nurse explains that in addition to being pregnant she also has high blood pressure. This problem needs to be treated and monitored or it could become dangerous. He asks, "What can I do about this?" You repeat the teaching you did with his wife and instruct him about how to take a blood pressure. After successful return demonstration, you ask that he take the blood pressure every day as soon as he gets home from work and record it to show the nurse at the next visit. If the blood pressure goes up greater than 10 points he should call the nurse. The nurse makes an appointment to see the couple again.

NOW WHAT? At the third visit the nurse takes the blood pressure and it is still elevated (150/98). The nurse asks to see a record of the blood pressures that the husband has taken. She notices that the blood pressure has been slowly creeping up over the last two days. The wife states she has been staying in bed but she has been getting restless and bored. She states "I've only been getting up a couple of times a day. I don't know what to do with myself."

NOW WHAT? **What could you suggest to help her?** Rather than getting up, you could have her lie on her right side occasionally if it is too hard to stay on her left side all of the time. We could also suggest some activities to decrease her boredom such as crafts, puzzles, or reading. The next week the husband calls and tells the nurse that his wife has a severe headache and is seeing spots before her eyes. The husband explains, "When I came home from work she was sitting there crying. She told me she couldn't take the dust anymore and had to clean the place."

NOW WHAT? The nurse knows that these are worsening signs and if untreated could lead to seizures. The nurse instructs the husband to tell his wife to lie down. She tells the husband to take her blood pressure. It is 160/110. The nurse calls the doctor. The doctor instructs the nurse to have the client go to the emergency department by ambulance.

NOW WHAT - CEREBROVASCULAR ACCIDENT

A 67-year-old man was just admitted with a left hemispheric cerebrovascular accident (CVA).

NOW WHAT? **What would you assess first?** What do you know about a CVA? A CVA or stroke occurs when there is a decrease or lack of blood supply to part of the brain. **Knowing that this is an attack to the brain, what would you need to think about?** Breathing is a major concern. The client knows to take a breath because his brain tells him to. We would need to assess his respirations for quality and rate. We note that he is breathing normally with a rate of 20 breaths per minute right now. **Why else would you be concerned about his breathing?** If the brain responds to the attack by swelling (cerebral edema) then we would need to be concerned about increased intracranial pressure (ICP).

NOW WHAT? **How might you know if your client had increased ICP?** The increased pressure in the brain could decrease the cerebral blood flow, causing the pressure to rise and the pulse to decrease. You take the client's blood pressure and pulse and note that they are 160/98 and 66.

NOW WHAT? Knowing that the client probably has increased ICP from the cerebral edema caused by a stroke, **how would you position him to decrease the pressure?** You would want to elevate the head of bed to promote venous drainage. The pressure could also cause him to vomit so how could you keep this from endangering the client? You could put him on his side so if he would vomit, he would not aspirate. You might also want to have suction equipment available in case he would vomit.

NOW WHAT? **What else needs to be assessed? What will be affected if this is a left hemispheric CVA?** You could perform a neurological assessment. The left side of the brain controls the right side of the body so we would check his ability to move and the amount of strength in his arm and leg. **How would you do this?** You could ask him to squeeze your hands with his, noting strength and symmetry. You could also ask him to push his feet against your hands. When you do these, you note that he has a weak right pedal push and weak right hand grasp. The motor strength in his left hand and foot are intact. You also see that he has a right facial droop and his tongue deviates to the right.

NOW WHAT? **What else would you assess?** Remembering that the speech area (Broca's area) is located very near the motor area of the brain, you might also expect him to have difficulty with communication. You noted earlier that when you asked him to squeeze your hand that he did. Therefore, he is able to understand simple directions. **What else might you want to assess?** Communication is a two way process so you also want to find out if he can clearly expresses his thoughts. **How would you do this?** You could ask him to tell you his name. He tries, but what he says is not understandable. You realize that he has expressive aphasia.

NOW WHAT? As part of the neurological examination you also assess his sight. **What would you expect to find?** If only one side of the brain is affected, in this case the left side, you would only expect half of the optic nerve to be affected. **What would this mean for the client?** If only half of the nerve is affected, you would expect half of his sight to be affected. More simply, he will only be able to see out of the left side of each eye. This is known as homonymous hemianopsia.

NOW WHAT? **What kind of interventions would be necessary for this client?** We have already positioned him to facilitate breathing and to reduce increased ICP. Knowing that he has right-sided weakness, **what else do you need to think about when positioning him?** We might be concerned about contractures. **How could you prevent them?** You could use splints, footboards, pillows or rolls to maintain body alignment. You would also want to change the client's position at least every two hours to prevent pressure sores. **How might you have the client move his weak extremities?** You could assist him by performing passive range-of-motion.

NOW WHAT? Knowing that the client can see out of only the left side of his eyes, **how would you want to adjust your care?** You could place objects such as the phone and bedside table on his left side. If approaching him from the right side, **what could you do so that he would not be startled by your "sudden" appearance?** You could talk to him as you approach. You could also tell his family members to do the same. His daughter does this but then comments to you "I know he is listening to me because he does what I tell him but his speech is so garbled, that he doesn't make sense."

NOW WHAT? You might want to explain that because of the CVA he has difficulty expressing his thoughts but he does seem to understand what people are saying. You might want to help the client express himself by encouraging him to use gestures, a picture board or even writing what he wants to say.

NOW WHAT - EMPHYSEMA

A 62-year-old client comes to the emergency department complaining of dyspnea on exertion and greenish sputum. He has a 5-year history of emphysema.

NOW WHAT? **What would you assess first? What do you know about emphysema?** Emphysema is a chronic condition in which the client has difficulty with expiration due to destruction of the alveoli. This could be causing the dyspnea on exertion. Therefore, you would want to improve his gas exchange by increasing his ability to expel air. Your first concern would be to help him breathe better. **How could you do that?** If his dyspnea is caused by exertion, the first thing you would want him to do is rest. You could check to see if he has a prescription for a bronchodilator and oxygen. You find out that he does and you administer them. **What do you know about oxygen administration for this client?** Knowing that if he has difficulty expelling air, the CO_2 would build up and hypoxia becomes the stimulus to breathe. If you give too much oxygen, he will have no drive to take a breath. He is prescribed 2L/min of O_2 via nasal cannula.

NOW WHAT? You know that 2L/min is within normal parameters. **What else would you do to help him breathe?** You could encourage him to breathe by using his belly muscles instead of his chest to help him get the air out. You might also teach him pursed lip breathing for the same reason.

NOW WHAT? The client also has greenish colored sputum. We know this is not normal and may be the result of a lung infection; therefore, we might want to obtain a prescription for a sputum culture. The sputum comes back positive and antibiotics are prescribed. While you are teaching the client how to take his antibiotics, he states "I don't know why I'm still having so much trouble breathing; I haven't had a cigarette for 3 months."

NOW WHAT? Even though he has quit smoking, you know that emphysema is a chronic condition in which irreversible damage to the lungs has occurred. **So what would you tell the client?** You reinforce that stopping smoking helps to prevent further damage. Since he does not believe he is improving since he quit smoking, you may also want to see what else could be contributing to his problem.

NOW WHAT? You could do an environmental assessment. You find out that he lives near a factory that emits a grey cloud of smoke all of the time. You could ask if anyone else in the home smokes. You find out that the client's wife also quit smoking when her husband did. She now asks, "What else can we do?"

NOW WHAT? You could teach the client not to go out when there is a high humidity or when the pollution is high. You would also want him to stay away from the factory as much as possible. **What else would you want to teach this client?** He was admitted with an infection and difficulty breathing. You could teach him ways to prevent an infection. **How would you do that?** You could encourage him to drink 6 to 8 glasses of fluids every day to keep the secretions moist and easier to cough up. You could encourage him to use his abdominal muscles to breathe and cough so he does not get too tired. Since he came in with dyspnea on exertion, you would want to encourage him to take frequent rest periods to conserve his energy. You could also suggest he see his doctor for routine check-ups, not just when he is sick. In order to prevent an infection, you might also suggest that he be immunized against the flu and Streptococcus Pneumoniae. The client agrees to try these but then asks, "How will I know if I do have an infection?"

NOW WHAT? **What would you teach him to look for?** He came in with greenish colored sputum. You teach him to look for a color change, an increase in thickness or increased amount of sputum. You know that infection is also associated with a fever so we could teach him to check his temperature. He also had an episode of dyspnea which could be caused by an infection so you would teach him to report any breathing difficulty to his doctor.

NOW WHAT- TYPE 2 DIABETES MELLITUS

A 50-year-old woman is admitted with a diagnosis of hyperglycemic, hyperosmolar nonketotic syndrome (HHNS).

NOW WHAT? **What do you know about HHNS?** It is a condition that occurs in people with type 2 diabetes where they become hyperglycemic with fluid loss. Unlike diabetic ketoacidosis (DKA) they do not lose large amounts of ketones and become acidotic. So, now that you know what it is **what should you assess first?** You could check her blood glucose to see how high it is. It is 389. If the client is having fluid loss you would be concerned about dehydration. **How would you know if the client is dehydrated?** Well, you could look at her skin and mucous membranes. You note that her skin turgor is poor and her mucous membranes are dry. **How else could you tell if she was dehydrated?** You could take her vital signs. You know that hypotension, tachycardia and increased temperature are all associated with dehydration. Her vital signs are: T-38.4°C, P-96, R-20, BP-102/68. **What else would you expect to be altered if she were dehydrated?** You could check her lab results to see if she had an electrolyte imbalance. You note that her serum sodium is 130 and her serum potassium is 3.0.

NOW WHAT?
What needs to be done to correct the HHNS? Well, if she is hyperglycemic, you would want to give something that would help lower those levels. Both insulin and oral hypoglycemics do this so **which would you expect to give?** You know that severe hyperglycemia can be dangerous and lead to neurological impairment, so **what would help the glucose drop faster?** Insulin would definitely work faster than an oral hypoglycemic which would have to go through the GI tract prior to being utilized. **What kind of insulin would you expect to be prescribed?** Again, you would want the one that would work the fastest. Intravenous drugs generally work faster than ones given subcutaneously; therefore you would expect to give regular insulin since it is the only one that can be given intravenously.

NOW WHAT?
What else do you need to do for this client? Remember she is also dehydrated and has an electrolyte imbalance. You would expect that the physician would prescribe fluids. You would want to replace the fluid loss as quickly as possible so you would expect that they would be given intravenously. **What kinds of fluids would you expect to be prescribed?** If the client is hyperglycemic, you would not want to start with fluids that have dextrose. Therefore, you could give an isotonic solution such as 0.9% NSS or 0.45% NSS. This would also help correct the sodium imbalance. **How could you correct the potassium imbalance?** The physician could prescribe that potassium be added to the solution. **When would this be done?** You know that potassium is excreted by the kidneys and if the kidneys can't excrete it, the potassium will build up in the client's bloodstream. So, you would want to make sure that the client could void before you would add any potassium to the solution. You rehydrate the client and give insulin as prescribed and the HHNS resolves.

NOW WHAT?
Before sending the client home, what might you want to assess? If the HHNS was caused by hyperglycemia, you might want to find out how she became hyperglycemic. **You could ask her to tell you about her day before she was admitted.** She reports that she has had the flu for the past week. Knowing that an illness such as the flu could lead to hyperglycemia with dehydration, **could this client have done anything to prevent the HHNS?** Well, you might ask if she followed the sick day rules for diabetics. She tells you that she has had diabetes for five years but has never heard of sick day rules. You then teach her the sick day rules.

NOW WHAT?
If this client has had diabetes for five years but never knew about sick day rules, **what else might she not know? How could you find out?** You might want to review diabetic teaching, but **where would you start?** You could start by assessing where the learner is and ask **what she knows about diabetes.** She tells you, "It means that I have 'sugar' so I have to take a pill everyday and I'm not allowed to eat foods that have a lot of sugar in them."

NOW WHAT? Based on this statement, **what would you teach her? What else would you want to know about her diet?** You might want to ask if she understands the exchange lists for diabetics. She tells you that she learned them once, but she thought that after they put her on the oral hypoglycemic she did not have to be so careful. She thought she only had to watch how much sugar she ate.

NOW WHAT? You could review the diabetic exchange lists and stress the importance of staying on it whether or not she is taking an oral hypoglycemic. **How would you know she understood the plan?** You could have her plan a mock menu for one week to see if she would be able to maintain the prescribed amount of exchanges. **What else could you do?** She tells us that she tries to eat foods without sugar. **So how could you teach her that sugar is not the only thing to consider?** You could teach her to read labels of foods to determine the amounts of calories, fat and other essential nutrients. She then says "If I do all of this, will I lose weight too? My doctor told me I'm 50 pounds over weight and I don't know how I'll ever lose that much."

NOW WHAT? **What else could you do to help her lose weight?** You could suggest daily exercise, such as walking. The client agrees to try this. If this client is going to walk daily, **what else would you want to teach her?** Knowing that foot and leg problems are associated with diabetes, **what specifically could you teach her? How could you prevent these problems from occurring?** You could teach her to inspect her feet daily as well as how to care for them by making sure no moisture gets in between the toes. **What about shoes?** You could teach her to wear shoes that fit well (not too tight, not too loose), not to have open toes and are comfortable for walking. **What kinds of things would you want to teach her to avoid in order to protect her feet?** You could discourage barefoot walking, using heating pads or shaving calluses. She agrees to do the above. The client is discharged to home and is scheduled for a follow-up visit in one month.

NOW WHAT - KNEE ARTHROPLASTY

A 64-year-old woman with a history of rheumatoid arthritis is admitted for arthroplasty of the right knee.

NOW WHAT? Knowing that an arthroplasty is the replacement of a joint, **what would you assess first?** You would want to know what her mobility is prior to surgery. She tells you that she has difficulty walking for long periods of time and cannot walk up and down steps without having severe pain. Because this woman is undergoing surgery, **what else could you assess?** You know that postoperative infection is always a concern, so you would want to make sure that she is free of infection prior to surgery. **How would you know that?** You would expect that the surgeon would prescribe a CBC with differential and a urine specimen for culture and sensitivity. Both tests are normal and surgery is performed. The client returns to the unit for postoperative care.

NOW WHAT? **What would you assess first?** You would want to make sure that the circulation to the knee and leg are adequate. **How would you do that?** You could conduct a neurovascular check to the affected leg and compare it to the unaffected leg. The toes are pink, warm and dry with quick capillary refill. Pedal, post-tibial and popliteal pulses are strong and regular. **What else would you need to assess?** You would also want to assess the flexion of the new joint. **How would you do that?** You could begin to put the knee through partial range-of-motion using a continuous passive motion (CPM) machine with predetermined settings that were prescribed by the surgeon. You find out that the client is able to move her leg in the CPM machine but tells you she would rather not use it because it hurts too much.

NOW WHAT? **What could you do for the pain?** You notice that she is prescribed patient controlled analgesia (PCA) but when you check the pump, you note that she has not given herself any medication since she returned from surgery two hours ago.

NOW WHAT? You need to find out why she is not using the pump. **How could you do that?** You ask why she is not using the pump and she says, "Someone came in to explain it to me but I was so sleepy, I don't think I heard much of what he had to say."

NOW WHAT? You need to re-teach her how to use the pump for pain control and ask her to give a return demonstration in the use of the pump. She does. When you check on her again in 15 minutes, she says she feels a little better, but points to the drainage bag and asks "Is all that blood from my knee? Is something wrong?"

NOW WHAT? **What would you tell the client?** Before responding to the client, you check the drainage bag and you note that there is 75ml of bloody drainage in the bag. **Is this normal?** You realize that most clients who have a total knee replacement have about 200ml of bloody drainage during the first 8 hours after surgery. So you could tell the client that this is normal.

NOW WHAT? **What else do you need to do for this client?** Other than pain medication, would you expect her to get any other types of medications? Knowing that she is at risk for a postoperative infection because of the large incision, **what might you expect the physician to prescribe?** Most likely you would be giving IV antibiotics prophylactically over the next two days. **What other complication of this type of surgery would you need to be concerned about?** What about a pulmonary embolus from a clot in the leg secondary to stasis? **What drugs would the surgeon prescribe to prevent this from happening?** The client would probably be prescribed either Heparin or Coumadin. **How would you know they are working? What lab values would you need to check?** PTT

91

for Heparin and PT for Coumadin. **How else could you check for an embolus?** You could check for a positive Homan's sign. **How would you do that?** You could ask the client to dorsiflex her foot and see if she has any calf pain. She has a negative Homan's sign and PTT and PT are within normal limits. Other than range of motion (ROM) exercises and anticoagulant therapy, **what else could you do to prevent a thrombus from forming?** If the thrombus would most likely form in the leg, you might want to apply antiembolic stockings as prescribed. The client has been steadily improving and is to be discharged on her fifth day after surgery. She will continue with physical therapy on an outpatient basis.

NOW WHAT? **What kind of discharge planning and teaching needs to be done?** Knowing that the client will probably need the assistance of a walker for a while, **what would you need to assess for in the home?** You would want to make sure her environment is safe, so **how could you do that?** You could ask if anyone will be at home to help her. She tells you that her husband is home and that her daughter will be coming in every day to see if she needs anything.

NOW WHAT? Now that you know that family members will be involved in this client's care, **how could you include them in discharge planning?** You could make sure you conduct discharge teaching when one of them is available. Both come in that evening to help plan for discharge. **What could you teach them so they could ready the home for the client's arrival?** Remembering that she will be using a walker, you might want them to remove scatter rugs or any cords that would cause her to trip. She will have difficulty navigating stairs but her husband tells you they live in a ranch style home without stairs. **What else would you want to teach?** What could go wrong after the client is discharged. You know that infection is always a concern after surgery so **how would she know if the wound became infected? What symptoms would you teach the client and her family to be alert for?** You would want them to check the incisional site for redness, warmth, swelling or drainage. You would also want her to report increased pain or fever as these are also signs of infection. **What else could happen when she gets home that would need to be reported?** You would also be concerned that the artificial knee would dislocate. **How would you know if that happened?** Well, if it were malaligned that would be one way. If that happened, **what would most likely occur?** The client would not be able to use that leg and would be in severe pain. The client and family verbalize comprehension of the discharge plan and go home to ready the house for the client's arrival.

NOW WHAT - SICKLE CELL ANEMIA

An 8-year-old boy is brought to the hospital by his parents. He has had a sore throat for 3 days and is now diagnosed as having a vaso-occlusive sickle cell crisis.

NOW WHAT? **What do you know about sickle cell anemia (SCA)?** It is a genetic disorder in which normal red blood cells are replaced by sickled ones. **So what is a vaso-occlusive crisis?** In vaso-occlusive crisis the sickled cells obstruct the blood vessels. It is often precipitated by an infection. Knowing this, **what would be your major concern?** If the blood vessels become occluded, this could lead to ischemia and necrosis.

NOW WHAT? **So what would you assess first?** If this could cause ischemia and necrosis, you might first want to make sure that it has not done any irreversible damage. **What systems would be particularly vulnerable to sickled cells occluding the vessels?** Knowing that ischemia to the brain could lead to a stroke or other types of brain damage; you might want to perform a neurological exam. You do, and the child is neurologically intact. If the small blood vessels in the lungs became occluded, this could lead to the child having difficulty breathing and eventually death if it is not treated. Knowing that this complication of SCA is also called chest syndrome, **how would you know if your client had it?** Well, if the vessels in the lungs were obstructed, the child would probably complain of chest pain. He would also have rapid respirations and difficulty breathing. If he was having a hard time trying to breathe, **what else would you see?** You might note nasal flaring or abdominal retractions. He might also have a fever or a congested cough. You take his vital signs and note: T-38.2°C, P-92, R-24 and BP-112/70. You realize that his temperature and pulse are slightly elevated but his respirations and blood pressure are normal. He denies any difficulty breathing but complains of "a lot of pain in my arms and legs."

NOW WHAT? **What could you do for the pain?** You would probably expect that the physician has prescribed some type of analgesic. **What do you think it would be and how would it be given?** The child told you that he was in "a lot of pain." **What does that mean?** You could ask him to rate his pain on a scale of 1 to 10, but **what if he was not able to do that? How else could you tell how much pain he was in?** You could ask him to show you by using the FACES scale and pointing to the face that matches how he feels. He does and rates the pain as a 5 on the FACES scale of 0 to 5. Knowing that the pain is severe you would expect him to be prescribed a narcotic such as morphine. **How would you expect that it would be given to provide maximum pain relief?** Continuous IV infusion would be better than oral medication because the client would get a steady amount of the medication instead of having to tolerate peaks and troughs. The child is prescribed morphine sulfate via IV continuous drip. When the parents see that you are giving their child morphine, they ask: "How will you know he won't become addicted?"

NOW WHAT? **What would you tell the parents?** Knowing that it is extremely rare for children with SCA to become addicted to pain medication, you could reassure the parents that addiction is highly unlikely. **How else could you help to minimize the pain?** The child complained of pain in his arms and legs. You know that this is due to the sickled cells clumping in the vessels, so what could you do to help dilate the blood vessels. You could apply hot packs or do passive range of motion to improve circulation.

NOW WHAT? **What else would you expect to be prescribed to help treat the crisis?** Knowing that this crisis was preceded by a sore throat, you would probably expect that the physician would prescribe an antibiotic after first determining that it was bacterial. **How would this be done?** The physician could prescribe a throat culture. An antibiotic is prescribed when the child's culture comes back positive for Streptococcus Pneumoniae. Keeping in mind that a vaso-occlusive crisis occurs when the sickled red blood cells are clumped together, **what could be done to change that?** Diluting the blood might help give the sickled cells more room and they would be less likely to cause an occlusion. **So what would you expect to be prescribed to dilute the blood?** The physician prescribed that the child receive IV fluids at a rate of 150ml/kg/day. **How else might you increase the amount of fluid the child receives?** You could encourage the child to drink more. His mother tells you he hates to drink water and rarely drinks anything unless it is with a meal. **What other sources of fluid could you suggest for this child?** You might try flavored ice pops, soups, pudding, gelatin or ice cream. The parents agree to encourage fluids but now ask, "How will we know if he is getting enough fluids?"

NOW WHAT? **What would you teach them? What are the signs of dehydration in an 8 year old?** You could teach them to check his weight (for a sudden loss), skin turgor and mucous membranes. They verbalize comprehension of these instructions. While you are teaching the parents, they tell you that they read that the purpose of red blood cells is to carry oxygen so should they also learn how to give their son oxygen at home?

NOW WHAT? **Is oxygen appropriate for children in vaso-occlusive crisis?** Knowing that the blood vessels have clumps of cells; **would the oxygen get to them?** Probably not. **What else could happen if the child gets too much oxygen?** It can cause bone marrow depression which would make the anemia worse. You teach the parents this and now they state: "Our son was diagnosed with SCA as a baby, but this is the first time we have ever had to bring him to the hospital. What can we do to prevent this from happening again?"

NOW WHAT? **What would you teach the parents about how to prevent a sickle cell crisis?** Knowing that red blood cells carry oxygen, you would want to teach the parents how to avoid things that would decrease the tissue oxygenation in their son. **What could those things be?** Well if the child were involved in strenuous activities such as contact sports that could use up his oxygen. The parents tell you that he is not involved in any contact sports, but he loves to swim. They ask, "Is he allowed to do this?" **How could you promote tissue oxygenation and still allow him to swim?** You can teach them to make sure he gets plenty of rest periods and does not tire himself out. **What else would lead to tissue deoxygenation? What kinds of environments would have low levels of oxygen?** You could teach the parents to avoid high altitudes or nonpressurized airplane rides. Knowing that the crisis was precipitated by an infection, **what could you teach**

the parents? You might want to teach them to keep their son away from anyone who they know has an infection.

NOW WHAT? **What else would you want to teach the parents?** Remembering that dehydration worsened the problem of vaso-occlusive crisis, you would want to teach them to keep their son well hydrated using the strategies presented earlier. The parents state they will now incorporate them into their routine at home. The child's crisis resolves and he is discharged to home with a follow-up visit in 2 weeks.

NOW WHAT - COLORECTAL CANCER

A 62-year-old man is admitted for a bowel resection and possible colostomy for cancer of the descending colon.

NOW WHAT? **What would you do to prepare this client for surgery?** If he were having surgery on his bowel, you would want to make sure it was empty. **How would you do that?** You would probably expect that the surgeon would prescribe enemas or laxatives. **What else would be prescribed to help keep the bowel clear?** If he ate, the residue would accumulate in the bowel, so you would probably expect that he would be on a full liquid diet until midnight before surgery. **What would happen then?** He would probably be NPO to keep the bowel clear and to keep him from aspirating during surgery. If the client is not allowed anything by mouth, **how would you keep him hydrated?** You would probably expect that he would be prescribed IV fluids. Knowing that a postoperative infection is a risk of surgery, **how could it be prevented?** You might also expect to be giving him prophylactic antibiotics as prescribed.

NOW WHAT? **What else would you be concerned about prior to sending the client to surgery?** You would want to do some preoperative teaching. While you are teaching the client what to expect postoperatively he asks, "Am I going to have to wear a bag for the rest of my life?"

NOW WHAT? **What would you say to the client?** Knowing that the colostomy is a possibility, you would not want to falsely reassure the client. You know that you need to further assess the client's needs. You could first find out what the client already knows by asking, "What have you been told?" He states, "The doctor told me he didn't know whether I would need one. I'm hoping I don't have to have one, but I guess I won't know until I wake up from surgery." **How would you respond to this client?** Often when clients make comments such as this, you feel uncomfortable hearing the client's distress, but you know that the client needs to express his concerns about surgery and the possibility of a colostomy. You overcome your anxiety and encourage the client to express his fears. You honestly answer any question he has.

The client has surgery and returns to your unit with an abdominal incision with staples and a dressing, a Jackson Pratt drain, an NG to low continuous suction, a Foley catheter, a descending colostomy, an IV infusion of D5 1/2 NSS with 20meq KCl/L, and prescriptions for IV antibiotics and narcotic analgesics.

NOW WHAT? **What would you assess?** You conduct a head to toe assessment and note: Respirations dry and unlabored, Lungs clear to auscultation in all lobes, Apical pulse strong and regular, Abdomen soft and nondistended with hypoactive bowel sounds, NG draining greenish brown fluid, Surgical dressing dry and intact, JP draining serosanguinous fluid, Stoma is brick red and slightly edematous, The IV is infusing without difficulty and the insertion site is without redness, warmth, swelling or drainage. The client progresses as expected. It is now the third postoperative day and you plan to do colostomy care teaching with the client.

NOW WHAT? **Where would you start?** You might start by telling the client to watch you as you change the bag and inspect the stoma. The client agrees to watch. You begin by getting out all of the equipment and proceed with the bag change. As you are doing this, he is looking out through the window.

NOW WHAT? **What would you need to do?** You would want to talk with the client about why he is not paying attention. You might ask, "It seems like you are having difficulty paying attention." He states, "Who would want to learn this, it's disgusting. I'm not going to learn this because I'm not going to do this." **How would you respond?** You might want to empathize with him by saying, "I understand that this is very difficult and takes some time to get use to." Knowing that it is important not to force the client to care for the colostomy before he is ready, you state. "You won't have to do this today, you can watch several more times before you have to do it." The nurse changes the bag and inspects the stoma. She then sits by the client's bedside and asks what specifically he is concerned about. He tells you, "This isn't normal, I won't be able to go out in public, it smells. What if I have a bowel movement while at work, everyone will know. I just don't see how I'm going to manage with this."

NOW WHAT? **What could you do to help him?** Based on the clients concerns you might consider contacting the ostomy society. You tell the client that the ostomy society is made up of people who have learned how to live effectively with their ostomies. You ask if he would like someone from this group to talk with him. He tells you that he would like to think about it. While he is considering his options, you discuss it with the treatment team. The next day the client tells you he would like to talk with someone with an ostomy. A meeting is arranged for the next day.

SUMMARY
This chapter offers several ideas of games that can be incorporated into the student's study sessions. The key here is that learning does not have to be as dry or boring as you

may think. Make a game of your study material and your recall of the material will be improved.

Eye Disorder Crossword Puzzle Answers

ACROSS
1. MACULAR DEGENERATION
4. DIPLOPIA
6. HYPEROPIA
7. HALO
9. LOOK UP
10. CANTHUS
12. CORNEA
15. ULCERS
16. WEB
17. STRABISMUS
19. CONES
20. AGE
23. RETINAL DETACHMENT
25. LENS
26. TUMORS
27. MONTH

DOWN
1. MYOPIA
2. DEPTH
3. OS
5. MASSAGE
8. FLOATERS
11. IRRIGATE
12. CONJUNCTIVITIS
13. ACUTE
14. PTOSIS
18. KERATITIS
21. GLAUCOMA
22. LENS OPACITY
24. TONOMETER

Connective Tissue and Arthritis Crossword Puzzle Answers

ACROSS
1. COLCHICINE
2. BRAIN
4. REHABILITATION
6. FUNCTION
8. INFLAMMATION
11. ANA TITER
12. DEGENERATIVE JOINT DISEASE
14. ULCERS
15. GI BLEEDING
16. DIET
17. ASA
19. LYME DISEASE
21. HAND RAILS
22. THROMBOSIS
24. OSTEOARTHRITIS
26. RENAL
27. NSAIDS
28. SYSTEMIC

DOWN
1. CHRONIC
3. INFORMATION
5. ASPIRATION
7. BUTTERFLY
9. X RAY FINDINGS
10. SJÖGRENS
13. GOUTY ARTHRITIS
15. DEMARDS
18. YOUNG
19. LOW RISERS
20. SEPTIC
23. STRESS
25. RUGS

10

DEVELOPING AN INDIVIDUALIZED PLAN OF ACTION

In this chapter we want to focus on helping you put all of the information together in order to develop your own individualized plan of action. Think about it as if you were developing a nursing care plan for yourself. You have written many nursing care plans for clients, now it is your turn to write a nursing care plan for yourself. Writing this plan will allow you to take care of yourself and take charge of your own test preparation whether it is for your first nursing exam or preparation for the NCLEX.

The first step in developing an individualized plan of action is self-assessment. Throughout the first 9 chapters you have been given many opportunities for self-assessment. Let's start by trying to pull your assessment factors together. Ask yourself:

1. "What are my patterns (strengths and weaknesses) as a test taker? What does my visual assessment tell me? In other words, what do I see in my practice answer sheets? What are my content weaknesses? Can I identify any specific areas of nursing content that will require more preparation?"

2. "How is my timing? Am I a slow starter? Am I a frenzied finisher? Can I usually do a nursing multiple choice question in about 50 to 60 seconds? How much time do I take? Do I procrastinate with studying and test preparation? What are my prestudy tactics?"

3. "What about my thinking during a test, or for that matter, while I study? Do I have a lot of negative thoughts that impair my test performance? Do I feel nervous? Do I experience the symptoms of test anxiety?"

4. "What about test taking or reasoning errors? Do I misread questions or 'what if' by adding information to the question that is not presented to me?"

5. "Do I have problems remembering information that I have studied? Does my mind draw a blank during the test?"

After carefully completing the self-assessment, you must develop interventions for your identified test taking problems. Now ask yourself the question, how you can best utilize the time you have to prepare for your upcoming test, taking into account the information that you know about yourself as a test taker? What specific strategies would you implement to address your specific test taking patterns?

Let's look at a few examples of student plans.

DJ'S PLAN

DJ is preparing for his comprehensive final in his first nursing course. As he conducts a self-assessment, he realizes several problematic test taking patterns. DJ recognizes that he has a problem with getting started. He has first question freeze. By the time he is half way through the test he has missed many questions. He gets better as the test goes on but by that time he has already done significant damage. DJ gets very nervous before a test. He gets butterflies in his stomach and sometimes gets a pounding headache. He frequently worries that he is going to be too sick to finish the test and worries that he is not going to know the answer to the next question. He definitely has symptoms of test anxiety.

DJ decides that he has to do something to calm himself down at the beginning of the test. The best way for him to do this is twofold: first he needs to start progressive relaxation training (discussed in chapter 4) and secondly, to work on some of his negative thoughts. To do this, he decides to try some cognitive restructuring and keep a journal separating his thoughts, feelings and behavior so that he can evaluate his thoughts in terms of how realistic they are. For individuals who have high levels of anxiety about starting a test, these two techniques have been the most helpful.

EMILY'S PLAN

Let's look at Emily, who is preparing to take the NCLEX. Emily has approximately one month to prepare for the NCLEX. What would be the most cost effective way for her to use this time?

As Emily looks at her self-assessment data, she notices that she makes a lot of test taking or reasoning errors, in that she misses questions because she misreads or misunderstands the questions. She also notices that she misses clumps of questions in a row. What would be the best way for Emily to utilize her time to prepare? First of all, Emily has two problems; her first problem is that she is making reasoning errors. For this she needs to do practice questions on a regular basis. Emily's best solution for this is to get several NCLEX or nursing test taking question books and do practice questions every day. Keep in mind that everyone preparing for the NCLEX (or any major nursing exam) should be doing practice questions, but because Emily's problem is in reasoning errors, she needs to make doing practice questions a daily routine. If test taking errors are a major problem for you, reviewing your text book and class notes will not solve the problem. Reviewing nursing content will help you brush up on areas that you are weak in but will not help your reasoning and problem solving skills that are necessary to pass the NCLEX. Emily's second problem is clumping. We have found that one of the best treatments for this is thought stopping (discussed in chapter 6). Other strategies to be used in combination with thought stopping, would be cognitive restructuring and/or completing a worry log, because usually the clumping is brought on by repeated negative thoughts that start to occur at the first question in the clump of questions missed.

KEN'S PLAN

Ken notices that he also makes reasoning errors during a test. When he reviews the test with his teacher, he finds himself arguing with her about what the question is asking and tries to prove to the teacher that his answer is right. Ken needs to do practice questions on a regular basis and also review the test taking principles discussed in chapter three.

Ken assesses medical-surgical nursing as an area of content weakness. He studies chapter one to review the visual assessment skills. After several days of doing medical-surgical questions, he is able to be more specific about his knowledge deficits. It seems that only endocrine and cardiac questions cause him difficulty. Ken then decides to review those chapters in his medical-surgical textbook.

SARAH'S PLAN

Sarah's problem with test taking occurs before she even gets to the test. Her problem starts with test preparation. Sarah puts in many hours of study time; however, her test scores never reflect this effort. She is becoming increasingly frustrated and asks classmates and teachers for suggestions. She wonders what she is doing wrong. When

Sarah did talk with her teacher about her test preparation problem, her teacher suggested she use some of the metacognitive strategies. Sarah develops a plan to change her study habits and make them more effective. She incorporates mnemonics, talk to the textbook and the think out loud techniques into her plan of action.

These are a few examples of student self-assessments and plans of action. Remember, everyone's plan will be different. Do not assume that your testing strengths and weaknesses are the same as your classmates and, therefore, your test preparation should be the same as well. The following are general guidelines to utilize in selecting strategies for enhancing test performance. If you have a problem with feeling anxious prior to or during a test, the first strategy you may want to try is progressive relaxation. If you are troubled with repeated negative thoughts about your ability to succeed, try cognitive restructuring. If you are a clumper (missing several questions in a row) consider the thought stopping technique. If you have trouble maintaining your focus and miss the majority of your questions at the end of the test or practice session, try timing yourself and increasing the number of practice questions you do every day. If you have trouble with procrastination or ineffective studying, try the metacognitive and gaming techniques. In conclusion, if you select any of the strategies to enhance your test taking skills and find that they are helpful by decreasing your anxiety or just make you feel good about yourself as a test taker, use them. Remember, test taking success is individual and a combination of many variables. Your success will depend on your willingness to take a good, honest look at your strengths and weaknesses as a test taker. When you do this, you can develop strategies or interventions that are specific and individualized for you and you can take charge of your journey throughout your nursing education.

SUMMARY

Some final thoughts.....

1) Take control --- Don't wait for someone else to spoon feed you information. Become actively involved in enhancing your test taking skills.

2) Keep doing practice questions. Even though they scare you and make you nervous, they are one of the best ways to enhance your thinking.

3) Stay focused and set realistic goals. Keep plugging away. Doing a little bit every day will keep you from getting overwhelmed.

4) Be a cost effective learner. You want the most effective learning for the least amount of preparation time. Instead of studying in a haphazard fashion, try a systematic approach. Spend the majority of your time studying that information which is least familiar to you.

5) Believe in yourself. Everybody has weaknesses, so find yours and fix them. Remember there is a connection between your beliefs and your behavior. **It is the thought that counts!**

Last but not least we leave you with this poem. It expresses our belief that you can use good thinking skills to become successful on the NCLEX

THE NIGHT BEFORE NCLEX

Twas the night before NCLEX and all thru the schools

Not a GN was studying, they all felt like fools.

The textbooks were scattered in every room

With an air of anxiety and impending doom

The morning arrived for the career threatening event.

They dressed and they traveled to the big testing tent.

They stood and they trembled, as more people appeared

Their knees started knocking; hearts pounded with fear.

More rapid than eagles, they flocked and they gawked

They talked louder and louder, can this waiting last? Did you study?

Are you ready? Do you think you will pass?

I don't know, they kept asking, Am I up to this task?

Be quiet; don't talk now, the proctors exclaimed!

As they lined them all up and called them by name.

They stared at the questions, on the monitor screen

Where did they get these? They exclaimed in a plea.

They squirmed and they twisted in their uncomfortable seats,

Keep trying, they thought, don't admit to defeat.

Things started changing, a break long over due.

How did this happen? Here's one that I knew.

They started relaxing, they changed their cognitions,

Imagined they passed and got all of their wishes.

Their thinking became clearer as they completed the test.

Its over they sighed, we all did our best.

They traveled back home to wait on their fate

Some worried, some wondered and some overate.

The hours creped by, ever so slow

The high spirits they started with were becoming quite low

Then one bright sunny morning,

They awoke with a start

This must be the day, they felt in their hearts.

They went to their mailboxes nailed to a post,

They peered quickly inside; they were white as a ghost,

There it was in an envelope behind the new TV Guide,

If it isn't good news they'd just have to hide.

They opened the envelope and screamed with delight

Their hopes and their dreams had reached greater heights.

I did it! I did it! Look everyone. See,

I finally did it; it's a license for me!!!!

PRACTICE SESSIONS

with

ANSWERS AND RATIONALES

PRACTICE SESSION: 1

> **Instructions: Allow yourself 30 minutes to complete the following 30 practice questions. Use a timer to notify yourself when 30 minutes are over so that you are not constantly looking at your watch while completing the questions.**

1. A 44-year-old woman is admitted with pneumonia. She tells the nurse she has been taking hormone replacement therapy for menopausal symptoms. What finding during the admission assessment would most concern the nurse?
    a. Diminished breath sounds in the bases of the lungs.
    b. Redness and warmth of the right leg.
    c. Cough, productive for thick green sputum.
    d. Fatigue and muscle weakness.

2. A client is being evaluated for Addison's disease. The nurse understands that the client is more at risk of developing this disease if he currently has which diagnosis?
    a. Diabetes mellitus.
    b. Hepatitis.
    c. Sickle cell anemia.
    d. Irritable bowel syndrome.

3. A 60-year-old client with ovarian cancer arrived for her third chemotherapy treatment. Her white count is 1,500/mm. In addition to notifying the physician the nurse should:
    a. administer the prescribed chemotherapy.
    b. initiate bleeding precautions.
    c. instruct the client to increase high iron foods in her diet.
    d. instruct the client to report any increase in temperature.

4. A client is admitted following surgery for a ruptured appendix. The nurse would suspect the client has developed peritonitis if which was noted?
    a. The drainage in the NG tube suddenly decreases.
    b. Bowel sounds are hyperactive.
    c. Urine specific gravity decreases.
    d. A distended abdomen with rebound tenderness.

5. A client has been diagnosed with pernicious anemia. The nurse recognizes the client understands the teaching when which statement is made?
    a. "My disease is due to faulty absorption of minerals."
    b. "My daughter cannot inherit this disease."
    c. "My disease can be controlled by taking monthly vitamin B_{12} injections."
    d. "I will need to take vitamin B_{12} for about a month to be cured."

6. In planning nursing care for a client with auditory hallucinations, the nurse should consider that:
    a. silence indicates active hallucinatory behavior.
    b. distraction is an effective nursing intervention.
    c. seclusion may be used to stop the hallucinations.
    d. explanations that the voices are not real is effective.

7. While placing an IV in a client with dementia, the nurse is bitten on the arm by the client. The charge nurse should instruct the nurse to wash the arm with soap and water and:
    a. return to giving care.
    b. make an appointment with her primary care provider to be seen at the end of the shift.
    c. report to human resources to fill out an incident report.
    d. report immediately to the emergency department for evaluation.

8. A nurse is teaching a client about levothyroxine sodium (Synthyroid). The nurse documents that the client understands symptoms of hypothyroidism when she knows to report:
    a. poor appetite with weight loss.
    b. weakness and sleepiness.
    c. agitation and nervousness.
    d. heat intolerance.

9. A client is admitted with severe burns of the face and chest. During the acute burn period, which change in serum laboratory values would the nurse expect to see?
    a. Hypernatremia, hypokalemia.
    b. Increased serum albumin, hypernatremia.
    c. Decreased serum albumin, hypokalemia.
    d. Hyponatremia, hyperkalemia.

10. A client who had a brain tumor resection is being bathed by the nurse. The client looks down at the floor and quietly says; "I feel like such an invalid, I can't do anything for myself." The most therapeutic response would be:
    a. "It is difficult right now, I understand, but in time, you will feel better."
    b. "I think you need to understand more about what has happened to you."
    c. "Are you saying that you are feeling helpless right now?"
    d. "You sound angry, let's talk about how you are feeling right now."

11. A client is four hours postpartum and ready to ambulate for the first time. What is the appropriate nursing action?
    a. Assist the mother to first dangle her legs before slowly getting out of bed.
    b. Tell the mother how to use the call light in case she feels faint.
    c. Instruct the mother to walk very slowly the first few times out of bed.
    d. There is no special nursing intervention required.

12. A client who had a myocardial infarction in the morning has improved greatly and asks the nurse if she would help her to the bathroom. The nurse should base her response on the knowledge that:
    a. since the client is feeling better, she can increase activity as tolerated.
    b. the first 24 hours post-myocardial infarction is the most critical and the infarction could still extend.
    c. the client should be permitted to do as much as possible to decrease the stress level.
    d. clients on intravenous morphine sulfate (Morphine) should not be permitted out of bed due to possible orthostatic hypotension.

13. The nurse is educating a client who is diagnosed with a cystocele. Further teaching would be necessary if which statement is made?
    a. "I'll need to tell my doctor I have a latex allergy."
    b. "I should remove and clean the pessary every night."
    c. "I will practice Kegal exercises at least 30 times a day."
    d. "This is probably the reason I am incontinent when I cough."

14. A 6-month-old infant is brought to the well child clinic for administration of immunizations. After determining that the infant is well and has no contraindication to any required immunizations, the nurse will administer:
    a. Hepatitis A, Inactivated polio, Hemophilus Influenza B, Tetanus, Diphtheria, Pertusis, and Pneumococcal Conjugate vaccines.
    b. Hepatitis B, Inactivated polio, Hemophilus Influenza B, Tetanus, Diphtheria, Pertusis, Pneumococcal Conjugate, and Influenza vaccines.
    c. Hepatitis A, Hepatitis B, Inactivated polio, Hemophilus Influenza B, Tetanus, Diphtheria, Pertusis, Pneumococcal Conjugate, Influenza, and Varicella vaccines.
    d. Hepatitis B, Inactivated polio, Tetanus, Diphtheria, Pertusis, Measles, Mumps, Rubella and Influenza vaccines.

15. A woman just diagnosed with pelvic inflammatory disease is going to be treated at home. The nurse would include which instructions when conducting discharge teaching? Select all that apply.
    a. "Take your antibiotic with an antacid such as Mylanta to avoid stomach irritation."
    b. "Encourage your partner to be tested and treated."
    c. "Avoid sexual intercourse for four weeks."
    d. "Increase your water intake to ten glasses per day."
    e. "Take your temperature twice per day."
    f. "Return to the clinic for a follow-up evaluation in three weeks."

16. A nurse is caring for a client who has had a prostatectomy earlier that day. The client is complaining of severe abdominal pain. What should the nurse do first?
    a. Irrigate the urinary catheter as prescribed.
    b. Call the physician.
    c. Medicate as prescribed with a belladonna and opium suppository.
    d. Teach the client perineal exercises.

17. While a client is on heparin sodium (Heparin) therapy, it is the nurse's responsibility to monitor results of the:
    a. partial thromboplastin time.
    b. prothrombin time.
    c. potassium and calcium levels.
    d. hemoglobin levels.

18. A client with a history of rheumatoid arthritis is admitted to the hospital. The nurse would expect which symptoms when assessing the client?
    a. Joint crepitus.
    b. Heberden's nodes.
    c. Butterfly rash.
    d. Spongy joint swelling.

19. A client diagnosed with Type 2 diabetes is admitted to the hospital with complaints of frequent voiding, weakness and tiredness. A urine reduction reveals glycosuria; fasting blood glucose is 400mg/100ml. The nurse recognizes the manifestations as impending:
    a. diabetic acidosis.
    b. diabetic neuropathies.
    c. hyperglycemic hyperosmolar nonketotic coma.
    d. hypoglycemia.

20. A woman visiting her husband in the hospital says to the nurse, "I've had it, I can't take it anymore, unless he gets help with his drinking, I'm leaving him." The primary goal of the nurse's response is to:
    a. encourage the wife to attend an Alanon meeting.
    b. encourage the wife to attend an Alcoholics Anonymous (AA) meeting.
    c. tell the wife that she is doing the right thing.
    d. explain to the wife that her husband needs her now.

21. A client is prescribed a positron emission tomography (PET) scan of the head because the physician suspects a glioma. The client asks why he should have this test instead of a computerized axial tomography (CT) or a magnetic resonance imaging (MRI). The nurse bases her response on the fact that the:
    a. MRI might disturb the glioma.
    b. CT scan is a more invasive study.
    c. PET scan can locate the tumor much quicker.
    d. PET scan measures the tissue metabolism of the brain.

107

22. The nurse smells smoke coming from an unoccupied room. When she investigates, she notices that the trashcan is on fire. What should she do next?
    a. Pull the fire alarm.
    b. Put out the fire with a carbon dioxide extinguisher.
    c. Turn off the main oxygen valve.
    d. Evacuate the clients.

23. A client receiving hemodialysis is given a nursing diagnosis of: risk for injury related to folic acid deficiency secondary to hemodialysis. Based on this diagnosis, what would the nurse be alert for?
    a. Hypotension.
    b. Fatigue.
    c. Drop in PTT.
    d. Disequilibrium syndrome.

24. What teaching would be included in preparing a client with a new colostomy for discharge?
    a. The stoma will enlarge as the muscles relax.
    b. Sexual activity may be resumed.
    c. High fiber foods are restricted.
    d. Colostomy irrigations are contraindicated.

25. A 38-year-old man has been trying to stop smoking with the aid of a transdermal nicotine (Nicoderm) patch. Which client statement would indicate that he was having toxic effects?
    a. "I get a rash at the site of the patch."
    b. "I'm very constipated lately."
    c. "My mouth is so dry."
    d. "I'm nauseated all of the time."

26. A client in cardiac arrest is noted to have ventricular fibrillations. The nurse understands that this is happening because:
    a. the ventricles are quivering and cardiac output is minimal.
    b. electrical activity in the heart is at a standstill.
    c. the ventricles are beating too rapidly.
    d. the atria have stopped and only the ventricles are beating.

27. The nurse at adult day care suspects one of the clients is being abused by the home caregiver. The best course of action would be to:
    a. validate the findings with other sources.
    b. confront the caregiver.
    c. document the suspicions.
    d. refer the family for counseling.

28. When conducting health teaching about the medication prescribed for the client with gastroesophageal reflux disease (GERD), the nurse would include which statement?
    a. "Open the capsule and sprinkle the medication on your food."
    b. "Take your omeprazole (Prilosec) 30 minutes before breakfast."
    c. "You can decrease the dosage once you are feeling better."
    d. "Take your omeprazole (Prilosec) two hours after meals."

29. The correct sequence of cardiopulmonary resuscitation during a code situation is:
   a. Assess the level of consciousness, open the airway, initiate artificial ventilation, assess circulation, and initiate external cardiac compressions.
   b. Assess the level of consciousness, assess circulation, open the airway, initiate artificial ventilation, and initiate external cardiac compressions.
   c. Open the airway, initiate artificial ventilation, assess the level of consciousness, assess circulation, and initiate external cardiac compressions.
   d. Open the airway, assess the level of consciousness, initiate artificial ventilation, assess circulation, and initiate external cardiac compressions.

30. The charge nurse returns from break. Which situation should the nurse address first?
   a. A physician is waiting to give a verbal prescription for a STAT dose of promethazine (Phenergan).
   b. The emergency department is on the telephone to give report on a new admission.
   c. A maintenance worker is lying on the ground next to a ladder.
   d. An aide is reporting that a client's blood transfusion is complete.

STOP. You have now completed Practice Session: 1. Now take a few minutes and correct your answers. Calculate your accuracy rate by dividing the number of questions you completed correctly by the total number of questions you completed (30).

Correct answers ÷ total number of questions completed = accuracy rate.

_____ ÷ _____ = _____

ANSWERS AND RATIONALES
Practice Session 1

1. **The correct answer is b.** The question is asking what assessment finding would be vital for the nurse to know when caring for a client with pneumonia who is also prescribed hormone replacement therapy for menopausal symptoms. Estrogen has been implicated in thromboembolic disease. Redness and warmth of the leg would indicate a possible thrombus. A client with pneumonia would be expected to have diminished breath sounds (option a). Thick green sputum is indicative of an infection, which is consistent with the diagnosis of pneumonia (option c). Fatigue and muscle weakness are also symptoms that would be expected in a client with pneumonia (option d).
   Nursing Process: Assessment   **Client Need:** Physiological Integrity

2. **The correct answer is a.** The question is asking for a risk factor of Addison's disease. One risk factor of Addison's disease is history of other endocrine disorders. Hepatitis (option b) is a metabolic disease. Sickle cell anemia is a hematologic disorder (option c). Irritable bowel syndrome is an elimination disorder (option d).
   Nursing Process: Assessment   **Client Need:** Physiological Integrity

3. **The correct answer is d.** The question is asking what action is necessary when the white blood count is significantly low. Low white counts make the client more susceptible to infection. Reporting a temperature allows for prompt treatment of the existing infection, which then increases the chance of survival. Chemotherapy is contraindicated with a white count less than 2,000/mm (option a). No information is given about platelet counts (bleeding) (option b) or red blood cell count and indices (anemia) (option c).
   Nursing Process: Implementation   **Client Need:** Physiological Integrity

4. **The correct answer is d.** The question is asking how a nurse would know a client who had a ruptured appendix is developing peritonitis. Significant causes of peritoneal irritation include abdominal distention, rebound tenderness over the inflamed area and muscular rigidity. A sudden decrease in NG drainage may indicate the tube is obstructed (option a). Placement needs to be verified and tubal patency restored. Clients with peritonitis would experience hypoactive or absent bowel sounds (option b). Peritonitis can lead to hypovolemia that would cause an increase in urine specific gravity (option c).
   Nursing Process: Assessment   **Client Need:** Physiological Integrity

5. **The correct answer is c.** The question is asking what is true about treatment of pernicious anemia. Treatment of choice for pernicious anemia is vitamin B_{12} injections. Pernicious anemia is due to a deficiency of vitamin B_{12}, which may be treated with injections of vitamin B_{12} (option a). At first, B_{12} is given daily but then clients are managed with a 100mcg injection monthly (option d). The disease tends to run in families (option b).
   Nursing Process: Evaluation   **Client Need:** Physiological Integrity

6. **The correct answer is b.** The question is asking what to plan for a client who hears voices. Distraction is an effective nursing intervention because it provides a concrete alternative to the hallucinatory thought processes and helps define reality. Silence does not necessarily indicate that the client is hallucinating (option a). Seclusion is not a usual intervention with hallucinations. Hallucinations may still occur in seclusion, as it does nothing to interrupt them and may actually increase them due to stress or withdrawal from others (option c). Telling the client that the hallucinations are not real is usually ineffective because this is a defense the client uses and part of that client's reality. It will interrupt rapport with the client (option d).
   Nursing Process: Planning   **Client Need:** Psychosocial Integrity

7. **The correct answer is d.** The question is asking what should be done when a nurse sustains a human bite. A variety of human pathogens, including hepatitis, tetanus and HIV can be found in the mucous membranes of the mouth and can be transmitted through a puncture wound when blood from each individual can mix. The nurse must seek immediate attention so that

prophylactic tetanus and antibiotic measures can be instituted. Serum antibody levels can be drawn to determine if the nurse has been exposed to any specific pathogen and treatment can be started. The sooner these measures can be instituted, the better the prognosis for the nurse (options a & b). An incident report should be filed but this can be done after the nurse is evaluated and treated (option c).
Nursing Process: Implementation   **Client Need:** Safe, Effective Care Environment

8.   **The correct answer is b.** The question is asking what are symptoms of low thyroid. Hypothyroidism is a condition where metabolism is slowed resulting in symptoms such as weakness and sleepiness. Hyperthyroidism would result in poor appetite with weight gain (option a). The client would appear fatigued, apathetic and depressed (option c). Cold intolerance would be evident (option d).
     Nursing Process: Evaluation   **Client Need:** Physiological Integrity

9.   **The correct answer is d.** The question is asking what blood laboratory values would be present in a client with severe burns. Hyponatremia and hyperkalemia would be expected. Sodium is lost in large amounts into the interstitial fluid (options a & b). Normal sodium is 135 to 145. Potassium is released into the blood when cells are destroyed. This leads to hyperkalemia (option c). Albumin is also lost as capillaries become more permeable and albumin leaks into interstitial spaces (option b).
     Nursing Process: Assessment   **Client Need:** Physiological Integrity

10.   **The correct answer is c.** The question is asking how to respond to a client who expresses an inability to care for self. The nurse is attempting to help the client develop a clearer understanding of her specific feelings. This is necessary because the client's statements are not always straight forward when she is upset. Therefore, the nurse clarifies for both the client and herself. Option (a) is an example of false reassurance; the nurse does not know if the client will feel better. Option (b) avoids the client's feelings altogether. There is no evidence to indicate the client is angry (option d).
     Nursing Process: Implementation   **Client Need:** Psychosocial Integrity

11.   **The correct answer is a.** The question is asking how best to assist a post-birth client who is getting up to walk for the first time. Dangling first allows the body to compensate for possible orthostatic hypotension due to fluid loss during the birth process. Options (b) and (c) are also correct but not until after the client has been assisted out of bed. Option (d) is incorrect because dizziness and/or faintness may occur as a result of medications, fatigue, blood loss or hypoglycemia.
     Nursing Process: Implementation   **Client Need:** Physiological Integrity

12.   **The correct answer is b.** The question is asking what is true for clients' post-myocardial infarction. The first 24 hours after a myocardial infarction are the most critical. The goal of care during this period is to lower oxygen demands of the heart. Most clients are maintained on bed rest for 24 hours (option a). The client may feel as though she can be active, but should stay as calm and rested as possible to keep oxygen demands lower and lessen the chance of extending the injury (option c). Clients on intravenous morphine sulfate may be prone to hypotension and should be ambulated with caution (option d).
     Nursing Process: Analysis   **Client Need:** Physiological Integrity

13.   **The correct answer is b.** The question is asking which statement is wrong regarding the treatment for a client with a cystocele. A cystocele occurs when the bladder wall protrudes into the vaginal orifice causing the vaginal wall to bulge downward. Pessaries are used to keep the bladder in proper alignment. These devices are fitted and inserted by the gynecologist. They remain in place until the next gynecological exam. Many pessaries are made of latex; therefore, it would be important for the physician to know if the client had a latex allergy (option a). Kegal exercises are used to strengthen the pelvic muscles (option c). Symptoms of a cystocele include urinary incontinence, frequency and urgency (option d).
     Nursing Process: Analysis   **Client Need:** Physiological Integrity

14. **The correct answer is b.** The question is asking which immunizations are indicated for a 6-month-old infant. All required immunizations are listed in option (b) (Note: some states do require administration of Hepatitis A.) Hepatitis B and Influenza are missing from option (a). Varicella, Measles, Mumps, and Rubella are not administered until 12 months of age making options (c) and (d) incorrect.
Nursing Process: Implementation   **Client Need:** Health Promotion & Maintenance

15. **The correct answers are b, d and e.** The question is asking what the nurse should teach a client who was just diagnosed with pelvic inflammatory disease (PID). Oral antibiotics are given for 14 days. PID is most often contracted sexually; therefore, partners should be examined and treated as necessary. Increased fluid intake helps to rid the body of the causative organism. The client should be taught to monitor temperature to assess for worsening infection. Antibiotics should not be taken with antacids as they decrease effectiveness (option a). Sexual intercourse may be resumed after the course of antibiotics is completed (usually 14 days). If the partner is also infected, sex may be resumed 48 hours after being started on antibiotics and a condom is used (option c). The client should be seen in the clinic 48 to 72 hours after initial antibiotic treatment for evaluation of effectiveness (option f).
Nursing Process: Implementation   **Client Need:** Physiological Integrity

16. **The correct answer is a.** The question is asking how to respond to a client post prostatectomy who, complains of abdominal pain. First, the nurse should think about what might cause abdominal pain in this client. Blood clots can cause obstruction of the tubing and lead to over distension of the bladder. The pain can be relieved by ensuring the patency of the tubing by irrigating the catheter with 50ml of hypotonic glycerine solution. Calling the physician at this time is unnecessary (option b). Belladonna and opium (B&O) suppositories are often prescribed for bladder spasms; however, catheter irrigation should occur first (option c). Perineal exercises will strengthen perineal muscles and would be appropriate following discharge to enhance the ability to void; however, it will not help the pain caused by clots in the catheter commonly found on the day of surgery (option d).
Nursing Process: Implementation   **Client Need:** Physiological Integrity

17. **The correct answer is a.** The question is asking what laboratory value must be monitored in a client receiving heparin sodium (Heparin). Partial thromboplastin time (PTT) is performed routinely during heparin sodium (Heparin) administration. Prothrombin time (PT) (option b) monitors warfarin sodium (Coumadin) derivatives. Potassium, calcium and hemoglobin (options c & d) are unrelated to heparin sodium (Heparin) therapy.
Nursing Process: Evaluation   **Client Need:** Physiological Integrity

18. **The correct answer is d.** The question is asking what symptoms relate to rheumatoid arthritis. Joint swelling that is spongy or soft to the touch is a classic sign of rheumatoid arthritis. Joint crepitus (option a) and Heberden's nodes (option b) are symptoms of degenerative arthritis. Butterfly rash (option c) is a sign of systemic lupus erythematosus.
Nursing Process: Assessment   **Client Need:** Physiological Integrity

19. **The correct answer is c.** The question is asking which of the symptoms listed indicate a client with Type 2 diabetes. Hyperglycemic hyperosmolar nonketotic coma is seen when the function of insulin is severely inhibited with clients who have Type 2 diabetes. The condition results in very high glucose levels and glucose spilling into the urine. Resulting hyperosmolality initiates a major fluid shift resulting in diuresis and dehydration. Diabetic ketoacidosis is seldom observed in Type 2 diabetes because the client continues to produce insulin and utilizes some glucose thereby preventing the breakdown of fats (option a). Hypoglycemia is low blood glucose levels, usually below 50mg/100ml (option d). Diabetic neuropathies, while observed in both forms of diabetes, occur over a longer period of time and contribute to autonomic neuropathies and diabetic foot problems (option b).
Nursing Process: Analysis   **Client Need:** Physiological Integrity

20. **The correct answer is a.** The question is asking how the nurse should respond to a wife upset by

her husband's drinking problem. Alcoholism is a family disease. The nurse's responsibility is to guide the client/family into treatment and not tell them what to do (options c & d). Alanon is for the family members, especially the spouse (option a), while Alcoholics Anonymous (AA) is for the alcohol abuser (option b).
Nursing Process: Planning   **Client Need:** Psychosocial Integrity

21.   **The correct answer is d.** The question is asking why a positron emission tomography (PET) scan is used to check for the brain tumor rather than a different type of scan. PET scans measure tissue metabolism. This is done when the client inhales a radioactive gas or is injected with a radioactive substance that will emit a positively charged particle. This test can measure blood flow, tissue metabolism, blood volume and tissue density. This test is specific for gliomas because they have good perfusion with little oxygen consumption. A magnetic resonance imaging scan (MRI) utilizes a high magnetic force and reflects what is in the area being scanned but does not disturb it (option a). Computerized tomography (CT) scans are noninvasive studies (option b). CT scans; MRI and PET scans can all locate tumors (option c).
Nursing Process: Analysis   **Client Need:** Health Promotion & Maintenance

22.   **The correct answer is a.** The question is asking what should be done first when the nurse finds a fire in an empty room. The fire alarm should be pulled so trained personnel can fight the fire if it spreads. The nurse can then attempt to put out the fire with an extinguisher (option b). The main oxygen valve is then turned off (option c). There were no clients in immediate danger because the room was empty; therefore, evacuation was unnecessary (option d).
Nursing Process: Implementation   **Client Need:** Safe, Effective Care Environment

23.   **The correct answer is b.** The question is asking what the nurse should watch for if a client has a nursing diagnosis of risk: for injury related to folic acid deficiency secondary to hemodialysis. Think first about folic acid deficiency. Folic acid is lost during hemodialysis resulting in anemia and fatigue. Hypotension and disequilibrium syndrome (options a & d) are related to rate of fluid removal. The PTT (partial thromboplastin time) would be expected to increase, not drop, with heparinization (option c).
Nursing Process: Assessment   **Client Need:** Physiological Integrity

24.   **The correct answer is b.** The question is asking what teaching should be presented to a client being discharged with a colostomy. Sexual activity may be resumed. The nurse should promote discussion of concerns and strategies, which may facilitate comfort for the client and spouse. The stoma is expected to begin shrinking in size one week postoperatively (option a). Persons with colostomies resume normal diets and are not restricted unless other problems arise (option c). However, persons with ileostomies should avoid high fiber foods. Persons with colostomies may decide to manage their colostomies with regular irrigations, which may begin when the stool becomes soft, about one week after surgery (option d).
Nursing Process: Planning   **Client Need:** Health Promotion & Maintenance

25.   **The correct answer is d.** The question is asking what is a toxic effect of transdermal nicotine (Nicoderm). Nausea, vomiting, diarrhea (option b), salivation (option c) and dizziness are symptoms of nicotine toxicity, which need to be reported to the physician. A skin rash indicates an allergic sensitivity but not toxicity (option a).
Nursing Process: Analysis   **Client Need:** Physiological Integrity

26.   **The correct answer is a.** The question is asking what happens with ventricular fibrillation. The ventricles are quivering and there is minimal if any cardiac output. When electrical activity has stopped, the rhythm is called asystole (option b). Option (c) refers to ventricular tachycardia. The atria contribute only a small amount to the total cardiac output (option d).
Nursing Process: Analysis   **Client Need:** Physiological Integrity

27.   **The correct answer is c.** The question is asking what the nurse should do when it is suspected that an adult client is being abused. The nurse should document background information, any symptoms noted (such as bruising) and their severity. The caregiver and client's explanations of

how injuries occurred, other illnesses the client has (acute and chronic), self-care problems, and the client's social climate are also included. This information can then be used when reporting the incident. In some states, reporting suspected elder abuse or neglect is mandatory. Validating evidence from other sources (option a) takes time and also may be a breach of confidentiality. If a criminal case occurs, the police may investigate with the neighbors but it is not the role of the nurse to gather such evidence. Confronting the caregiver (option b) can be dangerous to the client. If anything, the nurse should try to work with the caregiver and client to resolve the problem. Referral of the family to counseling (option d) may be an appropriate intervention but can be analyzed and a proper plan of care devised for the family.

Nursing Process: Implementation　　　**Client Need:** Safe, Effective Care Environment

28.　**The correct answer is b.** The question is asking which statement would indicate the client understands the teaching regarding gastroesophageal reflux disease (GERD). Omeprazole (Prilosec) decreases gastric acid production and should be taken prior to meals, not after meals (option d). The capsules should be swallowed whole to promote absorption (option a). The dose should not be decreased or discontinued without consulting a physician (option c).

　　Nursing Process: Evaluation　　　**Client Need:** Physiological Integrity

29.　**The correct answer is a.** The question is asking about the correct sequencing of cardiopulmonary resuscitation during a code situation. The sequencing is logical. The nurse first checks the level of consciousness, and then opens the airway. If the client is not breathing, artificial ventilation is performed. The pulse is then checked. If it is absent, chest compressions are delivered. Option (b) is incorrect as the sequence is incorrect. Opening of the airway follows assessing of consciousness. Option (c) is incorrect, as one needs to assess the level of consciousness first, then open the airway, and proceed with artificial ventilation, assessing of circulation and cardiac compressions. Option (d) is incorrect, as the airway needs to be opened as the second step, followed by artificial ventilations, assessment of circulation and cardiac compressions.

　　Nursing Process: Implementation　　　**Client Need:** Physiological Integrity

30.　**The correct answer is c.** The question is asking which of four scenarios should be addressed first. Recognition of life-threatening illness or injury is one of the most important aspects of nursing care. Before a diagnosis can be made, recognition of dangerous clinical signs and symptoms with initiation of interventions to reverse or prevent a crisis is essential. Therefore, the nurse must first complete an initial assessment of the maintenance worker described in option (c) to determine the presence of actual or potential threats to life and then initiate appropriate interventions for the worker's condition. Therefore, options (a, b & d), which are not emergencies, would not be the nurse's first priority.

　　Nursing Process: Analysis　　　**Client Need:** Safe, Effective Care Environment

> **Instructions: Allow yourself 30 minutes to complete the following 30 practice questions. Use a timer to notify yourself when 30 minutes are over so that you are not constantly looking at your watch while completing the questions.**

1. The nurse is teaching the client with irritable bowel syndrome (IBS) about dietary management of the condition. Which client statement indicates understanding? "I will:
    a.   avoid all fresh fruits and vegetables."
    b.   drink three glasses of milk and eat two slices of bread every day."
    c.   eat bran cereal and fresh fruits."
    d.   eat lean meats and chicken."

2. A client with systemic lupus erythematosus (SLE) is admitted to the medical unit. The nurse would expect to assess:
    a.   joint pain, stiffness, decreased mobility and fatigue.
    b.   butterfly rash across the nose.
    c.   progressive loss of joint cartilage.
    d.   history of viral infection with latent paralysis.

3. A client is prescribed subcutaneous heparin sodium (Heparin). What is the appropriate technique for administering subcutaneous heparin sodium (Heparin)?
    a.   Inject the needle, carefully aspirate and, following the injection, gently massage the area.
    b.   Aspirate before injection but do not massage.
    c.   Do not aspirate before the injection but gently massage the area.
    d.   Neither aspirate before the injection nor massage after the injection.

4. What outcome would indicate that a client with a right-sided cerebrovascular accident (CVA) is responding appropriately to the treatment plan? The client:
    a.   performs active range-of-motion (ROM) to her right side.
    b.   appropriately dresses herself.
    c.   is cheerful and cooperative.
    d.   expresses herself clearly.

5. A 3-year-old child and his parents have come to the pediatric clinic to be screened for infantile autism. The nurse asks if there have been any behavioral changes. Which reply by the parents might relate to childhood autism?
    a.   "He says he hears a voice that tells him to hurt himself."
    b   "He panics when we are out of his sight."
    c.   "We rearranged the furniture in his room and he had a temper tantrum."
    d.   "He doesn't talk, but he will use his hands to gesture what he needs or wants."

6. A staff nurse is working with a student who is caring for a client who has a chest tube. The fluid in the apparatus does not rise with inspiration. The nurse should intervene when the student plans to:
    a.   check that the tubing is not looped.
    b.   milk the chest tube.
    c.   notify the physician.
    d.   ask the client to cough.

7.   The nurse plans to check placement of a nasogastric feeding tube prior to initiating feedings. The safest way to check placement would be to:
       a.   introduce air into the tube and listen for the "pop" with a stethoscope.
       b.   place the end of the tube in a glass of water to watch for bubbling.
       c.   listen for interrupted breathing patterns with a stethoscope.
       d.   aspirate the tube and observe for gastric contents.

8.   While preparing to teach a new mother about breastfeeding, the nurse remembers which hormones are responsible for initiating the mother's lactation?
       a.   Decreased levels of oxytocin.
       b.   Increased levels of prolactin with decreased levels of estrogen and progesterone.
       c.   Decreased levels of prolactin with increased levels of estrogen and progesterone.
       d.   Decreased levels of oxytocin with decreased levels of prolactin.

9.   The nurse is conducting a rectal cancer-screening program at a local church. The nurse teaches that a definitive diagnosis for rectal cancer is made through a:
       a.   sigmoidoscopy.
       b.   carcinoembryonic antigen (CEA) level.
       c.   colonoscopy.
       d.   biopsy specimen.

10.   A client has problems sleeping at night because of pain. An appropriate goal would be that the client would:
       a.   report an improved sense of self.
       b.   demonstrate a greater tolerance for activity.
       c.   decrease her anxiety level prior to sleep.
       d.   state she is receiving adequate rest.

11.   Which symptoms would the nurse expect a client with Meniere's disease to exhibit?
       a.   Vertigo, tinnitus and hearing loss.
       b.   Tinnitus, pain and increased appetite.
       c.   Vertigo, fever and headache.
       d.   Headache, hearing loss and fever.

12.   The nurse reinforces teaching of a diabetic diet with a client who states, "I can't afford to go out and buy all the diabetic foods needed for a diabetic diet." The nurse's best response would be:
       a.   "The physician can regulate your medicine to meet your usual dietary pattern."
       b.   "The diabetic diet is low in protein and high in simple carbohydrates so the diet isn't as expensive as you think."
       c.   "Your meal plan can be arranged to include foods regularly eaten in amounts needed to attain a desirable weight."
       d.   "The only special foods required are those substituting fructose for glucose."

13.   When teaching a client the correct use of a diaphragm for birth control, what should be included?
       a.   How to check for the string.
       b.   Proper time for insertion and removal.
       c.   Proper fit should be rechecked after a weight loss or gain of five pounds.
       d.   It can be safely left in place for several days.

14.   The nurse on the surgical unit realizes that the most significant factor in the development of postoperative respiratory complications in a liver transplant client is:
       a.   recumbency and inactivity.
       b.   hypoventilation.
       c.   irritation from an endotracheal tube.
       d.   irritation from a nasogastric tube.

15. A client with a basilar skull fracture is suspected of having cerebrospinal rhinorrhea when she complains of bloody drainage from her right nare. What test result would confirm the nurse's suspicion?
    a.   Drainage tests positive for glucose.
    b.   Drainage yields a positive guaiac test.
    c.   Presence of the "halo" or "ring" sign.
    d.   Presence of the Battle's sign.

16. During a dressing change, the nurse notes drainage from the abdominal incision. The nurse would be most concerned if the incision contained what?
    a.   Moderate amount of bleeding.
    b.   Small amount of liquid stool.
    c.   Large amount of purulent drainage.
    d.   Moderate amount of serosanguinous fluid.

17. A client is diagnosed with a pheochromocytoma after a tumor is found on the adrenal medulla. The nurse would also expect to find:
    a.   decreased blood glucose levels.
    b.   elevated blood pressure.
    c.   decreased pulse and respirations.
    d.   increased appetite with weight gain.

18. A client admitted to the labor suite is suspected of having placenta previa. The nurse should:
    a.   assess the client for vaginal bleeding.
    b.   assess cervical dilation.
    c.   monitor the uterus for board-like rigidity.
    d.   force fluids to maintain urinary output.

19. A client about to undergo cataract surgery is prescribed neosynephrine hydrochloride ophthalmic solution 10% one drop to each eye. The client asks the reason for the drops. The nurse would reply that the drops:
    a.   increase visualization of the eye.
    b.   reduce intraocular pressure.
    c.   constrict the pupils.
    d.   decrease pain after surgery.

20. The nurse walks into a room to check vital signs and finds the client is unresponsive. The initial action of the nurse would be to:
    a.   call a cardiac arrest code.
    b.   check for the presence of a carotid pulse.
    c.   deliver a precordial thump.
    d.   tilt back the head and observe for spontaneous respirations.

21. A client is prescribed 6mg/kg of theophylline ethylenediamine (Aminophylline) IV as a loading dose. The client weighs 75kg. The pharmacy sends two vials of theophylline ethylenediamine (Aminophylline). Each vial contains 250mg dissolved in 10ml. How many milliliters would the nurse draw up?

    _____

22. A nurse is assessing a liver transplant client. The nurse understands that the top of the client's T-tube was placed in the:
    a.   cystic and hepatic ducts.
    b.   common bile duct.
    c.   hepatic duct and duodenum.
    d.   pancreatic duct.

117

23. A psychotic client develops a dystonic reaction on the evening shift. The nurse's initial action should be to:
    a. observe the client to see if the symptoms worsen.
    b. call the physician for a prescription of diphenhydramine (Benadryl).
    c. tell the client to lie down and the symptoms will disappear.
    d. apply heat to the affected area.

24. A client is receiving furosemide (Lasix) 40mg BID. The nurse would be alert for which side effect?
    a. K^+ = 5.5mEq/dL.
    b. Ca^{++} = 7mg/dL.
    c. K^+ = 3.4mEq/dL.
    d. Ca^{++} = 11mg/dL.

25. A client was admitted to a psychiatric unit because of an inability to function at work. He believes he "doesn't have what it takes any more." Which nursing diagnosis would be most appropriate at this time?
    a. Dysfunctional grieving.
    b. Impaired social interaction.
    c. Alteration in thought processes.
    d. Disturbance in self-concept.

26. A client with pancreatitis has been prescribed parenteral hyperalimentation. The preferred site for the infusion of hyperalimentation is the:
    a. superior vena cava.
    b. subclavian vein.
    c. jugular vein.
    d. brachial vein.

27. In the immediate postoperative period for a client who has just undergone an aortic dissection, what is the priority intervention?
    a. Administer intravenous antihypertensive agents as prescribed.
    b. Assess urinary output every hour.
    c. Keep the client supine.
    d. Monitor vital signs, especially pulse and blood pressure, every hour.

28. A client hospitalized for tuberculosis is being discharged. The most important principle the nurse should emphasize in preventing the transmission of tuberculosis should include:
    a. explaining how tuberculosis is spread and the measures necessary to prevent its spread.
    b. explaining basic food groups and how a nutritionally adequate diet prevents recurrence.
    c. stating the name, dosage, actions, and side effects of prescribed medications.
    d. stating plans for ongoing follow-up care.

29. The nurse notes that a client's psoriasis is improving by decreased:
    a. keratinous silver scales.
    b. pustular hair follicles.
    c. sebaceous cysts.
    d. fibrotic yellow scales.

30. A nurse working in a prenatal clinic suspects utero-tracheoesophageal fistula (TEF) when the client exhibits:
    a. oligohydramnios.
    b. polyhydramnios.
    c. placenta previa.
    d. meconium stained amniotic fluid.

STOP. You have now completed Practice Session: 2. Now take a few minutes and correct your answers. Calculate your accuracy rate by dividing the number of questions you completed correctly by the total number of questions you completed (30).

Correct answers ÷ total number of questions completed = accuracy rate.

_____ ÷ _____ = _____

ANSWERS AND RATIONALES
Practice Session 2

1. **The correct answer is c.** The question is asking which statement about diet is accurate for a client with irritable bowel syndrome (IBS). Clients with IBS need to increase fiber in the diet to decrease symptoms. Eating bran cereal and eating fresh fruits will increase fiber in the diet. Avoiding fresh fruits and vegetables is incorrect, because that would decrease fiber consumption (option a). Milk, bread, lean meats, and chicken, while they may be healthy, are not high sources of fiber (options b & d).
    Nursing Process: Evaluation   **Client Need:** Health Promotion & Maintenance

2. **The correct answer is b.** The question is asking what symptoms pertain to systemic lupus erythematosus (SLE). The butterfly rash across the nose is the distinctive characteristic of SLE. SLE is a chronic autoimmune collagen vascular disease that involves multiple systems. The symptoms in option (a) are characteristic of rheumatoid arthritis. Option (c) is the major contributor to osteoarthritis. Option (d) is the pathology of gouty arthritis.
    Nursing Process: Assessment   **Client Need:** Physiological Integrity

3. **The correct answer is d.** The question is asking what is the appropriate technique for giving subcutaneous heparin. The nurse should not aspirate before the injection or massage following the injection. Aspiration (options a & b) can damage small blood vessels and could lead to hematoma. Massaging the area (option c) will increase the likelihood of bleeding. These actions are, however, appropriate following most injections.
    Nursing Process: Implementation   **Client Need:** Safe, Effective Care Environment

4. **The correct answer is b.** The question is asking for positive outcome behaviors in a client with a right-sided cerebrovascular accident (CVA). Clients with a right-sided CVA have paralysis on the left side and the brain does not acknowledge that the left side exists. If she is able to dress herself that would mean that she is acknowledging the left side of her body. The client would have no difficulty performing range-of-motion (ROM) on the uninvolved side of the body (option a). Clients with a right-sided cerebrovascular accident (CVA) often tend to be euphoric (option c). Since the left side of the brain is dominant for language ability in most people, speech difficulties would be apparent in a client who had a right-sided CVA (option d).
    Nursing Process: Evaluation   **Client Need:** Physiological Integrity

5. **The correct answer is c.** The question is asking what behavior change occurs with childhood autism. Autistic children prefer routines and repetition; therefore, changes in the environment of the child can cause extreme distress and anger. Hallucinations and delusions are not found in autistic children but may be found in schizophrenia (option a). Autistic children are socially isolative and are focused on their own world. These children would usually not notice if a person was in the room or not as long as the person did not interfere with his own space (option b). Autistic children have poor language skills with peculiar speech and lack of hand gestures for communication (option d).
    Nursing Process: Assessment   **Client Need:** Psychosocial Integrity

6. **The correct answer is c.** The question is asking which intervention is wrong. Although the chest tube has stopped fluctuating, options (a), (b) and (d) should be performed before contacting the physician (unless contraindicated). Tubing that is looped will allow fluid to accumulate and decrease the effectiveness of the chest tube (option a). Gently squeezing or milking the tube will help move phlegm and clots to the collection chamber and keep the tube patent (option b). Coughing will also help move trapped particles in the chest tube to the collection chamber (option d). If no cause can be found and corrected, then the physician would be notified.
    Nursing Process: Planning   **Client Need:** Safe, Effective Care Environment

7. **The correct answer is d.** The question is asking the best way to check for nasogastric tube placement prior to a feeding. Gastric contents would best demonstrate correct nasogastric

placement, as they would not be found elsewhere. In many clients, the other methods (options a, b, & c) may not demonstrate displacement even if the tube is located in the lungs.
Nursing Process: Evaluation   **Client Need:** Safe, Effective Care Environment

8. **The correct answer is b.** The question is asking what hormones start milk flowing in a breast-feeding mother. Prolactin levels increase and estrogen and progesterone levels are decreased to cause an increase in the volume of milk secreted as well as total output of nutrients (option c). Increased (not decreased) oxytocin can promote lactation (options a & d).
Nursing Process: Analysis   **Client Need:** Health Promotion & Maintenance

9. **The correct answer is d.** The question is asking the only definitive way to diagnose rectal cancer. Cancer of the rectum can be accurately diagnosed by pathologic examination through a biopsy specimen of the lesion during an endoscopic examination. Sigmoidoscopy and colonoscopy (options a & c) examinations can visualize the bowel and provide a method to obtain a biopsy but do not provide a definitive diagnosis. CEA levels are not useful as a screening test for colorectal cancer (option b).
Nursing Process: Implementation   **Client Need:** Health Promotion & Maintenance

10. **The correct answer is d.** The question is asking the appropriate goal for problems with sleep. Even though the reason for the lack of sleep is pain, the actual goal deals with the sleep. Stating adequate rest for her needs demonstrates the pain has been relieved or is being tolerated in a way that the client can now get sufficient sleep. Reporting an improved sense of self (option a) relates to an altered self-concept. Demonstrating a greater tolerance for activity (option b) relates to impaired physical mobility. Decreasing anxiety level prior to sleep (option c) relates to anxiety and might be a strategy for the identified problem if the client's pain is related to anxiety.
Nursing Process: Planning   **Client Need:** Physiological Integrity

11. **The correct answer is a.** The question is asking what are the symptoms in a client with Meniere's disease. Meniere's disease is not diagnosed until the triad of symptoms; vertigo, tinnitus and hearing loss, is present. Pain, increased appetite and fever are not typical symptoms of the disease (options b, c & d). Headache, nausea and vomiting may be present as secondary symptoms.
Nursing Process: Assessment   **Client Need:** Physiological Integrity

12. **The correct answer is c.** The question is asking how to assist a client who thinks special expensive food is required on a diabetic diet. A detailed diet history is completed with the client. Food preferences are incorporated into daily distribution of food groups. There are no special foods required on a diabetic diet. Restricted foods are primarily those containing refined sugar. Portion sizes are carefully controlled. The diet is limited because of possible complications of diabetes, therefore, medication is not changed to fit dietary patterns (option a). The American Diabetes Association recommends that 55% to 60% of calories come from carbohydrates but there should be a balanced mix between simple and complex carbohydrates, 12% to 20% from protein, and less than 30% from fat (option b). While fructose does not significantly increase postprandial blood glucose, it does have the approximate equivalent to sugar in calories (option d). It is not required in the diabetic diet.
Nursing Process: Implementation   **Client Need:** Physiological Integrity

13. **The correct answer is b.** The question is asking the correct instructions for using a diaphragm for birth control. In order for the diaphragm to be effective, proper instruction on insertion and removal is important. The diaphragm does not have a string as an intrauterine device (IUD) may have (option a). The proper fit should be rechecked after a weight loss or gain of 10 to 20 pounds (option c). A diaphragm should not be left in place for extended periods of time due to incidence of infection and increased risk of toxic shock syndrome (option d).
Nursing Process: Implementation   **Client Need:** Health Promotion & Maintenance

14. **The correct answer is b.** The question is asking why respiratory complications might occur in a client post-liver transplant. High abdominal incisions are made in liver transplants; therefore the

client becomes prone to postoperative respiratory congestion. This is due to the considerable incisional pain causing the client to take shallow breaths rather than deep breathing. Recumbency and inactivity (option a) are usually not a problem because postoperative clients are ambulated as soon as possible after surgery. The endotracheal tube (option c) may irritate but assists with ventilation. The nasogastric tube (option d) does not interfere with the respiratory status.
Nursing Process: Analysis   **Client Need:** Physiological Integrity

15.   **The correct answer is c.** The question is asking which is a positive sign of cerebrospinal fluid (CSF). The nurse permits the drainage to drip on a gauze pad or towel and observes for a circle with a pinkish center surrounded by a yellowish "ring" or "halo." The yellowish ring is CSF. Since there is blood in the drainage and both blood and CSF contain glucose, a positive glucose test (option a) would not help to determine whether CSF is present in the drainage. Guaiac test (option b) is a test for occult blood and blood is readily apparent in the drainage. Battle's sign (option d) is bruising behind the ear in the mastoid area.
Nursing Process: Analysis   **Client Need:** Physiological Integrity

16.   **The correct answer is b.** The question is asking which finding would indicate the client needs immediate attention. Liquid stool at the incision site would be indicative of a bowel perforation. The client needs immediate surgery to repair this leak. Any delay could lead to peritonitis, hemorrhage and septic shock. A moderate amount of bleeding (option a) would need to be further assessed but would not take precedence over a perforated bowel. A large amount of purulent drainage (option c) does indicate a possible infection, however, this could be treated with antibiotics. It also would not take priority over a bowel perforation. Serosanguinous fluid is often expected with an abdominal incision (option d).
Nursing Process: Analysis   **Client Need:** Physiological Integrity

17.   **The correct answer is b.** The question is asking what symptoms would occur in a client diagnosed with a pheochromocytoma. Hypertension is the most common manifestation usually sustained and resistant to treatment. The blood glucose levels will be increased due to excessive secretion of epinephrine and norepinephrine (option a). Increased pulse and respirations result from secretion of epinephrine and norepinephrine (option c). An increased metabolic rate would result in weight loss (option d).
Nursing Process: Assessment   **Client Need:** Physiological Integrity

18.   **The correct answer is a.** The question is asking what to do for a client who may have placenta previa. The nurse would assess the client for vaginal bleeding and monitor vital signs because visible bleeding may not be indicative of true blood loss. In order to assess cervical dilation, a vaginal examination would be done. This is contraindicated in suspected placenta previa because severe hemorrhage may result with even mild manipulation (option b). A rigid board-like uterus is related to concealed bleeding as in abruptio placenta (option c). The client is kept NPO because the treatment of choice is a cesarean delivery (option d).
Nursing Process: Implementation   **Client Need:** Safe, Effective Care Environment

19.   **The correct answer is a.** The question is asking why he is getting the eyedrops for cataract surgery. Neosynephrine is a potent mydriatic. Mydriasis or dilation of the pupil is helpful during surgery and examination to allow better visualization of the inside of the eye. (Remember mydriatic has the letters dia for dilate.) Miotics constrict the pupils (option c). Although these drugs decrease intraocular pressure (option b) and pain (option d) they are not required for cataract surgery. They are used to treat glaucoma.
Nursing Process: Implementation   **Client Need:** Physiological Integrity

20.   **The correct answer is d.** The question is asking what the nurse should do when finding a client who is unresponsive. Tilt back the head and observe for spontaneous respirations. Opening the airway by tilting back the head is the first step in cardiopulmonary resuscitation. It may be premature to call a code (option a) since cardiac or respiratory arrest has not been established. The airway should be opened before checking for a pulse (option b). The precordial thump (option c) is used in a monitored client who has had a cardiac arrest.

21. **The correct answer is 18.** The question is asking how much to give in the loading dose intravenously. First, find the total number of mgs desired by multiplying the body weight by the number of mg/kg.
75 x 6 = 450mg (what you desire to give).
Then determine how many mgs you have on hand.
250mg x 2 vials = 500mg in 20ml.
Now use the formula <u>desired</u> x quantity
                    on hand
$\frac{450mg}{500mg}$ x $\frac{20ml}{1}$ = 18mls

Nursing Process: Planning   **Client Need:** Physiological Integrity

22. **The correct answer is b.** The question is asking where a T-tube is placed in a liver transplant client. A T-tube is inserted into the common bile duct during surgery when biliary reconstruction is part of the surgical procedure. An end-to-end anastomosis of the donor and recipient common bile duct is performed. This ensures patency of the duct until the edema produced by the trauma has subsided. It also allows the excess bile to drain (options a, c & d).
Nursing Process: Planning   **Client Need:** Physiological Integrity

23. **The correct answer is b.** The question is asking how to respond to a dystonic reaction. An acute dystonic reaction requires immediate action. Symptoms will worsen if action is not taken and further observation alone is insufficient (option a). Symptoms will not be relieved by rest (option c) but only by administration of an anti-parkinsonian agent. Applying heat (option d) will do nothing to alleviate the symptoms.
Nursing Process: Implementation   **Client Need:** Physiological Integrity

24. **The correct answer is c.** The question is asking what is a side effect of furosemide (Lasix). Furosemide (Lasix) and other thiazide diuretics cause urinary loss of potassium. Clients with a potassium level of less than 3.5 (hypokalemia) are prone to cardiac arrhythmias and are also more sensitive to other medications such as lanoxin (Digoxin) (option a). Calcium levels (options b & d) are not as widely changed by furosemide (Lasix).
Nursing Process: Evaluation   **Client Need:** Physiological Integrity

25. **The correct answer is d.** The question is asking for a nursing diagnosis for a client who believes he has an inability to function. Self-devaluation would lead to a nursing diagnosis of low self-esteem. There are no assessment data to substantiate delayed grieving (option a), impaired social interaction (option b) or impaired thinking (option c).
Nursing Process: Analysis   **Client Need:** Psychosocial Integrity

26. **The correct answer is b.** The question is asking which vessel would be best to use for hyperalimentation. The physician performs the placement of the catheter into a large central vein. The vein most commonly used is the subclavian. The subclavian vein empties into the superior vena cava (option a). The innominate jugular veins (option c) may be used but are not the most common or preferred sites. The brachial vein (option d) is not a central vein and would be too small for this purpose.
Nursing Process: Planning   **Client Need:** Physiological Integrity

27. **The correct answer is a.** The question is asking which measure will maintain systolic blood pressure in the desirable range immediately after surgery is performed to repair an aortic dissection. Maintenance of blood pressure is critical to prevent complications in the immediate postoperative period. Intravenous blood pressure medications are given and the client is closely monitored. Assessing urinary output is an indication of renal perfusion and is more sensitive to poor perfusion than high blood pressure (option b). Clients are kept in a semi-Fowler's position to maintain blood pressure at an acceptable level (option c). They are not kept in the supine position.

Monitoring vital signs is done more often than every hour in the immediate postoperative period and does not alter the blood pressure (option d).
Nursing Process: Implementation   **Client Need:** Physiological Integrity

28.   **The correct answer is a.** The question is asking how best to prevent tuberculosis from spreading. Client teaching to prevent transmission of tuberculosis includes preventing contamination of air with tuberculosis and taking antituberculosis drugs as prescribed. While options (b), (c), and (d) are all-important in the discharge teaching plan, they are not emphasized in preventing the transmission.
Nursing Process: Implementation   **Client Need:** Health Promotion & Maintenance

29.   **The correct answer is a.** The question is asking which symptom relates to psoriasis. When psoriasis improves, it is freed of the plaques and shows healthy skin again. Pustular hair follicles may indicate folliculitis (option b). A sebaceous cyst involves sebaceous glands and hair follicles (option c). Yellow scales may relate to skin diseases such as seborrheic dermatitis (option d).
Nursing Process: Evaluation   **Client Need:** Physiological Integrity

30.   **The correct answer is b.** The question is asking what symptom in the mother might show that the fetus potentially has tracheoesophageal fistula (TEF). TEF must be ruled out in any infant born to a woman with polyhydramnios. A normal infant swallows amniotic fluid during intrauterine life. An infant with TEF is able to swallow the fluid but cannot retain fluid due to the closed esophagus. Oligohydramnios is an insufficient amount of amniotic fluid, which is primarily associated with urinary tract anomalies (option a). Placenta previa (option c) and meconium stained amniotic fluid (option d) are not associated with congenital anomalies.
Nursing Process: Analysis   **Client Need:** Physiological Integrity

PRACTICE SESSION: 3

> **Instructions: Allow yourself 30 minutes to complete the following 30 practice questions. Use a timer to notify yourself when 30 minutes are over so that you are not constantly looking at your watch while completing the questions.**

1. The unit secretary on the orthopedic unit reports that four clients are complaining and asked for the nurse. Which client should be seen first? The client:
   a. with Buck's traction complaining of constipation.
   b. in a leg cast complaining of pain unrelieved by the medicine.
   c. one day post-external fixation insertion complaining of wetness at the pin sites.
   d. in a cervical halter asking for pain medication.

2. A client with major depression is admitted to the psychiatric unit. What is most important in assessing this client?
   a. Amount of withdrawal.
   b. Self-destructive thoughts.
   c. Variations in mood.
   d. Type of sleep disturbance.

3. In planning care for a group of clients, which client would be most appropriate for the registered nurse to assign to the LPN?
   a. A client who requires discharge teaching on home IV antibiotic therapy.
   b. A client who is being admitted with a diagnosis of pneumonia.
   c. A newly diagnosed insulin-dependent diabetic client who is scheduled to perform return demonstration on self-administration of insulin.
   d. A client who is two days post-bowel resection with a nasogastric (NG) tube.

4. A client asks the nurse, "Is everything I say to you strictly confidential? I mean, you won't tell anyone." The most appropriate response by the nurse would be:
   a. "Of course, you can trust me, I will not repeat anything you say."
   b. "I cannot promise to keep something confidential when I don't know what it is."
   c. "Are you telling me that you find it difficult to confide in me."
   d. "That is a difficult question to answer, I'm not sure I understand."

5. A client has been receiving a tube feeding for the last three days. The client begins to have diarrhea. The nurse would suspect the cause of this problem is:
   a. an electrolyte imbalance.
   b. air in the tube.
   c. a full bowel obstruction.
   d. bolus feedings.

6. The nurse is reviewing arterial blood gas results for a newly admitted client. The results are: pH=7.30; $PaCO_2$=50; PaO_2=80; and HCO_3=24. The nurse realizes this is indicative of:
   a. metabolic acidosis.
   b. respiratory acidosis.
   c. metabolic alkalosis.
   d. respiratory alkalosis.

7. A nurse is caring for a client in renal failure. The nurse should plan interventions to manage which problems? Select all that apply.
   a. Hyperphosphatemia.
   b. Hypophosphatemia.
   c. Hyperkalemia.
   d. Hypokalemia.
   e. Hypercalcemia.
   f. Hypocalcemia.

8. A client is to wear knee-high elastic stockings to lower the risk of developing deep vein thrombosis. An appropriate intervention when applying elastic stockings is to:
   a. use stockings to relieve pitting edema.
   b. apply stockings prior to getting out of bed and standing.
   c. remove stockings once every 24 hours.
   d. apply stockings that are tight, smooth and wrinkle free.

9. An albuterol (Ventolin) inhalant is prescribed for a client who is diagnosed with asthma. The nurse would instruct the client to:
   a. inhale normally through the mouth and in mid-inhalation depress the inhaler.
   b. wait at least 10 minutes before repeating if more than one inhalation is prescribed.
   c. hold the breath for 45 seconds after inhalation.
   d. inhale deeply five or six times before inhaling the medication.

10. The nurse is interviewing a teenager who admits to using androgenous drugs in an effort to increase his overall muscle mass. With this information, what would be the appropriate nursing action for his general health maintenance?
    a. Be certain that milk is on every meal tray.
    b. Encourage a very liberal fluid intake.
    c. Make sure bananas and/or oranges are eaten daily.
    d. Arrange for extra desserts to be provided.

11. A client's intravenous access has extravasation. The nurse discontinues the intravenous access at that site because:
    a. a clot has formed at the end of the catheter.
    b. there is no longer a blood return from the catheter.
    c. the catheter tip has pierced the wall of the vessel.
    d. fluid has leaked into the intracellular space.

12. The nurse suspects that a client who has delivered a baby may have an infection. What would be indicative of a possible infection in a woman who is two days postpartum?
    a. Temperature of 101°F (38.3°C).
    b. Lochia flow moderate, rubra.
    c. Diaphoresis.
    d. Increased white blood cell count.

13. A nurse is conducting a group session for people with anorexia nervosa. A goal of the group may be that the clients realize that their continued eating behavior is due to:
    a. revenge.
    b. self-punishment.
    c. hunger.
    d. control.

14. A 29-year-old client with hemophilia is admitted to the emergency department following a minor traffic accident. Assessment reveals a swollen, very painful, right knee. In order to prevent deformity, the nurse would:
   a. administer aspirin and apply ice packs.
   b. apply a pressure dressing and ice packs.
   c. perform passive range-of-motion exercises.
   d. immobilize the leg and apply warm compresses.

15. The nurse is attempting to comfort a woman whose husband just died of a myocardial infarction. The nurse bases her approach on the concept that the grief this woman will probably experience is:
   a. a pathologic situation requiring therapy.
   b. a normal response to any loss or anticipated loss.
   c. an abnormal response leading to depression.
   d. a form of regression to an earlier stage of development.

16. A child with sickle cell anemia is at risk for infection because:
   a. the spleen has become dysfunctional with fibrosis.
   b. the cardiac output is significantly decreased.
   c. the skin barrier is broken with tissue necrosis.
   d. renal failure has increased circulating waste.

17. A client in the labor and delivery suite tells the nurse, "I think my water broke." The nurse should assess the:
   a. fetal heart tones and color of amniotic fluid.
   b. time since the last contraction.
   c. client's vital signs.
   d. results of the client's CBC with differential.

18. A client with dependent personality disorder stops working on her project and starts crying. She states, "I just can't do this. I need someone to help me and you won't do it. You don't understand that I'm sick." The best response by the nurse would be:
   a. "Just put the project away. You can start something easier tomorrow."
   b. "Sometimes you say this when things get hard and you don't want to stick to your task."
   c. "Yes, this task is hard but I guess you just aren't up to it."
   d. "I'm sorry but you have to stay until the task is finished no matter how long it takes."

19. A client was to be NPO after midnight due to morning surgery. The nurse notes the client received enteral feedings by gastric tube from 12:00AM to 6:00AM at a rate of 120ml/hour. The operating room has called to premedicate the client. The nurse should:
   a. premedicate the client and send to surgery as scheduled.
   b. notify the physician.
   c. call the operating room and cancel the surgery.
   d. ask the operating room nurse if the surgery can be rescheduled for a later time of day.

20. A home care nurse visits a 67-year-old client who lives with her husband. The client had a cerebrovascular accident. What is the priority assessment?
   a. Nature of the illness.
   b. Impact of the illness on the family.
   c. Degree of disability.
   d. Long-term care requirements.

21. When a postoperative client is in hemorrhagic shock, the client will probably exhibit which symptom first?
   a. Cold extremities.
   b. Tachycardia.
   c. Anuria.
   d. Cyanosis.

22. A client at the outpatient mental health clinic complains of increased anxiety when asked to speak in front of large groups at work. The nurse would expect the client to report which symptoms?
   a. Palpitations, shortness of breath, sweaty palms.
   b. Blunted affect, ambivalence, loose associations.
   c. Body image disturbance, flat affect, perfectionism.
   d. Illusions, increased salivation, depersonalization.

23. Following a seizure, a man with a brain tumor is confused and difficult to arouse. The client's wife asks, "What's wrong with him? Why won't he wake up?" The most appropriate nursing response would be:
   a. "This is probably a result of the hypoxia."
   b. "This is called the postictal period of a seizure."
   c. "There is usually a temporary period of confusion after a seizure."
   d. "Don't worry, he will be fine in a few minutes."

24. A client has undergone repair of a left fractured hip. Which assessment data may indicate a decrease in tissue perfusion to the operative extremity?
   a. Client complains of feeling pressure from the bed sheet on his toes.
   b. Client is unable to move the left toes.
   c. Left foot is cooler than the right foot.
   d. Pink color noted on toes of the affected foot.

25. A 13-year-old client is admitted to the emergency department with suspected inhalant abuse (huffing). The nurse would initiate which measure first?
   a. Administer epinephrine as prescribed.
   b. Assess for psychological risk factors.
   c. Insert a nasogastric tube to facilitate lavage.
   d. Prepare for ventilatory support.

26. A child comes to the emergency department after getting hit in the eye with a hockey puck. He is diagnosed with a hyphema of the right eye. Discharge instructions would include resting the eye and maintaining the child in what position?
   a. Right Sims'.
   b. Supine.
   c. Semi-Fowler's.
   d. Left Sims'.

27. What should be included in the plan of care for a client with hepatitis A?
   a. Teach the client's spouse about immune serum globulin.
   b. Tell the client to avoid intimate contact with the spouse.
   c. Schedule the client's large meal in the early afternoon.
   d. Encourage the client to ambulate three times a day.

28. How would a nurse position a client to prevent contractures?
   a. Lateral, head in line with spine, shoulders and elbows flexed and pillows supporting the head and upper arm.
   b. Supine with elbows extended, legs in a neutral position and the feet in plantar flexion.
   c. Prone, head turned laterally and supported by a pillow, arms adducted and a flat support under the pelvis.
   d. Supine, arms adducted and externally rotated, back supported by a pillow and the hips in adduction.

29. A client with chronic obstructive pulmonary disease (COPD) is being discharged from the hospital after an episode of pneumonia. Which statement by the client indicates understanding of the teaching about COPD?
   a. "My cigarette smoking has done damage but stopping now won't make any difference."
   b. "Next time I get a cold, I'll treat it early with cold medicine."
   c. "I'm going to start walking a little each day as much as I'm able."
   d. "For the Christmas holidays, I'm going to visit my son in Colorado."

30. A client is prescribed oxygen via nasal cannula. The nurse would best determine the effectiveness of this therapy by:
   a. auscultation of lung sounds.
   b. monitoring pulse oximetry.
   c. checking the nail beds for cyanosis.
   d. monitoring level of consciousness.

STOP. You have now completed Practice Session: 3. Now take a few minutes and correct your answers. Calculate your accuracy rate by dividing the number of questions you completed correctly by the total number of questions you completed (30).

Correct answers ÷ total number of questions completed = accuracy rate.

_____ ÷ _____ = _____

ANSWERS AND RATIONALES
Practice Session 3

1.   **The correct answer is b.** The question is asking which client's problem would be the priority from the four clients. Think about what each of the symptoms may mean. Pain unrelieved by medication may be a symptom of compartment syndrome where swelling may occlude the circulation causing ischemia. The physician should be notified immediately. Constipation (option a) may occur due to immobility of clients in traction. Increased fluids and fiber should be given to assist with positive bowel habits. Pin sites in external fixation devices should be cleaned every eight hours for the first few days. Some drainage in the beginning is normal and may feel wet to the client (option c). The sites should be assessed for signs of infection. Pain may occur while clients are in traction (option d). Nurses should teach clients to ask for medication before pain becomes too severe or it should be offered if the client does not request it.
Nursing Process: Analysis   **Client Need:** Physiological Integrity

2.   **The correct answer is b.** The question is asking what should be assessed with a depressed client. Assessment for self-destructive thoughts and behavior, including suicide, is the priority in order to maintain the safety of the client. Amount of withdrawal (option a), variations in mood (option c), and the type of sleep disturbance (option d) would all be necessary in proper assessment but would not be considered the highest priority.
Nursing Process: Assessment   **Client Need:** Safe, Effective Care Environment

3.   **The correct answer is d.** The question is asking which of four clients would be best to assign to a LPN. The part of the nursing process most readily delegated involves the components of intervention. Procedures such as NG tube care and IV therapy fall into this category. Nursing activities that are not within the scope of sound nursing judgment to delegate are: client health teaching described in option (a); nursing activities which require an evaluation of the client's response to the care provided, i.e. a client who is performing a return demonstration, as described in option (c); and nursing activities which require nursing assessment, as described in option (b).
Nursing Process: Planning   **Client Need:** Safe, Effective Care Environment

4.   **The correct answer is b.** The question is asking how to respond when the client is concerned about keeping all information confidential. The client must understand that information pertinent to his care and safety must be communicated to other health care professionals as appropriate. Information about the client should be held in strict confidence and not divulged to anyone who is not directly involved in the client's care. However, certain information may be shared with outsiders such as police when a client is suicidal and needs assistance (option a). The client is not indicating difficulty with trust but is asking for the parameters of the nurse-client relationship (option c). The client asked specifically about confidential information (option d) and is understandable.
Nursing Process: Implementation   **Client Need:** Psychosocial Integrity

5.   **The correct answer is d.** The question is asking what might cause diarrhea in a client receiving tube feedings. Bolus feedings can lead to diarrhea in individuals receiving tube feedings because it may be too much for the bowel to handle at once and absorption is inadequate. Electrolyte imbalance is often the effect of diarrhea, not the cause (option a). Air in the tube can cause nausea, not diarrhea (option b). Full or total bowel obstruction would produce absence of stool, not diarrhea (option c).
Nursing Process: Analysis   **Client Need:** Physiological Integrity

6.   **The correct answer is b.** The question is asking for an analysis of the blood gases. These blood gases represent respiratory acidosis. Normal pH is 7.35 to 7.45. To evaluate arterial blood gases, follow this procedure: First, evaluate the pH, a value below 7.35 indicates acidosis, a value above 7.45 indicates alkalosis (options c & d). Second, evaluate the carbon dioxide. If the carbon dioxide and the pH go in opposite directions, the problem is respiratory (e.g.; respiratory acidosis or respiratory alkalosis) (option a). In this client, a pH value of 7.30 indicates acidosis, and a

carbon dioxide value of 50 (normal $PaCO_2$ levels are 35-45mmHg) is high so it is respiratory acidosis.

Nursing Process: Analysis **Client Need:** Physiological Integrity

7. **The correct answers are a, c and f.** The question is asking what usual problems occur in a client with chronic renal failure. Hyperphosphatemia and hypocalcemia are present due to the decreased ability of the kidneys to excrete phosphate with a decrease in ionized serum calcium (options b & e). Potassium ion excretion is also impaired resulting in hyperkalemia (option d). Anemia may also be present because the kidney cannot produce erythropoietin, a hormone that stimulates red blood cell production, and red blood cell production is suppressed.

    Nursing Process: Planning **Client Need:** Physiological Integrity

8. **The correct answer is b.** The question is asking for the correct way to apply elastic support stockings. Applying stockings prior to getting out of bed prevents dilation of the veins and venous stasis. Elastic stockings are used to increase circulation and decrease the risk of venous thrombosis not to relieve pitting edema (option a). Stockings should be removed at least once every 24 hours to assess skin integrity (option c). Stockings should be smooth and wrinkle free so as not to impede circulation. Stockings should not be tight or they may impede circulation. The proper size should be determined by measuring the client's legs for a proper fit (option d).

    Nursing Process: Implementation **Client Need:** Safe, Effective Care Environment

9. **The correct answer is a.** The question is asking how to use an inhaler. The client should be instructed to exhale completely, and then begin to inhale, insert the inhaler, activate it and finish fully inhaling. Usually a minute is adequate between inhalations (option b). Forty-five seconds is much too long to instruct the client to hold her breath, 10 to 15 seconds is adequate (option c). Instructing the client to hyperventilate may be detrimental (option d).

    Nursing Process: Implementation **Client Need:** Safe, Effective Care Environment

10. **The correct answer is b.** The question is asking what to do for a client who has used androgenous drugs. These drugs have sometimes been ingested to "build up" or increase the muscle mass of the user. Use of androgenic drugs will often lead to elevated levels of sodium, potassium, creatinine, and especially calcium. Calcium intake may need to be limited, and adequate hydration assured to aid in the proper excretion of the mineral. Milk (option a) contains calcium, which is already elevated and will increase the problem. Bananas and oranges (option c) have potassium, which is already increased due to the drug and will worsen the condition. Extra desserts (option d) may provide extra calories but will not play a role in correcting the condition.

    Nursing Process: Implementation **Client Need:** Physiological Integrity

11. **The correct answer is c.** The question is asking why an intravenous access should be discontinued due to extravasation. The catheter tip pierces the wall of the vein or becomes dislodged from the vein, thus allowing fluid to leak into the interstitial space. The signs and symptoms of extravasation include: pain, swelling, a decrease in flow rate, and a cool clammy area surrounding the intravenous site. Option (b) does not answer the question and is also a common misconception. If the catheter tip has gone through the vein, blood may seep into the tissue and backflow into the catheter. Option (a) would result in the cessation of flow. Option (d) is also incorrect, fluid leaks into the interstitial spaces not intracellular spaces.

    Nursing Process: Analysis **Client Need:** Physiological Integrity

12. **The correct answer is a.** The question is asking for a sign of infection for this post-birth woman. Normal processes such as wound healing and dehydration may cause a temperature elevation to 100.4°F (38.0°C). Any elevation higher than that should alert the nurse to look for other clinical signs of infection. The other options (b, c & d) are normal postpartum occurrences.

    Nursing Process: Evaluation **Client Need:** Physiological Integrity

13. **The correct answer is d.** The question is asking what the dynamic is of people who have anorexia nervosa. Food and its consumption becomes a control issue in clients with anorexia

nervosa. The anorexic client's eating behavior is not usually motivated by revenge, self-destruction or hunger (options a, b & c).
Nursing Process: Planning   **Client Need:** Psychosocial Integrity

14. **The correct answer is b.** The question is asking which of the measures will prevent joint deformity in a hemophiliac with an acute injury. Controlling bleeding into the joint is the most effective way of preventing deformity. Application of pressure and cold is the best selection, offered to do this. Aspirin, range-of-motion, and heat will promote increased bleeding in the joint, thus leading to potential deformity (options a, c, & d).
Nursing Process: Implementation   **Client Need:** Physiological Integrity

15. **The correct answer is b.** The question is asking the type of grief this woman is experiencing. Grief is a natural reaction to an anticipated, real or imagined loss. Everyone experiences the pain and suffering of grief sometime during life. It is not pathological or abnormal unless the reaction is delayed or results in depression (options a & c). Although some behaviors may be regressive (crying), grief itself is not regressive but normal (option d).
Nursing Process: Analysis   **Client Need:** Psychosocial Integrity

16. **The correct answer is a.** The question is asking why a person who has sickle cell anemia can get infections easily. The spleen is, at first, quite enlarged from engorgement with sickled cells, and it has reduced phagocytic and reticuloendothelial functions. The spleen becomes progressively small and fibrotic due to repeated infarctions. The children become increasingly susceptible to infection because the spleen can no longer filter bacteria and release phagocytic cells. Option (a) is the primary reason for increased risk of infection, although options (b), (c) and (d) can exist and complicate the status of the child with sickle cell disease.
Nursing Process: Analysis   **Client Need:** Safe, Effective Care Environment

17. **The correct answer is a.** The question is asking what should be assessed first for a mother who has just released her amniotic fluid. Amniotic fluid must be present for the fetus to thrive. Determination of fetal heart tones is one way to assess the fetus' well being. If the color of the amniotic fluid is dark, this could be a sign of fetal distress. The fluid should be clear. Contractions would still be timed but safety of the fetus is a priority (option b). The mother's vital signs are not directly affected by the presence or absence of amniotic fluid (option c). Blood loss and/or infection are not evident, so CBC (complete blood count) would not be a priority at this time (option d).
Nursing Process: Assessment   **Client Need:** Health Promotion & Maintenance

18. **The correct answer is b.** The question is asking how to respond to a client with dependent personality disorder who cries and wants to quit her task. The client is being manipulative. In order to foster independent behavior, the nurse should encourage the client to identify manipulative behaviors that may block her abilities to succeed. This is the first step in helping the client follow through on her treatment goals. Option (a) allows the client to stop and rewards her manipulation. Option (c) also allows her to give up and reinforces dependent behavior. Option (d) will start into a power struggle with the client.
Nursing Process: Implementation   **Client Need:** Psychosocial Integrity

19. **The correct answer is b.** The question is asking what the nurse should do when enteral feedings were given to a client who is NPO prior to surgery. Food and fluid consumption is restricted eight to ten hours prior to any surgical procedure because of potential aspiration. Although the client was to be NPO, gastric tube feedings should also be held because these feedings could be vomited which leads to aspiration (option a). It is the physician's responsibility to cancel (option c) or reschedule (option d) surgery.
Nursing Process: Implementation   **Client Need:** Physiological Integrity

20. **The correct answer is b.** The question is asking the most important assessment parameter by the home care nurse. Since the husband will be caring for the wife when the home care nurse is not available, the impact of the illness on the family unit will determine the type of care and support

needed over a long-term basis. The family's beliefs about the illness may cause differences in the nature of the illness and the degree of disability. Nature of illness (option a), degree of disability (option c), and long-term care requirements (option d) are necessary to assess but may change as a result of how the illness impacts on the family.

Nursing Process: Assessment   **Client Need:** Health Promotion & Maintenance

21.   **The correct answer is b.** The question is asking the first way the body shows shock from hemorrhage or fluid loss. Tachycardia is one of the first signs of fluid volume deficit in postoperative clients. A decrease in circulating blood volume leads to a decrease in cardiac output resulting in hypotension and tachycardia. As the decrease in cardiac output persists, the client will exhibit signs of cold extremities, anuria and cyanosis (options a, c & d).

Nursing Process: Assessment   **Client Need:** Physiological Integrity

22.   **The correct answer is a.** The question is asking what symptoms occur with increased anxiety. Palpitations, shortness of breath and sweaty palms are typical symptoms related to anxiety. Blunted affect, loose associations and ambivalence (option b) are related to schizophrenia. Body image disturbance and perfectionism are related to eating disorders. A flat affect is seen in clients with depression (option c). Illusions, increased salivation and depersonalization (option d) are behaviors seen with use of hallucinogens.

Nursing Process: Assessment   **Client Need:** Psychosocial Integrity

23.   **The correct answer is c.** The question is asking what the usual behavior is of a person with a brain tumor who has just had a seizure. The statement that there is usually a period of confusion after a seizure both gives the family information and reassures them that this is normal. Option (a) is incorrect; although this is a possibility, it is unlikely and would worry the family. Option (b) is a true statement, but gives the wife information that will probably not be understood and will not help. Option (d) is nontherapeutic communication and is called giving false reassurance; although this is probably true, there is no way for the nurse to know this for certain.

Nursing Process: Implementation   **Client Need:** Health Promotion & Maintenance

24.   **The correct answer is c.** The question is asking for a sign of decreased circulation to an extremity. The decrease in temperature may be related to a decrease in perfusion to the extremity. When a client has a musculoskeletal dysfunction, the circulatory and neurological status must be assessed as well as the muscle function. To prevent complications, the position, color, temperature, pulses, capillary refill, motor function and sensation of the affected extremity are assessed. Intact sensation (such as feeling pressure from the bed sheet) is a normal neurological finding (option a). The inability of the client to move his toes is a neurological problem, which may be related to tissue swelling or nerve damage (option b). Pink toes are a normal finding for a circulatory assessment (option d).

Nursing Process: Assessment   **Client Need:** Safe, Effective Care Environment

25.   **The correct answer is d.** The question is asking which measure is a priority when caring for an acute case of inhalant abuse. Inhalants can lead to respiratory and fatal cardiac arrythmias. Maintaining cardio-pulmonary function is the top priority in cases of abuse. Epinephrine is contraindicated, because this may increase the risk of fatal arrythmia, and increase agitation and aggression frequently seen in these clients (option a). The nurse should question this prescription. Assessing for psychological risk factors (option b) should be initiated after the client is no longer at risk of dying from the acute effects of the substance. Lavage will have no effect on removing substances that have been inhaled (option c).

Nursing Process: Implementation   **Client Need:** Physiological Integrity

26.   **The correct answer is c.** The question is asking what is the best position for a child who has a hyphema. A hyphema is blood in the anterior chamber of the eye. The child is kept in an upright position to keep the blood from moving around in the eye. This allows the blood to gradually reabsorb. Sim's and supine positions (options a, b & d) are likely to increase the intraocular pressure. Gravity also prevents the blood from invading the optical center of the cornea. The child is kept still to reduce the chance of rebleeding.

27. **The correct answer is a.** The question is asking what is true for care of a client with hepatitis A. Immune serum globulin is recommended for family members who have been exposed. It provides passive immunity. Intimacy (option b) does not have to be avoided with hepatitis A because it is not transmitted through intimate contact. Large meals (option c) should not be offered. Because of the severe nausea and anorexia, most clients with hepatitis cannot eat a large meal and small frequent feedings should be encouraged. Rest, and often, strict bed rest, should be encouraged to promote liver healing (option d).
Nursing Process: Planning   **Client Need:** Physiological Integrity

28. **The correct answer is a.** The question is asking how to keep a person from developing contractures through correct body alignment. The correct lateral position is maintained when the head is in line with the spine, the shoulders and elbows are flexed and pillows are supporting the head and upper arm. If the client is in a supine position the elbows should be flexed, not extended (option b). The arms should be abducted and the mattress, not a pillow, supports the back. The hips should be slightly abducted to prevent internal rotation (option d). If the client is prone, the arms are abducted not adducted (option c).
Nursing Process: Implementation   **Client Need:** Physiological Integrity

29. **The correct answer is c.** The question is asking what would be a correct statement about chronic obstructive pulmonary disease (COPD). While exercise has not been shown to improve pulmonary function tests in clients with COPD, it shows that it improves skeletal muscle functioning, improves endurance and strengthens the heart. Smoking is one of the main contributors to COPD, and clients should be recommended to try a program to help them stop. Further damage can be avoided if the client stops smoking (option a). Swift treatment of any respiratory infection may prevent acute exacerbations of the COPD. However, over the counter medications may be contraindicated. The client should seek medical attention for any respiratory infection (option b). Travel in an airplane and vacationing in high altitudes may be contraindicated in clients with hypoxemia. The atmospheric pressure of oxygen is lower at high altitudes and in airplane cabins (option d).
Nursing Process: Evaluation   **Client Need:** Health Promotion & Maintenance

30. **The correct answer is b.** The question is asking how to know that the oxygen is helping the client. Pulse oximetry measures the oxygen saturation of the hemoglobin. A probe is placed on the finger and a sensor monitors the saturation of the blood by sending light signals generated by the oximeter and reflected by the pulsating blood in the finger. Checking the nail beds and level of consciousness are also ways to monitor the ventilatory status of a client, but they are highly subjective (options c & d). Auscultation of lung sounds may provide important data, but does not provide information about how much oxygen is getting into the blood (option a).
Nursing Process: Evaluation   **Client Need:** Physiological Integrity

PRACTICE SESSION: 4

> **Instructions: Allow yourself 30 minutes to complete the following 30 practice questions. Use a timer to notify yourself when 30 minutes are over so that you are not constantly looking at your watch while completing the questions.**

1. A client admitted with severe burns needs to have his dressings changed. To help the client cope with this experience, the nurse gives the client which combination of prescribed medications before the procedure?
    a. Collagenase (Santyl) and lorazepam (Ativan).
    b. Ranitidine (Zantac) and fentanyl (Sublimaze).
    c. Meperidine (Demerol) and siver sulfadiazine (Silvadene).
    d. Morphine Sulfate (Morphine) and midazolam (Versed).

2. A couple with one child with cystic fibrosis asks the nurse what the chances are of having another child with the disease. The nurse's most appropriate response would be:
    a. "Each baby has a 25% chance of having cystic fibrosis."
    b. "One baby out of four will have cystic fibrosis."
    c. "Cystic fibrosis is an autosomal dominant disease."
    d. "This child will probably be your only baby with cystic fibrosis."

3. A nurse is assisting a physician to perform a thoracentesis. During the procedure the client is monitored for a pneumothorax. What symptom would indicate that a pneumothorax might have occurred?
    a. Decreased respiratory rate.
    b. Blood-tinged sputum.
    c. Tachycardia.
    d. Increased temperature.

4. The nurse manager is orienting a new nurse to the use of patient-controlled analgesia (PCA) pumps. The nurse teaches that clients who use PCA pumps are:
    a. found to have increased side effects resulting from the direct bolus doses of medication.
    b. able to use traditional methods of pain relief in conjunction with PCA.
    c. likely to have inadequate control of pain relief when initiating painful activities.
    d. found to use a greater amount of medication than traditional methods of pain relief.

5. A nurse would plan what nursing action to prevent foot drop in a client?
    a. Have the client lie laterally with the toes suspended over the edge of the mattress.
    b. Ask the family to bring in hightop tennis shoes for the client to wear in bed.
    c. Place a trochanter roll between the ileum and the midthigh.
    d. Flex the knees so that the plantar portion of the foot is against the mattress.

6. Which nursing action has the highest priority for a client who is about to receive preoperative medications?
    a. Be sure that the operative permit is signed.
    b. Check that dentures have been removed.
    c. Raise the bedside rails.
    d. Make sure the client has voided.

7. The emergency department nurse is giving discharge instructions to a client who suffered a mild head injury. The client should return to the emergency department if he exhibits:
   a. vomiting.
   b. a headache.
   c. rapid speech.
   d. loss of memory for the accident.

8. Which is the most appropriate action for the nurse to take when the client first arrives in the post-anesthesia care unit (PACU)?
   a. Listen to the report from the operating room team.
   b. Obtain baseline vital signs.
   c. Assess the dressing.
   d. Position the client.

9. What would be most helpful in preventing lymphedema in a client who has just had a modified radical mastectomy?
   a. Massage and intermittent compression.
   b. Intermittent compression and elevation.
   c. Exercise and massage.
   d. Elevation and exercise.

10. A nurse is caring for a depressed client. Which client behavior would warrant further investigation by the nurse? The client:
    a. starts to tell you he can see that his thinking is disturbed.
    b. begins to verbalize his feelings of sadness and loneliness.
    c. starts to plan a vacation for himself.
    d. gives his baseball season tickets to his brother-in-law.

11. A client with Cushing's syndrome has just undergone a unilateral adrenalectomy. Two days after surgery the client asks the nurse why her adrenocortical steroid medications have been decreased when her adrenal gland was removed. The best reply of the nurse would be:
    a. "I'll recheck the medication prescription with the physician."
    b. "Your blood sugar will be monitored once per day to determine your medication dosage."
    c. "Your body can no longer handle so much medication with your adrenal gland missing."
    d. "The remaining adrenal gland will begin to produce hormones to replace those lost."

12. A client has been placed on anticoagulant medication after a heart attack. The nurse would assess the client for:
    a. hypersalivation.
    b. daytime drowsiness.
    c. petechiae.
    d. seizure activity.

13. A client with a permanent tracheostomy is learning how to care for his tracheostomy at home. Which client statement indicates a need for further teaching?
    a. "I can wear a turtleneck sweater to cover the hole."
    b. "I should use hairspray to keep my hair from getting into my tracheostomy."
    c. "I can shower if I use a shower guard."
    d. "I should suction the tracheostomy as needed using clean technique."

14. It is important for the nurse to take appropriate precautions to prevent which postoperative complication associated with a draining nasogastric tube?
    a. Atelectasis.
    b. Hydration.
    c. Electrolyte deficit.
    d. Nausea.

15. The most important concern of the nurse caring for a client who has suffered an intracapsular fracture of the femur is assessment for:
    a. hypovolemic shock.
    b. infection.
    c. fat embolism.
    d. pain due to muscle spasm.

16. A diabetic client delivers a 10-pound (4.54 kg) baby. The nurse should assess the baby for:
    a. hypercalcemia.
    b. hypoglycemia.
    c. hyperglycemia.
    d. infant gestational diabetes.

17. An obese client has been placed on a weight reduction plan to help control her hypertension. The client returns to the clinic in two weeks and has not lost any weight. Which factors are most important in assessing the client's lack of success with dieting?
    a. The duration of the obese state.
    b. Family history of obesity.
    c. Past-weight reduction practices.
    d. Desire to lose weight.

18. A client admitted for acute glomerulonephritis begins to complain of nausea and headache. The nurse notes that the blood pressure is elevated and urine output has significantly decreased in the last few hours. What would the nurse do next?
    a. Assess urine for presence of blood or protein.
    b. Note if client has an elevated temperature.
    c. Check the BUN & creatinine levels.
    d. Call the physician.

19. A client continually washes her hands especially after talking with someone. The nurse analyzes this behavior as:
    a. regression.
    b. displacement.
    c. projection.
    d. undoing.

20. A nurse is caring for a client who has a decubitus ulcer that is positive for methicillin-resistant staphylococcus aureus (MRSA). The client needs to have a central line dressing change. What should the nurse wear prior to going into the room? Select all that apply.
    a. Gloves.
    b. Gown.
    c. Mask.
    d. Goggles.
    e. Shoe covers.
    f. Surgical cap.

21. The nurse evaluates that a client on a low-residue diet understands his therapy when he states that he should avoid:
    a. milk.
    b. carbonated beverages.
    c. fish.
    d. smooth peanut butter.

22. A client has just had a bowel resection with a colostomy. During the first postoperative day, the nurse would expect the stoma to produce:
    a. flatus.
    b. fecal drainage.
    c. serosanguinous secretion.
    d. bile.

23. A 33-year-old has been diagnosed with endometriosis. She states she does not want to have children. What would the appropriate treatment be for this woman?
    a. Hormone replacement therapy.
    b. Therapeutic surgery.
    c. Hysterectomy.
    d. Oophorectomy.

24. An 80-year-old client is ordered 1,000ml of D_5W + 40mEq of KCl at 100ml/hour. The nurse comes out of shift report and finds that the client's intravenous solution is behind by 500ml. The correct intervention would be to:
    a. increase flow rate to 150ml for the next 10 hours to make up the 500ml.
    b. ask the physician to change the intravenous infusion to a higher rate.
    c. notify the physician and maintain the intravenous infusion at the same rate.
    d. force oral fluids by 500ml to compensate for the loss of intravenous fluids.

25. A client is walking in the hall four days postoperatively. She suddenly screams, "My stitches are coming loose and my insides are falling out, help me!" She grabs her abdomen and stoops over. The nurse should:
    a. place the client flat in bed and approximate wound edges.
    b. cover exposed intestines with a dry sterile dressing.
    c. using aseptic technique, return the exposed intestine to the abdominal cavity.
    d. cover the exposed intestines with a moist sterile dressing.

26. A client with schizophrenia is admitted to the psychiatric unit. During assessment the client tells the nurse, "I had to leave college in a hurry, the dean was going to have a computer implanted in my brain." The nurse understands that this statement is an example of a (n):
    a. delusion of grandeur.
    b. idea of reference.
    c. somatic delusion.
    d. persecutory delusion.

27. The nurse teaches a new mother which facts about proper positioning of an infant during breast-feeding?
    a. Most infants prefer to be cradled in their mothers' arms while feeding.
    b. The maternal side-lying position is the best position for feeding.
    c. Using varied positions for nursing is a good technique to decrease nipple soreness.
    d. The football hold does not facilitate complete emptying of the breast.

28. A physician has written a prescription for a client to receive oral contraceptives. The nurse would question the prescription if the client:
    a. drinks one beer per day.
    b. is over 30 years of age.
    c. smokes a pack of cigarettes per day.
    d. has a history of multiple pregnancies.

29. The nurse is preparing a client with peripheral vascular disease for discharge. Discharge instructions would include:
   a. bathe feet daily with warm water, walk one to two miles per day.
   b. if feet hurt at night, wrap a heating pad in a towel and place it on feet on a low setting.
   c. walk to the point of discomfort, then rest and attempt again.
   d. keep the legs elevated as much as possible while sitting.

30. A client is scheduled for a cardiac catheterization. The nurse realizes the client understands the teaching when he makes which statement?
   a. "I will be injected with a dye for visualization of my abdominal aorta."
   b. "This test will allow the doctor to measure the pressures within the chambers and blood vessels of my heart."
   c. "Upon return, I can expect a large pressure dressing to the side of my neck."
   d. "Streptokinase (Streptase) therapy may be used to help unblock my clogged arteries."

STOP. You have now completed Practice Session: 4. Now take a few minutes and correct your answers. Calculate your accuracy rate by dividing the number of questions you completed correctly by the total number of questions you completed (30).

Correct answers ÷ total number of questions completed = accuracy rate.

_____ ÷ _____ = _____

ANSWERS AND RATIONALES
Practice Session 4

1. **The correct answer is d.** The question is asking what combination of drugs will help a client cope with the pain associated with debridement of burn wounds. Morphine is used to decrease pain and midazolam (Versed) acts as a short-term (usually lasts 30-60 minutes) amnestic. This keeps the client from remembering the painful event. Lorazepam (Ativan) is used to decrease anxiety prior to a dressing change. Collagenase (Santyl) is an enzymatic preparation that is used to debride the wound, it would not be used to help the client cope with the procedure (option a). Fentanyl (Sublimaze) may be used to sedate a client who is about to undergo a dressing change. Ranitidine (Zantac) is used to treat GI distress associated with Curling's ulcers. It would not be given to promote comfort during a dressing change (option b). Meperidine (Demerol) may be used to decrease pain incurred during a dressing change. Silver sulfadiazine (Silvadene) is used to decrease the microbial population in the wound (option c).
Nursing Process: Planning   **Client Need:** Physiological Integrity

2. **The correct answer is a.** The question is asking the chance of each child having cystic fibrosis in a family. Each baby conceived has a one in four chance of developing cystic fibrosis. Cystic fibrosis is an autosomal recessive trait, which means that both parents are carriers of the gene (option c). To tell a mother that she will probably have only one child with cystic fibrosis is giving false hope (options b & d).
Nursing Process: Implementation   **Client Need:** Health Promotion & Maintenance

3. **The correct answer is c.** The question is asking for the symptom of a pneumothorax. A thoracentesis is the removal of fluid from the pleural cavity through a large needle. A pneumothorax can occur if the lung is punctured during the procedure. If a pneumothorax occurs, the pulse and respirations will increase (option a). Blood-tinged sputum would indicate that blood vessels have been punctured by the needle (option b). Increased temperature is a sign of infection, not pneumothorax (option d).
Nursing Process: Evaluation   **Client Need:** Physiological Integrity

4. **The correct answer is b.** The question is asking what is true about patient controlled analgesia (PCA) pumps. Traditional methods of pain relief can be used along with PCA. Traditional methods would include oral, intramuscular, subcutaneous, intravenous or spinal routes. Side effects are few with adequate control of pain and the safety measures programmed into the pump (option a). Clients are found to have a more consistent level of analgesia when using PCA. The client is able to administer the analgesia with increased pain or painful activities resulting in decreased pain (option c). The amount of medication administered by the client is no greater than traditional methods (option d).
Nursing Process: Analysis   **Client Need:** Physiological Integrity

5. **The correct answer is b.** The question is asking how best to prevent foot drop in a client. Foot drop occurs when the client cannot dorsiflex the foot. Hightop tennis shoes are used to maintain the foot in dorsiflexion to prevent foot drop. If a client is lying laterally, the feet should be supported by a footboard or pillows (option a). A trochanter roll is used to prevent internal rotation of the hip, not foot drop (option c). The knees should be extended and the plantar portion of the foot supported by pillows or a footboard (option d).
Nursing Process: Planning   **Client Need:** Physiological Integrity

6. **The correct answer is a.** The question is asking the nurse to prioritize the actions given for a preoperative client who is about to be medicated prior to surgery. The operative permit must be signed and witnessed before any medication that will alter consciousness is administered. Dentures could be removed after the client is medicated, if needed (option b). Raising the bedside rails is a safety measure performed by the nurse after the medication is administered (option c). Making sure the client has voided before medication is administered is not a priority. The client may not be able to get up and walk to the bathroom but could use a bedpan or urinal (option d).

Nursing Process: Analysis   **Client Need:** Safe, Effective Care Environment

7. **The correct answer is a.** The question is asking what would be a symptom of a problem in a head injured client. Vomiting would be an indication that the intracranial pressure (ICP) has increased. Increased ICP is a potentially life-threatening situation and help should be sought immediately. A headache and loss of memory for the accident (options b & d) are common and expected symptoms of a mild head injury. Slurred speech not rapid could indicate a neurological change (option c).
    Nursing Process: Evaluation   **Client Need:** Physiological Integrity

8. **The correct answer is d.** The question is asking the nurse to prioritize activities in the post-anesthesia care unit (PACU) when a client is newly admitted. The client should be properly positioned to ensure a patent airway whether the client is unconscious or semi-conscious. Oxygen is applied unless contraindicated. After the client is properly positioned, the baseline vital signs are taken, level of consciousness is determined (option b) and the dressing is assessed (option c). Drains, intravenous lines and other equipment are also assessed and the nurse listens to report (option a).
    Nursing Process: Implementation   **Client Need:** Safe, Effective Care Environment

9. **The correct answer is d.** The question is asking the best way to keep edema from occurring in a client who has had a mastectomy where lymph tissue has been removed. Think about how the lymph system helps to drain the fluid away and now it is no longer fully intact. Massage, intermittent compression and exercise are each used as treatment measures for lymphedema (options a, b & c). However, the use of exercise and elevation of the affected extremity are most crucial to the prevention of lymphedema occurrence following a mastectomy.
    Nursing Process: Planning   **Client Need:** Physiological Integrity

10. **The correct answer is d.** The question is asking what assessment data would indicate a problem that needs to be further assessed. Giving away prized items such as season baseball tickets is a behavioral clue that may show the person does not intend to be around in the future to use them. This is a sign of suicidal intent, which must immediately be addressed by the nurse. Recognizing distorted thinking (option a) and verbalizing feelings (option b) are positive signs that the client is progressing in treatment. Planning a vacation (option c) shows the client is talking about the future, which is also a positive sign.
    Nursing Process: Assessment   **Client Need:** Psychosocial Integrity

11. **The correct answer is d.** The question is asking why a person's steroid medication would be decreased when one of the glands that produce that steroid has been removed. Blood glucose may begin to elevate in client's taking steroid medication. Insulin coverage may be necessary. Decreasing the dosages of the adrenocortical steroids after 48 hours allows for the remaining adrenal gland to gradually resume hormone secretion (option c). The blood glucose level for this client should be monitored four times per day (option b) and will not cause steroid levels to change. The medication dose may need to be rechecked but the dose will decrease over time (option a).
    Nursing Process: Implementation   **Client Need:** Physiological Integrity

12. **The correct answer is c.** The question is asking for a symptom relating to anticoagulant therapy where the clotting time is lengthened. A major complication of anticoagulant therapy is bleeding, which occurs from delayed clotting time of blood. One sign of this bleeding is petechiae. Hypersalivation, daytime drowsiness and seizure activity do not relate to anticoagulant therapy (options a, b & d).
    Nursing Process: Assessment   **Client Need:** Physiological Integrity

13. **The correct answer is b.** The question is asking which client statement about home tracheostomy care is incorrect. Hair sprays and powders should be avoided because they can get into the tracheostomy and cause tracheal damage, leading to infection. Covering the tracheostomy enhances the appearance of the client. It also protects the tracheostomy and warms the inhaled air

(option a). A shower guard is a device that fits over the tracheostomy to keep water from entering the stoma during contact with water (option c). Tracheostomy suctioning can be performed using clean technique at home, emphasizing hand washing as extremely important before beginning the procedure (option d).
Nursing Process: Evaluation   **Client Need:** Health Promotion & Maintenance

14.   **The correct answer is c.** The question is asking what problem is related to a nasogastric tube that drains the gastrointestinal (GI) tract. GI tract drainage is a principle cause of dehydration and electrolyte deficits because it pulls out drainage before the needed substances are usually absorbed into the system in the lower GI tract. Atelectasis is related to pulmonary problems such as aspiration of vomitus and the depressive effects of narcotics (option a). Dehydration would be a concern not hydration (option b). Overload is related to an excessive amount of intravenous fluids or inadequate renal function. Nausea is associated with the disease condition or the administration of anesthetic agents and narcotics (option d).
Nursing Process: Assessment   **Client Need:** Safe, Effective Care Environment

15.   **The correct answer is a.** The question is asking the nurse to prioritize the possible problems of a client with an intracapsular femur fracture. The femur is very vascular; therefore, large quantities of blood may be lost in femoral and pelvic fractures. Hypovolemic shock resulting from hemorrhage and loss of extracellular fluid into damaged tissues may occur in fractures of the extremities, thorax, pelvis, and spine. Infection is a concern, but not an immediate one (option b). Fat embolism can occur within 48 hours but is secondary to hypovolemic shock (option c). Pain due to muscle spasm is an immediate nursing concern, however, when prioritizing, the nurse should be most concerned about assessment for hypovolemic shock that can be life-threatening (option d).
Nursing Process: Assessment   **Client Need:** Physiological Integrity

16.   **The correct answer is b.** The question is asking what to look for in a large infant born to a diabetic mother. A baby weighing 10 pounds (4.54 kg) is considered to be large for gestational age. This would increase his need for glucose and put the infant in hypoglycemia. Hypercalcemia may become a problem but it is not an early complication of large gestational age (option a). Since the mother is diabetic, glucose passes through the placenta and the fetus increases insulin to compensate and, thus, potential for hypoglycemia exists, not hyperglycemia (option c). The infant is not at risk for gestational diabetes (option d).
Nursing Process: Assessment   **Client Need:** Health Promotion & Maintenance

17.   **The correct answer is d.** The question is asking why the client had trouble losing weight. Although options (a), (b) and (c) are all-important, the client's motivation and desire to lose weight are the most important.
Nursing Process: Assessment   **Client Need:** Psychosocial Integrity

18.   **The correct answer is c.** The question is asking for the priority nursing action when a client with glomerulonephritis has an elevated blood pressure and decreased urine output. A major complication of acute glomerulonephritis is renal failure. Signs of renal failure include fatigue, nausea, vomiting, headache, hypertension, edema, sudden onset of oliguria, and a sudden rise in BUN and serum creatinine. The nurse would need to know the BUN & creatinine levels before calling the physician (option d). You would already expect this client to have hematuria and proteinuria (option a) and possibly a low-grade fever (option b).
Nursing Process: Analysis   **Client Need:** Physiological Integrity

19.   **The correct answer is d.** The question is asking what defense mechanism is being used when a client constantly washes her hands. Ritualistic behavior may be performed to undo certain feelings such as guilt when the person believes perfectionistic standards have not been attained. Regression occurs when a person resorts to an earlier level of functioning that is more comfortable (option a). Displacement occurs when a person discharges emotions to another person or object (option b). Projection occurs when a person denies feelings and attributes them to another person (option c).

20.   **The correct answers are a and b.** The question is asking what precautions must be taken for a central line dressing change in a client with methicillin resistant staphylococcus aureus (MRSA). Contact isolation measures are indicated for this client. MRSA colonizes on the skin easily; so gloves and gowns are indicated. Masks are recommended for clients with MRSA pneumonia (option c). Goggles, shoe covers and surgical caps are not necessary (options d, e & f).
Nursing Process: Planning   **Client Need:** Safe, Effective Care Environment

21.   **The correct answer is a.** The question is asking what does not belong on a low-residue diet. A low-residue diet results in decreased fecal matter passed through the bowel. Milk is high-residue and is restricted on the diet. Carbonated beverages, fish and smooth peanut butter are allowed on a low-residue diet (options b, c & d).
Nursing Process: Evaluation   **Client Need:** Physiological Integrity

22.   **The correct answer is c.** The question is asking what the stoma drainage should be one day post-colostomy. The stoma drainage initially is mucus and serosanguinous secretion. Flatus and fecal drainage (options a & b) usually begin in four to seven days postoperatively for a colostomy. Bile (option d) is unrelated to colostomy drainage.
Nursing Process: Evaluation   **Client Need:** Physiological Integrity

23.   **The correct answer is a.** The question is asking what treatment would be appropriate for a client in childbearing years without children. Hormone replacement therapy (HRT) would be the most conservative treatment for this case. Therapeutic surgery would occur if HRT were not successful (option b). A hysterectomy would be the last resort (option c). Even though the client has said she has no desire to bear children, she is still in childbearing years and may change her mind. Oophprectomy (removal of ovaries) has been occasionally performed in severe cases of endometriosis but once again should be a last resort in childbearing years (option d).
Nursing Process: Analysis   **Client Need:** Physiological Integrity

24.   **The correct answer is c.** The question is asking how to intervene when a client's intravenous solution is behind by 500ml. The nurse must notify the physician and maintain the intravenous infusion at the prescribed rate until speaking with the physician. The nurse does not have the authority to change intravenous infusion rates. Increasing the intravenous infusion rate on an elderly client may cause circulatory overload (option a). Due to normal degenerative changes, elderly clients do not always have adequate cardiac output to handle extra circulatory fluids (option b). Oral fluids will not compensate for intravenous fluids and forcing fluids plus administering the intravenous fluids may again place the elderly client in jeopardy (option d).
Nursing Process: Implementation   **Client Need:** Physiological Integrity

25.   **The correct answer is d.** The question is asking what to do when a client's surgical wound opens and the intestines protrude. When disruption of a wound occurs, the surgeon is notified at once. The protruding coils of intestines should be covered with sterile dressing moistened with sterile saline. The isotonic solution maintains the usual body environment and keeps the tissue from drying. If evisceration of an abdominal wound has occurred, place the client in a mid-Fowler's position with knees drawn up to relieve tension on the abdomen (option a). If the intestines are externalized, cover with sterile saline soaked pads and place dry sterile pads over them (option b). Do not attempt to replace the intestines (option c). Notify the surgeon immediately.
Nursing Process: Implementation   **Client Need:** Physiological Integrity

26.   **The correct answer is d.** The question is asking the nurse to analyze the data provided in the client's statement. A delusion is a fixed false belief that cannot be dispelled by logic. A persecutory delusion is the belief that someone is plotting or conspiring to harm the client. The client states that she believes the dean is implanting something in her brain or trying to harm her so the client's statement is a persecutory delusion. A delusion of grandeur is the belief that one is endowed with special powers or is a person of great importance (option a). Ideas of reference are remarks by other people that the client mistakenly believes refer to her (option b). A somatic

delusion is the belief that one has some type of disease process that cannot be medically substantiated (option c).
Nursing Process: Analysis   **Client Need:** Psychosocial Integrity

27.   **The correct answer is c.** The question is asking which option is true regarding infant position and breastfeeding. Recommending varied positions rather than only one position alters the focus of greatest stress to the nipples and promotes complete breast emptying (options a, b & d).
Nursing Process: Implementation   **Client Need:** Health Promotion & Maintenance

28.   **The correct answer is c.** The question is asking what would cause the nurse to question the physician about prescribing oral contraceptives. Women who smoke heavily and use oral contraceptives have a significant risk of cardiovascular disease. Oral contraceptives are not contraindicated in women who consume alcoholic beverages in limited use (option a). Thirty-five is usually the age to consider alternative methods of birth control because of increased risk of complications associated with oral contraceptives (option b). Multiple pregnancies have not been associated in problems with oral contraceptives (option d).
Nursing Process: Analysis   **Client Need:** Health Promotion & Maintenance

29.   **The correct answer is c.** The question is asking what is a correct instruction about peripheral vascular disease. Walking to the point of discomfort then resting and attempting again will gradually increase the client's tolerance as well as improve arterial circulation. The client should not walk past the point of discomfort (option a). Heating pads should never be used nor should hot water because sensation is decreased and tissue damage may occur (option b). Elevating the legs will make it more difficult for blood to get into the feet and will increase pain (option d).
Nursing Process: Planning   **Client Need:** Health Promotion & Maintenance

30.   **The correct answer is b.** The question is asking which statement is true about cardiac catheterization. During the cardiac catheterization, pressures in the heart chamber can be measured. The heart rate and surrounding vessels can be visualized. Abdominal vessels are not routinely checked during the procedure (option a). The catheter is usually introduced through the groin and/or the antecubital space (option c). Streptokinase (Streptase) therapy is instituted to dissolve clots in major coronary arteries (option d). This therapy is not normally associated with a cardiac catheterization, but is done during the procedure known as angioplasty. Angioplasty is the procedure done for revascularization of coronary arteries.
Nursing Process: Evaluation   **Client Need:** Physiological Integrity

PRACTICE SESSION: 5

Instructions: Allow yourself 30 minutes to complete the following 30 practice questions. Use a timer to notify yourself when 30 minutes are over so that you are not constantly looking at your watch while completing the questions.

1.   A client with chronic renal failure is admitted to the dialysis unit with a nonfunctioning left atrioventricular (AV) fistula. The client's intake was 400ml and output was 10ml of concentrated urine over an eight-hour period. The nurse should:
   a.   notify the physician of a urine output less than 30ml per hour.
   b.   encourage the client to increase fluid intake.
   c.   straight catheterize the client for a post-void residual.
   d.   record 10ml in the output record.

2.   A client comes to the emergency department with severe abdominal pain. The nurse suspects acute pancreatitis when which lab result is reported?
   a.   Bilirubin 2mg/dL.
   b.   WBC 4,000.
   c.   Amylase 40units/L.
   d.   Calcium 11mg/dL.

3.   After receiving verbal report at 3:00PM, which client should be assessed initially by the nurse?
   a.   A 46-year-old client who returned from an abdominal hysterectomy at 12:00PM.
   b.   An elderly client who is confused and is wearing a waist restraint.
   c.   A 36-year-old postoperative craniotomy client who has had a urine output of 360ml in the last two hours.
   d.   A client with Type 1 diabetes that is taking prednisone (Deltasone) for her rheumatoid arthritis and has a glucose level of 200.

4.   A client with hallucinations is admitted to the psychiatric unit. The nurse's initial approach would be to:
   a.   give haloperidol (Haldol) 5mg p.o. as prescribed for agitation.
   b.   give a tour of the unit so the client can feel secure in her new environment.
   c.   introduce oneself to the client and show her to her room.
   d.   introduce the client to other clients already on the unit.

5.   Documentation after a client fall reads: Heard loud noise in client room. Upon investigation, found client on floor in pool of urine. Client apparently got up without assistance. Probably slipped in urine. Client assisted up and to bathroom. No red marks found. Client states, "I'm okay." The nurse could be held liable due to which part of the documentation?
   a.   Upon investigation, found client on floor in pool of urine.
   b.   Probably slipped in urine.
   c.   Heard loud noise in client room.
   d.   No red marks found. Client states, "I'm okay."

6.   The nursing process for clients with eating disorders focuses on:
   a.   a knowledge base to develop insight.
   b.   a behavioral change program.
   c.   an increase in socialization factors.
   d.   drug therapy.

7. A client with a myocardial infarction is placed on heparin sodium (Heparin). The nurse should make sure the antidote is available, which is:
   a. vitamin K.
   b. protamine sulfate.
   c. platelet infusion.
   d. calcium.

8. A client undergoing blood transfusions is found to have a hemolytic reaction to the blood. The correct action of the nurse should be to discontinue the transfusion and:
   a. give the p.r.n. antihistamine for hives and itching.
   b. give the p.r.n. acetaminophen (Tylenol) to decrease fever.
   c. call the physician and request an antibiotic.
   d. call the physician and observe for bloody urine.

9. Following a cerebrovascular accident, a client has minimal movement and sensation in the right arm. To prevent contracture, the nurse should:
   a. place a footboard at the foot of the bed.
   b. teach the client to perform active range-of-motion to his right side.
   c. place a pillow under the affected arm with arm and fingers slightly flexed.
   d. place a pillow under the affected arm with arm and fingers extended.

10. A client with a medical diagnosis of age-related macular degeneration would complain of:
    a. loss of sensation, pain and paresthesia of the extremities.
    b. progressive loss of central vision.
    c. low back pain with muscle spasms.
    d. progressive loss of hearing.

11. The nurse is caring for a client admitted to the hospital with frostbite. The right hand and fingers are bright red, painful and edematous. The nurse should plan to:
    a. keep his hand immobile to decrease pain.
    b. massage his fingers gently to increase blood circulation.
    c. place his hand in a warm water bath.
    d. elevate his hand above the heart to decrease edema.

12. A fiberoptic bronchoscopy is preformed for biopsy of a previously inaccessible tumor. An initial nursing intervention post-bronchoscopy should be to:
    a. order a diet of clear liquids.
    b. give nothing by mouth.
    c. give ice chips as tolerated.
    d. order a soft diet.

13. The nurse is assisting a terminally ill client with his bath when the client tearfully says, "The doctor says I'm dying." The nurse plans her approach recognizing that most people with life-threatening illnesses:
    a. want to gradually learn the reality of their conditions.
    b. would rather not know the truth.
    c. want to pretend they do not know.
    d. want their families to be told instead of them.

14. A client with a leg fracture is ordered Buck's traction. While preparing to apply the traction, the nurse knows this is done primarily to:
    a. prevent soft tissue swelling.
    b. maintain fracture immobility.
    c. reduce the fractured femur.
    d. maintain the fracture reduction.

15. A client suspected of having tuberculosis has been prescribed a sputum culture, tuberculin skin test and chest X-ray. The nurse anticipates that the route of administration for the tuberculin test will be:
    a.   subcutaneous.
    b.   intramuscular.
    c.   intradermal.
    d.   transdermal.

16. Three days after the insertion of a chest tube to treat a pneumothorax, the nurse notes there is continuous bubbling in the water-seal chamber. The nurse should:
    a.   check for an air leak.
    b.   decrease the suction.
    c.   do nothing it is normal.
    d.   increase the suction.

17. The charge nurse on a pediatric transplant unit receives a call from the parents of a child admitted yesterday afternoon. The child's sister was diagnosed with chickenpox today. What is the priority action of the nurse?
    a.   Notify the physician and request a prescription for acyclovir (Zovirax) for the child.
    b.   Assess the child for development of a pruritic vesicular rash on the trunk.
    c.   Determine if the child was involved in any playroom activities today.
    d.   Inform the parents that they would not be able to visit their child for seven days.

18. In a client with expressive aphasia, the nurse should communicate by:
    a.   speaking loudly and distinctly.
    b.   avoiding use of gestures.
    c.   presenting one idea at a time.
    d.   encouraging group participation.

19. A client is admitted to the nursing unit post-total-laryngectomy. The nurse should consider which nursing diagnosis as the highest priority?
    a.   Ineffective tissue perfusion related to tissue edema and disruption of blood flow and lymphatic drainage.
    b.   Imbalanced nutrition: less than body requirements related to surgical procedure, edema and dysphagia.
    c.   Risk for impaired gas exchange related to low tidal volume breathing secondary to pain, sedation, and increased mucous production.
    d.   Ineffective airway clearance related to alteration in upper airway, presence of tracheostomy tube and difficulty expectorating sputum.

20. The client comes into the emergency department and is diagnosed with right-sided heart failure. The nurse would expect the client to exhibit which major symptom?
    a.   Pulmonary congestion.
    b.   Dependent edema.
    c.   Dyspnea, cough and fatigue.
    d.   Accumulation of fluid into the pericardial sac.

21. A nurse is reinforcing diet teaching to a client previously diagnosed with Type 1 diabetes. Which statement indicates that the client understands the diabetic diet?
    a.   "I am going to save Friday's bread exchanges and use them on Saturday nights when I go out for dinner."
    b.   "I do not like the corn, so I will substitute it with broccoli."
    c.   "I do not like to eat so much for lunch, so I am going to save my fruit for an afternoon snack."
    d.   "The dietician has been in to see me on several occasions, and I don't have any questions about my diet."

22. The most important nursing concern when caring for a ventilator dependent client on high levels of positive end expiratory pressure (PEEP) would be to:
   a.   auscultate lungs a minimum of every two hours.
   b.   monitor ventilator checks every hour.
   c.   prevent infection.
   d.   suction client every two hours.

23. In a client with pernicious anemia, the nurse would expect to see:
   a.   increased PT, PTT and decreased platelet levels.
   b.   bone pain and an enlarged spleen.
   c.   an abnormal hemoglobin A.
   d.   smooth, sore, red tongue and abdominal pain.

24. The nurse is teaching a client about her scheduled cystoscopy. Further teaching is needed when the client states:
   a.   "The doctor will visually inspect my bladder and urethra."
   b.   "After the examination, I may see some blood in my urine."
   c.   "I can tolerate the contrast material because I have no allergies."
   d.   "After the examination, I may feel some discomfort when I urinate."

25. The parents of a newborn ask why Apgar scores are given to their infant. The nurse replies that the Apgar score:
   a.   determines the infant's cardiac adjustment to extrauterine life.
   b.   provides an index for quickly assessing the infant's cardiac, respiratory, and neuromuscular status.
   c.   measures the infant's alertness and reactivity after delivery.
   d.   indicates the infant's motor coordination, respiratory status and interaction with the environment.

26. A client with a gunshot wound to the chest is brought to the emergency department. An open pneumothorax is apparent and the nurse applies a petroleum gauze dressing. The following signs appear: hypotension, anxiety, displaced point of maximal impulse and subcutaneous emphysema in the neck. The nurse analyzes these signs as:
   a.   a tension pneumothorax.
   b.   a need for a higher oxygen concentration.
   c.   heart damage from the bullet.
   d.   a nonocclusive dressing to the pneumothorax.

27. The nurse should suspect benign prostatic hypertrophy (BPH) in a client who reports which signs and symptoms?
   a.   Urinary frequency and constipation.
   b.   Difficulty beginning urinary stream and terminal dribbling.
   c.   Impotence and oliguria.
   d.   Epigastric pain and night sweats.

28. The physician prepares to insert a central venous pressure (CVP) line. The client asks the nurse why this is necessary. The nurse should base the response on the knowledge that the CVP line measures:
   a.   pulmonary artery pressure.
   b.   right atrial pressure.
   c.   left ventricular pressure.
   d.   cardiac output.

29. A rape victim's family asks the nurse how they can help. The nurse evaluates that the family is able to give positive support when they:
   a. use distraction to prevent the victim from thinking about the rape.
   b. state concerns about how friends will react to the rape.
   c. listen to the victim identify ways the rape could have been prevented.
   d. plan ways for the victim to change locks and telephone number.

30. A client is prescribed a magnetic resonance image (MRI) of the brain. When obtaining the client's history, the most important factor the nurse must assess is that the client:
   a. is acrophobic.
   b. had a pacemaker implanted five years ago.
   c. has been NPO for 24 hours.
   d. had taken a dose of phenytoin (Dilantin) this morning.

STOP. You have now completed Practice Session: 5. Now take a few minutes and correct your answers. Calculate your accuracy rate by dividing the number of questions you completed correctly by the total number of questions you completed (30).

Correct answers ÷ total number of questions completed = accuracy rate.

_____ ÷ _____ = _____

ANSWERS AND RATIONALES
Practice Session 5

1. **The correct answer is d.** The question is asking what to do when a client with chronic renal failure has an intake of 400ml and an output of 10ml. Think about what you know of chronic renal failure. Renal failure is when the kidneys are not doing their job. Chronic means this has happened over time and is not new. As renal failure progresses, urine output decreases until anuria occurs. Recording 10ml in the output record is the correct answer. There would be no need to notify the physician (option a) or catheterize the client (option c) since 10ml would be within normal findings for a chronic renal failure client. Encouraging fluid intake (option b) would be contraindicated since fluid intake is adjusted according to dialysis schedule and urine output.
   Nursing Process: Implementation   **Client Need:** Physiological Integrity

2. **The correct answer is a.** The question is asking which lab value would be indicative of pancreatitis. An elevated bilirubin (normal: 0.1-1mg/dL) may indicate compression of the common bile duct, a manifestation of acute pancreatitis. The white blood cell (normal: 4,500-10,000) count is usually elevated due to the inflammatory process (option b). In pancreatitis, the amylase (normal: 25-125) will be markedly elevated (option c). Hypocalcemia (normal: 8.9-10.3mg/dL) occurs in approximately one fourth of clients with pancreatitis (option d).
   Nursing Process: Analysis   **Client Need:** Physiological Integrity

3. **The correct answer is c.** The question is asking which client should be assessed first following verbal report. This client is exhibiting signs of diabetes insipidus. This needs to be verified by the nurse so that interventions to compensate for fluid loss and electrolyte imbalance are begun. The postoperative hysterectomy client (option a) also needs to be assessed, but not first. The elderly client who is confused is also not a priority at this time since this is not a change in condition (option b). Elevated glucose levels are an expected finding in both Type 1 diabetes and in response to corticosteroid therapy. This client also needs to be assessed but is not in immediate danger (option d).
   Nursing Process: Planning   **Client Need:** Physiological Integrity

4. **The correct answer is c.** The question is asking what the initial action would be when admitting a client with hallucinations. Remember the client with hallucinations is vulnerable to stimuli and has problems interpreting reality. The nurse's first task is to establish contact with the client. Introducing oneself and showing the client to her room allows the nurse to proceed slowly in developing an atmosphere of trust while being sensitive to the client's vulnerability. Haloperidol (Haldol) would not be indicated at this time, as the client does not show signs of agitation (option a). Giving the client a tour of the unit, detailed instructions about unit activities, or introducing the client to others may be overwhelming when the client is first admitted (options b & d).
   Nursing Process: Implementation   **Client Need:** Psychosocial Integrity

5. **The correct answer is b.** The question is asking which part of the documentation is wrong and could lead to a liability suit. The word "probably" makes an assumption about what happened. There is no evidence as to whether the client slipped in the urine or the client voided after falling. Since the nurse did not witness the event, no statement can be made as to what happened. The nurse can only document what is actually seen or heard. All other options (a, c & d) are objective statements of what the nurse saw or heard.
   Nursing Process: Analysis   **Client Need:** Safe, Effective Care Environment

6. **The correct answer is b.** The question is asking the focus of nursing in clients with eating disorders. Change is a process, starting with acceptance of the seriousness of the problem and moving through a process of behavioral changes supported by a changing belief system. Knowledge does not create change (option a). Socialization without other assistance may increase the problem (option c). Drugs can be used as a part of an ongoing program, but would not be the focus of nursing intervention (option d).
   Nursing Process: Planning   **Client Need:** Psychosocial Integrity

7.   **The correct answer is b.** The question is asking about the antidote for heparin sodium (Heparin). Protamine sulfate is the antagonist for heparin sodium (Heparin) and should always be available due to the possibility of bleeding. Vitamin K is administered for the treatment of excessive warfarin sodium (Coumadin) therapy (option a). While platelets and calcium are necessary for the clotting process, they are not administered as an antidote for heparin sodium (Heparin) therapy (options c & d). However, an infusion of plasma may be administered for bleeding associated with warfarin sodium (Coumadin) therapy.
Nursing Process: Analysis   **Client Need:** Physiological Integrity

8.   **The correct answer is d.** The question is asking what the nurse should do after stopping the transfusion in a client having a hemolytic reaction to the infusing blood. First, think of what a hemolytic reaction is. A hemolytic reaction is the most dangerous type of transfusion reaction that occurs when the donor blood is incompatible with that of the recipient. The reaction must be recognized and the transfusion discontinued immediately. When blood types are incompatible, the red blood cells tend to clump and get caught in small blood vessels. These clumps may disintegrate, releasing the hemoglobin into the circulatory system. The body will try to rid itself of the hemoglobin as the circulation filters through the kidneys. However, hemoglobin often crystallizes and obstructs the renal tubules producing kidney (renal) damage. Antihistamines (option a) may be given for an allergic reaction. Some clients may develop hives or generalized itching. Antibiotics (option c) may be used for infection. The client may develop a fever during a transfusion because of the presence of bacterial pathogens. Septic reaction is a severe reaction resulting from the transfusion of blood contaminated with bacteria and can also result in a fever as well as chills. Acetaminophen (Tylenol) can be used to reduce the fever (option b).
Nursing Process: Implementation   **Client Need:** Safe, Effective Care Environment

9.   **The correct answer is c.** The question is asking how to prevent contractures in a client with paresis of the right arm. A pillow is placed under the arm to prevent edema and resultant fibrosis. The fingers and arm are slightly flexed to maintain the most functional position (option d). A footboard would not prevent contractures to the paralyzed arm (option a). The client cannot perform active range-of-motion on a paralyzed limb. Active exercise requires voluntary muscle movement, which is not present in this client (option b).
Nursing Process: Implementation   **Client Need:** Physiological Integrity

10.   **The correct answer is b.** The question is asking what subjective assessment data indicates age-related macular degeneration. Damage or deterioration of photoreceptor cells in the area of the macula cause central vision loss. Age-related macular degeneration is the leading cause of severe vision loss in the 65 and older age group. A client with peripheral neuropathy would complain of loss of sensation, pain and paresthesia (tingling, prickling) of the extremities (option a). Lumbar disc herniation would cause low back pain and muscle spasms (option c). A client with Meniere's disease would complain of progressive hearing loss (option d).
Nursing Process: Assessment   **Client Need:** Physiological Integrity

11.   **The correct answer is c.** The question is asking how to plan care for a client who has had frostbite. Placing the hand in a warm water bath with temperature at 43°C (110°F) for rapid rewarming is the correct treatment for frostbite. Blood flow to the affected extremity is increased with gentle exercise. Immobilization (option a) may decrease tissue perfusion of vital oxygen. Massaging fingers (option b) would cause tissue damage. The affected extremity is elevated after rewarming (option d).
Nursing Process: Planning   **Client Need:** Physiological Integrity

12.   **The correct answer is b.** The question is asking how to take care of a client who just had a fiberoptic bronchoscopy. An anesthetic is given to the throat, which calms the gag reflex and prevents pain or discomfort while the tube is in the throat. After the procedure, the initial intervention is to give the client nothing by mouth until the gag reflex returns; otherwise the client could choke or contract aspiration pneumonia. The NPO status is then usually followed by ice chips (option c), progresses to clear liquids (option a) and then to a soft diet (option d).
Nursing Process: Implementation   **Client Need:** Safe, Effective Care Environment

13. **The correct answer is a.** The question is asking what statement is true for terminally ill clients. Clients have the right to accurate information. This promotes trust within the care giving relationship and directly influences the client's ability to fully participate in care. Sources suggest that people want to be told the truth (option b). Often, when they pretend they do not know, it is usually to protect loved ones (options c & d). Pretending (option c) is different than denial and means a person knows but chooses to say otherwise. Denial is a defense used when the truth is too painful to bear. Often, people go through periods of realizing death will occur and denying that truth. This is normal and a part of the grieving process.
Nursing Process: Planning　　　　**Client Need:** Health Promotion & Maintenance

14. **The correct answer is b.** The question is asking why Buck's traction is used. Remember that Buck's traction is a type of skin traction placed on the outside of the leg. Buck's traction is used to maintain temporary immobility prior to surgical repair of leg fractures to relieve muscle spasm. Buck's traction does not prevent soft tissue swelling or reduce the fracture (options a & c). After the fracture has been reduced, Buck's traction is not usually prescribed (option d).
Nursing Process: Planning　　　　**Client Need:** Physiological Integrity

15. **The correct answer is c.** The question is asking how a tuberculin test is given. The intradermal route is most commonly used to determine the presence of a disease such as tuberculosis. The needle is inserted with the bevel up. When the substance is injected, a wheal elevates the skin in the area of the injection. The subcutaneous route is often used for giving insulin (option a). The intramuscular route is often used for vaccinations (option b). The transdermal route is often used for medications given via patch, such as the nicotine patch (Nicoderm) (option d).
Nursing Process: Planning　　　　**Client Need:** Safe, Effective Care Environment

16. **The correct answer is a.** The question is asking what to do when the water seal chamber bubbles three days after insertion. When a chest tube is inserted to treat a pneumothorax, continuous bubbling should be present for only a few minutes after insertion. Persistent bubbling indicates an air leak. Decreasing the suction (option b) would not lessen the air leak. Decreased pressure would also keep the lung from re-expanding properly. Doing nothing (option c) would place the client in danger as the system is not functioning properly and the pneumothorax might continue to develop. Increasing suction (option d) places the client in danger of lung tissue damage as it is sucked into the tube.
Nursing Process: Implementation　　　　**Client Need:** Safe, Effective Care Environment

17. **The correct answer is c.** The question is asking what the nurse should do first when it is discovered that there has been a potential exposure to chickenpox. Chickenpox is a very contagious virus that is airborne. Chickenpox is potentially fatal for anyone who is immunosuppressed. It is important for the nurse to determine if anyone on the unit was exposed to the child whose sister was diagnosed with chickenpox. Chickenpox is contagious from the day before the rash occurs until the first crop of vesicles crusts over. Acyclovir (Zovirax) is an antiviral medication that may be indicated for a child who has been exposed to chickenpox, however, it is more important to determine who has been exposed first (option a). It is important to see if the child has a rash, however, since he may be contagious it is more important to determine if he has exposed any other children to this disease (option b). If the parents have had chickenpox or have been vaccinated against the disease, they may visit the child (option d).
Nursing Process: Planning　　　　**Client Need:** Safe, Effective Care Environment

18. **The correct answer is c.** The question is asking the best method of communicating with someone who has expressive aphasia. Expressive aphasia is an impairment of the motor function of speech. It differs from receptive aphasia in that generally comprehension of speech is not impaired. These clients can be easily frustrated; therefore, option (c) is correct. The aphasic client should not be overwhelmed with multiple thoughts at one time. This may be too confusing. Option (a) is incorrect as the client is able to hear and speaking loudly will not help comprehension or expression of ideas. Gestures are often an effective way to communicate with an aphasic client, as

interpretation of gestures is usually unimpaired (option b). Group participation, including multiple person conversations, is often initially overwhelming to the aphasic client (option d).
Nursing Process: Implementation   **Client Need:** Physiological Integrity

19.   **The correct answer is d.** The question is asking which nursing of four nursing diagnoses would be first priority for a client post-total-laryngectomy. Inflammation in the surgical area may compress the trachea and interfere with normal movement of mucus up and out of the bronchial tree. After surgery, maintenance of a patent airway is a priority nursing diagnosis immediately after surgery and for several days postoperatively. Although the other diagnoses are appropriate for this client, ineffective airway clearance takes priority over ineffective tissue perfusion, imbalanced nutrition and risk for impaired gas exchange in options (a, b & c).
Nursing Process: Planning   **Client Need:** Physiological Integrity

20.   **The correct answer is b.** The question is asking what symptoms are exhibited in right-sided congestive heart failure. In left-sided heart failure, the lungs are involved. In right-sided heart failure the rest of the system is involved. When the right ventricle fails, congestion of the viscera and peripheral tissue occurs and can lead to venous engorgement of the liver. In left-sided heart failure, pulmonary congestion (option a), dyspnea, cough and fatigue (option c) are seen when congestion backs into the lungs. Accumulation of fluid into the pericardial sac (option d) is a major symptom of pericardial effusion.
Nursing Process: Assessment   **Client Need:** Physiological Integrity

21.   **The correct answer is c.** The question is asking which statement shows understanding of a diabetic diet. The number of designated exchanges can be divided into a meal/snack pattern that is consistent with lifestyle and medications. The total number of exchanges for a day is determined from the total number of calorie, carbohydrate, fat and protein prescribed. They must be evenly distributed on a consistent daily basis so that the medication remains effective (option a). Corn is a bread exchange; broccoli is a vegetable exchange. Foods within one exchange group can be substituted, but not foods in different exchange groups (option b). Evaluation of a client's understanding is best accomplished through application of knowledge (option d).
Nursing Process: Evaluation   **Client Need:** Health Promotion & Maintenance

22.   **The correct answer is a.** The question is asking how to best care for a client on high levels of PEEP. The words "most important" are key and mean you should prioritize any answers, which might be correct. The number one complication associated with PEEP is a pneumothorax secondary to a constant positive pressure exerted on the lungs. Though the nurse should monitor ventilator checks, this is primarily the responsibility of the respiratory therapist (option b). Though prevention of infection is always a concern, it is not the most important concern of a client on PEEP (option c). Suctioning (option d) does not affect PEEP.
Nursing Process: Planning   **Client Need:** Physiological Integrity

23.   **The correct answer is d.** The question is asking what symptoms are present in pernicious anemia. Pernicious anemia is the absence of intrinsic factor and vitamin B_{12}. This is caused by an atrophic gastric mucosa leading to a smooth red tongue and abdominal pain. Increased PT, PTT and decreased platelet counts (option a) are signs of disseminated intravascular coagulation. Bone pain and a large spleen (option b) are seen in thalassemia, not pernicious anemia. When a client has abnormal hemoglobin A this is indicative of sickle cell disease (option c).
Nursing Process: Assessment   **Client Need:** Physiological Integrity

24.   **The correct answer is c.** The question is asking what further teaching would be needed for a cystoscopy. Contrast material is not used during a cystoscopy. The cystoscope is inserted through the urethra into the bladder. The scope has an optical lens system that allows for visualization of the bladder and urethra (option a). The client may feel burning (option d) and have blood-tinged urine (option b) because of trauma to the mucous membranes during the examination.
Nursing Process: Evaluation   **Client Need:** Safe, Effective Care Environment

25.   **The correct answer is b.** The question is asking the reason Apgar scores are given to newborn

infants. A score of 0, 1, or 2, based on definite criteria, is given to the infant's heart rate, respiratory effort, muscle tone, reflex irritability, and color based on assessment. The Apgar score does not measure motor coordination or the baby's interaction with the environment (option d). Options (a) and (c) are partially correct, but do not address all aspects of Apgar scoring.
Nursing Process: Implementation   **Client Need:** Health Promotion & Maintenance

26.   **The correct answer is a.** The question is asking the nurse to analyze the set of symptoms. Note they occurred after the occlusive dressing was placed over the open pneumothorax. When applying an occlusive dressing to an open pneumothorax, the nurse must watch closely for a developing tension pneumothorax. Signs of a tension pneumothorax include: restlessness, cyanosis, mediastinal shift, possible subcutaneous emphysema, and shock. The air that has already gained entrance through the pneumothorax has no place to go, so it shifts other tissue to make room. To relieve the client's respiratory distress, oxygen could be administered, but this does not provide a complete analysis of what has occurred (option b). Likewise, the ricochet effect of the bullet may have damaged the client's heart, but this does not account for the situation described in this question (option c). The dressing has indeed acted occlusively, converting the open pneumothorax to a tension pneumothorax (option d).
Nursing Process: Evaluation   **Client Need:** Physiological Integrity

27.   **The correct answer is b.** The question is asking what symptoms are present in benign prostatic hypertrophy (BPH). The enlarged prostate obstructs the flow of urine causing difficulty beginning the urinary stream and terminal dribbling. Although urinary frequency and epigastric pain are also signs of (BPH), night sweats and constipation are not (options a & d). Impotence is a complication of a total prostatectomy, not a symptom of BPH. Oliguria is not related to BPH but may be related to renal problems (option c).
Nursing Process: Assessment   **Client Need:** Physiological Integrity

28.   **The correct answer is b.** The question is asking what a central venous pressure (CVP) line measures. Think of where it goes in the body. A CVP line is positioned in the right atrium (where the great veins of the body empty) and measures fluid volume in the veins. Pulmonary artery pressure and left ventricular pressure are best measured by a Swan Ganz multilumen pulmonary artery catheter (options a & c). Cardiac output equals stroke volume times heart rate and is also measured by Swan Ganz catheter (option d).
Nursing Process: Planning   **Client Need:** Safe, Effective Care Environment

29.   **The correct answer is c.** The question is asking how to evaluate when the family will be supportive to the victim. Listening to the client relive the experience and try to figure out ways to keep this from happening is a positive response. It helps the client believe certain behaviors could change to keep this from happening again and gives her a sense of control over the incident. Keeping the victim from talking about the rape (option a) does not help the client relieve stress and prevent withdrawal. The client should be encouraged to talk at her own pace as she works through the trauma and grief. Stating concern about how others will think about the rape (option b) may show an attitude that the client is unclean or to blame for the attack. However, others should only be told about the rape, as the client feels ready for others to know. Planning for ways the client can change locks and telephone numbers (option d) may be positive and is a usual behavior but should be initiated by the client, if desired, not the family.
Nursing Process: Evaluation   **Client Need:** Psychosocial Integrity

30.   **The correct answer is b.** The question is asking what would be important in the history of a client about to undergo magnetic resonance imaging (MRI). Because MRI uses a high magnetic field to obtain an image, all metallic objects should be removed. If the client has any internal metal objects, such as a pacemaker, a MRI could cause severe harm. The client should be assessed for claustrophobia (a fear of small places), not acrophobia (a fear of high places) (option a) because the client may lie inside a tube-like machine. The client does not need to be NPO prior to a MRI (option c) since food does not interfere with the scan. Anticonvulsants, such as phenytoin (Dilantin) will not change the outcome of a MRI (option d).
Nursing Process: Assessment   **Client Need:** Physiological Integrity

PRACTICE SESSION: 6

> **Instructions: Allow yourself 30 minutes to complete the following 30 practice questions. Use a timer to notify yourself when 30 minutes are over so that you are not constantly looking at your watch while completing the questions.**

1. A nurse is preparing a client to undergo a paracentesis for severe ascites. What must be done prior to this procedure?
   a. Monitor vital signs, especially blood pressure.
   b. Have the client assume a supine position.
   c. Instruct the client to void.
   d. Administer salt poor albumin IV as prescribed.

2. A nurse is bathing a toddler. The child's mother had to work and is unable to be at the hospital with her son until afternoon. The child asks the nurse, "Where's mommy?" The nurse's best response is:
   a. "Mommy had to go home for a while, but she will be here today."
   b. "Mommy will be here after lunch."
   c. "Mommy always comes back to see you."
   d. "Mommy told me yesterday that she would be here today after noon."

3. The nurse is planning care for a client with acute gastritis. Initially, the nurse should plan to:
   a. monitor intake and output for signs of dehydration.
   b. keep the client NPO until symptoms subside.
   c. assess electrolyte values every 24 hours for fluid imbalance.
   d. evaluate the client's knowledge about gastritis.

4. A client with burns on the back and legs is complaining of severe pain. The appropriate action of the nurse at this time is to:
   a. administer a narcotic analgesic as prescribed.
   b. explain to the client that pain medication must be held because of the inability to absorb it.
   c. administer aspirin (Ecotrin) or acetaminophen (Tylenol) as prescribed.
   d. explain to the client that narcotics must be used very sparingly.

5. Following a stroke, a client is to be started on oral feedings. Prior to initiating oral feedings the nurse should evaluate the gag reflex by assessing which cranial nerves?
   a. Oculomotor, trochlear and abducens.
   b. Trigeminal and facial.
   c. Glossopharyngeal and vagus.
   d. Hypoglossal and spinal accessory.

6. The emergency department nurse assesses four clients. Which client should be cared for first? A client:
   a. who presents with complaints of sudden onset of severe, constant abdominal pain, a distended, rigid abdomen with high-pitched bowel sounds and borborygmi.
   b. with schizophrenia who is hearing the voice of his dead father.
   c. who is gravida III, para II with ruptured membranes contracting every four to five minutes and fetal heart rate of 156.
   d. complaining of blurred vision and severe headache. Reports weight loss despite an increased appetite and excessive thirst. Voiding large quantities of clear yellow urine.

7. A client is admitted to the medical unit of the hospital due to physical problems related to chronic alcoholism. What would be the priority nursing diagnosis?
   a. High risk for injury related to self-destructive behavior.
   b. Alteration in nutrition related to excessive alcohol intake.
   c. Disturbance in self-concept related to hospitalization.
   d. High risk for sensory-perceptual alterations related to alcohol withdrawal.

8. A client is admitted with Cushing's syndrome. The nurse would expect the physician to treat the client with:
   a. fluid replacement therapy.
   b. levothyroxine (Synthroid) therapy.
   c. a transsphenoidal hypophysectomy.
   d. corticosteroid replacement therapy.

9. The physician prescribes a client to perform incentive spirometry following surgery. What should be included in the client teaching?
   a. Begin to use the spirometer the day after surgery.
   b. Inhale as the mist is dispersed.
   c. Take several normal breaths in between use of the spirometer.
   d. Use the spirometer 20 to 30 times per hour while awake.

10. A nurse is caring for a client who had a radical neck dissection the day before. The nurse observes that the client has 115ml of serosanguinous fluid from portable suction. Based on this finding, the nurse should:
    a. apply a pressure dressing.
    b. document the drainage in the nursing notes.
    c. notify the physician.
    d. assess the client's vital signs.

11. During the assessment, the nurse would expect a client with peptic ulcer disease to describe the pain as:
    a. a localized sharp sensation in the umbilical region.
    b. intensifying with the intake of food.
    c. becoming less severe toward the end of the day.
    d. not present upon arising in the morning.

12. A client with psoriasis asks the nurse why the red patches go away in the summer and return in the fall. The nurse explains that the remission is probably related to:
    a. vitamin A released by the sun.
    b. ultraviolet rays of the sun.
    c. the humid climate that prevents dehydration.
    d. the dry climate that promotes sloughing of tissues.

13. A nurse walks into the room of a client with Meniere's disease to give a bath and finds the client curled in a fetal position. The client states, "Please don't make me move, it will make me sick." The appropriate response by the nurse at this time is:
    a. "We won't do the bath now, but at least let me help you onto your other side."
    b. "If you don't try to move around a little you won't know when the attack has passed."
    c. "A bath really isn't necessary, I'll check to see if you feel up to one later."
    d. "I'll get you a shot for nausea and we'll do the bath in an hour."

14. A client with severe pruritis has scratched raw several areas of the skin. What would be an appropriate nursing intervention at this time?
    a. Tell the client that if the scratching doesn't stop, mitts can be applied for protection.
    b. Give the client an alcohol rub to cool the skin.
    c. Offer to sit with the client for a while.
    d. Administer antihistamines as prescribed.

15. A client presents to the emergency department with complaints of increased shortness of breath that has been going on for the past six months. Blood gases drawn reveal the following: pH 7.35, PaCO$_2$ 60 and HCO$_3$ 37. The nurse analyzes these blood gases as:
    a. normal findings.
    b. compensated respiratory acidosis.
    c. uncompensated respiratory acidosis.
    d. respiratory alkalosis.

16. A nurse is conducting teaching with a client being discharged on tranylcypromine (Parnate). What topics should the nurse include? Select all that apply.
    a. Risk of blood dyscrasias.
    b. Low-tyramine diet.
    c. Importance of regular blood pressure monitoring.
    d. Potential for addiction.
    e. Potential medication interactions.
    f. Adherence to low-sodium diet.

17. A client with dementia is to be discharged to a nursing home. The nurse would ensure that this client's needs are best met by:
    a. sending a copy of the written care plan to the nursing home.
    b. assisting the client to meet all of his goals during hospitalization.
    c. teaching the family to meet the client's needs so they stay involved.
    d. calling the nursing home and giving instructions about the client's care.

18. What would the nurse expect to assess in a client with Crohn's disease?
    a. Nausea and vomiting.
    b. Edema and weight gain.
    c. Abdominal cramps and diarrhea.
    d. Abdominal rigidity and constipation.

19. A client with giardiasis is placed on oral metronidazole (Flagyl) therapy. When instructing the client on the medication, the nurse should teach the client to:
    a. avoid alcohol while taking the medication.
    b. avoid taking it with antacids or milk products.
    c. take the medication on an empty stomach.
    d. stop taking the medication if diarrhea subsides.

20. Four days after liver transplant surgery, the client complains that "It feels like something let go in my stomach." Which assessment data indicates that wound dehiscence has occurred?
    a. Redness and edema accompanied with pain at the incision site.
    b. A two (2) cm opening in the middle of the incision with serosanguinous drainage.
    c. Approximated wound edges with purulent drainage.
    d. Elevated and discolored wound edges.

21. A woman who was battered by her husband is to be discharged. The nurse finds her crying and states, "I just can't go home with him there." The most appropriate nursing response would be:
   a. "Why don't you have a restraining order placed against him?"
   b. "Have you discussed this with your doctor?"
   c. "You seem frightened about going home."
   d. "He is in jail right now where he can't hurt you."

22. The physician prescribes an intravenous urogram for a client with suspected renovascular hypertension. When the client asks the nurse to explain this procedure, the nurse responds by stating that:
   a. an instrument will be inserted to visualize problems directly.
   b. the client will be given a solution to drink and X-rays will show kidney function.
   c. a catheter will be threaded up to the kidney and pictures will be taken.
   d. a dye will be given by vein and X-rays taken as the kidneys excrete the dye.

23. The neurology unit is completely full when the nursing supervisor informs the staff that a head injured client is to be admitted. What would be the most appropriate solution to this problem?
   a. Transfer a client with spina bifida admitted for a shunt revision to the general surgical unit.
   b. Transfer a client with a cerebrovascular accident to the medical intensive care unit.
   c. Transfer the client with a spinal cord injury of two days ago to the rehabilitation unit.
   d. Suggest that the new admission be sent to the intensive care unit.

24. A client with a history of cardiac disease is experiencing signs of electrolyte imbalance. When the initial laboratory studies reveal hypokalemia, the nurse realizes that this state is most likely caused by:
   a. vomiting.
   b. nasogastric suctioning.
   c. diarrhea.
   d. diuresis.

25. A young primipara, in her last trimester, is undergoing tests. The nurse would look for which test result that demonstrates fetal distress?
   a. A reactive non-stress test.
   b. Decreasing estriol levels.
   c. An increasing lecithin-sphingomyelin (L/S) ratio.
   d. A negative oxytocin challenge test (OCT).

26. When administering hyperalimentation to a client, what should be monitored to prevent complications of this therapy?
   a. Weight and peripheral edema.
   b. Blood pressure and urine output.
   c. Blood and urine glucose.
   d. Hemoglobin and hematocrit.

27. Which observation is most indicative of urinary retention in a postoperative client?
   a. Anxiety and restlessness.
   b. Not voiding within eight hours after surgery.
   c. Distended urinary bladder.
   d. Lower abdominal pain.

28. The nurse notes that a client with symptoms of mania does not usually eat the food on the meal tray. The client tells the nurse, "I don't have time to eat, there is too much to do. Besides, this food is slop." The best way for the nurse to increase the client's intake is to:
   a. give the client finger foods that can be carried.
   b. increase the client's fluid intake.
   c. give the client foods low in sugar to decrease hyperactivity.
   d. serve meals on an attractive tray with fresh flowers.

29. A 65-year-old woman with Type 1 diabetes is admitted with an exacerbation of her peripheral vascular disease. She complains of a great deal of pain in her right foot even at rest. Her right great toe is cyanotic. The nurse evaluates that the pain is probably caused by:
   a. acute venous insufficiency.
   b. ischemia due to inadequate blood supply.
   c. hyperactivity of sympathetic nerve fibers secondary to diabetes.
   d. necrosis of the cyanotic tissue.

30. A nurse is admitting a woman who has been taking more than her prescribed dosage of diazepam (Valium) while drinking heavily. The client states she is not an addict because the diazepam (Valium) was prescribed and she only drinks "socially", that it is her husband who has the drinking problem. In planning this client's care, the nurse understands that the:
   a. defense mechanisms of denial, rationalization and projection are being used.
   b. defense mechanisms of undoing, projection and displacement are being used.
   c. client and her husband are having marital problems and she is not addicted to either alcohol or drugs.
   d. client is dealing with her feelings toward her husband in a passive-aggressive manner.

STOP. You have now completed Practice Session: 6. Now take a few minutes and correct your answers. Calculate your accuracy rate by dividing the number of questions you completed correctly by the total number of questions you completed (30).

Correct answers ÷ total number of questions completed = accuracy rate.

_____ ÷ _____ = _____

ANSWERS AND RATIONALES
Practice Session 6

1. **The correct answer is c.** The question is asking the preparation of a client having a paracentesis. Paracentesis is the removal of fluid from the abdominal cavity through a small incision made in the abdominal wall. Having the client void prior to the procedure will decrease the chance of puncturing the bladder during the procedure. Blood pressure should be monitored during the paracentesis, as vascular collapse is a possible complication, however, it is not necessary to monitor blood pressure prior to the procedure (option a). The client should be sitting up not lying down to keep the intestines away from the puncture site (option b). Salt poor albumin is often given after a paracentesis to replace any lost protein during the procedure, but is not necessary beforehand (option d).
    Nursing Process: Implementation   **Client Need:** Safe, Effective Care Environment

2. **The correct answer is b.** The question is asking how to tell a toddler when his mother is coming to visit. A sense of time for toddlers is still considerably circumscribed but they are beginning to learn about time sequences (i.e., one event follows another). Routines in a toddler's life help him distinguish sequences, such as breakfast-bath-play-lunch. Telling a toddler specific time (options a & d) does not mean anything to him. Also, telling him that Mommy always comes back does not mean anything cognitively either (option c). Telling the toddler that Mommy will be here after lunch is a concrete example that he can understand.
    Nursing Process: Implementation   **Client Need:** Health Promotion & Maintenance

3. **The correct answer is b.** The question is asking the best way to care for a client with an inflamed stomach lining. Symptoms of gastritis are vomiting, nausea, heartburn and fatigue. An initial nursing intervention would be to keep the client NPO until symptoms subside. All other options (a, c & d) are correct but keeping the client NPO may avert dehydration and electrolyte imbalance. The client is not usually amenable for teaching while in the acute stage of the illness.
    Nursing Process: Planning   **Client Need:** Physiological Integrity

4. **The correct answer is a.** The question is asking how to respond to a burn client's complaints of pain. Medication should be given as prescribed when the client complains of pain. Narcotics such as morphine sulfate (Morphine); meperidine (Demerol), codeine and hydromorphine (Dilaudid) are usually used in the postburn phase. Withholding pain medication is unethical and unnecessary (option b) and actually impedes the healing process. Acetaminophen (Tylenol) and aspirin (Ecotrin) are indicated for mild to moderate pain (option c). There is no need to use morphine sulfate sparingly. Burns often cause severe pain. If the client is complaining of pain, he should be given pain medication as prescribed (option d).
    Nursing Process: Implementation   **Client Need:** Physiological Integrity

5. **The correct answer is c.** The question is asking which cranial nerves supply the gag reflex. The glossopharyngeal and vagus cranial nerves mediate the gag reflex. The sensory component is the glossopharyngeal nerve and the motor response is mediated by the vagus nerve. An intact gag reflex is a safety factor when initiating oral feedings to prevent choking or aspiration. The oculomotor, trochlear and abducens nerves (option a) are responsible for eye movement, pupil reactivity and extraocular movements. The trigeminal and facial nerves (option b) are responsible for jaw and facial movements. The hypoglossal nerve is responsible for tongue movements and the spinal accessory nerve is responsible for shoulder shrugs (option d).
    Nursing Process: Evaluation   **Client Need:** Physiological Integrity

6. **The correct answer is a.** The question is asking which of the four clients should be cared for first. This client has typical clinical manifestations of an intestinal obstruction. However, the severe, constant pain coupled with abdominal rigidity suggests that strangulation has occurred (i.e. volvulus). Gangrene is likely to develop if treatment is not immediate; therefore, this client is the priority. The client in option (b) is actively hallucinating however he is not a danger to himself or others and is not the priority. The client described in option (c) is stable with a stable fetus who is

in the early stage of active labor. The client described in option (d) is experiencing classic symptoms of Type 1 diabetes. This is not an emergency situation.
Nursing Process: Planning   **Client Need:** Physiological Integrity

7.   **The correct answer is b.** The question is asking the most important problem in a client with alcoholism. All of the options are correct but option (b) is the priority. Problems related to the alteration in nutrition due to excessive alcohol intake are usually the reason for medical hospitalization. This is also a short-term diagnosis while option (c) is a long-term diagnosis. Options (a) and (d) are potential but not actual or immediate problems.
Nursing Process: Analysis   **Client Need:** Physiological Integrity

8.   **The correct answer is c.** The question is asking which treatment would be utilized for a client with Cushing's syndrome. Cushing's syndrome results from overactivity of the adrenal gland, with subsequent hypersecretion of glucocorticoids. Seventy percent of cases of Cushing's syndrome are caused by pituitary hypersecretion and pituitary tumors. The resection of most pituitary tumors causing Cushing's is performed via transsphenoidal hypophysectomy. Sodium and water retention may be present because of the mineralcorticoid effects of cortisol. Therefore, fluid replacement therapy (option a) would be incorrect. Levothyroxine (Synthroid) therapy (option b) is the drug of choice to treat hypothyroidism. Corticosteroid replacement therapy is used to treat Addison's disease (option d).
Nursing Process: Implementation   **Client Need:** Physiological Integrity

9.   **The correct answer is c.** The question is asking how a client should be instructed to use incentive spirometry. Incentive spirometry is used to measure gradually increased inhaled volume. The client inhales deeply through a mouthpiece, pauses then exhales. Normal breaths are taken in between use of the spirometer so as not to tire the client. The spirometer should be used immediately following surgery as atelectasis can occur within an hour of hypoventilation (option a). No mist is involved in incentive spirometry. A mini-nebulizer delivers a mist of medication for the client to inhale (option b). The spirometer should be used approximately 10 times an hour while awake. Twenty to 30 times per hour can fatigue the client (option d).
Nursing Process: Implementation   **Client Need:** Health Promotion & Maintenance

10.   **The correct answer is b.** The question is asking what to do if 115ml drainage is observed. First, decide if this is normal for a one-day postoperative radical neck dissection. Most clients who undergo a radical neck dissection are expected to drain 80ml to 120ml of serosanguinous fluid through portable suction. This information needs to be documented. A radical neck dissection is the removal of all of the neck tissue under the skin including lymph nodes and muscles and usually performed due to cancer. A pressure dressing is only required if wound suction is not available. It is not optimal, as it needs to be rechecked and changed frequently (option a). Because the amount drained is within normal parameters and the color is also an expected color, the physician does not need to be called and vital signs do not need to be assessed at this time (options c & d).
Nursing Process: Implementation   **Client Need:** Physiological Integrity

11.   **The correct answer is d.** The question is asking which option best typifies the pain from a peptic ulcer. There is no ulcer related pain when the client awakens in the morning because the flow of gastric acid is at its lowest level at that time. Pain would be felt in the midepigastric region, not the umbilical region (option a), and may be described in a number of ways. Pain typically is relieved quite promptly by the intake of food, since the acid digests with the food and not the stomach lining (option b). Pain becomes more severe toward the end of the day because the acidic juices have been flowing due to food intake and activity (option c).
Nursing Process: Assessment   **Client Need:** Physiological Integrity

12.   **The correct answer is b.** The question is asking why psoriasis is less apparent in the summer and recurs in the fall. Ultraviolet light is a treatment for psoriasis and this occurs naturally with sunlight. Sunlight is not a source of vitamin A, but D (option a). A humid climate would promote

dehydration rather than prevent it and is unrelated to psoriasis treatment (option c). A dry climate (option d) does not promote tissue sloughing and is also unrelated to psoriasis treatment.
Nursing Process: Implementation   **Client Need:** Physiological Integrity

13.   **The correct answer is c.** The question is asking what to do when a client with Meniere's disease is noted to be in the fetal position. Meniere's disease is a dysfunction in the inner ear that causes balance problems, dizziness, nausea, tinnitus and hearing loss in the affected ear. During an acute attack of Meniere's disease, the client should be allowed to stay in whatever position is comfortable. A bath is not a priority at this time. The client should only be moved for essential care, therefore options (a) and (b) are incorrect. The client has not complained of nausea and, if the bath were to be planned for a later time, the client should be reevaluated at that time (option d).
Nursing Process: Implementation   **Client Need:** Physiological Integrity

14.   **The correct answer is d.** The question is asking what to do when a client scratches raw an area of skin. Administer antihistamines as prescribed. It is obvious that the client is very uncomfortable. Pruritis can be very exhausting to the client. Antihistamines, such as diphenhydramine (Benadryl), may provide relief for this condition. Clients who cannot stop scratching even with treatment may need mitts so the area can heal (option a). An alcohol rub would further dry the skin and aggravate the problem although lotions and emollients may be soothing (option b). Sitting with the client (option c), while supportive, does nothing to ease the discomfort and some action should be taken first.
Nursing Process: Implementation   **Client Need:** Physiological Integrity

15.   **The correct answer is b.** The question is asking for an evaluation of the arterial blood gases (ABGs). The values given represent respiratory acidosis with metabolic compensation. Normal pH is 7.35 to 7.45, normal $PaCO_2$ is 35 to 45 and normal HCO_3 is 22 to 26. Always approach ABGs the same way. First, look at the pH and determine if it is high or low. Then draw an arrow next to it (down for acidosis and up for alkalosis). Now look at the $PaCO_2$ and draw an arrow up if it is elevated and down if it is low. If the pH and $PaCO_2$ arrows go in opposite directions, it is a respiratory problem. If the pH and $PaCO_2$ arrows go in the same direction, it is a metabolic problem. If it is a respiratory problem, the HCO_3 will try to correct it by going in the opposite direction of the pH. This is known as compensation. If it is a metabolic problem, the $PaCO_2$ will try to correct it. If the $PaCO_2$ is normal, there is no compensation. If both the $PaCO_2$ and the pH arrows are going in the same direction, then there is compensation. Although the pH is normal, the $PaCO_2$ and the HCO_3 are elevated, therefore option (a) cannot be correct. The high CO_2 reflects the CO_2 retention from respiratory disease. The increased HCO_3 is the body's method of normalizing the pH. For option (c) to be correct the pH would need to be below 7.35 combined with a normal or low HCO_3. For option (d) to be correct the pH would need to be above 7.45.
Nursing Process: Analysis   **Client Need:** Physiological Integrity

16.   **The correct answers are b, c and e.** The question is asking what the nurse would teach a client who is prescribed tranylcypromine (Parnate). Tranylcypromine (Parnate) is a monoamine oxidase inhibitor (MAOI). In general MAOIs are used when clients do not respond to other classifications of antidepressants. The most serious risk of the MAOIs is hypertensive crisis. To avoid this, clients must be placed on tyramine-restricted diets (avoiding foods that contain tyramine such as aged cheeses, raisins, bananas, fish and processed meats) (option b). MAOIs block the enzyme MAO that breaks down tyramine; it can build up in the body. When a client taking a MAOI, like tranylcypromine (Parnate) eats foods high in tyramine, a hypertensive crisis can occur. The client's blood pressure must be carefully monitored (option c) on a regular basis to avoid this. Side effects of tranylcypromine (Parnate) can be severe when this drug is mixed with other medications (option e). The risk of blood dyscrasias is a risk of neuroleptic medications (option a). Addiction to tranylcypromine (Parnate) is not a concern (option d).
Nursing Process: Planning   **Client Need:** Health Promotion & Maintenance

17.   **The correct answer is a.** The question is asking how best to meet the needs of a client being discharged to a nursing home. Written documentation is more powerful communication and leaves no doubt about the plan as it was being carried out in the hospital. Meeting all needs

(option b) is unrealistic. The family will be unable to meet all of the needs or the client would not need supervised care (option c); however, family involvement in care is essential. Telephoning the nursing home (option d) may lead to miscommunication and the person who receives the call may forget what is told to her in verbal communication.

Nursing Process: Implementation   **Client Need:** Health Promotion & Maintenance

18. **The correct answer is c.** The question is asking what symptoms relate to Crohn's disease. Diarrhea is usual with crampy or colicky pain, and as the disease progresses, there is weight loss and dehydration (option b). Abdominal rigidity and constipation (option d) are associated more with perforation of the bowel and peritonitis. Nausea and vomiting are related to diverticulitis (option a).

Nursing Process: Assessment   **Client Need:** Physiological Integrity

19. **The correct answer is a.** The question is asking which option is correct teaching about taking this medication. Metronidazole (Flagyl) may induce a reaction if taken with alcohol. This medication should be taken with meals or with milk or antacids to decrease gastrointestinal distress (options b & c). The medication should be taken for its full course of treatment (option d).

Nursing Process: Implementation   **Client Need:** Physiological Integrity

20. **The correct answer is b.** The question is asking which option defines wound dehiscence. The major clinical manifestations of wound dehiscence are the client's complaint of a sensation of something letting go and the appearance of a wound opening with serosanguinous drainage (option b). Elevated and discolored wound edges are signs of possible hematoma at the site (option d). Redness, edema, pain and purulent drainage (options a & c) are manifestations of a wound infection.

Nursing Process: Assessment   **Client Need:** Physiological Integrity

21. **The correct answer is c.** The question is asking for a therapeutic response to the client's statement. Option (c) uses restating, a therapeutic communication technique designed to show empathy and to help the client talk about her fears. Option (a) gives advice and does not allow the client to express her own thoughts. Option (d) does not address the fact that the client is upset. Option (b) tells the client to speak to the doctor when the nurse could respond.

Nursing Process: Implementation   **Client Need:** Health Promotion & Maintenance

22. **The correct answer is d.** The question is asking what happens in a urogram. A radiopaque dye is given by vein and X-rays are taken as the dye passes through the kidneys and urinary tract. A scope passed into the bladder is a cystoscopy (option a). There is no procedure where a client drinks fluid, which later shows the kidneys (option b). A very small renal catheter can be threaded through to the kidneys, but pictures are not taken with this method (option c).

Nursing Process: Planning   **Client Need:** Safe, Effective Care Environment

23. **The correct answer is a.** The question is asking what to do when the unit is full but another client is being admitted. A client with spina bifida admitted for shunt repair will have a shunt placed to drain excess cerebrospinal fluid. It is placed in the ventricle by a neurosurgeon and threaded under the scalp and skin to the peritoneum. Because this is a surgical procedure, any nurse who works on a surgical floor would know how to assess the site and shunt tract for complications of surgery. Transferring a client to the intensive care unit that does not require intensive care is costly to the client and also uses a bed space that is needed for more critical clients (options b & d). A client who has just suffered a spinal cord injury two days ago is not ready for rehabilitation. Management begins with immobilization and reduction of the dislocation. It is often followed by surgery to further stabilize the client. The team needs to assess and treat any complication prior to transfer to the rehabilitation unit (option c).

Nursing Process: Analysis   **Client Need:** Safe, Effective Care Environment

24. **The correct answer is d.** The question is asking the cause of hypokalemia in a client with heart disease. Although large quantities of potassium can be lost in a number of ways, (options a, b & c) diuresis is the prime cause of potassium depletion. Also, many medications used in heart

disease create a better functioning heart, which increases renal perfusion causing increased urine output.
Nursing Process: Analysis　　　　　**Client Need:** Physiological Integrity

25.　**The correct answer is b.** The question is asking what test relates to fetal distress. Decreasing estriol levels are associated with a fetus in distress as well as a poorly functioning placenta. All the other options listed are utilized to determine the results of a compromised fetus. A reactive non-stress test (option a) means the fetal activity is within normal limits. Increasing L/S ratio (option c) is a positive sign, although this may be misleading as a sign of prevention of respiratory distress syndrome. A negative OCT (option d) indicates no placental insufficiency.
Nursing Process: Evaluation　　　　　**Client Need:** Physiological Integrity

26.　**The correct answer is c.** The question is asking how the nurse could prevent complications in the client receiving hyperalimentation. The nurse should monitor blood and urine glucose to assess for glucose imbalances. Altered blood sugar is one of the identified clinical problems associated with hyperalimentation. Nursing interventions include monitoring blood glucose levels daily and checking urine sugar and acetone every four hours. Monitoring weight, edema, blood pressure, urine output, hematocrit and hemoglobin (options a, b & d) would not specifically identify any of the other clinical problems associated with hyperalimentation.
Nursing Process: Assessment　　　　　**Client Need:** Physiological Integrity

27.　**The correct answer is c.** The question is asking which option is the best sign of urine left in the bladder after voiding. A distended bladder indicates urinary retention. Clients unable to void the retained urine may develop some tachycardia related to discomfort, restlessness and anxiety associated with the difficulty (option a). Not voiding eight hours after surgery (option b) and lower abdominal pain (option d) are signals to the nurse to assess the client for possible urinary retention; however these may also be symptoms of other complications of surgery.
Nursing Process: Assessment　　　　　**Client Need:** Physiological Integrity

28.　**The correct answer is a.** The question is asking how to improve nutritional intake of a client who is manic and will not sit down to eat. A client in a manic state finds it difficult to remain still long enough to eat a meal. Nutrition becomes a problem. Finger foods or foods that can be carried will help meet the nutritional needs of the client. Increasing the client's fluid intake (option b) will not meet nutritional requirements. Giving the client foods low in sugar will not decrease hyperactivity (option c) since sugar is not the reason for the hyperactivity. Serving meals on an attractive tray with fresh flowers (option d) is not appropriate since he is unable, voluntarily, to slow down to eat a meal.
Nursing Process: Implementation　　　　　**Client Need:** Physiological Integrity

29.　**The correct answer is b.** The question is asking what causes the pain in a client with peripheral vascular disease. Pain is related to ischemia due to inadequate blood supply. Ischemic tissue is still alive with functioning nerve and pain receptors. Clients with diabetes have loss of autonomic nerve fibers not hyperactivity of sympathetic nerve fibers (option c). Necrotic tissue (option d) has no sensation; it is the ischemic tissue surrounding it that causes pain. Acute venous insufficiency (option a) results in edema of the area that may or may not result in discomfort.
Nursing Process: Analysis　　　　　**Client Need:** Physiological Integrity

30.　**The correct answer is a.** The question is asking the nurse to analyze this clinical situation. Denial, rationalization and projection are the trilogy of addiction defense mechanisms (denial: not an addict; rationalization: drinks socially and only takes prescription drugs; projection: husband is the addict). Undoing, projection and displacement are incorrect (option b). Alcoholism is a primary disease, which affects the family and causes marital problems (option c). The client is not showing passive-aggressive behavior (option d). Passive-aggressive behavior is a term describing indirect expression of anger.
Nursing Process: Analysis　　　　　**Client Need:** Psychosocial Integrity

PRACTICE SESSION: 7

> **Instructions: Allow yourself 30 minutes to complete the following 30 practice questions. Use a timer to notify yourself when 30 minutes are over so that you are not constantly looking at your watch while completing the questions.**

1. A client admitted with chest trauma is diagnosed with a myocardial contusion. The nurse plans care based on the understanding that:
   a. associated precordial pain is the result of myocardial infarction.
   b. dysrhythmias may be present.
   c. the contusion is due to pericardial rupture.
   d. coronary vasodilators are indicated.

2. What is the most effective nursing measure in reducing nosocomial infections with the surgical client?
   a. Encourage the client to cough and deep breathe every hour.
   b. Administer antibiotics as prescribed.
   c. Maintain asepsis during wound care.
   d. Frequent hand washing.

3. Which lab values would be consistent with the drive to breathe in a client with chronic obstructive pulmonary disease (COPD)?
   a. PaO_2 of 90 and a pH of 7.3.
   b. $PaCO_2$ of 48 and a PaO_2 of 91.
   c. $PaCO_2$ of 33 and a HCO_3 of 30.
   d. HCO_3 of 28 and a pH of 7.33.

4. A client has been diagnosed with asthma and a history of hypertension. While the nurse is explaining the use of the inhaler, she asks what other medications the client is taking. The nurse would notify the physician if the client were taking which medication?
   a. Propanolol (Inderal).
   b. Nifedipine (Procardia).
   c. Verapamil hydrochloride (Calan).
   d. Methyldopa (Aldomet).

5. A client comes to the maternity clinic for a pregnancy test that results in positive findings. The client has one son, three years of age. She previously had a spontaneous abortion at 11 weeks gestation. Which statement best describes the client?
   a. Gravida II, para III.
   b. Gravida II, para II.
   c. Gravida III, para I.
   d. Gravida II, para I.

6. When the nurse takes a central venous pressure (CVP) reading, the water in the manometer rises during inspiration and falls during expiration. The appropriate action of the nurse would be to:
   a. relevel the manometer and attempt another reading.
   b. notify the physician immediately.
   c. check the manometer for air bubbles.
   d. record the level at expiration as the CVP.

7. A 32-year-old male client, married for five years, comes to the mental health clinic complaining of feeling uncomfortable about sex and fear that he might be homosexual. The first step in the assessment process would be to:
    a. conduct a complete sexual history on the client.
    b. examine the nurse's own feelings and thoughts about homosexuality.
    c. include the client's wife in the assessment process.
    d. assess the client's childhood sexual development.

8. A client recovering from abdominal surgery complains of considerable gaseous distension. Which nursing measure would be considered most effective in alleviating the excess gas?
    a. Inserting a rectal tube for a period of 20 minutes.
    b. Assisting the client to walk in the corridor.
    c. Administering a carminative enema as prescribed.
    d. Applying a hot water bottle to the abdomen.

9. A client sustains a fracture of the right arm. The fracture is stabilized and the client has a closed reduction of the right arm and cast application. After the plaster cast has been applied, the nurse bases further actions on the fact that the cast:
    a. is slightly wet but rigid.
    b. will now have maximum strength.
    c. may be dented with pressure from fingers or hands when being moved.
    d. needs quick drying.

10. What is the most important nursing intervention for a client who is vomiting postoperatively?
    a. Turn the client to a side-lying position.
    b. Support the abdominal incision.
    c. Administer oral hygiene.
    d. Accurately measure the vomitus.

11. A client is admitted to the hospital after suffering a cerebral vascular accident (CVA). In order to assess the client's visual loss the nurse should perform which examination?
    a. Direct pupillary response.
    b. Consensual pupillary response.
    c. Visual field examination.
    d. Accommodation and convergence.

12. The nurse should plan to explain to a client who will be receiving a spinal anesthetic that he will:
    a. become drowsy from the anesthetic agent that is used to numb his legs.
    b. have a gradual loss of sensation and motion after the anesthetic agent is administered.
    c. be able to move his legs but will not have any sensation below the waist.
    d. have a gradual return of movement and sensation in his legs.

13. A 9-month-old child is admitted with inspiratory stridor, a barking cough and fever. On admission, his respiratory rate is 42, his heart rate is 160 and his temperature is 101°F. The nurse assesses the child 30 minutes later and his respirations are now 64, his heart rate is 168 and his temperature is 102°F. Based on these changes which intervention should be eliminated from this child's care?
    a. Encourage oral fluids.
    b. Administer nebulized epinephrine as prescribed.
    c. Place child in orthopneic position.
    d. Humidify all oxygen.

14. The nurse would include which discharge instructions for a client with a total hip replacement?
    a. May use full weight bearing as desired.
    b. Continue to do exercises such as bend over at the waist and touch your toes.
    c. Advise that increased pain is normal upon ambulation.
    d. Use an elevated toilet seat.

15. A client is scheduled for a gastroscopic examination to rule out a peptic ulcer. During the procedure the nurse is primarily responsible for:
    a. assembling the equipment needed for the procedure.
    b. attending to the client's physical and psychosocial needs.
    c. assisting the physician with the procedure.
    d. providing mouth care and cleaning the work area following the procedure.

16. A client admitted with schizophrenia tells the nurse she no longer hears voices. When evaluating the plan of care for alteration in thought processes, the nurse decides that:
    a. the problem can be resolved since she no longer hears voices.
    b. more information is needed since she may be "covering up."
    c. it is not unusual for "voices" to abruptly disappear.
    d. she should discuss discharge with the treatment team.

17. The nurse is caring for a client admitted to the surgical unit for repair of a rectal fistula. In caring for a client with an anorectal incision, the nurse knows that healing will be enhanced by:
    a. maintaining a wet-to-dry dressing.
    b. inserting an indwelling urinary catheter.
    c. warm sitz baths.
    d. frequent dressing changes.

18. A client has been diagnosed with diabetes insipidus. Which statement would indicate that the client needs further teaching?
    a. "I will have my urine checked daily for glucose."
    b. "My disease cannot be controlled by limiting my intake of fluids."
    c. "Until my disease is corrected, I will continue to excrete large volumes of urine."
    d. "My disease is related to a disorder of the posterior lobe of the pituitary."

19. When collecting assessment data, the nurse notes which symptoms that may be indicative of hyperthyroidism?
    a. Increased appetite with accompanying weight gain over the past month.
    b. Increased body temperature and intolerance to heat.
    c. Skin pale, cool and dry.
    d. Constipation and goiter.

20. A client with alcoholism decides to go to an alcohol and drug treatment center. The nurse knows that the most important factor for the client's rehabilitation is:
    a. family support.
    b. motivation.
    c. past coping skills.
    d. self-esteem.

21. A client is admitted with leukorrhea and intermenstrual bleeding. Colposcopy and biopsy results reveal stage III cervical cancer. Brachytherapy is scheduled for a three-day period. The nurse caring for this client must be aware that:
    a. Care must be organized so that a limited amount of time is spent with the client.
    b. A shield must be worn each time the client's room is entered.
    c. The client is not considered to be radioactive during the time the source is in place.
    d. The client's skin will be marked to identify the area to be radiated.

22. An 8-year-old child is being evaluated for Legg-Calve-Perthes disease (LCP). The nurse may expect to assess which early sign of LCP?
    a. Inflammation of the affected femur.
    b. Enlargement of the calf muscles.
    c. A limp, that may or may not be painful.
    d. Loss of sensation to the affected extremity.

23. A client recently diagnosed with Type 2 diabetes is placed on an oral hypoglycemic agent. The nurse would teach the client to:
    a. avoid ingesting large amounts of aspirin (Ecotrin).
    b. increase the dosage when experiencing an infection or febrile illness.
    c. limit exercise when taking the medication.
    d. take the medication one-half hour prior to each meal.

24. A nurse is documenting intake and output of her postoperative client during the 3:00PM to 11:00PM shift. The client ate two cups of broth, one-half cup of gelatin and an eight-ounce glass of juice for dinner. He received a maintenance intravenous infusion of D_5 1/2 NSS at a rate of 100ml/hour. At 2:00PM, his Jackson Pratt (JP) drained 130ml of serosanguinous fluid that was prescribed to be replaced 1/2ml per ml of loss over four hours from 3:00PM to 7:00PM with maintenance intravenous fluid. At 10:00PM the nurse emptied the Foley catheter bag of 925ml dark yellow urine. The JP was emptied of 90ml serous fluid. How many milliliters did the client take in during the nurse's shift?

    _____

25. A client with chronic obstructive pulmonary disease (COPD) is suspected of having a bowel obstruction and is scheduled for an outpatient barium enema. What client statement would the nurse need to clarify?
    a. "I won't eat any solid foods after dinner tonight, but I can have apple juice."
    b. "I will take my morning furosemide (Lasix) with only a sip of water the day of the test."
    c. "I will report any dark colored stools to the doctor."
    d. "I will have my son take me home after the test."

26. The nurse is caring for a client newly admitted to a nursing home from the hospital. The client has a history of dementia, hypertension and urinary incontinence. A Foley catheter is patent for adequate amounts of clear yellow urine. The nurse should expect the physician to:
    a. discontinue the Foley catheter.
    b. prescribe intermittent catheterization.
    c. suggest surgical intervention to the family.
    d. leave the Foley catheter in place until continence is achieved.

27. A 16-year-old adolescent with meningitis has been in respiratory isolation for the last six days. She begins to improve, although she is irritable and has no interest in eating or in activity. The nurse would base her plan of care on the understanding that this behavior is:
    a. part of her illness.
    b. a reflection of her "normal" behavior.
    c. a serious mental depression.
    d. sensory deprivation.

28. In evaluating an open wound, the nurse identifies granulating tissue and documents it as:
    a. pink with a moderate amount of beginning scar tissue.
    b. necrotic with firm borders.
    c. red and blanches white with digital pressure.
    d. pink to red and bleeds easily.

29. The nurse evaluates that a client with bulimia is improving when she states that eating disorders generally develop in response to:
    a. the inability to cope with life stressors effectively.
    b. rebellious acts against society.
    c. lack of will power and initiative to change.
    d. an economically and socially deprived background.

30.   During a discharge interview a client expresses vague suicidal ideation. The nurse confirms that
        the client is currently suicidal. Place the interventions in the order that the nurse would complete
        them.
        a.   Report the situation to the treatment team.
        b.   Conduct a room search for dangerous objects.
        c.   Place the client on one-to-one observation.
        d.   Carefully document the client's conversation and the nurse's response.

**STOP. You have now completed Practice Session: 7. Now take a few minutes
and correct your answers. Calculate your accuracy rate by dividing the
number of questions you completed correctly by the total number of
questions you completed (30).**

Correct answers ÷ total number of questions completed = accuracy rate.

_____ ÷ _____ = _____

ANSWERS AND RATIONALES
Practice Session 7

1. **The correct answer is b.** The question is asking how to best take care of a client with a myocardial contusion. The heart has been damaged. Hemorrhage occurs in the myocardium as a result of the contusion. The heart's contractility, cardiac output and blood pressure may diminish. Dysrhythmias such as tachycardia, conduction problems and ventricular fibrillation may be present. A client with a myocardial contusion may experience precordial pain that only mimics that of myocardial infarction (option a). Precordial rupture (option c) is generally considered to be fatal. It can be caused for the same reasons as myocardial contusion, which includes rapid force deceleration and physical force such as in a car accident. The contusion pain is not alleviated by coronary vasodilators (option d).
   Nursing Process: Planning   **Client Need:** Physiological Integrity

2. **The correct answer is d.** The question is asking the best way to prevent nosocomial (hospital) infections in a surgical client. Precautions to prevent nosocomial infections and avoid infecting oneself begin with the understanding that unrecognized or subclinical infections are prevalent and that precautions begin before a diagnosis of infection is made. Routine techniques, such as hand washing, should be emphasized and enforced. Conscientious hand washing is essential for every person who comes in contact with clients and moves from one client to the next. The other three options (a, b & c) are good supporting measures but mean little without hand washing.
   Nursing Process: Implementation   **Client Need:** Safe, Effective Care Environment

3. **The correct answer is b.** The question is asking what lab values would indicate that a client automatically knows to breathe in chronic obstructive pulmonary disease (COPD). In a client with COPD, the drive to breathe is an elevated carbon dioxide ($PaCO_2$) level (option c). Normal $PaCO_2$ is 35 to 45mm Hg. In a person with a chronically elevated $PaCO_2$, the brain becomes insensitive to this and the drive to breathe becomes a low PaO_2 (option a). A normal PaO_2 is 80 to 100mm Hg. Giving too high a concentration of oxygen to this client could cause respiratory arrest. The pH and the HCO_3 are related to the acid base balance in the blood, not the drive to breathe (options a & d).
   Nursing Process: Analysis   **Client Need:** Physiological Integrity

4. **The correct answer is a.** The question is asking which medication would cause a problem for a client with asthma. Though propanolol (Inderal) is known as an effective antihypertensive, it is contraindicated in clients with asthma. Propanolol (Inderal) is a beta-blocker. By blocking beta cells it can cause bronchoconstriction and lead to brochospasm, which can be detrimental to clients with asthma. All other options (b, c & d) are acceptable antihypertensive agents and can be safely used with asthma.
   Nursing Process: Analysis   **Client Need:** Physiological Integrity

5. **The correct answer is c.** The question is asking what is the gravida and para for this client. Gravida refers to pregnancies of any duration. Para denotes past pregnancies that have resulted in an infant of viable age, regardless of the fate of that infant. It is advisable to remember that the terms gravida and para refer solely to pregnancies. The client is currently pregnant and had two previous pregnancies, which makes her gravida III. She has carried one pregnancy to a viable age, thus, she is para I (options a, b & d).
   Nursing Process: Analysis   **Client Need:** Health Promotion & Maintenance

6. **The correct answer is d.** The question is asking what the nurse should do if the water rises during inspiration and falls at expiration. First, you have to determine if this is normal and it is. The fluid fluctuates because of the change in intrathoracic pressure during respirations. The measurement should be recorded at the level at expiration as the central venous pressure. Nurses must be consistent when measuring the reading at expiration. This will increase the accuracy of the results. The nurse should relevel the manometer (option a) only if a very high or low result is obtained. The described fluctuation is a normal response and the physician does not need to be

notified (option b). Air bubbles (option c) would not prevent fluctuation, but would alter the reading.
Nursing Process: Implementation   **Client Need:** Safe, Effective Care Environment

7.   **The correct answer is b.** The question is asking the first step in the assessment process if a client believes he is homosexual. In caring for the homosexual client, the first step in the assessment phase is self-assessment of the nurse. It is important for the nurse to examine personal thoughts and feelings before attempting to care for the homosexual client. Sexual issues are extremely value-laden and emotionally charged. Nurses often fall victim to societal myths and misinformation about homosexuality, which can affect the quality of nursing care that is provided for clients. Option (c) is not a priority at this time. Option (d) is beyond basic sexual history taking and usually requires advanced experience. Sexual history taking (option a) is within the scope of nursing practice. The first priority in the assessment phase is self-assessment of the nurse.
Nursing Process: Assessment   **Client Need:** Health Promotion & Maintenance

8.   **The correct answer is b.** The question is asking for the most effective action to alleviate gaseous distension in a client recovering from abdominal surgery. "Most effective" means that more than one answer may be a way to relieve gas but one is better than the rest. Exercise is the most effective way to expel flatus and it is also the most natural. Walking is the best method. If that is not possible, moving about in the bed will help. A rectal tube, carminative enema and hot water bottle (options a, c & d) may be tried if exercise is not sufficient to reduce the flatus.
Nursing Process: Implementation   **Client Need:** Physiological Integrity

9.   **The correct answer is c.** The question is asking which option is true about a newly applied plaster cast. After the cast is applied, the plaster cast is still wet and somewhat soft, not rigid (option a). It does not have its full strength until dry. While damp, it can be dented if handled with the fingertips instead of the palms of the hands. The cast should dry naturally and requires 24 to 72 hours to dry, depending on the thickness of the cast and the environmental drying conditions (options b & d).
Nursing Process: Analysis   **Client Need:** Physiological Integrity

10.   **The correct answer is a.** The question is asking what is the most important intervention for a postoperative client who is vomiting. Since safety would be of prime consideration to prevent aspiration and maintain an open airway, the client would be placed in a side-lying position unless contraindicated by the surgical procedure. If the client is supine, the head should be turned to the side to avoid aspiration. The threat of aspiration is a constant concern when vomiting is severe. The client who cannot adequately care for himself should be placed in a semi-Fowler's or side-lying position. Dressings over the wound will act as a support (option b). The client may or may not experience nausea and oral hygiene will not affect vomiting during the postoperative period (option c). Measuring vomitus (option d) is important for fluid balance but is not the most important intervention.
Nursing Process: Implementation   **Client Need:** Physiological Integrity

11.   **The correct answer is c.** The question is asking which test is used to assess visual loss associated with a cerebral vascular accident (CVA). When a client experiences a CVA, the ability to see out of one side of the eyes may be lost. This is known as homonymous heminopsia. Confrontation visual field examination will help the nurse identify the extent of the visual field loss. The other examinations will determine the function of the eye muscles and the intactness of the optic nerve but will not demonstrate a field deficit (options a, b & d).
Nursing Process: Assessment   **Client Need:** Physiological Integrity

12.   **The correct answer is d.** The question is asking what will happen when a client receives a spinal anesthetic. The return of movement and sensation in the lower extremities is gradual with the return of motion first and then sensation. This type of anesthetic does not cloud or alter the client's level of consciousness (option a). Within minutes after the injection of the anesthetic

agent into the subarachnoid space, the client will experience a loss of sensation and paralysis of the extremities (options b & c).
Nursing Process: Implementation   **Client Need:** Physiological Integrity

13.   **The correct answer is a.** The question is asking what the nurse should not do when a child admitted with croup is experiencing increasing respiratory distress. Oral fluids are contraindicated when the respiratory rate is above 60 breaths per minute. Encouraging the child to drink can lead to aspiration. Nebulized epinephrine will cause bronchodilation (option b). Placing the child in an orthopneic position (sitting upright) will facilitate lung expansion (option c). Humidifying the oxygen (option d) will liquefy and loosen secretions.
Nursing Process: Implementation   **Client Need:** Physiological Integrity

14.   **The correct answer is d.** The question is asking what instructions would be given to a client after a total hip replacement. Use of an elevated toilet seat helps to prevent dislocation of the hip. Crossing the legs, bending from the waist to touch the toes (option b), and sitting on low lounge chairs are all situations, which could possibly lead to a hip dislocation. Partial weight bearing is the norm with progression towards full weight bearing (option a). Increased pain may be related to a hematoma and should be investigated (option c).
Nursing Process: Planning   **Client Need:** Health Promotion & Maintenance

15.   **The correct answer is b.** The question is asking the nurse's primary responsibility during a gastroscopy. The nurse may assist with all of the options (a, c & d). However, the primary responsibility for the nurse should be supporting and advocating for the client.
Nursing Process: Implementation   **Client Need:** Physiological Integrity

16.   **The correct answer is b.** The question is asking how to evaluate hallucinations objectively based on the client's statement that she no longer hears voices. Options (a), (c) and (d) assume that there are no more "voices" just because the client reports such. Validation of data collection is needed to confirm such assumptions.
Nursing Process: Evaluation   **Client Need:** Psychosocial Integrity

17.   **The correct answer is c.** The question is asking how healing would be helped in a client with an anorectal incision. Warm baths or sitz baths are soothing and promote cleansing of the incision. The warm water may also promote the drainage of purulent secretions. Warm sitz baths assist in tissue debridement, provide comfort, and increase circulation to the area. Moist heat causes vasodilation, which allows more oxygen to flow to the affected area. Side-to-side positioning and short walks are better than sitting. A wet-to-dry dressing (option a) will not necessarily enhance the healing process in this case. An indwelling catheter (option b) might be necessary for a vesicovaginal fistula but is not necessary for a rectal fistula. Frequent dressing changes (option d) may be a source of irritation, lengthening the healing process.
Nursing Process: Planning   **Client Need:** Physiological Integrity

18.   **The correct answer is a.** The question is asking when further teaching is needed for a client with diabetes insipidus (DI). This means one option is wrong and the other three are correct. Clients with DI do not have the need to be checked for glucose because there is no glucose in urine. DI is a disorder of the posterior pituitary gland (option d) due to a deficiency in vasopressin. The antidiuretic hormone (vasopressin) creates a condition characterized by great thirst and large volumes of dilute urine. Until the disease is corrected with adequate replacement of vasopressin, the client will continue to void large volumes of dilute urine (option c). The disease cannot be corrected by limiting the intake of fluids, (option b) because loss of fluid continues without fluid replacement; it does not correct the underlying cause.
Nursing Process: Evaluation   **Client Need:** Physiological Integrity

19.   **The correct answer is b.** The question is asking what symptoms relate to hyperthyroidism. Think about the fact that metabolism would be increased. Increased body temperature and intolerance to heat result from an increased metabolic rate. Increased appetite will be accompanied by increased weight loss due to increased metabolism (option a). Skin is warm and

172

moist due to vasodilation (option c). Goiter is a symptom of hyperthyroidism, however, there is increased frequency of stools and stools are less formed in clients with hyperthyroidism (option d).
Nursing Process: Assessment   **Client Need:** Physiological Integrity

20.   **The correct answer is b.** The question is asking which factor is most important for client rehabilitation. That means that more than one may be true but the question asked you to prioritize. The person with alcoholism often does not want to stop drinking, but only to slow down. Only when persons with alcoholism have the motivation to get help to stop drinking, can they stop drinking. Although the family, coping ability and self-esteem play a role in the treatment process, it is motivation that will keep the person from drinking (options a, c & d).
Nursing Process: Assessment   **Client Need:** Psychosocial Integrity

21.   **The correct answer is a.** The question is asking which concept the nurse should be aware of when caring for a client receiving brachytherapy. Brachytherapy consists of implantation of radioactive materials directly into the tumor or in close proximity to the tumor. The amount of time and proximity to the client is determined by the dose of the implant; therefore, principles of time and distance are used when caring for a client with an implant. Nurses must limit the amount of time in direct contact with the client. Caregivers must wear a film badge to indicate radiation exposure. Shielding should be used when in close proximity to the client, but not each time the room is entered (option b). The client is considered to be radioactive during the time the source is in place (option c). The client's skin is marked for external beam radiation, not internal radiation (option d).
Nursing Process: Implementation   **Client Need:** Safe, Effective Care Environment

22.   **The correct answer is c.** The question is asking for an early sign of Legg-Calve-Perthes (LCP) disease. Early is a key word and means that both early and late signs may be in the options. LCP occurs when there is avascular necrosis to the femoral head. This causes the child to limp. Hip pain is sometimes accompanied with the limp. The pain may radiate, but is usually relieved by rest. Inflammation may occur at the hip, not the femur. Femur inflammation would be indicative of osteomyelitis (option a). Enlargement of the calf muscles is found in muscular dystrophy (option b). Children with LCP do not usually lose sensation of the extremity, but may do so with a neurological disorder (option d).
Nursing Process: Assessment   **Client Need:** Physiological Integrity

23.   **The correct answer is a.** The question is asking what option is true for hypoglycemic agents. Aspirin (Ecotrin) potentiates the actions of oral hypoglycemic agents. Clients may need to take insulin instead of, or with their oral hypoglycemic agent during periods of infection or illness (option b). Clients need to follow a prescribed diet and maintain a regular exercise program (option c); oral hypoglycemics differ in the rate they are absorbed from the gastrointestinal system. Long-acting agents are administered once daily (option d). More rapid-acting agents are administered twice daily, not with each meal.
Nursing Process: Implementation   **Client Need:** Health Promotion & Maintenance

24.   **The correct answer is 1,705.** The question is asking the intake for the 3:00PM to 11:00PM shift. All routes of fluid intake and loss must be recorded. The client took in a total of 840ml orally (480ml broth, 120ml gelatin, 240ml juice) and 865ml parenterally (800ml IV maintenance and 65ml replacement fluid--130ml x 1/2ml = 65ml) for a total input of 1,705ml. Output from 3:00PM to 11:00PM includes 925ml of urine and 90ml of JP drainage for a total output of 1,015ml.
Nursing Process: Analysis   **Client Need:** Physiological Integrity

25.   **The correct answer is b.** The question is asking which statement needs to be clarified by the nurse. Clarified is the key word, as it means one option is wrong and the other three are correct concerning the barium enema. A client should be NPO after midnight in preparation for a barium enema. This includes oral medications. The client scheduled for a barium enema the following day should have clear liquids until midnight (option a). The client should be taught to monitor stools for consistency and color following a barium enema. Stools should be light in color for the

first two to three days. Dark stools may indicate bleeding or a bowel perforation (option c). Barium enemas can cause excessive fatigue and the client should be instructed to rest and not drive home (option d).
Nursing Process: Evaluation   **Client Need:** Health Promotion & Maintenance

26.   **The correct answer is a.** The question is asking what the nurse can expect from the physician for a newly admitted client. A Foley catheter is used only when absolutely necessary and should be discontinued when urine output is adequate and urine is assessed for urinary tract infections. Intermittent catheterizations (option b) are prescribed for inadequate urine output. Surgical intervention (option c) would only be used when a malformation causing incontinence is present. Foley catheters are a leading cause of infection and should be removed as soon as possible.
Nursing Process: Analysis   **Client Need:** Physiological Integrity

27.   **The correct answer is d.** The question is asking the nurse to analyze the girl's behavior. Think about an adolescent's needs and the fact that the client is improving. Very common reactions of the client, who is "isolated" particularly when use of a private room is indicated, are rejection, loneliness, and sometimes guilt feelings. The behavior is not a part of the meningitis but a result of necessary treatment (option a). A change in this client's behavior should first be assessed as a result of sensory deprivation and not assumed to be a component of "normal" behavior (option b). If the behavior continues after intervention, depression may be a factor (option c).
Nursing Process: Analysis   **Client Need:** Psychosocial Integrity

28.   **The correct answer is d.** The question is asking which option shows granulating tissue. An open wound will heal by secondary intention, which means it heals from the inside out. The necrotic tissue which lines the walls of an open infected wound will gradually disintegrate and the open cavity will fill with red, soft sensitive tissue that bleeds very easily. This is known as granulation. Scar tissue forms as healing is completed and, if necrotic tissue is evident, granulation has not yet occurred; therefore, cannot be identified (options a & b). Tissue that blanches white is an indication that tissue perfusion is intact but is not a test for presence of granulation tissue (option c).
Nursing Process: Evaluation   **Client Need:** Physiological Integrity

29.   **The correct answer is a.** The question is asking which option is true about how bulimia develops. A person does not learn how to deal with stress effectively and eating or not eating becomes an ineffective way to survive, numb or control life stressors. Rebellious acts against society are seen in people with antisocial personality disorder (option b). Lack of will power is not related to eating disorders (option c). There is no evidence to support that bulimia is related to economic and social deprivation (option d).
Nursing Process: Evaluation   **Client Need:** Psychosocial Integrity

30.   **The correct order of the options is: c, b, a, d.** The question is asking the correct order of interventions necessary when a client is suicidal. The first priority of the nurse is to place the client on one-to-one observation to keep him safe (option c) while the staff searches his room for potentially dangerous objects e.g. knives, glass objects, scissors, etc. (option b). The nurse then informs the charge nurse, physician and treatment team members of the client's intent (option a) and then specifically documents the client's comments and the nurse's assessment and specific interventions to protect the client (option d). The specific charting also helps protect the nurse legally, as it shows that she did everything reasonable to keep the client safe.
Nursing Process: Implementation   **Client Need:** Psychosocial Integrity

> **Instructions:** Allow yourself 30 minutes to complete the following 30 practice questions. Use a timer to notify yourself when 30 minutes are over so that you are not constantly looking at your watch while completing the questions.

1. A 16-year-old client has just found out that her parents are moving the family to another state. Although the rest of the family is eagerly anticipating the move, the adolescent is experiencing frequent crying spells and difficulty concentrating at school. In working with this adolescent, the nurse's initial task would be to:
   a. assess the client's perception of the event.
   b. establish a therapeutic trusting relationship.
   c. help the client accept the reality of the move.
   d. teach the client stress management techniques.

2. A female client with spina bifida is being taught how to perform urinary self-catheterization. Which client statement would indicate an understanding of the teaching plan?
   a. "I should catheterize myself every eight hours while awake."
   b. "I need to maintain sterile technique while catheterizing myself."
   c. "I will clean myself with alcohol using a front to back motion before I catheterize myself."
   d. "I will wash the catheter with soapy water after I am done so that I can use it again later."

3. A client with a fractured femur is placed in Buck's traction. Nursing care for this client would include:
   a. keeping the buttocks off the mattress.
   b. asking the client to dosiflex the toes and foot every four hours.
   c. inspecting and cleaning pin sites every four hours.
   d. applying traction weights of 10 to 20 lbs (4.5 to 9.1 kg).

4. A nurse caring for a client with a chest tube would plan to:
   a. immediately clamp the tube if excessive bubbling occurs.
   b. put the arm and shoulder on the side of the chest tube through vigorous range-of-motion exercises twice per day.
   c. clamp the tube during transport.
   d. encourage the client to cough and deep breath each shift.

5. Which position would be indicated to decrease venous return and promote comfort for a client with acute pulmonary edema?
   a. Trendelenburg.
   b. Sitting upright with legs dangling over the bed.
   c. High-Fowler's.
   d. Semi-Fowler's with legs slightly elevated.

6. A 4-month-old infant with suspected epiglottitis is being admitted to the pediatric unit. On the admission assessment, the nurse should avoid direct examination of the throat because:
   a. it may precipitate vomiting, which would cause sudden laryngospasms.
   b. it may precipitate sudden laryngospasms leading to death.
   c. the infant may have strep throat and this disease is very contagious.
   d. it is impossible to visualize the throat of a 4-month-old infant.

7.	A graduate nurse (GN) is caring for a client with acute respiratory distress syndrome (ARDS). The GN questions her own ability regarding suctioning. What finding would indicate that the GN performed this procedure successfully?
   a.	Respiratory rate is now 30/minute.
   b.	Pulse rate is now 120/minute.
   c.	Blood pressure is now 120/80.
   d.	Breath sounds are now clear bilaterally in all fields.

8.	A nurse is admitting a Puerto Rican client to the emergency department. The client was injured at work and brought to the hospital by ambulance. The client's wife and children arrive shortly afterward. The nurse might alter the assessment of this family because:
   a.	note taking is considered to be rude.
   b.	family members probably are bilingual.
   c.	they might consider some questions too private.
   d.	of the belief the hospital is only a place to die.

9.	What would be included in the discharge instructions for a client with hepatitis C?
   a.	Alcohol is permitted in moderation.
   b.	Vitamin supplements are desirable to enhance dietary nutrition.
   c.	No medication should be taken until its effect on the liver is determined.
   d.	Antiemetics should be taken if nausea and vomiting become severe.

10.	A child with cyanosis and difficulty breathing is admitted. The characteristics that will implicate cardiovascular disease rather than respiratory distress are demonstrated in the child whose cyanosis:
   a.	decreases with crying.
   b.	decreases with feeding.
   c.	increases with crying.
   d.	improves with oxygen.

11.	A client with acquired immune deficiency syndrome (AIDS) is admitted to a hospice. The role of the nurse caring for a dying client should be to:
   a.	encourage the family in finding alternative curative methods.
   b.	assist the client and family to anticipate and plan for death.
   c.	support the family's denial if they choose to remain there.
   d.	tell the family to call the nurse if emergencies occur.

12.	The registered nurse uses appropriate decision making skills in assigning a LPN to which client?
   a.	A 3-year-old girl admitted after a situation, which appears she was sexually molested.
   b.	An 18-year-old boy who is awaiting discharge instructions after sinus surgery.
   c.	A 12-year-old girl admitted with fractured femur in balanced suspension traction.
   d.	An 8-year-old boy who requires dietary discharge teaching after a bout with gastroenteritis.

13.	The nurse realizes that a client understands her high-fiber diet when she selects which foods at mealtime?
   a.	Milk, cottage cheese, refined grain cereals.
   b.	Applesauce, vegetable juices, fish.
   c.	White bread, carrots, creamy-style peanut butter.
   d.	Whole wheat bread, apples, oatmeal cookies.

14. A 12-year-old student was reported to the school nurse for suspected drug abuse. When contacted by the nurse, the parents state the child is old enough now to take care of this problem by himself. The nurse would also expect to assess what characteristic in the child?
    a. Self-fulfillment.
    b. Child-like lifestyle.
    c. Adult-like lifestyle.
    d. Low self-esteem.

15. A client in the post-anesthesia care unit is experiencing inspiratory stridor and sternal retractions after removal of an endotracheal tube. The nursing priority is to:
    a. call the physician.
    b. suction the client.
    c. administer the p.r.n. oxygen.
    d. turn the client on his side.

16. A client with a history of violence is admitted to a psychiatric unit with a diagnosis of chronic paranoid schizophrenia. He has not been taking his prescribed respiridone (Respirdal). What would be the priority diagnosis?
    a. Altered thought process related to aggression.
    b. Noncompliance related to medication side effects.
    c. Risk for violence related to history of aggressive acts.
    d. Powerlessness related to restrictions of the hospital environment.

17. A nurse is reviewing a new graduate nurse's plan of care for a client experiencing an acute asthma attack. Which intervention would need to be rewritten to ensure the client's safety?
    a. Auscultate breath sounds.
    b. Encourage fluid intake.
    c. Plan rest periods.
    d. Sedate client when restless.

18. After determining that two periods of variable decelerations of fetal heart rate have occurred, the nurse would immediately:
    a. position the client on her left side.
    b. prepare the client for delivery.
    c. instruct the client to bear down with each contraction.
    d. prepare the client for oxytocin (Pitocin) augmentation.

19. A client with a hip injury is being fitted for crutches. The teaching plan would include:
    a. wear soft-soled shoes.
    b. rest the axilla on the crutch top.
    c. when seated, place crutches on the unaffected side.
    d. allow one inch between the crutch top and axilla.

20. A child is ordered 375mg of ampicillin (Omnipen) orally every 6 hours. Ampicillin (Omnipen) liquid is available in 250mg per 5ml. How many milliliters should be given per dose?

    _____

21. At the initial prenatal visit; a client reports that she last started her menstrual period August 10. She asks the nurse when the baby will be due. Based on Nagele's rule, the baby is due:
    a. December 10.
    b. May 17.
    c. June 22.
    d. March 19.

22. A client is experiencing persecutory hallucinations. Therefore the nurse must be alert for signs of:
   a. depression and suicide.
   b. countertransference and transference.
   c. compulsive behavior to compensate for anxiety.
   d. nutritional deficits due to fear of eating.

23. A client is receiving methotrexate sodium (Mexate) for treatment of rheumatoid arthritis. The nurse should monitor the client for:
   a. hepatotoxicity.
   b. T-cell suppression.
   c. bone marrow stimulation.
   d. lymphotoxicity.

24. Which nursing intervention is indicated for a client with cerebrospinal rhinorrhea?
   a. Place a piece of sterile cotton in the nares.
   b. Encourage client to frequently blow the nose.
   c. Gently use nasotracheal suctioning to remove secretions.
   d. Tape a loose sterile gauze pad under the nose.

25. A nurse is administering a unit of blood to a postoperative client. Which assessment finding would be most suggestive of a blood transfusion reaction?
   a. Bibasilar rales.
   b. An irregular pulse.
   c. Temperature of 37°C.
   d. Blood pressure of 134/88.

26. A toddler is scheduled for a temporary colostomy. The nurse brings an ostomy bag for the child to examine. The child's mother questions this activity. The nurse explains that this activity will help the child:
   a. master the ostomy concept.
   b. learn how to care for himself.
   c. reduce the fear of a strange activity.
   d. understand the new toileting ritual.

27. The nurse suspects a client has a pleural effusion of the left lung with what assessment finding?
   a. Dull percussion over affected area.
   b. Normal breath sounds in all lobes.
   c. Distinct pleural friction rub.
   d. Productive coughing of sputum.

28. A client starts to have a seizure. The priority action of the nurse is to:
   a. place pillows around the head area.
   b. call an emergency code.
   c. administer oxygen by nasal cannula.
   d. loosen clothing.

29. The nurse enforces a bed rest order for a client with chronic obstructive lung disease (COPD) primarily to:
   a. decrease need of oxygen by tissues.
   b. encourage sleep to alleviate anxiety.
   c. decrease the respiratory rate.
   d. improve oxygen transport.

30. A woman who is two weeks postpartum develops mastitis. The nurse's teaching would include that the most common causative organism in mastitis is:
   a.   chlamydia.
   b.   cytomegalovirus.
   c.   herpes simplex type I.
   d.   staphylococcus aureus.

STOP. You have now completed Practice Session: 8. Now take a few minutes and correct your answers. Calculate your accuracy rate by dividing the number of questions you completed correctly by the total number of questions you completed (30).

Correct answers ÷ total number of questions completed = accuracy rate.

_____ ÷ _____ = _____

ANSWERS AND RATIONALES
Practice Session 8

1. **The correct answer is a.** The question is asking what the nurse should do first when working with an adolescent who is experiencing symptoms related to moving. Assessment of the client's balancing factors: perception of the event, support systems and coping mechanisms are the nurse's initial task in crisis intervention. Options (b), (c) and (d) are all potentially appropriate interventions in working with a client in crisis, however assessment is the initial nursing role.
    Nursing Process: Assessment   **Client Need:** Psychosocial Integrity

2. **The correct answer is d.** The question is asking which statement is true regarding urinary self-catheterization outside of the hospital. Sterile technique is used in the hospital because of the increased chance of infection; however, at home the client is instructed to use clean technique and reuse the catheter (option b). The client should catheterize herself every three to six hours. Eight hours leaves the bladder distended. It should not be filled with more than 300ml (option a). Sterilizing solutions are not required to cleanse the perineum. Alcohol is very drying to the skin (option c).
    Nursing Process: Evaluation   **Client Need:** Health Promotion & Maintenance

3. **The correct answer is b.** The question is asking how the nurse should care for a client in Buck's traction. Buck's traction is skin traction that is used to maintain alignment until skeletal traction can be applied during surgery. The nurse should perform neurovascular assessments every four hours. Asking the client to dorsiflex the toes and foot assesses peroneal nerve deficit. The buttocks should be kept off the mattress when Bryant's traction is used (option a). Pin care is performed for clients who have skeletal traction (option c). Weights for Buck's traction should not exceed 10-lbs (4.5 kg) as this can lead to pressure damage to the skin (option d).
    Nursing Process: Implementation   **Client Need:** Physiological Integrity

4. **The correct answer is d.** The question is asking how to care for a client with a chest tube. The client should be encouraged to cough and deep breathe to maintain the airway and prevent pneumonia. Putting the affected arm and shoulder through vigorous range-of-motion may cause the tube to dislodge (option b). If excessive bubbling occurs (option a), this could indicate an air leak, and the physician should be notified. The chest tube should never be clamped for transport (option c). This places more pressure on the chest cavity, which could create a pneumothorax.
    Nursing Process: Planning   **Client Need:** Safe, Effective Care Environment

5. **The correct answer is b.** The question is asking what position best assists a client in acute pulmonary edema. Sitting upright with legs dangling in a dependent position would decrease venous return, thus lowering the pressure in the pulmonary circulation. Options (a) and (d) would be contraindicated as they would increase venous return. Option (c) would be correct if the client is unable to dangle, but making the legs dependent would be more effective in reducing venous return.
    Nursing Process: Planning   **Client Need:** Physiological Integrity

6. **The correct answer is b.** The question is asking why direct examination of the throat in an infant with suspected epiglottitis should be avoided. Attempts to visualize the epiglottis directly may precipitate sudden laryngospasm, complete obstruction and death. Therefore, the nurse does not attempt examination of the throat. Examination is made by a trained practitioner; with intubation or tracheostomy equipment within reach. Correct examination of the throat should not precipitate vomiting, as the gag reflex should not be touched (option a). Although strep throat is contagious, nurses should use proper infection control precautions with all clients (option c). It is possible to visualize the infant's throat through careful assessment (option d).
    Nursing Process: Assessment   **Client Need:** Safe, Effective Care Environment

7. **The correct answer is d.** The question is asking about assessment findings relative to suctioning procedure effectiveness. Graduate nurses are sometimes overwhelmed by attempting to determine, which assessment information would indicate that their actions have improved a client

condition. From a practical standpoint, the breath sounds being clear bilaterally in all fields indicates that the suctioning was successful. The respiratory and pulse rates are high and the blood pressure is normal. However, the vital signs listed are not indicators of suctioning success. The respiratory rate is too high, and does not indicate whether suctioning was successful or not (option a). The pulse rate is too high, and gives no input into the effectiveness of suctioning (option b). Blood pressure is not an indicator of suctioning success (option c).
Nursing Process: Evaluation   **Client Need:** Physiological Integrity

8. **The correct answer is c.** The question is asking how the teaching approach should be different when addressing someone of the Puerto Rican culture. The Puerto Rican culture considers family matters private and some questions may seem insulting to the family. Note taking is considered to be rude by the Native American culture, not the Puerto Rican culture (option a). Puerto Rican family members may be bilingual, but this is not true of all persons (option b). Some clients may speak a type of English or may only speak Spanish. Puerto Ricans may be suspicious of hospital care. Often Hispanic Americans believe hospitals are a place to die (option d).
Nursing Process: Assessment   **Client Need:** Physiological Integrity

9. **The correct answer is c.** The question is asking which is true about treatment for hepatitis C. Many medications are hepatotoxic and none should be taken in an indiscriminant manner. Although vitamin K supplements may be advised if prothrombin time is longer than normal, other vitamin supplements are not generally necessary in uncomplicated hepatitis C. This is, of course, dependent upon a diet adequate in nutrition (option b). Alcohol should be avoided, as it is hepatotoxic (option a). Antiemetics can be obtained, if needed, but first must be reviewed for their effect on liver function (option d).
Nursing Process: Implementation   **Client Need:** Physiological Integrity

10. **The correct answer is c.** The question is asking how cyanosis differs in cardiovascular disease versus respiratory disease. Cyanotic heart defects usually result from anomalies that change the cardiac pressure so that blood shunts from the left side to the right side of the heart. Many congenital cardiac anomalies create situations (i.e. septal defects, patent ductus arteriosis) where oxygenated and venous blood mix. This mixing of blood can lead to cyanosis. Cyanosis indicates that low oxygen in the arterial blood is present, but decreased tissue oxygenation may not necessarily occur. Anything that causes an increased demand for oxygen (options a & b) will result in cyanosis. Oxygen may not help since the hypoxemia results from a structural defect (option d).
Nursing Process: Analysis   **Client Need:** Physiological Integrity

11. **The correct answer is b.** The question is asking the nurse's role with a dying client. Anticipatory grieving is most beneficial for the client and family. In this way, they can anticipate emergencies and how to deal with them rather than waiting for them to occur (option d). The family may wish to explore alternatives (option a) and the nurse may assist with this discussion but should still be assisting the client and family deal with possible death. Supporting denial (option c) will create delayed or unresolved grief.
Nursing Process: Implementation   **Client Need:** Health Promotion & Maintenance

12. **The correct answer is c.** The question is asking about the delegation of which client to a LPN. The LPN is best assigned to clients who require skill, but who have predictable clinical conditions and outcomes. The RN must retain the aspects of assessment, discharge planning, and she would be critical to the situation of the 3-year-old with possible molestation. The 12-year-old girl with established traction is an ideal choice for a LPN assignment. Option (a) is incorrect, as this child who may have been molested should be in the care of a RN. Option (b) is incorrect, as the RN must conduct discharge education/planning. Option (d) is incorrect, as this client also needs discharge teaching, which must be done by a RN. LPNs are not to be conducting initial assessments or discharge planning, which would require teaching.
Nursing Process: Implementation   **Client Need:** Physiological Integrity

13. **The correct answer is d.** The question is asking what are high-fiber items. Items listed in option (d) are high fiber foods. Milk products are usually low in fiber (option a). Although fruits and vegetables are typically higher in fiber, applesause and fruit juices are not (option b). White bread is lower in fiber that whole wheat bread. Creamy peanut butter is also low in fiber (option c).
Nursing Process: Evaluation   **Client Need:** Health Promotion & Maintenance

14. **The correct answer is d.** The question is asking what assessment finding might accompany drug abuse. Low self-esteem is another factor related to suspected drug use. Self-fulfillment (option a) is a positive characteristic. Students with a sense of self-fulfillment usually do not need to try drugs. A mixture between child-like (option b) and adult-like (option c) lifestyles is normal in an adolescent, but is not necessarily a factor in drug abuse as is low self-esteem.
Nursing Process: Assessment   **Client Need:** Psychosocial Integrity

15. **The correct answer is c.** The question is asking what to do when a client experiences respiratory problems after an endotracheal tube is removed. Inspiratory stridor and sternal retractions may indicate laryngospasms. Laryngospasms are most likely to occur after removal of the endotracheal tube. The first action of the nurse is to prevent hypoxia from airway obstruction by providing oxygen and pulling the mandible forward. The anesthesiologist is called to assess the client after the initial nursing actions (option a). Suctioning the client (option b) can further irritate the airway. Repositioning the client is an action used to prevent aspiration of vomitus (option d). In this situation the client's oxygenation status and airway need to be supported.
Nursing Process: Analysis   **Client Need:** Physiological Integrity

16. **The correct answer is c.** The question is asking the most important problem of this client. Although all options are applicable, prevention of violence is the priority diagnosis due to its potential disastrous effects. The aggression is probably a result of altered thought processes (option a). There is no evidence that side effects are causing noncompliance (option b). Powerlessness may be true; however, it is not the priority because of safety (option d).
Nursing Process: Analysis   **Client Need:** Psychosocial Integrity

17. **The correct answer is d.** The question is asking which option is the wrong approach in caring for an asthma attack in a client. The client experiencing an asthma attack should be sedated very cautiously to avoid respiratory depression. Restlessness could be due to oxygen deprivation or anxiety and needs to be investigated. Restlessness due to anxiety can be relieved through the presence of the nurse and/or family members. Breath sounds (option a) should be auscultated often to observe for changes in wheezing. Fluids should be encouraged (option b) to promote removal of secretions. Fatigue is a problem that can result in respiratory arrest and should be guarded against by scheduling rest periods throughout the day (option c).
Nursing Process: Planning   **Client Need:** Physiological Integrity

18. **The correct answer is a.** The question is asking what immediate action should be taken when the nurse notes two variable decelerations (lowered fetal heart rates). First, think if this is normal or something to be concerned about. This is a dangerous situation as it means the fetus is not receiving enough oxygen. Positioning the client on her left side will relieve pressure on the great vessels; therefore, circulation will be increased to the fetus. This may be the only action that needs to be taken at this time to resolve the symptom of fetal distress (options b & c). If the client is receiving oxytocin (Pitocin) and has persistent, severe variable decelerations, the oxytocin (Pitocin) infusion should be stopped until the physician has the opportunity to evaluate the tracing.
Nursing Process: Implementation   **Client Need:** Physiological Integrity

19. **The correct answer is c.** The question is asking for the correct instruction for someone with crutches. When the client starts to sit, the crutches are placed on the unaffected side. Then use the hand on the affected side to balance on the armrest while bending at the waist and lowering self into the chair. Firm soled shoes (option a) will keep the feet from injury. At least two inches should be between the top of the crutch and the axilla (option d) and the axilla should never rest on the crutch top (option b) because damage can occur to the brachial plexus.
Nursing Process: Planning   **Client Need:** Safe, Effective Care Environment

20. **The correct answer is 7.5.** The question is asking how many milliliters per dose should be given.

dose desired x quantity = amount
dose on hand

$\frac{375mg}{250mg}$ x 5ml = 7.5ml

Nursing Process: Planning   **Client Need:** Physiological Integrity

21. **The correct answer is b.** The question is asking the nurse to determine the due date. Nagele's rule states that estimated date of delivery equals the first day of the last menstrual period (LMP) plus seven days and minus three months. LMP = August 10 + 7 days = August 17 - 3 months = May 17.
Nursing Process: Implementation   **Client Need:** Health Promotion & Maintenance

22. **The correct answer is a.** The question is asking what the nurse should further assess in a client who believes others are out to harm him in some way. The other responses are important but not as vital as the need to prevent self-harm. If a client believes there is no way to get away from the people or to resolve the situation, hopelessness often occurs which leads to depression and thoughts of suicide. Countertransference is a phenomenon of the nurse's reaction to a client; transference occurs when the client unconsciously has similar feelings and attitudes toward the nurse as were felt toward others in early life (option b). Compulsions (option c) are acts to decrease anxiety but are usually unrelated to hallucinations. Fear of eating (option d) implies self-persecutory acts but suicide would be most important and more inclusive.
Nursing Process: Assessment   **Client Need:** Psychosocial Integrity

23. **The correct answer is a.** The question is asking what precautions to check in a client receiving methotrexate (Mexate). While the drug can be effective against rheumatoid arthritis, it is also toxic to the liver and bone marrow (option c). T-cell suppression (option b) and lymphotoxicity (option d) are not involved with this drug.
Nursing Process: Evaluation   **Client Need:** Physiological Integrity

24. **The correct answer is d.** The question is asking how to deal with cerebrospinal fluid (CSF) draining from the nose. A dressing will permit the nurse to monitor the amount and type of the drainage and provide for client comfort by absorbing the drainage. Cotton in the nares (option a) promotes infection as bacteria in the nose can colonize on the cotton and CSF will promote bacterial growth. Blowing the nose (option b) and nasotracheal suctioning (option c) promote increased loss of CSF.
Nursing Process: Implementation   **Client Need:** Physiological Integrity

25. **The correct answer is a.** The question is asking which data shows symptoms of a blood transfusion reaction. During the administration of the blood, the nurse should look for early signs of distress in the respiratory system, such as rales, tachypnea, dyspnea, and wheezing. Other signs of a transfusion reaction include: bradycardia, tachycardia, change in blood pressure and an increase in temperature. An irregular pulse (option b) does not indicate a transfusion reaction. A temperature of 37°C (option c) and blood pressure of 134/88 (option d) are normal readings.
Nursing Process: Evaluation   **Client Need:** Safe, Effective Care Environment

26. **The correct answer is c.** The question is asking why the nurse allows the toddler to play with the ostomy equipment. Allowing the child to observe the equipment and materials may decrease anxiety and fear. The toddler needs to feel in control. Simple explanations in toddler terms with actual equipment for the toddler to manipulate and examine, will help the toddler understand and master the experience in a more autonomous way. The toddler's comprehension of words is good even when verbal ability is not fully developed. Encouraging the toddler's autonomy with the new activity may promote more cooperative behavior. The toddler cannot cognitively master the concepts or physically care for himself (options a, b & d). However, the child's cooperation will increase as the fears decrease.

27.   **The correct answer is a.** The question is asking which assessment data may suggest pleural effusion. With the presence of fluid in the pleural space, percussion will be dull. Breath sounds will be diminished in the area of pleural effusion (option b). A pleural friction rub is indicative of pleurisy (option c). Any cough would be non-productive since the fluid is in the pleural space (option d).
Nursing Process: Analysis   **Client Need:** Physiological Integrity

28.   **The correct answer is d.** The question is asking the priority action for a client having a seizure. Loosen clothing so that the client is less likely to be injured. Do not leave the client. Arrange the client on the side to maintain airway clearance. Do not restrain the client. Place a pillow or blanket under the head for protection (option a). Oxygen does not need to be administered (option c) at this time. Do not force anything into the client's mouth, but an airway may be inserted while the client is relaxed. A code is unnecessary (option b). After discharge, the client and family should be instructed to call emergency services if a seizure lasts longer than five minutes.
Nursing Process: Implementation   **Client Need:** Safe, Effective Care Environment

29.   **The correct answer is a.** The question is asking why a client with chronic obstructive pulmonary disease (COPD) should be on bed rest. Oxygen is compromised getting into the tissues because of the COPD. Impaired gas exchange is often a problem during an exacerbation. The goal of oxygen therapy is to have an oxygen saturation of at least 90% during low flow oxygen therapy. Bed rest reduces body metabolism and, therefore, reduces the need of tissue cells for oxygen. This helps to accomplish the goal of low oxygen therapy. Sleep and decreased anxiety (option b) are both desirable, but they can be accomplished with bed rest. Decreased respiratory rate (option c) and increased oxygen transport (option d) occurs because the oxygen demand is decreased with bed rest.
Nursing Process: Analysis   **Client Need:** Physiological Integrity

30.   **The correct answer is d.** The question is asking the usual cause of mastitis. Mastitis refers to an inflammation of the breast generally caused by staphylococcus aureus, which is often found on the skin and primarily seen in breastfeeding women. Chlamydia, cytomegalovirus and herpes simplex are sexually transmitted diseases and are not typical in breastfeeding (options a, b & c).
Nursing Process: Analysis   **Client Need:** Health Promotion & Maintenance

> **Instructions: Allow yourself 30 minutes to complete the following 30 practice questions. Use a timer to notify yourself when 30 minutes are over so that you are not constantly looking at your watch while completing the questions.**

1. The nurse would instruct a client on antacid therapy to take it:
   a. one hour prior to the meal.
   b. with the meal.
   c. one hour after the meal.
   d. two hours after the meal.

2. A postoperative client is restless and tachypneic. She is pale and her pulse pressure is narrowing. Her urinary output has been 25ml per hour for the last two hours. Which nursing measure should be taken?
   a. Elevate the head of the bed to facilitate adequate ventilation.
   b. Administer oxygen as prescribed.
   c. Monitor vital signs every hour.
   d. Provide emotional support because these symptoms are caused by the transient stress of injury.

3. The plan of care for a client with rheumatoid arthritis is based on the knowledge that the swelling of the finger joints is due to:
   a. infiltration of pus into the muscles and fibrous tissue surrounding the joint.
   b. blood seeping from skin capillaries into the subcutaneous tissues.
   c. formation of bony spurs on the edges of the articulating surfaces in the joint.
   d. distension of the joint capsule by an increased amount of synovial fluid.

4. A client who just had a left upper lobectomy asks the nurse, "Why do I have two chest tubes? Did something go wrong?" The most appropriate response by the nurse would be that the:
   a. upper tube is for removal of air; the lower for removal of fluid.
   b. upper tube is for the removal of fluid; the lower for removal of air.
   c. anterior tube is placed in the pleural space; the posterior is placed in the subpleural space.
   d. lower tube is a backup in case the upper tube becomes clotted.

5. A home care nurse has been caring for a client with a decubitus ulcer on the coccyx. The wound is granulating. How should the nurse care for this client?
   a. Clean the wound with hydrogen peroxide.
   b. Apply a wet-to-dry dressing.
   c. Encourage a low-cholesterol, low-sodium diet.
   d. Keep the head of bed flat.

6. Immediately following the evacuation of an epidural hematoma, the most important goal the nurse should plan for is prevention of:
   a. pneumonia.
   b. wound infection.
   c. thrombophlebitis.
   d. increased intracranial pressure.

7. The nurse knows that teaching regarding treatment for a pheochromocytoma has been effective when the client states:
   a. "I realize I will have to take steroids for the rest of my life after surgery."
   b. "When I wake up after surgery, I will be in the intensive care unit for at least one day."
   c. "I will avoid any movement following surgery because of the large incision and slow healing."
   d. "I will maintain a special low-carbohydrate diet for the rest of my life, because of the risk of high glucose levels."

8. The most valuable action that a nurse can take when emergency triage involves a dirty bomb is to first:
   a. protect themselves.
   b. keep clients outside of the building.
   c. understand that the bomb is generally chemical but not radiological in content.
   d. place a detection badge on their scrubs to ensure that any radiological input is calculated.

9. A client, addicted to cocaine is attending group therapy. The nurse is discussing the relationship between cocaine and seizure activity. The nurse would determine that group members understand this relationship when they state:
   a. taking an anticonvulsant such as phenytoin (Dilantin) will prevent cocaine-related seizures.
   b. people with epilepsy or other seizure disorders are usually those who get cocaine-related seizures.
   c. cocaine-related seizures occur with long-term use and high doses of cocaine.
   d. any amount of cocaine can produce a seizure in anyone.

10. Based on the developmental capabilities of a 6-year-old child with diabetes, the nurse would expect which goal to be met prior to discharge? The child will:
    a. perform blood or urine glucose testing with supervision.
    b. mix two insulins in one syringe and give the injection.
    c. plan his own meals and snacks.
    d. identify limitations in the exercise plan.

11. A client with Addison's disease is admitted to the medical unit. Which client complaint would need to be addressed first?
    a. Dizzy when arising or moving fast.
    b. Rash and normal temperature.
    c. Fatigue, weakness and dyspnea.
    d. Drinks three liters of fluid per day.

12. A client is diagnosed as having pericarditis. The nurse should expect what assessment data?
    a. Heart murmur.
    b. S-3.
    c. S-4.
    d. Friction rub.

13. A child with Type 1 diabetes is prescribed four insulin injections each day. His mother asks the nurse why he can't have one injection like his father. The appropriate nursing response would be:
    a. "We believe that children should try to get used to the injections, so we give them more than once a day."
    b. "We are trying to provide insulin at times and quantities similar to a normally functioning pancreas."
    c. "We want you to become used to giving injections, then we will reduce the dosage to once a day."
    d. "With the types of insulin available for children, this is the only regimen that is proven effective for glucose control."

14. When working with the parents of a stillborn baby, the nurse understands that:
    a. privacy is needed to deal with the death.
    b. the parents need the presence of others to cope.
    c. the nurse's presence is usually seen as an intrusion.
    d. referral should be made to social service.

15. A nurse working in the post-anesthesia care unit (PACU) has just received a client from surgery. Immediate postoperative assessment by this nurse should include:
    a. thorough medical history, type of surgery, and estimated blood loss.
    b. type of surgery, allergies, and family medical history.
    c. type of anesthesia, problems during surgery, and estimated blood loss.
    d. respiratory status, type of anesthesia, and immunization history.

16. A hospitalized toddler is extremely anxious in this new environment. On the fourth day of hospitalization the child seems to calm down and is unconcerned about seeing her parents. This behavior indicates the:
    a. parents should visit less frequently.
    b. child has successfully adjusted to the hospital environment.
    c. child may be in a denial-detachment stage and unwilling to trust.
    d. child has transferred his allegiance to the nursing staff.

17. The nurse understands that the development of trust with a client diagnosed with schizophrenia, although crucial to the nurse-client relationship, is difficult due to client reluctance. The nurse understands the reason for this reluctance may include: Select all that apply.
    a. They are struggling to trust their own thoughts.
    b. Previous rejection in relationships.
    c. Medications interfere with their ability to communicate.
    d. Engaging in an interaction is too overwhelming.
    e. They fear the nurse will not believe they are sick.

18. Following the spontaneous rupture of amniotic membranes in a woman in labor, the nurse notes a decrease in the fetal heart rate and that the amniotic fluid is meconium stained. The nurse realizes this is indicative of:
    a. fetal distress.
    b. increased fetal activity.
    c. maternal dehydration.
    d. normal labor.

19. A client is using a cane to walk for balance and support. Proper instruction for stair climbing would include to:
    a. step up on the unaffected leg, follow with the cane and affected leg.
    b. place the cane on the step following with the affected leg, then the unaffected leg.
    c. step up with the affected leg, follow with the cane and the unaffected leg.
    d. place the cane on the step following with the unaffected leg, then the affected leg.

20. Which room assignment would be most appropriate for a client with hyperthyroidism?
    a. A semi-private room next to the nurse's station.
    b. A private room.
    c. A room with a talkative client.
    d. A room with a quiet client.

21. A client is prescribed nitroglycerine sublingually for his angina. The nurse would alert the client to expect:
    a. a slow heart beat.
    b. a headache.
    c. high blood pressure.
    d. drowsiness.

22. During the assessment of a client with placenta previa, the nurse would expect to find:
    a. bright-red bleeding.
    b. dark-red bleeding.
    c. brownish-red spotting.
    d. no vaginal bleeding.

23. A client had a hemorrhoidectomy. What should be included in the postoperative nursing care plan?
    a. Administer saline enemas until the area heals.
    b. Encourage a low-residue diet.
    c. Avoid warm sitz baths.
    d. Drink plenty of fluids.

24. The nurse is reviewing a postoperative client's arterial blood gas results. The client is on two liters of oxygen by nasal cannula. The results are determined to be normal when they read:
    a. pH 7.46, $PaCO_2$ 33, PaO_2 110.
    b. pH 7.35, $PaCO_2$ 36, PaO_2 64.
    c. pH 7.40, $PaCO_2$ 40, PaO_2 164.
    d. pH 7.42, $PaCO_2$ 46, PaO_2 100.

25. A client has just had a mastectomy and the nurse notes that the surgical dressing is stained with blood. The nurse should:
    a. notify the physician.
    b. circle the area on the dressing.
    c. check the client's axilla for moisture.
    d. evaluate the operative site.

26. A 55-year-old farmer diagnosed with cancer tells the nurse, "It's over. My farm is ruined. I wanted to give it to my grandchildren but now I'll have to sell it." The nurse understands that the client is:
    a. engaging in life review.
    b. probably organically depressed.
    c. worried about his impending death.
    d. concerned about his livelihood.

27. A client is scheduled for a pelvic ultrasound. The nurse would teach the client that:
    a. "A small amount of radioactive dye is introduced into the pelvic area and scans are taken."
    b. "High frequency sound waves are directed to the pelvic area to record a cross sectional structural view."
    c. "Laser beams are used to find the normal and abnormal structures in the pelvic area."
    d. "A large machine will take small sectional pictures of the pelvic area to determine if extra tissue is present."

28. Prior to the administration of an enema the nurse would assist a client into which position?
    a. Dorsal recumbent.
    b. Right Sims'.
    c. Left semi-Fowler's.
    d. Left Sims'.

29. A client with bronchogenic carcinoma develops syndrome of inappropriate antidiuretic hormone (SIADH). The nurse would expect this client to exhibit:
    a. hypermotility in the gastrointestinal tract.
    b. hyponatremia with increased urinary sodium.
    c. polydipsia and decreased urine specific gravity.
    d. severe dehydration and hypovolemic shock.

30. A nurse is preparing a client for discharge following surgery for a detached retina. What statement would indicate the client understands the teaching?
   a. "You said I could wash my hair in two days."
   b. "I can pick up small objects."
   c. "I will clean my eyelid with sterile cotton balls from the outer to inner canthus."
   d. "I have to wear that eye shield only at night now."

STOP. You have now completed Practice Session: 9. Now take a few minutes and correct your answers. Calculate your accuracy rate by dividing the number of questions you completed correctly by the total number of questions you completed (30).

Correct answers ÷ total number of questions completed = accuracy rate.

_____ ÷ _____ = _____

ANSWERS AND RATIONALES
Practice Session 9

1. **The correct answer is c.** The question is asking when an antacid should be taken. The antacid should be given for optimal effect at a time of maximal acidity within the stomach. That period is approximately an hour after the ingestion of food, not with the meal (option b). Histamine antagonists such as famotadine (Pepcid) are often given before a meal to decrease gastric acid secretion (options a). Sucralfate (Carafate), a drug used to coat a gastric ulcer, can be given two hours after a meal (option d).
Nursing Process: Planning   **Client Need:** Physiological Integrity

2. **The correct answer is b.** The question is asking the nurse to analyze the presenting data and choose the option that best responds to the data. The signs and symptoms indicate hypovolemic shock. For a client in shock, a patent airway must be maintained and administration of oxygen ensures adequate tissue oxygenation. A client in hypovolemic shock should be placed in a supine position and, if hemorrhaging is severe, the legs can be elevated 20 to 30 degrees (option a). Due to the acute and emergency nature of hypovolemic shock, vital signs must be monitored more frequently than every hour until they become stabilized (option c). Although symptoms such as cool and clammy skin, restlessness, and tachypnea may be caused by the transient stress of injury, the other signs listed in the question indicate hypovolemic shock (option d).
Nursing Process: Analysis   **Client Need:** Physiological Integrity

3. **The correct answer is d.** The question is asking why the joints swell in a client with rheumatoid arthritis. The pathophysiology begins by an inflammation of the synovium with edema, vascular congestion, and cellular infiltrates. The infiltration of pus into surrounding tissue would be indicative of an infection (option a). Seepage of blood into the subcutaneous tissue is indicative of a contusion (option b). Bony spurs occur with osteoarthritis not rheumatoid (option c).
Nursing Process: Analysis   **Client Need:** Physiological Integrity

4. **The correct answer is a.** The question is asking the purpose of the two drainage tubes in the chest after a lobectomy. Usually two chest catheters are inserted, the upper being for drainage of air, the lower for drainage of fluid (options b & d). Option (c) is incorrect because both chest tubes are in the pleural space.
Nursing Process: Analysis   **Client Need:** Physiological Integrity

5. **The correct answer is d.** The question is asking what is the appropriate care for a client with a pressure ulcer. The head of the bed should be kept flat to avoid sacral pressure. Granulating tissue is healthy tissue. Hydrogen peroxide is cytotoxic and should not be used on healthy tissue (option a). A wet-to-dry dressing is used for debridement, not for granulating tissue (option b). A diet rich in protein and calories is suggested for clients with pressure ulcers (option c).
Nursing Process: Implementation   **Client Need:** Physiological Integrity

6. **The correct answer is d.** The question is asking the priority potential problem for a client who had an epidural hematoma removed. Increase in the intracranial pressure may cause further neurological deterioration and death, as intracranial pressure compromises cerebral perfusion. This client is at risk for increased intracranial pressure because of the potential for rebleed and presence of cerebral edema. Nursing and medical interventions are designed to prevent or reduce increased intracranial pressure. Options (a), (b) and (c) are all appropriate goals for this client, but are not more important than option (d) which can be rapidly life threatening.
Nursing Process: Planning   **Client Need:** Physiological Integrity

7. **The correct answer is b.** The question is asking what is true about treating pheochromocytoma. Pheochromocytoma is a small tumor on the adrenal gland. It produces symptoms such as anxiety and high blood pressure. Surgery to remove that adrenal gland is usually performed. The client is usually sent to the ICU to be monitored for Addisonian crisis and fluid and electrolyte imbalance. Steroid support may be necessary postoperatively; it will be slowly withdrawn as the remaining adrenal gland assumes the function of releasing an adequate amount of hormone for daily

activities and additional stressors (option a). The client should be instructed in splinting the incision while turning and deep breathing (option c). A normal diet should be expected. The elevated glucose will be alleviated with surgery. In addition, high glucose is not corrected with a low-carbohydrate diet (option c).

Nursing Process: Evaluation   **Client Need:** Physiological Integrity

8.   **The correct answer is a.** The question is asking what the most valuable action a nurse can take when emergency triage involves a dirty bomb. Dirty bombs are extremely dangerous and the nurse needs to protect herself first before she can assist others. The bombs are generally radiological in content and, although there needs to be triage for the clients, the location of their decontamination can be varied. Wearing a detection badge is not the priority here. Keeping the caregivers safe so that they can adequately care for others is the key. Option (b) is incorrect as it is not a priority action. Although these clients need to be decontaminated that is not necessarily done outside. Option (c) is incorrect as the dirty bomb is radiological in content. Option (d) is incorrect as this is a measure to identify cumulative radiological input and is worn by those who work in and around areas where radiology is used.

Nursing Process: Implementation   **Client Need:** Safe, Effective Care Environment

9.   **The correct answer is d.** The question is asking the relationship between seizures and cocaine. No matter how little cocaine is used, it can cause a seizure, which is one of the most serious side effects of cocaine use. Anticonvulsant medication, such as phenytoin (Dilantin), will not prevent seizures in cocaine abuse (option a). Although epileptics are more prone to cocaine-related seizures, anyone using cocaine can have a seizure (option b). Continued use of cocaine can lead to a reverse tolerance to the drug's seizure producing properties, that is, less and less of the drug would produce seizures (option c).

Nursing Process: Evaluation   **Client Need:** Physiological Integrity

10.   **The correct answer is a.** The question is asking what task a 6-year-old diabetic child can do in self-care. The child at age six or seven can perform blood or urine tests, record results, may need reminding and will need supervision. Mixing insulins (option b) and planning meals (option c) are not usually expectations before age 14. There are no limitations in the exercise plan (option d).

Nursing Process: Planning   **Client Need:** Health Promotion & Maintenance

11.   **The correct answer is c.** The question is asking which data was most important. If the client has Addison's disease, the nurse would need to look for signs of Addisonian crisis. Fatigue, weakness and dyspnea are all signs of electrolyte imbalance, which may be a part of Addison's crisis. This is an emergency situation, which needs immediate intervention. Dizziness upon rising or moving (option a) is called orthostatic hypotension. It could occur with fluid imbalances, but more data would be needed. Rash and normal temperature (option b) are unrelated, but could be due to dermatitis. Fluid intake of at least three liters per day is essential for fluid balance (option d).

Nursing Process: Assessment   **Client Need:** Physiological Integrity

12.   **The correct answer is d.** The question is asking which data points toward inflammation of the sac surrounding the heart. When inflammation occurs anywhere, there is usually swelling. How might this show itself at the heart? Pericarditis (inflammation of the pericardium of the heart) causes an audible friction rub heard when auscultating heart sounds. S-3 is a third heart sound often associated with left ventricular heart failure. The S-3 heart sound is usually brought about due to impedance to diastolic filling of the ventricle in certain disease state (option b). S-4 is present when the ventricle is hypertrophied such as with aortic stenosis (option c). Heart murmurs are usually auscultated when there is an incomplete valve or with valvular regurgitation (option a).

Nursing Process: Assessment   **Client Need:** Physiological Integrity

13.   **The correct answer is b.** The question is asking why the diabetic child must have more than one insulin injection per day. Tightly controlled insulin therapy provides insulin as a normally functioning pancreas would. The normally functioning pancreas releases a low dose of insulin continuously into the blood stream; a bolus is released following meals. Multiple injection method has been found to significantly decrease the onset of complications. The number of

injections will not influence the child's "getting used to injections" (option a). The child is being maintained on four injections per day for tight control; this can never be maintained with one injection per day (option c). There are a variety of regimens available, each of them effective (option d).
Nursing Process: Implementation   **Client Need:** Physiological Integrity

14.   **The correct answer is b.** The question is asking how to assist parents of a stillborn infant. Talking with others assists the parents with reality testing and expression of the loss. Some privacy may be beneficial, but complete privacy promotes autistic thinking, which may lead to heightened feelings of guilt and depression (option a). The nurse's role is to support the parents and encourage expression of feelings (option c). Understanding the needs of parents is within the scope of nursing practice. Referral to social service is not a decision that the nurse would make alone (option d).
Nursing Process: Analysis   **Client Need:** Health Promotion & Maintenance

15.   **The correct answer is c.** The question is asking what to assess when a client is received in post-anesthesia care. An immediate postoperative assessment should be performed by the nurse and anesthesiologist, and should include: client's name, type of surgery, type of anesthesia and other drugs given, brief medical history, problems during surgery (shock, hemorrhage), intake and output, surgical drains, and an overall evaluation of the client's vital signs. Thorough medical history, family medical history and immunization history are not relevant at this time (options a, b & d).
Nursing Process: Assessment   **Client Need:** Physiological Integrity

16.   **The correct answer is c.** The question is asking what the behavior signifies in a hospitalized toddler. Children who seem to have settled in show signs of resignation and this is erroneously interpreted as recovery. It is an indication that children have defended themselves against grief and pain through repressing the image of and all feelings for their parents (options b & d). Visiting less frequently may reinforce feelings of rejection (option a).
Nursing Process: Analysis   **Client Need:** Health Promotion & Maintenance

17.   **The correct answers are a, b, and d.** The question is asking why clients with schizophrenia are hesitant to trust the nurse. Clients with schizophrenia often have difficulty forming a trusting relationship with anyone. Previous rejections (option b), experiencing hallucinations and delusions make it difficult for the client to sort out and trust their own thoughts (option a). The images of others may be frightening and distorted, thus making the prospect of working with the nurse totally overwhelming to the client (option d). Medications (option c) usually make the client more amenable to therapeutic interaction, not less able to communicate. Clients with schizophrenia often deny that they are mentally ill, they are usually not afraid that the nurse will not believe that they have an illness (option e).
Nursing Process: Analysis   **Client Need:** Psychosocial Integrity

18.   **The correct answer is a.** The question is asking for analysis of those fetal symptoms during labor. Fetal response to hypoxia includes relaxation of the anal sphincter, causing meconium to be released in utero, increased peristalsis, and reflex gasping. Decelerations of fetal heart rate can indicate several things. If they are early decelerations, usually no intervention is required. If they occur late, maternal and fetal assessments are intensified to help determine the cause. Severe variable decelerations can indicate cord prolapse, which causes fetal distress (options b, c & d).
Nursing Process: Analysis   **Client Need:** Physiological Integrity

19.   **The correct answer is a.** The question is asking how to instruct a client to use the cane while on the stairs. The cane should be held opposite the affected extremity, widening the base of support. The unaffected leg is placed on the step followed with the cane and affected extremity (options b, c & d).
Nursing Process: Implementation   **Client Need:** Safe, Effective Care Environment

20.   **The correct answer is b.** The question is asking where a client with hyperthyroidism should be

placed. Hyperthyroidism increases a client's metabolism. The nurse should take into account the needs of this client and potential roommates. In this case, the nurse should provide a restful environment, both physically and mentally. The private room enables the client to rest and prevents the client from disturbing others with hyperactive behavior. The presence of a roommate and the activity that centers at the nursing station will create stimulating environments; the goal is to provide a restful environment (option a). Option (c), a talkative roommate, is too stimulating. The client would be too hyperactive and disturbing for a quiet roommate (option d).

Nursing Process: Analysis   **Client Need:** Safe, Effective Care Environment

21.   **The correct answer is b.** The question is asking what to tell a client to expect if taking sublingual nitroglycerine, which is a nitrate. Side effects of nitrates include: flushing, pounding or pulsating headache, hypotension (option c) and reflex tachycardia (option a). Drowsiness (option d) is not a symptom of generalized systemic dilation but may be of other medications such as antianxiety drugs.

Nursing Process: Implementation   **Client Need:** Physiological Integrity

22.   **The correct answer is a.** The question is asking which assessment data relates to placenta previa. Usually bright-red vaginal painless bleeding occurring at the end of the second trimester is typical of placenta previa. Dark brown-red bleeding and brownish-red spotting are associated with abruptio placenta (options b & c). No vaginal bleeding is more often associated with concealed abruptio placenta (option d).

Nursing Process: Assessment   **Client Need:** Physiological Integrity

23.   **The correct answer is d.** The question is asking how to care for a client after hemorrhoid surgery. Good fluid intake is important to prevent constipation and injury to the operative area. Saline enemas may be indicated prior to surgery, however following surgery; enemas should be avoided because of potential trauma to the rectum (option a). A high (not low) residue diet will promote soft stools so the client can avoid straining and bleeding (option b). Warm sitz baths to the area will promote healing (option c).

Nursing Process: Planning   **Client Need:** Physiological Integrity

24.   **The correct answer is c.** The question is asking which were normal arterial blood gases for a client on two liters of oxygen by nasal cannula. Normal pH is 7.35 to 7.45. Normal $PaCO_2$ is 38 to 45, therefore, options (a) and (d) are incorrect. Normal PaO_2 on room air is 80 to 100; therefore, option (b) is incorrect. Clients on artificial oxygen will have a higher than normal PaO_2.

Nursing Process: Evaluation   **Client Need:** Physiological Integrity

25.   **The correct answer is c.** The question is asking what to do initially when observing a bloodstained dressing. The stained dressing may indicate that the client is bleeding from the surgical incision. The drainage would follow the line of gravity. Checking the axilla for any indication of moisture underneath will confirm if there is any additional leakage of blood and is the most appropriate initial response. Circling the area on the dressing (option b) and evaluating the operative site (option d) would be actions after checking the axilla. Notifying the physician (option a) would not be necessary unless further signs of hemorrhage were evident.

Nursing Process: Implementation   **Client Need:** Physiological Integrity

26.   **The correct answer is d.** The question is asking for an analysis of the client's statement. The client is 55-years-old so maybe developmental theory can give insight. The client has expressed concern about maintaining his livelihood and passing on the farm to his children. This is part of the developmental task for his age group. Life review (option a) generally occurs in later adulthood as preparation for death. Organic depression (option b) cannot be supported by the data. Concern about death (option c) is interpretation beyond the client's expressed meaning.

Nursing Process: Analysis   **Client Need:** Health Promotion & Maintenance

27.   **The correct answer is b.** The question is asking correct information about a pelvic sonogram. High frequency sound waves are directed to a part of the pelvic area and bounce back to form an image on a screen. Based on this image, the physician can diagnose any abnormalities.

Ultrasound examination does not include the use of radioactive dyes (option a). Laser beams (option c) are not generally used for diagnosis, but may be used later for excision of endometrial tissue. Small sectional pictures (option d) are generally true of computerized tomography (CT) scanning.

Nursing Process: Implementation   **Client Need:** Safe, Effective Care Environment

28.   **The correct answer is d.** The question is asking how to position a client who is to receive an enema. The client should be placed in the left Sims' or left side-lying position, which allows the enema solution to flow by gravity along the curve of the colon and, therefore, improves retention. Option (a), dorsal recumbent is sometimes useful for positioning children for an enema or an adult when left Sims' is contraindicated. Semi-Fowler's and right Sims' would necessitate that the fluid flow against gravity (options b & c).

Nursing Process: Implementation   **Client Need:** Safe, Effective Care Environment

29.   **The correct answer is b.** The question is asking for assessment data, which might indicate syndrome of inappropriate antidiuretic hormone (SIADH). SIADH refers to excessive antidiuretic hormone (ADH) secretion from the pituitary gland, even in the face of subnormal serum osmolarity. SIADH is often of nonendocrine origin. The syndrome may occur in clients with bronchogenic carcinoma in which malignant lung cells synthesize and release ADH. Clients with this disorder cannot excrete dilute urine. They retain fluids and develop a sodium deficiency. Clients with SIADH may gain body weight because of fluid retention. Clinically, serum sodium levels are below 135mEq/L, whereas the urinary sodium concentrations are elevated. Polydipsia, decreased urine specific gravity, severe dehydration and hypovolemic shock (options c & d) are signs of diabetes insipidus. Hypermotility would not be present (option a).

Nursing Process: Implementation   **Client Need:** Physiological Integrity

30.   **The correct answer is d.** The question is asking for proper care after surgery for detached retina. The client needs to wear the eye shield only at night when the eye can be inadvertently injured during sleep. Hair washing must wait for two weeks because vigorous washing can dislodge the retina again (option a). Small objects can be picked up, but only if the client does not bend at the waist, which would place more pressure on the eye and possibly disrupt the surgery (option b). The eye is always rinsed and cleaned from inner to outer corner (option c).

Nursing Process: Implementation   **Client Need:** Physiological Integrity

1. A family member is learning how to perform sterile dressing changes on her daughter. Which procedure should the nurse reinforce?
   a. Articles are considered sterile for a short time after opening.
   b. It is acceptable to use a wet outer package as long as the contents are dry.
   c. Skin surrounding the incision must be sterilized before the fresh dressing is applied.
   d. The edges of a wrapper containing sterile articles are considered unsterile.

2. You are the charge nurse on a pediatric unit. Due to staff shortages, a nurse from a medical-surgical unit is assigned to assist you. The nurse states that she has little pediatric experience. Which client can be most safely assigned to this nurse?
   a. An infant with a cleft lip repair who is scheduled for discharge in the morning.
   b. A toddler newly admitted following ingestion of a poison.
   c. A school-age child with pyelonephritis receiving IV antibiotics.
   d. A preschool child with sickle cell crisis.

3. The nurse is caring for a postoperative appendectomy client with a history of Type 1 diabetes. The client is on a regular glucose testing and insulin schedule. The physician advances the client's diet from NPO to clear liquids. The nurse should:
   a. order a diet of ginger ale, gelatin and chicken broth.
   b. order a diet of dietetic gelatin, sugar free ginger ale and chicken broth.
   c. order a diet of simple carbohydrates.
   d. call the physician to clarify the diet.

4. A nurse is examining a client's breasts. What would indicate an abnormality?
   a. A palpable transverse ridge of tissue at the lower edge of both breasts.
   b. Bilaterally large and pendulous breasts.
   c. Elevation of the left breast when standing erect.
   d. Darkened areola and pigmented breast follicles.

5. The nurse would teach a client with spinal cord injury to prevent autonomic dysreflexia by:
   a. assuming an upright position.
   b. evacuating bladder and bowel regularly.
   c. assessing for decubitus ulcers.
   d. decreasing emotional distress.

6. A nurse caring for a client with polycystic kidney disease (PKD) would be most concerned with which finding?
   a. Abdominal pain.
   b. Severe headache.
   c. Bloody urine.
   d. Distended abdomen.

7. A pregnant client is planning to breastfeed her baby. The nurse assesses that the client has inverted nipples. The nurse should instruct the client to:
   a. Use breast cups to treat the problem.
   b. Bottle feed her baby.
   c. Allow breasts to become engorged before feeding.
   d. Use anhydrous lanolin to prevent soreness.

8. When obtaining a throat culture, the nurse should:
   a.   have the client take a deep breath and cough into a sterile cup.
   b.   warm the specimen in an incubator prior to analysis.
   c.   have the client lie down.
   d.   quickly swab the pharynx.

9. A client with a fracture of the left leg is prescribed Buck's extension traction to the leg with five pounds of weight. Buck's traction is an example of:
   a.   skeletal traction.
   b.   skin traction.
   c.   balanced traction.
   d.   split-Russell traction.

10. After passing a kidney stone, a client is prepared for discharge. The client tells the nurse that he usually drinks between 600ml to 800ml of fluid per day. In order to prevent reoccurrence of the stone, the nurse would suggest that the client:
    a.   increase oral intake to 1,000ml per day.
    b.   decrease oral intake of protein products.
    c.   increase oral fluid intake to 2,000ml per day.
    d.   increase oral calcium intake.

11. Which client would be at the highest risk for malignant melanoma?
    a.   A woman of Scandinavian descent living in Buffalo, New York; using sunscreen with SPF of 30, occasionally in sun.
    b.   A 16-year-old adolescent, of Italian descent, living in Pennsylvania, on the swim team, using sunscreen with SPF of 20.
    c.   An African American man, living in Seattle, Washington, is a construction worker who uses no sunscreen.
    d.   An Asian women, living in Miami, Florida, who occasionally goes to beach and uses a sunscreen with SPF of 15.

12. The nurse is caring for a terminally ill client just diagnosed with an inoperable brain tumor. The nurse plans care knowing that the way most individuals cope with dying:
    a.   resembles the way they have coped with other losses in their lives.
    b.   depends on the attitudes of family and health care providers.
    c.   depends on the length of time between diagnosis and death.
    d.   reflects the ability to resolve conflicts and maintain control.

13. A client is about to be discharged with a new colostomy. The nurse is evaluating if the client understands how to irrigate his colostomy. Which client statement would indicate a need for further teaching?
    a.   "I will insert the catheter about three inches."
    b.   "I will use between 500ml and 1,000ml of warm water to irrigate."
    c.   "I will dilate my stoma with the stoma cone before irrigation."
    d.   "I will perform the irrigation every morning at 9:00AM."

14. A client, admitted with schizophrenia, is nearing discharge. The nurse should help the client meet her needs primarily by:
    a.   maximizing her coping skills.
    b.   increasing her interpersonal skills.
    c.   avoiding usual stresses.
    d.   eliminating her psychosis.

15. A client comes to the emergency department with severe chest injuries. Chest tubes are inserted and the client is admitted. The nurse would notify the physician immediately when the drainage is:
   a. 200ml/hour for five hours following insertion.
   b. 30ml every hour for 24 hours.
   c. 100ml for an eight hour shift.
   d. zero ml for three hours.

16. A nurse is teaching a 15-year-old client how to perform testicular self-examination. Which statement indicates a need for additional teaching? "I will:
   a. call my physician if I notice any hard lumps in my testicles."
   b. call my physician if one testicle is much larger than the other."
   c. examine my testicles every two months."
   d. examine my testicles in the shower."

17. A postoperative cholecystectomy client's T-tube drainage has increased from 200ml to 1,000ml per day. This would indicate that:
   a. bile production from the liver is improving.
   b. the T-tube is not functioning properly.
   c. the common bile duct is obstructed below the tube.
   d. the pancreatic duct is obstructed.

18. A client is scheduled to have a lumbar laminectomy with spinal fusion. The nurse should instruct the client that postoperatively he would be required to:
   a. sit up, deep breathe, and cough vigorously every two hours to promote effective airway clearance.
   b. lie in a prone position to maintain proper alignment of the spine and reduce pressure and pain at the operative site.
   c. have pillows or a bath blanket positioned under his knees to assist in relaxing lower back muscles.
   d. turn every two hours using a side-to-side log rolling technique to prevent twisting of the spine or hips.

19. The night prior to surgery, a client is prescribed to have soapsuds enemas until clear. The return of the third enema is brown solution and contains flakes of stool. What should the nurse do next?
   a. Insert a rectal tube.
   b. Wait one half hour and repeat the enema.
   c. Hold the enema and call the physician.
   d. Elevate the enema container prior to the next instillation.

20. A 9-year-old boy was injured and brought to the emergency department. His mother said he fell at home and twisted his ankle. A fracture of the ankle is diagnosed. This injury may be considered suspicious because:
   a. the fracture extends through the skin.
   b. the bone is splintered into several fragments.
   c. a break occurs across the entire section of the bone.
   d. the break coils around the bone.

21. A client who was brutally raped and strangled is brought to the emergency department in cardiac arrest. Although every attempt is made to revive her, the client dies. What should the nurse do while performing postmortem care?
   a. Remove all tubes and catheters used in the attempt to revive her.
   b. Place her clothing in a plastic bag and give it to the police.
   c. Wrap her hands in paper bags.
   d. Wash the body with hot soapy water.

22. A malnourished client on hyperalimentation (TPN) asks why she has to have "this tube." The nurse answers that TPN is used to treat malnourished clients because it:
   a. provides a highly concentrated solution of glucose and other nutrients.
   b. consists of a 10% dextrose solution, which contains 400 calories per 1,000ml of solution.
   c. is a method of providing needed fluids and electrolytes.
   d. is a complete form of a nutritionally balanced feeding.

23. A client is undergoing hemodialysis for end-stage renal disease. She is given epoetin alfa (Epogen) following the dialysis. The nurse understands that this drug is given to:
   a. treat anemia occurring with end-stage renal disease.
   b. increase lipid metabolism.
   c. decrease the incidence of infection.
   d. decrease blood pressure.

24. A client on a cardiac monitor is having six to seven premature ventricular contractions (PVCs) per minute. Appropriate intervention at this time would be to:
   a. continue to observe, because the number of PVCs is acceptable at this time.
   b. administer atropine 0.5mg intravenously as prescribed p.r.n.
   c. notify the physician immediately.
   d. assess the client's level of anxiety.

25. In evaluating the effectiveness of preoperative teaching, the nurse should expect the postoperative client to:
   a. use incentive spirometry every hour while awake.
   b. move unaffected areas in bed.
   c. refrain from asking for pain medicine between dosage times.
   d. void on arrival to the unit from the post-anesthesia care unit.

26. A client is scheduled to have an outpatient myelogram. What would the nurse teach the client? Select all that apply.
   a. "Drink one liter of water the morning of the test."
   b. "It is normal to expect some minor pain during the procedure."
   c. "You will need to stay in bed for six hours after the test."
   d. "Take the prescribed laxatives the day before the procedure."
   e. "You may eat whatever you want after the test."
   f. "It is important to wiggle your toes often during the test."

27. Prior to going into an isolation room, the nurse dons a mask, a gown and gloves. This is done because of the:
   a. virulence of the microorganisms involved.
   b. physical needs of the client.
   c. mode of transmission of the pathogens.
   d. security of other hospital clients.

28. A client is admitted with a diagnosis of sickle cell crisis. The charge nurse must put him in a semi-private room. Who would be the best choice for a roommate?
   a. A client who donated a kidney for transplantation.
   b. An elderly man with stage II decubitus ulcers.
   c. A trauma client with open fractures of both legs.
   d. A client with influenza being treated for dehydration.

29. A client with a history of migraine headaches is admitted to the hospital for unrelated surgery. The best way to assist this client postoperatively is to assess:
   a. if she usually has an aura before the migraine occurs.
   b. whether or not the migraine is precipitated by alcohol.
   c. for a family history of migraines or other types of headaches.
   d. whether she has ever been on oral contraceptive medication.

30. The nurse transcribes a prescription for an infant with epiglottitis to be NPO and receive an intravenous solution of D_5 in 1/4 NSS. The primary reason for this is to:
   a. meet calorie needs.
   b. decrease vagal stimulation.
   c. lessen physical exertion.
   d. relieve the laryngospasm.

31. A client admitted for pancreatitis admits to drinking nearly a case of beer daily until 36 hours prior to admission. The nurse should be alert for which sign of a complicated alcohol withdrawal?
   a. Anxiety.
   b. Tremors.
   c. Convulsions.
   d. Insomnia.

32. A client with Cushing's syndrome is being discharged after a carpal tunnel release was performed. Which client behavior best indicates that the discharge teaching was effective?
   a. The client identifies activities that increase the risk of infection.
   b. The client selects high sodium foods from a list of foods.
   c. The client states that there are no restrictions on her activity.
   d. The client identifies adrenal cortical deficit for the behavioral changes that she is experiencing.

33. A client with psoriasis should be further assessed for signs and symptoms of:
   a. Crohn's disease.
   b. arthritis.
   c. arteriosclerosis.
   d. Addison's disease.

34. Which nursing action would have the highest priority for a client presenting with active gastrointestinal bleeding?
   a. Prepare the client for an immediate endoscopy.
   b. Establish intravenous access.
   c. Treat the cause of the bleeding.
   d. Prepare the client for immediate surgery.

35. A client with colorectal cancer has just had an abdominoperineal resection and a colostomy construction. The nurse notes that the perineal dressing is saturated with serosanguinous drainage. The nurse should:
   a. notify the physician immediately.
   b. reinforce the dressing and recheck it shortly.
   c. check the vital signs and assess for possible shock.
   d. circle the drainage and recheck it in 15 minutes.

36. The nurse is assessing a client in the maternity clinic. What would be a positive sign of pregnancy?
   a. Amenorrhea.
   b. Positive pregnancy test.
   c. Fetal heart sounds.
   d. Quickening.

37. A nurse is writing a care plan for a client who had a spinal cord injury at S_5 and is having difficulty with constipation. Which intervention should be included in the plan of care?
   a. Stimulate the anal sphincter with a gloved lubricated finger.
   b. Massage the abdomen from left to right prior to defecation.
   c. Provide a bedpan at a specific time each day to attempt defecation.
   d. Have the client lean forward while attempting to defecate.

38. A client is hospitalized with acute thrombophlebitis of the right leg. The nursing assessment for this client would include which symptoms of the affected extremity?
   a. Intermittent claudication.
   b. Dry, scaly, shiny skin.
   c. Redness and warmth with edema.
   d. Absence of pulses distal to the occlusion.

39. A new father is watching his premature baby through the nursery window. He tells the nurse, "I would just like to hold my baby. I don't know how with all that equipment." An appropriate response by the nurse would be:
   a. "If you would like me to, I will tell you what the equipment is all about."
   b. "I'm sorry you can't hold the baby, the machines are helping her breath."
   c. "I can show you how to hold your baby so that the equipment isn't disturbed."
   d. "I am sorry you can't be near your baby now. Would you like to talk to her nurse?"

40. The nurse on a cardiac unit notices that her client is in ventricular fibrillation and has no pulse. The appropriate nursing action is to immediately notify the physician and:
   a. begin cardiopulmonary resuscitation (CPR).
   b. prepare to defibrillate.
   c. prepare for cardioversion.
   d. prepare one ampule of epinephrine.

41. A female client has stress incontinence. The nurse is teaching her Kegel exercises. To help her identify the muscle to be exercised, the nurse should have her:
   a. relax the muscles at the opening of the vagina by inserting a gloved finger.
   b. tighten her gluteal muscles and hold for 10 minutes.
   c. pretend that she is trying to hold back stool.
   d. bear down as if she is trying to have a bowel movement.

42. A woman involved in a motor vehicle accident with resultant chest trauma and blood loss is admitted to the emergency department. The priority nursing diagnosis would be:
   a. alteration in cardiac output: decreased related to hypovolemic shock.
   b. alteration in comfort: pain related to chest trauma.
   c. alteration in tissue perfusion related to hypovolemia.
   d. ineffective breathing pattern related to pain secondary to chest trauma.

43. Three hours after delivering her first baby, a woman complains of perineal discomfort at the site of her episiotomy. What is the appropriate nursing action?
   a. Report this discomfort to the physician.
   b. Administer a p.r.n. analgesic.
   c. Apply an ice pack to the perineal area.
   d. Apply a heat lamp to the perineal area.

44. An infant with cardiac disease is placed on lanoxin (Digoxin). The nurse should be alert for which signs of lanoxin (Digoxin) toxicity?
   a. Constant crying.
   b. Not eating.
   c. Confusion.
   d. Fever.

45. The nurse would teach a client on a low-cholesterol diet to avoid:
   a. egg whites.
   b. vegetable oils.
   c. liver.
   d. skim milk.

STOP. You have now completed Practice Session: 10. Now take a few minutes and correct your answers. Calculate your accuracy rate by dividing the number of questions you completed correctly by the total number of questions you completed (45).

Correct answers ÷ total number of questions completed = accuracy rate.

_____ ÷ _____ = _____

ANSWERS AND RATIONALES
Practice Session 10

1. **The correct answer is d.** The question is asking which is the correct information about sterile technique. The edges of a sterile wrapper are not sterile. Once articles are opened, they are no longer considered to be sterile because the air has germs, which could possibly contaminate the article (option a). Supplies are considered contaminated if any part is torn or wet (option b). Skin cannot be safely sterilized (option c). Cleansing with antiseptics and mechanical movements will reduce the numbers of both resident and transient bacteria.
    Nursing Process: Evaluation   **Client Need:** Safe, Effective Care Environment

2. **The correct answer is c.** The question is asking which client condition the medical-surgical nurse will be most familiar with and, therefore, able to deliver safe care. The treatment of pyelonephritis in children is basically the same as with adults. A medical-surgical nurse would be familiar with administration of intravenous antibiotics. Infants with cleft lip repair require specialized care related to feeding and suture care even when being discharged (option a). The toddler has been newly admitted and requires assessment skills the medical-surgical nurse may not have (option b). Sickle cell crisis occurs in children five years of age and younger requiring specialized assessment and intervention. It is unlikely that most medical-surgical nurses have experience with this (option d).
    Nursing Process: Implementation   **Client Need:** Safe, Effective Care Environment

3. **The correct answer is a.** The question is asking what to order when a client with Type 1 diabetes is advanced to a clear liquid diet. A diet of ginger ale, gelatin and chicken broth will increase glucose levels and decrease hypoglycemia. This helps to maintain nutritional status and promote wound healing. The glucose would be covered by the glucose testing and insulin schedule. Dietetic and sugar free foods would not meet calorie and nutritional needs of the client and would make the client hypoglycemic (option b). Ordering a diet of simple carbohydrates per se would not ensure a clear liquid diet (option c). There would be no need to clarify the diet with the physician (option d).
    Nursing Process: Analysis   **Client Need:** Physiological Integrity

4. **The correct answer is c.** The question is asking what would be an abnormal finding in a breast examination. An obvious elevation of a breast is always considered to be abnormal. Such a finding may be indicative of contraction of the underlying tissue that has resulted from tumor formation. The other options (a, b & d) are normal findings.
    Nursing Process: Analysis   **Client Need:** Physiological Integrity

5. **The correct answer is b.** The question is asking how to keep from having autonomic dysreflexia. A distended bladder or rectum will send stimuli into the cord and initiate the response. Assuming the upright position will lower blood pressure in the spinal cord injured client and is an initial measure taken when the client experiences autonomic dysreflexia (option a). Decubitus ulceration can cause this response, but it is not the most common causation (option c). Emotional distress does not cause the problem, as the sympathetic nervous system is not under higher cortical control (option d).
    Nursing Process: Implementation   **Client Need:** Health Promotion & Maintenance

6. **The correct answer is b.** The question is asking which symptom would require immediate attention in a client with polycystic kidney disease (PKD). A severe headache could indicate that the blood pressure is rising or a cerebral aneurysm has occurred, a life-threatening complication of PKD. Immediate medical attention is necessary. Abdominal pain, (option a), bloody urine (option c), and a distended abdomen (option d), while pertinent, are all symptoms common in PKD.
    Nursing Process: Evaluation   **Client Need:** Physiological Integrity

7. **The correct answer is a.** The question is asking what the nurse should tell a client who wants to

breastfeed but has inverted nipples. Inverted nipples should be assessed early so proper intervention can take place. Often, breast cups are used to assist the nipple to be presented to the infant. Often a nipple looks retracted or inverted, but actually functions properly when the infant is put to the breast (option b). Using breast cups and breast pumps assists the infant to suck on the breast. Allowing breasts to become engorged may make it more difficult for the infant to grasp the nipple and may promote nipple soreness (option c). Anhydrous lanolin is used to help with nipple soreness, but is unrelated to nipple inversion (option d).

Nursing Process: Implementation   **Client Need:** Health Promotion & Maintenance

8.   **The correct answer is d.** The question is asking how to properly obtain a throat culture. Quickly swabbing the pharynx avoids initiating the gag reflex and causing the client to be uncomfortable. Deep breathing and coughing into a sterile cup is the procedure for obtaining a sputum specimen, not a throat culture (option a). Warming the specimen is contraindicated, as it will cause microorganisms to grow and produce false results (option b). The client should assume a sitting position for increased visibility of the pharynx (option c).

Nursing Process: Implementation   **Client Need:** Physiological Integrity

9.   **The correct answer is b.** The question is asking what type of traction is Buck's traction. Buck's traction is a type of skin traction. Split-Russell traction is also a type of skin traction (option d). Skeletal traction (option a) places direct application through the bone itself; therefore, more use of weight can be tolerated. Balanced traction is a type of skeletal traction (option c).

Nursing Process: Planning   **Client Need:** Physiological Integrity

10.   **The correct answer is c.** The question is asking how a client can prevent further kidney stones. The two main principles used in preventing reoccurrence of renal stones are dilution and voiding. Ideally, fluid intake should be between 2,000ml and 3,000ml per day (option a). The high level of fluid intake will cause frequent voiding. The risk for some stones is related to dietary intake, but this situation did not indicate which type of stone was involved (options b & d).

Nursing Process: Planning   **Client Need:** Health Promotion & Maintenance

11.   **The correct answer is d.** The question is asking which client is at the highest risk for malignant melanoma. Even though people of Asian descent are the least susceptible, malignant melanoma differs from basal cell and squamous cell carcinoma in that malignant melanoma is due to intensity of the sun rather than duration of time in the sun. Being of Scandinavian descent (option a), a swim team participant (option b) and not using sunscreen (option c) are all risk factors for malignant melanoma, but the highest risk is the greatest intensity of the sun.

Nursing Process: Assessment   **Client Need:** Health Promotion & Maintenance

12.   **The correct answer is a.** The question is asking how most people cope with dying. Losses occur throughout life. People develop a pattern of responding to loss. The client will respond in the same way, depending on the meaning of this loss as compared with the meanings of previous losses. The other options (b, c & d) may also influence adaptation to a loss but a dying person faces the loss of all of those other things as well.

Nursing Process: Planning   **Client Need:** Health Promotion & Maintenance

13.   **The correct answer is c.** The question is asking what indicates that the client does not understand the colostomy irrigation teaching. Colostomy irrigation is done to stimulate peristalsis and allow evacuation. This allows the client to have a regular elimination pattern. If dilating the stoma is required, it should be done with a lubricated gloved pinky finger. As the finger is inserted, a massaging motion is used and progressively larger fingers are used until optimal dilation occurs. The catheter should be inserted three inches (option a). A stoma cone can be used to prevent perforation of the bowel or it can be attached to a catheter to keep the fluid from flowing out as fast as it goes in. Five hundred to 1,000ml of warm water should be used for irrigation (option b). The irrigation should be done daily, at the same time, to promote a pattern of regularity (option d).

Nursing Process: Evaluation   **Client Need:** Health Promotion & Maintenance

14. **The correct answer is a.** The question is asking how the nurse can best assist a client with schizophrenia prior to discharge. Nursing care focuses on maximizing coping skills. While increasing interpersonal skills is desirable (option b), it is not a major need at this time. Avoidance of usual stresses (option c) may be unrealistic. Elimination of psychosis may be impossible and is not in nursing's domain of practice (option d).
Nursing Process: Analysis   **Client Need:** Psychosocial Integrity

15. **The correct answer is a.** The question is asking what would be an abnormal sign in a client with chest injuries and who has a chest tube. Drainage of 200ml per hour for five to six hours is indicative of a serious problem. This may mean that more bleeding is going on. Therefore, the physician should be notified immediately and the client prepared for a possible thoracotomy. The other options are all acceptable amounts of drainage from chest tube secondary to trauma (options b, c & d).
Nursing Process: Analysis   **Client Need:** Physiological Integrity

16. **The correct answer is c.** The question is asking what information about self-testicular examination is incorrect and requires more teaching. Clients are instructed to examine their testicles every month, not every two months, in a warm, private place. Wet soapy hands make the process easier, making the shower, a good choice (option d). Clients are instructed to report hard lumps and an enlargement of one testicle (options a & b).
Nursing Process: Implementation   **Client Need:** Health Promotion & Maintenance

17. **The correct answer is c.** The question is asking what has happened if the T-tube drainage increases from 200ml to 1,000ml per day. When a client has a T-tube in place, part of the nurse's responsibility is to observe its function and drainage. A T-tube is a T shaped catheter that is placed in the common bile duct during a cholecystectomy to temporarily drain excess bile since the gall bladder has been removed. Increased bile flow from the tube, after it has started to decrease, is indicative of ductal obstruction below the tube placement. The presence of the tube does not change the amount of bile produced by the liver and, as long as the tube drains, it is functioning properly (options a & b). If the pancreatic duct does not function properly, the client would experience pancreatitis, not an increase in bile flow through a T-tube (option d).
Nursing Process: Evaluation   **Client Need:** Physiological Integrity

18. **The correct answer is d.** The question is asking what the client should do after undergoing a laminectomy. Log rolling assists in maintaining proper alignment of the spine and whole body to prevent twisting of the spine or hips. The bed (and client) should be kept flat (option a) to prevent flexion of the operative site. Vigorous coughing should be avoided to prevent strain on the back. The prone position (option b) should always be avoided to prevent strain or flexion at the surgical site. Pillows (option c) should not be placed under the popliteal space because of the risk of deep vein thrombosis.
Nursing Process: Implementation   **Client Need:** Safe, Effective Care Environment

19. **The correct answer is c.** The question is asking what to do after the third soapsuds enema does not come back clear. Soapsuds enemas are hypotonic solutions and repeated instillation can increase the blood volume and lead to water intoxication. Inserting a rectal tube will only facilitate the removal of flatus. It will not clean the rectum for surgery (option a). Adequate time, as determined by the physician, should be allowed between enemas to prevent the increase in blood volume (option b). Elevating the enema container will increase the rate of flow. It will not increase the amount of the return (option d).
Nursing Process: Implementation   **Client Need:** Physiological Integrity

20. **The correct answer is d.** The question is asking which injury might be considered suspicious. A break, which coils around the bone, is a spiral break, which often happens as a child twists to get away from someone. It is a sign to be investigated. The other options are not usually related to abuse. An open fracture is one that extends through the skin (option a). A comminuted fracture is when the bone is splintered into several fragments (option b). A transverse fracture is one that occurs across the entire section of the bone (option c).

21.   **The correct answer is c.** The question is asking how the nurse should care for a body that may contain hair tissue and skin samples of the perpetrator. The hands should be wrapped in a breathable container such as a paper bag. When an autopsy is performed, the body should be undisturbed. All tubes should remain in place (option a). Clothing should be placed in a breathable bag to preserve any evidence (option b). Washing the body may disturb evidence the medical examiner might find (option d).
     Nursing Process: Implementation   **Client Need:** Physiological Integrity

22.   **The correct answer is a.** The question is asking the purpose of total parenteral nutrition (TPN). Commercially prepared TPN base solution contains dextrose and nitrogen in the form of amino acids or protein hydrolysates. It also contains minimal amounts of electrolytes or vitamins. The hospital pharmacy will need to add electrolytes (option c), vitamins and trace elements. The usual solution contains from 15% to 25% dextrose. The 10% solution (option b) can be absorbed through a peripheral line, and if administering fluids and electrolytes was the only reason then this could be handled through a peripheral line. TPN is not a complete form of nutrition (option d) because it lacks essential fatty acids. These need to be administered separately as fat emulsions.
     Nursing Process: Analysis   **Client Need:** Physiological Integrity

23.   **The correct answer is a.** The question is asking what the drug epoetin alfa (Epogen) is used for. Epoetin alfa (Epogen), a synthetic form of erythropoietin, is used to treat the anemia associated with end-stage renal disease and hemodialysis. It does not affect lipid metabolism (option b). Filgastrin (Neupogen) is often used to decrease the incidence of infection by stimulating the proliferation of neutrophils (option c). Epoetin alfa (Epogen) will increase blood pressure, not decrease it (option d).
     Nursing Process: Analysis   **Client Need:** Physiological Integrity

24.   **The correct answer is c.** The question is asking what to do when a client has six to seven premature ventricular contractions in one minute. Notify the physician immediately. The number of PVCs is unacceptable (option a). Ischemic heart tissue is electrically unstable and is prone to fatal ventricular arrhythmias. Atropine (option b) is used to increase the heart rate in severe bradycardia and would not be appropriate. Anxiety (option d) may cause PVCs, however, at this point, it is more important to notify the physician to prevent more serious arrhythmias.
     Nursing Process: Implementation   **Client Need:** Safe, Effective Care Environment

25.   **The correct answer is a.** The question is asking which was correct teaching for a client who is having surgery. The nurse provides the client with information to promote respiratory and circulatory function during the postoperative period. If the client has understood the information, then postoperatively the client will perform deep breathing using the incentive spirometry. Early ambulation is indicated for the prevention of thrombophlebitis. When that is not possible, then moving all extremities in the bed is necessary to prevent clot formation (option b). Pain medication assists the client to be able to move and needs to be administered before the pain is severe in order for adequate relief to be obtained (option c). The client will not automatically void upon arriving to the unit. This will depend on fluid volume, type of anesthesia and the last time the client voided (option d).
     Nursing Process: Evaluation   **Client Need:** Health Promotion & Maintenance

26.   **The correct answers are c, d and e.** The question is asking for the appropriate client instructions prior to a myelogram. The client will need to remain in bed with the head of the bed-elevated 30° for 6 to 12 hours. Enemas and laxatives are used to enhance visualization of the lumbar region. The client is NPO the day of the test (option a), but may resume a normal diet as soon as the test is completed. A local anesthetic is used prior to needle insertion, therefore pressure may be felt but pain would be abnormal (option b). The ability to move the legs and wiggle the toes will be assessed frequently after the procedure, but not during (option f).
     Nursing Process: Implementation   **Client Need:** Physiological Integrity

27. **The correct answer is c.** The question is asking why isolation precautions are necessary. Infection is prevented or controlled by "breaking" the chain of infection so that the transmission of microorganisms is interrupted. Isolation measures do serve to protect others (personnel, clients, visitors) within the hospital setting (option d) and contain microorganisms regardless of virulence, (option a) but mode of transmission is the important factor in protecting others. The physical needs of the client (option b) must be met regardless of isolation techniques indicated.
Nursing Process: Planning   **Client Need:** Safe, Effective Care Environment

28. **The correct answer is a.** The question is asking the best room placement for a client with sickle cell crisis. A client in sickle cell crisis is at high risk for infection. Infection can prolong the crisis. The client who donates a kidney is considered to be very healthy and must be infection free prior to surgery. Decubitus ulcers (option b) in stage II are infected, so this person may pose a threat to the client with sickle cell disease. Open fractures (option c) occur when a skin wound extends to the fractured bone. Influenza (option d) is an infection caused by a virus.
Nursing Process: Planning   **Client Need:** Safe, Effective Care Environment

29. **The correct answer is a.** The question is asking what you need to know to help a postoperative client who has a history of migraines. A client having surgery will be NPO for a time pre and postoperatively and most medication used to treat migraines would not be given. The stress of surgery plus the lowered blood levels of preventive medication may make a person more prone to the headaches. Early warning where treatment can be initiated before the migraine is at its peak is the best method of assisting the client. Some clients who suffer from migraines report an aura of shimmering lights. This visual disturbance may be followed by neurological disturbances such as lip numbness, aphasia or drowsiness. Pain, nausea and vomiting follow soon afterwards. If the client has an aura, then measures may be taken to prevent or lessen the migraine. Alcohol is often a precipitant; however, there would be little reason to give her alcohol while hospitalized (option b). A family history of migraines (option c) might suggest she could also have migraines since they can be hereditary. However, this gives us no further assessment data since we already know she suffers from migraines. Oral contraceptive medication (option d) may precipitate a migraine but only if it is presently being used. History of use would not affect present migraines.
Nursing Process: Assessment   **Client Need:** Physiological Integrity

30. **The correct answer is c.** The question is asking why intravenous (IV) solution is given to an infant with epiglottitis, who is not allowed to have anything by mouth. When the infant sucks in order to eat, much physical exertion is required. Fluid by IV route is indicated with croup to decrease the chance of aspiration. The IV does not decrease vagal stimulation or reduce laryngospasms stimulation (options b & d). The amount of glucose does not meet the infant's calorie needs (option a). The physician usually realizes this and does not keep clients NPO for long periods of time; only until respirations decrease and aspiration is no longer a possibility.
Nursing Process: Implementation   **Client Need:** Physiological Integrity

31. **The correct answer is c.** The question is asking what would be a sign of a complicated (key word) withdrawal. The options show data that are usual symptoms of withdrawal and one that is a life-threatening complication. Anxiety, tremors and insomnia are symptoms of minor withdrawal (options a, b & d). A grand mal seizure is a more serious symptom and may occur anywhere from 6 to 48 hours after the last drink.
Nursing Process: Assessment   **Client Need:** Physiological Integrity

32. **The correct answer is a.** The question is asking what would be evaluation criteria for client teaching post-carpal tunnel release that also has Cushing's syndrome. The focus of nursing care for the client with Cushing's syndrome is to prevent potentially life-threatening infections and injury. Surgery results in a breakdown of skin and a possible conduit for infectious organisms. The client needs a low-sodium diet to maintain an adequate cardiac output (option b). The nurse and client need to identify and limit activities, such as hand movements and heavy lifting

which will increase the risk of injury related to the osteoporosis (option c). Behavioral changes are associated with adrenal cortical excess, not deficit (option d).
Nursing Process: Evaluation   **Client Need:** Health Promotion & Maintenance

33.   **The correct answer is b.** The question is asking what further assessment is needed from a client diagnosed with psoriasis. Approximately one third of clients with psoriasis also have arthritis. There is some evidence that psoriasis is related to the immune system, which causes cell proliferation. There is no direct connection with any of the other diseases (options a, c & d).
Nursing Process: Assessment   **Client Need:** Physiological Integrity

34.   **The correct answer is b.** The question is asking what the nurse does first for a client with active gastrointestinal bleeding. This means that more than one option may be true but only one is first. A client presenting with blood loss must have immediate intravenous access in order for fluids or blood to be given in an emergency situation. Eventually the client will require an endoscopy to visualize the esophagus and stomach (option a). However, this is not the number one priority. Treating the cause of the bleeding (option c) is also correct but not the number one priority. The cause should be corrected once determined. However, the client would need to receive fluid replacement quickly to prevent shock. Waiting until a cause is found could result in harm to the client. Though surgery may be needed, the client again needs to be stabilized with fluids or blood before surgery may be done (option d).
Nursing Process: Planning   **Client Need:** Safe, Effective Care Environment

35.   **The correct answer is b.** The question is asking how to respond when the dressing is full of drainage that is not bloody. The nurse should reinforce the dressing and recheck it shortly. The initial drainage from the perineal wound will be serosanguinous and profuse. This is not an emergency unless the client has large amounts of bloody drainage. It does not warrant notifying the physician immediately (option a). Option (c) is not necessary unless other symptoms that indicate shock are present. Option (d) is incorrect because the dressing is full of drainage and cannot be circled; it must be reinforced.
Nursing Process: Implementation   **Client Need:** Physiological Integrity

36.   **The correct answer is c.** The question is asking for a positive sign of pregnancy. A positive sign means a definite knowledge of pregnancy and generally involves some activity of the fetus. The distinct heartbeat of the fetus is a positive sign of pregnancy, usually heard at approximately the 20th week of gestation. Menstrual suppression/amenorrhea is a presumptive sign and may be caused by a variety of other conditions, such as thyroid disease or malnutrition in addition to pregnancy (option a). A positive pregnancy test (option b) is a probable sign, correct about 95% of the time, but may also be caused by ingestion of tranquilizers or oral contraceptives and can occur in postmenopausal women or women with thyroid disease. Quickening (option d) or a feeling of fetal movement is a presumptive sign and could be a misinterpretation of intestinal gas.
Nursing Process: Analysis   **Client Need:** Health Promotion & Maintenance

37.   **The correct answer is d.** The question is asking how to assist a client with constipation who also has a spinal injury at the S_5 level. Leaning forward increases the intra-abdominal pressure to facilitate movement of feces. Stimulating the anal sphincter is contraindicated in S_5 injuries, as the anus is relaxed and lacks tone (option a). Think of the path of the fecal material as it moves through the intestines. The abdomen should be massaged from right to left to facilitate feces movement, not from left to right (option b). Bedpans should be avoided (option c), as they would not foster normal movement (downward) for defecation. The client should assume a normal position for defecation by squatting and having the knees higher than the hips.
Nursing Process: Planning   **Client Need:** Physiological Integrity

38.   **The correct answer is c.** The question is asking for the symptoms of acute thrombophlebitis. Signs and symptoms of acute thrombophlebitis include redness and warmth along the vein and edema distal to the obstructed vein. The remaining options (a, b & d) are symptoms of peripheral arterial disease: intermittent claudication; dry, scaly shiny skin; and absence of pulses distal to the occlusion refer to arterial impairment of the extremities.

Nursing Process: Assessment   **Client Need:** Physiological Integrity

39.   **The correct answer is c.** The question is asking how to respond to a father who wants to hold his premature baby, but is afraid of the equipment. It is vital to the infant's well being for proper bonding to occur. This is fostered by the parents' participation in providing care for their infant (option d). This father did not really want to know about the equipment, he wanted to be near his baby (options a & b). By offering to go into the nursery with him so he could be near his baby, the nurse is offering herself and responding to the father's needs.
Nursing Process: Implementation   **Client Need:** Health Promotion & Maintenance

40.   **The correct answer is b.** The question is asking what to do when a client has no pulse or respirations but is in monitored ventricular fibrillation. Defibrillation is the treatment of choice in monitored ventricular fibrillation without pulse (option a). The purpose of defibrillation is to stop electrical activity in the heart so that when it restarts normal pacemakers will take over. Epinephrine (option d) is given during asystole to stimulate the heart into action. Cardioversion (option c) is a method of countershock used to correct less serious arrhythmias. The electrical impulse is synchronized with the R wave on the EKG.
Nursing Process: Implementation   **Client Need:** Safe, Effective Care Environment

41.   **The correct answer is c.** The question is asking the way to help a client identify the correct muscle for Kegel exercises. The nurse asks the client to pretend that she's trying to hold back stool so that the client can identify the pubococcygeus muscle. The pubococcygeus muscle is the muscle that one contracts to hold back stool and urine. The muscles at the vaginal entrance should be tightened, not relaxed (option a). Tightening gluteal muscles (option b) is incorrect because they are not the muscles involved in holding urine flow and will not prevent incontinence even if strengthened. Bearing down, as if trying to have a bowel movement, (option d) is incorrect because this identifies the wrong muscle and will not assist the client with the problem.
Nursing Process: Implementation   **Client Need:** Health Promotion & Maintenance

42.   **The correct answer is d.** The question is asking the priority nursing diagnosis in a client with chest trauma and blood loss. The first priority for any client is provision and maintenance of an open, effective airway. In addition, the situation has indicated the client has chest trauma, which would create an ineffective breathing pattern because of the associated pain. Options (a), (b) and (c) are appropriate for the client, but are not the priority diagnosis.
Nursing Process: Analysis   **Client Need:** Physiological Integrity

43.   **The correct answer is c.** The question is asking what the nurse would do for a client complaining of episiotomy pain three hours post-delivery. Ice is the treatment of choice for the first 24 hours to decrease edema and, therefore, decrease pain. Notification of the physician (option a) would not occur unless there was evidence of a developing hematoma or signs of infection. Analgesics (option b) are not usually used for perineal pain especially not as the first option. A heat lamp (option d) would increase swelling and pain at the area within the first 24 hours.
Nursing Process: Implementation   **Client Need:** Physiological Integrity

44.   **The correct answer is b.** The question is asking how to assess lanoxin (Digoxin) toxicity in an infant. Think about symptoms of this in an adult. An infant could not tell anyone if vision problems or nausea occurred. However, an infant who refuses to eat has anorexia, which is an early sign of toxicity. Since the client is an infant, confusion (option c) could not be assessed. A fever (option d) is not a sign of lanoxin (Digoxin) toxicity, nor is constant crying (option a). The infant could be crying for other reasons such as chest discomfort or fear.
Nursing Process: Evaluation   **Client Need:** Physiological Integrity

45.   **The correct answer is c.** The question is asking what foods are high in cholesterol. Liver is organ meat and contains 300mg cholesterol per 100g. Egg whites (option a) and vegetable oils (option b) contain none. Skim milk (option d) contains 3mg/100g.
Nursing Process: Implementation   **Client Need:** Physiological Integrity

PRACTICE SESSION: 11

Instructions: Allow yourself 45 minutes to complete the following 45 practice questions. Use a timer to notify yourself when 45 minutes are over so that you are not constantly looking at your watch while completing the questions.

1. A nurse is taking the history of a client complaining of visual changes. The nurse would further evaluate the client for other symptoms of cataracts if he complained of:
   a. gradual loss of peripheral vision.
   b. gradual loss of visual acuity.
   c. perception of haloes around lights.
   d. appearance of flashing lights.

2. A nurse is emptying the nasogastric suction drainage from a client who had a partial gastrectomy earlier that day. She observes that it looks like coffee grounds. After hematesting the drainage, what should the nurse do?
   a. Call the physician.
   b. Irrigate the nasogastric tube.
   c. Document the coffee ground drainage and hematest results.
   d. Increase the nasogastric suction from low intermittent to continuous.

3. What nursing intervention is necessary for a client receiving lactulose (Cephulac) for hepatic encephalopathy?
   a. Encourage the client to increase physical exercise.
   b. Monitor serum electrolytes daily.
   c. Increase dietary protein intake.
   d. Maintain a fluid restriction of 2,000ml/day.

4. A client is diagnosed with Buerger's disease. The nurse would further assess for a history of:
   a. cigarette smoking.
   b. diabetes mellitus.
   c. gouty arthritis.
   d. a high fat diet.

5. A client with excessive vomiting needs a nasogastric tube. In preparing the tube for placement, the nurse would measure from the:
   a. nose to the ear, then to the xiphoid.
   b. nose to the pubic area.
   c. top of the head to the nose, then to the xiphoid.
   d. nose to the xiphoid.

6. The nurse would especially monitor which client who just received sodium polystyrene sulfate (Kayexalate)? A client who has:
   a. chronic asthma.
   b. diabetes mellitus.
   c. frequent nosebleeds.
   d. congestive heart failure.

7. A client was rollerblading and was hit by a car. He sustained a maxillofacial fracture and has undergone an intermaxillary fixation. Following surgery, the client begins to vomit. What priority action should the nurse take?
   a. Cut the fixation wires.
   b. Suction the front of the mouth.
   c. Insert a nasogastric tube.
   d. Elevate the head of the bed.

8. While giving a bath to a client with Alzheimer's disease, he becomes loud and agitated. He waves his fist in the air and tells the nurse to stop rubbing poison all over him. The nurse should:
   a. Stop the bath and try again later.
   b. Set limits by stating, "Please put your fist down."
   c. Ask the client what is bothering him.
   d. Place the client in soft restraints to finish the bath.

9. Shortly after open-heart surgery, an elderly client develops atrial fibrillation on the monitor at a ventricular rate of 140. The nurse knows that this rhythm can be dangerous because it:
   a. may convert easily into ventricular fibrillation.
   b. involves all impulses from the AV node being blocked.
   c. causes the client to have a pulse deficit.
   d. promotes the formation of a thrombus.

10. The mother of a preschool child tells the nurse she's afraid her child is not making any friends. The nurse replies that the parent can help her child make friends by:
    a. being an active part of the child's play.
    b. closely watching over and directing the child's play.
    c. arranging for other children to come over and play.
    d. allowing the children to play without supervision.

11. The nurse is evaluating if a newly diagnosed diabetic understands the difference between NPH and regular insulins. The nurse knows that learning has occurred when the client states that:
    a. NPH is long-acting insulin that stays in the system for two days.
    b. regular insulin begins to act in one to two hours; it peaks in four to five hours; and it lasts 10 to 12 hours.
    c. regular insulin works faster, but not as long as NPH insulin.
    d. NPH does not peak, but stays in the system at low levels all day and night; regular insulin peaks in two to four hours after administration.

12. A client undergoing chemotherapy for leukemia is admitted to the emergency department following a car accident. Surgery is required. In addition to hematocrit and hemoglobin, what blood test would the nurse anticipate?
    a. Platelets.
    b. Electrolytes.
    c. Blood urea nitrogen.
    d. Blood glucose.

13. A nurse attempts a one-to-one interaction with a client admitted for suicidal ideation. The client states, "I would rather work things out myself than burden you with my problems." The most appropriate response by the nurse would be:
    a. "I can understand that you need your privacy; if you need me, let me know."
    b. "It is obvious that you have not been able to work things out by yourself."
    c. "Are you saying that nothing can be done to help you?"
    d. "It is difficult to discuss your problems with others, let's discuss your feelings about being a burden."

14. A client is being evaluated for possible diabetes insipidus following a craniotomy. The nurse should monitor the client for:
   a. excessive thirst and glucosuria.
   b. hypernatremia and weight loss.
   c. increased urine specific gravity and proteinuria.
   d. polyphagia and decreased serum osmolality.

15. On the first postpartal day, the nurse palpates a woman's fundus and expects it to be:
   a. boggy, midline and at the umbilicus.
   b. firm, dextroverted and one finger's breadth below the umbilicus.
   c. firm, midline and one finger's breadth below the umbilicus.
   d. boggy, midline and at the symphysis pubis.

16. The physician prescribes peritoneal dialysis for a client. When formulating a plan of care, the nurse would assign highest priority to which nursing action?
   a. Need for strict asepsis.
   b. Accurate intake and output.
   c. Maintenance of nutrition.
   d. Client teaching needs.

17. A client with a pressure ulcer is admitted to the long-term care facility. The nurse plans to clean the wound with:
   a. topical antiseptics.
   b. a gel wafer.
   c. normal saline.
   d. topical enzymes.

18. A nurse is planning care for a client with congestive heart failure and pulmonary edema. What would be an appropriate nursing diagnosis?
   a. Alteration in cardiac output: increased related to congestive heart failure.
   b. Fluid volume deficit: edema related to left ventricular failure.
   c. Activity intolerance related to decreased energy.
   d. Ineffective breathing pattern related to pain.

19. A client is about to undergo a modified radical mastectomy. When planning preoperative teaching, which nursing care measures should receive priority?
   a. Preventing postoperative complications.
   b. Establishing an individualized rehabilitation program.
   c. Identifying strategies for maintaining optimal self-concept.
   d. Alleviating anxiety and fears related to the surgery.

20. A nurse is called to the room by a family member and finds the client exhibiting tonic-clonic movements. The client also appears to be slightly cyanotic. The nurse's initial action would be to:
   a. attempt to insert a cloth or padded tongue blade in the mouth.
   b. attempt to restrain the client's limbs to prevent injury.
   c. administer oxygen.
   d. push aside the furniture, if possible.

21. The nurse is planning care for a woman who is having difficulty breastfeeding. The nursing care plan is based on the understanding that vasoconstriction in the breast is often caused by:
   a. increased prolactin.
   b. the presence of oxytocin.
   c. oversleeping.
   d. increased anxiety.

22. Bus accident victims are brought to the emergency department. Which client problem should be addressed first?
   a. A 54-year-old client with an irregular heartbeat.
   b. A 24-year-old client with high-pitched inspiration.
   c. A 72-year-old client with a strong cough and mucus expectoration.
   d. A 35-year-old client with a regular heart beat of 140.

23. The infection control nurse is walking by a client's room when she observes a student caring for a client. The nurse knows that the student is using correct procedure regarding standard precautions when she:
   a. wore gloves when emptying the client's bedpan of uncontaminated urine and feces.
   b. washed her hands with her gloves on prior to caring for the client in the next bed.
   c. wore sterile gloves to perform a finger stick blood glucose level.
   d. wore latex gloves when checking vital signs on a client receiving a blood transfusion.

24. A client is admitted with a cytomegalovirus (CMV) infection. Which precaution should be taken by the nursing staff to prevent transmission of the CMV?
   a. The client should be placed in reverse isolation.
   b. Pregnant nurses should not be assigned to care for the client.
   c. Gloves, gown and mask should be worn prior to entering the room.
   d. Begin penicillin G 1.2 million units intravenous every four hours as prescribed.

25. Upon assessment of a client with a C_7 spinal cord injury, the nurse would suspect autonomic dysreflexia when the client exhibits:
   a. hypotension and tachycardia.
   b. severe hypertension, bradycardia and sweating above the level of the lesion.
   c. nausea, vomiting and cardiac arrhythmias.
   d. heart block, bradycardia and cardiac arrest.

26. A client with a gunshot wound to the chest is brought to the emergency department. The client is alert and oriented but in pain. In caring for this client, the nurse understands that:
   a. application of a gauze dressing over the wound will prevent air from entering or leaving the chest.
   b. a sucking sound is likely to be heard over the wound.
   c. gunshot wounds are less serious than stab wounds.
   d. since the client arrived alert and oriented, his level of consciousness is likely to remain stable.

27. The nurse in the post-anesthesia care unit (PACU) notes that an unconscious client has begun to snore. The initial action of the nurse should be to:
   a. take no action and continue to observe.
   b. refer to the client's admission nursing assessment.
   c. immediately check the client's vital signs.
   d. manually move the lower jaw forward and upward.

28. A client has been prescribed nitrates for the treatment of angina. The nurse would evaluate these drugs looking for signs that show:
   a. dilation of both veins and arteries, therefore, increasing blood flow to the heart.
   b. increased cardiac output by enhancing the force of the contraction of the heart.
   c. a profound effect on the myocardial oxygen demands and supply.
   d. acceleration of the cardiac rate by creating a positive inotropic effect.

29. A nurse has administered morphine sulfate (Morphine) intramuscularly to a postoperative client. Which nursing observation best indicates the effectiveness of the medication?
    a.   The client's blood pressure, pulse and respirations are within normal limits.
    b.   The client describes his surgical pain as an 8 on the pain scale of 1 to 10.
    c.   The client's urinary output totaled 300ml for the last eight hours.
    d.   The client ambulated in the hall with the assistance of one nurse.

30. The nurse notifies the physician of a possible ectopic pregnancy after assessing which symptom?
    a.   Increased temperature.
    b.   Shoulder pain.
    c.   Pregnancy-induced hypertension.
    d.   Profuse vaginal bleeding.

31. A client is admitted to the hospital with complaints of diplopia, which worsens as the day moves on. The client is subsequently diagnosed with myasthenia gravis. The nurse would also expect to assess:
    a.   muscle wasting.
    b.   muscle fatigue even after rest.
    c.   eye drooping.
    d.   memory loss for recent events.

32. What would be an appropriate short-term goal for a client with paranoid schizophrenia? The client:
    a.   is no longer suspicious of others.
    b.   stays out of his room during the day.
    c.   leads group activities on the unit.
    d.   relates daily to two staff members

33. The nurse is making rounds prior to giving shift report. Which finding would need to be brought to the attention of unit personnel?
    a.   Intravenous bag with 150ml solution hanging.
    b.   Chest tube to suction with bubbling chamber.
    c.   Urinary catheter bag with 750ml of cloudy urine.
    d.   Soft restraint tied so that the client can move side-to-side.

34. A client presents in the emergency department with intensive eye pain, tearing and photophobia after scratching her right eye with a mascara brush. A diagnosis of corneal abrasion is made and treatment is initiated. Discharge instructions would include:
    a.   inspecting the right eye daily for evidence of infection.
    b.   avoiding the use of eye patches during the healing process.
    c.   applying ice compresses to the right eye to decrease pain and swelling.
    d.   avoiding bending the head below the waist to pick up items from the floor.

35. Preoperatively, the parents of a child with Hirschprung's disease are taught to give their son daily enemas. The nurse feels secure that they understand the procedure when they choose which enema?
    a.   Tap water.
    b.   Soapsuds.
    c.   Normal saline.
    d.   Hypotonic.

36. A client is prescribed 1,000ml D_5W with 10mEq of KCl over eight hours. With a drop factor of 15, what is the correct number of drops per minute?

_____

37. Following a Mantoux test, the skin reaction is more than 12mm induration. The client asks if this means he has tuberculosis. The nurse answers with the understanding that:
   a. the best purpose of skin testing is to positively diagnose tuberculosis.
   b. a positive skin test indicates active tuberculosis.
   c. a 12mm induration is only borderline significant for the Mantoux test.
   d. skin testing is primarily a screening device, which needs substantiation.

38. The primary nursing goal for a client with cerebrospinal rhinorrhea is to prevent:
   a. increased intracranial pressure.
   b. intracranial infection.
   c. loss of cerebrospinal fluid.
   d. further blood loss.

39. A client in sickle cell crisis becomes angry and starts to cry, "Why did it have to come back? Why does this have to happen at all?" The nurse's response would be:
   a. "You seem angry. You should talk about it."
   b. "Asking 'why' is always a difficult question in these cases."
   c. "You feel that life is treating you unfairly."
   d. "Sickle cell crisis is often caused by stress."

40. A client just delivered twins by cesarean section. The chief concern of the nurse would be:
   a. encouraging the client to ventilate her feelings about the birth and her self-image.
   b. assessing the client's vital signs, uterine fundus and abdominal dressing.
   c. reinforcing the client's knowledge regarding breastfeeding.
   d. providing early ambulation to prevent respiratory complications.

41. A 2-year-old toddler is being evaluated for autism. When the nurse finds this child in the playroom, he would expect him to be involved in which activity?
   a. Coloring in a book.
   b. Playing with a toy soldier.
   c. Finger painting on an easel.
   d. Rocking in a chair.

42. A client undergoes abdominal surgery. Postoperatively, the client shows signs of intestinal obstruction. The nurse would be the most concerned if which were noted?
   a. Burning pain.
   b. Dry heaves.
   c. Flatus.
   d. Bloody mucus.

43. A 3-day-old infant has developed physiological jaundice. The baby's father asks the nurse what causes this type of jaundice. The nurse tells the parents that it is due to:
   a. liver damage.
   b. increased production of bilirubin and liver immaturity.
   c. decreased production of bilirubin and immature red blood cells.
   d. an inborn error in metabolism.

44. A client with a detached retina has a nursing diagnosis of: risk for injury related to sensory deficit and anxiety. As you review the care plan, which intervention should be revised?
   a. Keep the bed in the lowest position and keep the side rails up on the affected side.
   b. Approach the client from the affected side so that he is not startled.
   c. Instruct the client to wear an eye shield at night or when taking a nap for two weeks after surgery.
   d. Instruct the client not to cough, sneeze or vomit. If this is a problem, tell the client to request a cough medication or an antiemetic.

45.	A man suffered a traumatic amputation of his right leg in a motor vehicle accident. One week later he is diagnosed with acute renal failure. Which factor is most likely a cause of the acute renal failure?

a.	Diabetes mellitus.
b.	Increased blood urea nitrogen (BUN).
c.	Hemorrhage.
d.	Hypertension.

STOP. You have now completed Practice Session: 11. Now take a few minutes and correct your answers. Calculate your accuracy rate by dividing the number of questions you completed correctly by the total number of questions you completed (45).

Correct answers ÷ total number of questions completed = accuracy rate.

_____ ÷ _____ = _____

ANSWERS AND RATIONALES
Practice Session 11

1. **The correct answer is b.** The question is asking for the symptoms of cataracts. In cataracts the ocular lens opacifies, thus leading to gradual loss of vision and/or blurry vision. Loss of peripheral vision and the appearance of haloes around lights are symptoms of glaucoma (options a & c), while the appearance of flashing lights is a symptom of retinal detachment (option d).
Nursing Process: Assessment   **Client Need:** Physiological Integrity

2. **The correct answer is c.** The question is asking what to do when a client has coffee ground colored drainage after testing it for blood. Coffee ground drainage is expected following gastric surgery. This should be documented with the results of the hematest. Because this is a normal finding it is unnecessary to call the physician (option a). Irrigating the nasogastric tube will clean the tube, but will not change the consistency of the drainage (option b). Increasing suction requires a physician's prescription (option d).
Nursing process: Implementation   **Client Need:** Physiological Integrity

3. **The correct answer is b.** The question is asking what the nurse must do when giving a client lactulose (Cephulac) to treat hepatic encephalopathy. Lactulose (Cephulac) is a laxative that acidifies the colonic contents and increases the osmotic pressure in the colon. This process decreases the ammonia level in the blood. The resultant increase in stools can lead to electrolyte deficiencies. An increase in exercise is not necessary when taking this medication (option a). An increase in dietary protein is contraindicated in clients with hepatic encephalopathy, as this leads to increased ammonia level (option c). Fluid restrictions can lead to dehydration in clients who are taking laxatives (option d).
Nursing Process: Implementation   **Client Need:** Physiological Integrity

4. **The correct answer is a.** The question is asking for a risk factor associated with Buerger's disease. Buerger's disease is inflammation of the small vessels of the legs and occasionally the upper extremities. Cigarette smoking aggravates the disorder. Some evidence suggests that it may be a causative factor as well. Diabetes mellitus is associated with atherosclerosis (option b). Gouty arthritis is the build up of uric acid in the joints (option c). A high fat diet is associated with atherosclerosis (option d).
Nursing Process: Assessment   **Client Need:** Physiological Integrity

5. **The correct answer is a.** The question is asking how to measure a client for a nasogastric tube. The measurement of the nasogastric tube should be accomplished with the client sitting in an upright position with head facing forward. The end of the tube should be placed at the end of the client's nose then extended to the bottom of the ear and then straight to the end of the xiphoid process (options b, c & d).
Nursing Process: Implementation   **Client Need:** Safe, Effective Care Environment

6. **The correct answer is d.** The question is asking which client may be in danger because of receiving sodium polystyrene sulfate (Kayexalate). This drug is used to help rid the body of excess potassium. Because sodium polystyrene sulfate (Kayexalate) exchanges sodium for potassium, it is more likely to precipitate volume overload in a client with a history of congestive heart failure (options a, b & c).
Nursing Process: Analysis   **Client Need:** Physiological Integrity

7. **The correct answer is b.** The question is asking what to do when a client, whose jaw is wired, vomits. The vomitus should be suctioned so as not to cause an airway obstruction. Often the vomitus can be suctioned without needing to cut the wires (option a). If the wires are cut, the surgeon must be notified to re-establish fixation. A nasogastric tube can be inserted to provide continuous or intermittent suction, however, it is not the priority when the client vomits (option c). The client's head should be turned to the side to promote drainage (option d).
Nursing Process: Implementation   **Client Need:** Safe, Effective Care Environment

8.   **The correct answer is a.** The question is asking how the nurse should intervene with a client who has Alzheimer's disease and becomes very agitated and delusional during his bath. Bath times may be particularly difficult. A very successful intervention with this client is to change the experience. The nurse can often decrease the client's agitation and anger by distracting or redirecting the client by stopping the bath and returning at another time. Giving the client basic directions would not be as helpful as distraction. Since the client has a cognitive impairment, he may not be able to respond appropriately (option b). The client believes the nurse is spreading poison on him. Asking him to further explain would encourage or "feed" this delusion (option c). Restraints are not necessary and will do little to decrease the client's agitation (option d).
Nursing Process: Implementation   **Client Need:** Psychosocial Integrity

9.   **The correct answer is d.** The question is asking why a ventricular rate of 140 is dangerous in a client with atrial fibrillation. In atrial fibrillation, the erratic contraction of the atria promotes the formation of a thrombus. This increases the risk for an embolic event, including stroke. Ventricular tachycardia can lead to ventricular fibrillation (option a). A complete heart block would occur when impulses from the AV node are being stopped, not when the atria are fibrillating (option b). Although a pulse deficit does occur with atrial fibrillation, it is a normal finding (option c).
Nursing Process: Analysis   **Client Need:** Physiological Integrity

10.   **The correct answer is c.** The question is asking how to help a preschool child make friends. If parents invite other children over to play, the children will learn better how to get along with each other. Active participation in play can further cement the parent-child bond, but does not foster making friends with the same age group (option a). Close watch and direction will make the children dependent on the adult for play ideas (option b). Allowing children to play without supervision (option d) may result in chaotic play and a child could be hurt.
Nursing Process: Implementation   **Client Need:** Health Promotion & Maintenance

11.   **The correct answer is c.** The question is asking for correct information about the two insulins. Learning has occurred when the client talks about the appropriate peaks and durations of the different insulins. As the effects of regular insulin are diminishing, the effects of NPH are increasing and can be utilized for glucose in the body during the basal hours of glucose release. NPH is intermediate-acting insulin with an onset of one to three hours; peak in 6 to 12 hours; and duration of 24 hours (options a & d). Regular insulin is short-acting with an onset of one-half to one hour; peaks in two to four hours and duration of eight hours (option b).
Nursing Process: Evaluation   **Client Need:** Health Promotion & Maintenance

12.   **The correct answer is a.** The question is asking what blood tests are drawn when a client who is presently having chemotherapy for leukemia must undergo surgery. Thrombocytopenia (low platelets) can occur with leukemia and chemotherapy. This results in clotting abnormalities, which might lead to hemorrhage. Electrolytes (option b) are drawn for older clients and those with a history of cardiac, renal or fluid balance problems. Blood urea nitrogen (BUN) (option c) may be checked in clients with renal disease, proteinuria or clients undergoing urologic procedures. Blood glucose (option d) may be drawn in clients with a history of diabetes mellitus or hypoglycemia.
Nursing Process: Planning   **Client Need:** Physiological Integrity

13.   **The correct answer is d.** The question is asking how to reply to the client's statement that she is a burden. In option (d), the nurse addresses the client's difficulty in relating her problem to the nurse and assists her in discussing her feelings of being a burden. The fact that the client was admitted for suicidal ideation and believes she is a burden means she needs to be further assessed immediately. Option (a) avoids the issue and allows the client to continue withdrawing, since depressed clients rarely request help. Option (b) is belittling the client's feelings and sense of self-worth. Option (c) is an incorrect interpretation of the client's comment by the nurse.
Nursing Process: Implementation   **Client Need:** Psychosocial Integrity

14. **The correct answer is b.** The question is asking for the symptoms of diabetes insipidus. Diabetes insipidus occurs when the pituitary gland does not secrete vasopressin, also known as antidiuretic hormone (ADH). It causes extreme thirst and polyuria. The urine is extremely dilute with a specific gravity of 1.001 to 1.005. To test for diabetes insipidus, fluids are withheld for 8 to 12 hours. The client with diabetes insipidus will have weight loss, excrete large volumes of urine, show decreased specific gravity (option c), have increased serum osmolality (option d), hypernatremia and decreased urine osmolality. Glucosuria (option a), proteinuria (option c) and polyphagia (option d) are symptoms of diabetes mellitus, not diabetes insipidus.
Nursing Process: Analysis   **Client Need:** Physiological Integrity

15. **The correct answer is c.** The question is asking what is normal for a woman one day postpartum. The uterine muscle must be firm (option a) if involuting and closing the maternal placental site sinuses is to take place. If the uterus is dextroverted (option b), the urinary bladder may be distended. The uterus involutes approximately one finger's breadth (1cm) per day in puerperium until it once again becomes a pelvic organ. Therefore, on postpartal day one, the nurse could expect to palpate the fundus at one finger's breadth below the umbilicus (option d).
Nursing Process: Evaluation   **Client Need:** Health Promotion & Maintenance

16. **The correct answer is a.** The question is asking the priority nursing action in caring for a client with peritoneal dialysis. The most common complication of peritoneal dialysis is peritonitis, and one of the primary causes of death in acute renal failure is sepsis. While accurate intake and output (option b), maintenance of nutrition (option c), and teaching needs of the client (option d) are important, problems relating to these areas are more easily dealt with than is infection.
Nursing Process: Analysis   **Client Need:** Safe, Effective Care Environment

17. **The correct answer is c.** The question is asking how to clean the wound. The goal of wound cleansing is to rid the wound of debris and bacteria so that the area does not become infected but heals properly. The wound area can be gently irrigated with saline, thus protecting the area without disturbing newly formed and healthy granulating tissue. Although some topical antiseptics may be used on occasion, often they do more harm to the cells and are only used to combat infected wounds (option a). Gel wafers may be used as a dressing for stage I and II ulcers once they are cleaned (option b). Topical enzymes are used for chemical debridement of a wound (option d).
Nursing Process: Analysis   **Client Need:** Physiological Integrity

18. **The correct answer is c.** The question is asking you to analyze the nursing problems of a client with a medical diagnosis of congestive heart failure and pulmonary edema. For this client, activity intolerance would be related to decreased energy or fatigue resulting from the inability of the heart to function effectively as a pump. For such a client, alteration in cardiac output would occur but would be decreased (option a). Edema would be related to left ventricular failure and would manifest itself as a fluid volume excess (option b). Option (d) would be an appropriate nursing diagnosis for a client with associated medical diagnoses that proclude pain, such as pleurisy, pneumonia, pulmonary embolus or pneumothorax.
Nursing Process: Planning   **Client Need:** Physiological Integrity

19. **The correct answer is d.** The question is asking how to plan preoperative teaching for a client about to undergo a mastectomy. Think about teaching-learning principles, especially readiness to learn. Following the diagnosis of cancer, it is not unusual for the client to exhibit anxiety and fear related to the treatment. It must be remembered that such behaviors influence the readiness of the client to learn. Before any content is addressed in preoperative teaching (options a, b & c), attempts to alleviate anxiety and fear must be initiated.
Nursing Process: Planning   **Client Need:** Safe, Effective Care Environment

20. **The correct answer is d.** The question is asking what to do when a client is having a seizure. The initial responsibility of the nurse is to move furniture to protect the client from injury. Attempting to restrain limbs or to insert anything between the teeth may cause more injury than

good, although in the past these were recognized interventions (options a & b). Oxygen might be administered if available, but this would not be the initial action (option c).
Nursing Process: Implementation   **Client Need:** Safe, Effective Care Environment

21.   **The correct answer is d.** The question is asking what causes the blood vessels in the breast to get smaller. Anxiety and tension inhibit the letdown reflex, which diminishes milk secretion. Prolactin, oxytocin and sleep benefit breastfeeding (options a, b & c).
Nursing Process: Planning   **Client Need:** Health Promotion & Maintenance

22.   **The correct answer is b.** The question is asking which client should be seen first. High-pitched inspiration with a weak cough is indicative of partial airway obstruction, which needs attention. If the client is coughing forcefully, the person should be monitored to make sure the obstruction is expelled. A client with a strong cough and expectorating mucus (option c) is not in danger of airway problems. Although cardiac problems (options a & d) are serious, airway problems take priority.
Nursing Process: Analysis   **Client Need:** Safe, Effective Care Environment

23.   **The correct answer is a.** The question is asking which is the correct way to use standard precautions when caring for a client. Gloves are required when emptying a bedpan, whether there is visible blood in nasal secretions, sputum, urine, feces, saliva, sweat, tears, vomitus or not. The gloves used in client care are not tough enough to withstand repeated or heavy use because they may weaken, tear or develop tiny holes (option b). Performing a finger stick blood glucose does not require the use of sterile gloves (option c). Performing vital signs on a client receiving blood does not require the use of latex gloves (option d). Gloves and goggles are necessary for protection when there is danger from being sprayed or splattered with blood or mucus and are not necessary when checking vital signs.
Nursing Process: Analysis   **Client Need:** Safe, Effective Care Environment

24.   **The correct answer is b.** The question is asking what precautions would prevent cytomegalovirus (CMV) transmission. Although CMV will cause mild symptoms in a healthy adult, it can lead to severe teratogenic effects in a developing fetus. Therefore, it is not advisable to assign pregnant nurses to care for CMV-infected clients. Reverse isolation is utilized to protect a client from further neutropenia, not prevent transmission (option a). Gloves should be worn with all infected clients, however, masks are not indicated and gowns are only indicated if soiling is highly likely (option c). Penicillin G is not indicated in the treatment of a virus (option d).
Nursing Process: Planning   **Client Need:** Safe, Effective Care Environment

25.   **The correct answer is b.** The question is asking when a client is having autonomic dysreflexia. The lesion is at C_7, leaving the sympathetic nervous system without higher cortical control. A stimulus initiates a systemic sympathetic response causing severe vasoconstriction and severe hypertension (option a). The baroreceptors in the carotid sinus and aortic arch sense the hypertension and stimulate the parasympathetic system via the vagus nerve. The heart rate decreases and sweating occurs, but the sympathetic stimulation is not altered because of the lesion (options c & d).
Nursing Process: Assessment   **Client Need:** Physiological Integrity

26.   **The correct answer is b.** The question is asking how to care for a client who has a chest wound from a gunshot. Sucking chest wounds are common in gunshot victims. When listening over the wound, a sucking sound is present as the client breathes. Gauze dressings allow air to seep in and out from the chest. An occlusive gauze dressing should be used (option a). Gunshot wounds are more serious than stab wounds, because gunshot wounds cause more rapid blood loss and severe lacerations, thereby compromising the client's respiratory status more quickly (option c). A fully oriented gunshot victim may rapidly become disoriented or unconscious from sudden respiratory deterioration (option d).
Nursing Process: Analysis   **Client Need:** Physiological Integrity

27. **The correct answer is d.** The question is asking what to do when an unconscious client snores. Snoring in an unconscious client often indicates airway obstruction and action should be taken immediately to correct this by neck hyperextension, jaw thrust or insertion of an oral airway. The other options (a, b & c) do not take immediate action to correct this airway problem and, therefore, are unsafe.
Nursing Process: Implementation **Client Need:** Physiological Integrity

28. **The correct answer is a.** The question is asking the action of nitrates. The action of nitrates is to dilate both veins and arteries to increase blood flow to the heart, thereby decreasing the incidence of angina. Option (b) is the action of digitalis preparations, which increase cardiac output by enhancing the force of the contraction of the ventricles. It is the drug of choice for congestive heart failure and atrial fibrillation. Option (c) is the action of calcium channel blockers, which are usually used to treat angina prophylactically. Option (d) is the action of cardiac stimulators such as atropine used to accelerate the heart rate.
Nursing Process: Analysis **Client Need:** Physiological Integrity

29. **The correct answer is d.** The question is asking for the best evaluation criteria related to pain relief. If the morphine sulfate (Morphine) is effective, the decrease in surgical pain will allow the client to ambulate early and with minimal assistance. A change in the client's vital signs (option a) may indicate a circulatory or respiratory complication from the opiate analgesic. On the standardized pain scale, one (1) is minimal and ten (10) is severe. An eight (8) on the pain scale indicates that the drug is ineffective (option b). One side effect of opiate analgesics is urinary retention (option c). The total urine output (300ml) is not indicative of a problem by itself.
Nursing Process: Evaluation **Client Need:** Safe, Effective Care Environment

30. **The correct answer is b.** The question is asking which symptom relates to ectopic pregnancy. Shoulder pain is caused by irritation of the diaphragmatic phrenic nerve when intraperitoneal blood is dispersed through the abdomen. Increased temperature is a sign of infection, such as appendicitis (option a). The incidence of pregnancy-induced hypertension is increased in hydatiform mole pregnancy (option c). Vaginal bleeding may occur, but can occur with other disorders as well, such as spontaneous abortion (option d).
Nursing Process: Assessment **Client Need:** Physiological Integrity

31. **The correct answer is c.** The question is asking what is a symptom of myasthenia gravis. Muscles of the face, neck and respiratory system are most affected. Two of the earliest signs of myasthenia gravis are diplopia (double vision) and ptosis (drooping eyelids). Muscle wasting (option a) does not generally occur. There should be no real neural deficit. There is no sensory loss; reflexes are normal and muscle atrophy is rare. The cells affected originate in the brainstem. Although muscle fatigue is progressive, improvement occurs after rest (option b). Memory cells remain unaffected (option d). Motor cells are usually affected.
Nursing Process: Assessment **Client Need:** Physiological Integrity

32. **The correct answer is d.** The question is asking what would be a short-term goal for a client who has difficulty perceiving reality and relating to others. A short-term goal is one, which can be accomplished in a shorter period of time than the others and should pertain to the client's problems. Relating to two other people deals with gaining relationships with people other than the nurse and also is shorter term. The other options; not suspicious of others, stays out of his room during the day and leads group activities on the unit (a, b & c) are unrealistic short-term goals.
Nursing Process: Evaluation **Client Need:** Psychosocial Integrity

33. **The correct answer is c.** The question is asking which option shows a problem that should be addressed. Cloudy urine is a sign of a possible urinary tract infection. The physician should be notified and a urine culture should be obtained so antibiotics can be started. The intravenous bag has enough solution hanging through the shift report (option a). A chamber should be bubbling if the suction to the chest tube is properly attached (option b). The client should be able to move while restrained, (option d) but should not be able to crawl out of bed.

34.   **The correct answer is a.** The question is asking for the discharge teaching for a client with a corneal abrasion. An abrasion to the cornea will cause the corneal epithelium to become compromised. Corneal epithelium is a barrier to microorganisms. The eye should be inspected daily for signs of infection. Patches (option b) are necessary for immobilization of the eyelids and promote comfort and healing. Ice compresses (option c) are used after enucleation surgery to control swelling, but is not necessary here. The ice may cause pressure and more problems. Bending the head below the waist (option d) is contraindicated after cataract surgery because it increases intraocular pressure. This does not affect corneal abrasions.
Nursing Process: Implementation   **Client Need:** Physiological Integrity

35.   **The correct answer is c.** The question is asking which enema is correct for a child with Hirschprung's disease. Because children with aganglionic disease do not have bowel movements, it is necessary for parents to administer daily enemas. It is important that the fluid used be normal saline and not hypotonic solutions like tap water since normal saline solutions are similar to the body's normal fluids (options a, b & d). Hypotonic solutions have led to the death of infants from cardiac congestion or cerebral edema (water intoxication).
Nursing Process: Evaluation   **Client Need:** Safe, Effective Care Environment

36.   **The correct answer is 31.** The question is asking the rate of the IV. The correct amount is 31 drops per minute.
First determine hourly rate:
$$\frac{1,000ml}{8\ hr} = \frac{125ml}{1\ hr}$$

Then determine the drop rate:
$$\frac{hourly\ rate \times drop\ factor}{60\ min} = \frac{125 \times 15}{60} = \frac{1,875}{60} = 31$$
Nursing Process: Planning   **Client Need:** Physiological Integrity

37.   **The correct answer is d.** The question is asking what the test means. Skin testing detects individuals who may be exposed and sensitized to the disease but not necessarily diseased. Skin testing is not a positive diagnostic technique, but should be substantiated with chest X-ray and sputum tests (option a). The positive skin test does not indicate active tuberculosis, but that the individual was exposed (option b). An induration of 10mm or greater indicates a significant Mantoux test result (option c).
Nursing Process: Implementation   **Client Need:** Health Promotion & Maintenance

38.   **The correct answer is b.** The question is asking the priority plan for a client with a leakage of cerebrospinal fluid through the nose. The presence of cerebrospinal fluid rhinorrhea indicates that there is a direct route from the "outside" into the intracranial cavity. The potential for infection exists because of this route. There is not more risk of increased intracranial pressure (option a) than would be normally. The small loss of cerebrospinal fluid and blood (options c & d) will continue until the tear in the meninges is corrected or healed. This does not pose as great a threat to the client as does intracranial infection.
Nursing Process: Planning   **Client Need:** Physiological Integrity

39.   **The correct answer is c.** The question is asking the nurse to respond to the client's psychological question of "why me?" This response shares the perception that the client believes having sickle cell is unfair. Option (a) does identify the feeling but goes on to give advice ("you should...") rather than collaboration. Option (b) does not respond to the client's need. Option (d) is a factual answer, which does not respond to the client's need and there are also no assessment data to indicate that the sickle cell crisis occurred in response to a stressor.
Nursing Process: Implementation   **Client Need:** Psychosocial Integrity

40. **The correct answer is b.** The question is asking what would be a potential problem for a mother who just delivered twin infants by cesarean section. The primary goal for the postoperative client following cesarean section is to monitor for signs and symptoms of postpartal hemorrhage. The remaining options (a, c & d) are correct, but not the chief factor during this immediate period. Monitoring the client's physical status is the most important goal.
Nursing Process: Planning   **Client Need:** Physiological Integrity

41. **The correct answer is d.** The question is asking which would be an activity in which an autistic child would engage. Children with autism prefer non-colorful, mechanistic, self-stimulating, repetitive activities such as rocking. Coloring in a book (option a) would not be usual activities for an autistic child. Playing with a toy soldier and finger painting on an easel (options b & c) also require more creative play not usually seen in autism.
Nursing Process: Assessment   **Client Need:** Psychosocial Integrity

42. **The correct answer is d.** The question is asking which symptom would indicate that the client might have an intestinal obstruction. The cardinal signs of intestinal obstruction include bloody mucus, colicky crampy pain, vomiting, distension and constipation with absence of stool and flatus (options a, b & c).
Nursing Process: Assessment   **Client Need:** Physiological Integrity

43. **The correct answer is b.** The question is asking why the newborn infant is yellow with jaundice or what is the cause of the jaundice in a 3-day-old infant. Physiological jaundice in newborns is related to an increased production of bilirubin and an immature liver. The jaundice is not due to liver damage, however, liver damage can occur if the condition remains untreated (option a). The jaundice is due to increased (not decreased) bilirubin. Immature red blood cells or fetal hemoglobin is normal for a newborn (option c). Newborn jaundice is unrelated to inborn errors of metabolism (option d).
Nursing Process: Implementation   **Client Need:** Health Promotion & Maintenance

44. **The correct answer is b.** The question is asking about interventions for a client with a detached retina. All of the options assist with client safety precautions, however approaching the client from the <u>unaffected</u> side, so that they can clearly see without a lot of head movement is important. The nurse would not question about keeping the bed in the low position and the side rails up on the affected side, as this is a safety measure taken for those with detached retinas (option a). One would not question about instructing the client to wear an eye shield at night or when taking a nap for two weeks after surgery, as this is an action taken with clients who have experienced detached retinas to protect the area from harm (option c). The nurse would not question about instructing the client not to cough, sneeze or vomit, as the goal is to limit pressure in the area of the retinal detachment so that further damage does not occur (option d).
Nursing Process: Evaluation   **Client Need:** Safe, Effective Care Environment

45. **The correct answer is c.** The question is asking what causes acute renal failure. Hemorrhage would cause a decrease in renal blood flow leading to decreased glomerular filtration, renal ischemia and tubular damage. Diabetes mellitus (option a) is a common cause of chronic renal failure but there is no evidence to suggest the client has the disease. An increased blood urea nitrogen (BUN) (option b) and hypertension (option d) are symptoms of renal failure, not causes of it.
Nursing Process: Analysis   **Client Need:** Physiological Integrity

Instructions: Allow yourself 60 minutes to complete the following 60 practice questions. Use a timer to notify yourself when 60 minutes are over so that you are not constantly looking at your watch while completing the questions.

1.   A client who recently had a myocardial infarction is prescribed morphine sulfate (Morphine) 2mg IV every 20 minutes as needed up to 10mg for pain. When the client complains of chest pain, the nurse should:
    a.   administer the medication and monitor blood pressure and respirations.
    b.   withhold the medication.
    c.   call the physician to clarify the prescription.
    d.   explain to the client that more medication can be given if needed.

2.   A postpartal client asks the nurse when she and her husband can resume sexual relations. The nurse responds that:
    a.   "You will not feel like having sexual relations until you have discontinued breastfeeding."
    b.   "Most couples wait six months to resume sexual activity."
    c.   "In about three to four weeks when the bleeding has stopped, if your episiotomy is not painful, you can start sexual activity."
    d.   "You can safely have sexual relations as soon as you like."

3.   A client undergoing allergy testing is required to receive several intradermal injections. What would the nurse plan to do?
    a.   Insert the needle at a 45-degree angle.
    b.   Massage the site following the injection.
    c.   Insert the needle through the dermis.
    d.   Withdraw the needle after a wheal appears.

4.   The nurse is assigned to care for a client who had a renal transplant three days ago. The client is prescribed hydralazine (Apresoline) for a systolic blood pressure greater than 140. The aide reports that the blood pressure is 148/96 and the client is medicated as prescribed. The nurse's next action should be to:
    a.   tell the aide to recheck the blood pressure within the next hour.
    b.   recheck the blood pressure personally in twenty minutes.
    c.   tell the aide to recheck the blood pressure in 30 minutes and report the results.
    d.   call the physician and report that the client's blood pressure is elevated.

5.   A renal function test is prescribed for a cardiac client. The client tells the nurse, "I have to save my urine for 24 hours for some test, but I forgot the name of it." Based on the 24-hour urine collection, which test was probably prescribed by the physician?
    a.   Renal concentration.
    b.   Creatinine clearance.
    c.   Serum creatinine.
    d.   Urea clearance.

6.   During a cardiac arrest a client is given lidocaine (Xylocaine). The nurse would expect to see which outcome?
    a.   Decreased hypoxemia.
    b.   Decreased ventricular dysrhythmia.
    c.   Corrected metabolic acidosis.
    d.   Increased myocardial contractions.

7. A client was admitted to the psychiatric unit with weight loss, crying, absence from work and profound sadness. The client and nurse walk together to the day room and the client sits down, lowers her head and covers her eyes. The nurse would document this behavior as indicative of:
   a. withdrawal.
   b. grieving.
   c. delusions.
   d. agitation.

8. A client is brought to the clinic from an area summer camp. The camp referral sheet states the client may have pediculosis. After the diagnosis is confirmed, what would the nurse expect the physician to prescribe?
   a. Apply corticosteroids to the affected area.
   b. Teach the client to take the full course of doxycycline (Vibamycin).
   c. Wash the hair thoroughly with lindane (Kwell).
   d. Inspect between the fingers and toes for burrows.

9. A nurse is assessing the fundus of a woman who delivered a baby one hour ago. The nurse would expect the fundus to be firm and:
   a. located below the symphysis pubis.
   b. midline and at the level of the umbilicus.
   c. deviated to the left side and above the umbilicus.
   d. deviated to the right side and above the umbilicus.

10. A woman has been experiencing auditory hallucinations and is brought to the hospital by her husband. She tells the nurse, "They don't like me." The nurse's best response would be:
    a. "Do you mean the voices?"
    b. "I like you and want to help you."
    c. "Who are 'they'?"
    d. "What makes you think that?"

11. The nurse is assessing a client diagnosed with a carpal tunnel syndrome. Expected findings would include:
    a. pain radiating down the dorsal surface of the forearm.
    b. aching pain from a round, firm, cystic swelling near the wrist.
    c. pain, numbness and paresthesia along the thumb, first and second fingers.
    d. numbness, tingling and white or blue skin color of the fingers.

12. As the nurse begins teaching regarding a bronchoscopy, the client interrupts and says, "Oh, you must have the wrong person, there's nothing wrong with my lung." The nurse knows that the physician talked with the client about the test this morning. The best reply of the nurse would be:
    a. "Maybe you're right. I'll check your chart."
    b. "Remember what the physician told you this morning."
    c. "Tell me more about the problem that brought you to the hospital."
    d. "What did the physician say this morning when you spoke?"

13. A client is prescribed a computed tomography (CT) of the brain with contrast. Following administration of the contrast, the nurse should observe for which side effects?
    a. Flushed face and complaint of a salty taste in the mouth.
    b. Warmth at injection site and bradycardia.
    c. Nausea and hypotension.
    d. Blurred vision and hand tremors.

14. A hurricane has hit a local community and victims are brought to the emergency department. Each inpatient unit is required to send a nurse to help triage and care for these clients. Which nurse should be sent? A nurse with a (n):
    a. bachelor's degree, two years of experience, who is caring for clients with an abdominal aneurysm, pelvic inflammatory disease and an appendectomy.
    b. associate degree, four years of experience, who is caring for clients with gallstones, a two-day postoperative below-the-knee amputation due to complications of diabetes and systemic lupus erythematosus.
    c. associate degree, 10 years of experience, who is caring for clients with a basilar skull fracture, a new postoperative thyroidectomy and cellulitis of the lower leg.
    d. bachelor's degree, 15 years of critical care experience, who is caring for clients with a pericardial drain for treatment of a cardiac tamponade, compartment syndrome following a radial fracture and terminal lung cancer.

15. A client is admitted for chronic renal failure. Blood work is prescribed to check for anemia. This client is predisposed to anemia due to:
    a. the kidney's inability to excrete potassium.
    b. defective hemoglobin molecules.
    c. the loss of blood during dialysis.
    d. a deficiency of erythropoietin.

16. An elderly client with Cushing's syndrome had a bilateral adrenalectomy. In evaluating the effectiveness of the steroid replacement therapy, the nurse should consider which assessment finding to be most important?
    a. Intact skin and mucous membranes.
    b. A 5 lb (2.3 kg) weight gain.
    c. An increased activity level.
    d. The client has eaten 75% of the meal.

17. A nurse is performing a physical examination on a client admitted with severe hypothyroidism. The correct method of palpating the thyroid gland would be to:
    a. ask the client to tighten the neck muscles to protect the gland.
    b. instruct the client to keep the chin up for unobstructed access.
    c. feel for the isthmus after asking the client to swallow.
    d. watch for the butterfly outline as the client swallows.

18. The nurse is caring for a client following an orchiectomy for stage I testicular cancer. In addition to pain medication, what would be most helpful for relieving pain?
    a. Application of ice packs.
    b. Avoiding scrotal support devices.
    c. Diversional techniques.
    d. Intermittent massage of the lower abdomen.

19. On the first postoperative day, which behavior should alert the nurse to the need for reinforcing the postoperative instructions? The client:
    a. splints the incision when coughing.
    b. is receiving pain medication every three to four hours.
    c. is turning over in bed every two hours.
    d. is using the incentive spirometer once every hour.

20. A client is being discharged from the same day surgical care unit after a hernia repair. Which client behavior would indicate to the nurse that the client understands the discharge instructions? The client:
   a. calls his daughter to pick him up from the hospital.
   b. signs the discharge instruction sheet.
   c. lifts his 5-year-old grandson.
   d. suggests that his daughter wait to fill the prescriptions.

21. During a prenatal wellness group discussion, the nurse encourages the members to stop smoking because it is associated with:
   a. cardiac anomalies in the fetus.
   b. low birth weight infants.
   c. longer labors.
   d. Down's syndrome.

22. A client is seen in the clinic and diagnosed with bacterial conjuctivitis. What would the nurse teach the client? Select all that apply.
   a. The symptoms should last for approximately one week.
   b. You should wear a patch over the affected eye.
   c. Wash your face with warm water only. Avoid using soap.
   d. You should expect the discharge to be yellow and decrease over time.
   e. A cool compress can be used to decrease the pain.
   f. Wear sunglasses when going outside.

23. A nurse from the pediatric ICU has been assigned to your medical-surgical ICU due to staffing shortages. Which client should she be assigned?
   a. A 50-year-old client with acute renal failure.
   b. A 45-year-old client with an acute myocardial infarction.
   c. A 35-year-old client in diabetic ketoacidosis.
   d. A 25-year-old client with a CVA.

24. A diabetic woman in the second trimester of pregnancy comes into the obstetrics clinic for a check-up. The nurse becomes very concerned when the client reports which symptom?
   a. Slight shortness of breath.
   b. Heartburn.
   c. Swelling of her face.
   d. Epistaxis.

25. The charge nurse is reviewing laboratory results for the unit. One client's chart shows a positive antibody test for acquired immunodeficiency syndrome (AIDS). The nurse analyzes this result to mean that:
   a. AIDS will probably be present in this client within the next year.
   b. the client has AIDS.
   c. antibodies to the AIDS virus are in the client's blood.
   d. the client has been infected with the AIDS virus but has not produced antibodies.

26. A client is required to go to an Alcoholics Anonymous (AA) meeting every day while in the rehabilitation program. Which client statement demonstrates knowledge of the principles about AA?
   a. "AA is part of the treatment; I will need to attend at least one meeting every month."
   b. "AA isn't for everyone."
   c. "The AA meetings help me to cope with and understand my past."
   d. "AA is going to help me stay sober."

27. A client with kidney stones complains of sharp pain in the left groin radiating into the scrotum. The nurse teaches the client and family that this type of kidney stone pain results from:
   a. ureteral lacerations.
   b. muscle spasms in the ureter.
   c. damage to the nephron.
   d. inflammatory response in the bladder.

28. A 5-month-old infant, 5.4 kg (11 lbs 14.5 oz), is diagnosed with nonorganic failure to thrive (NFTT). The nurse knows that this diagnosis is given to a child who:
   a. has a malabsorption problem causing weight loss.
   b. may be malnourished because of poor maternal attachment.
   c. is below the tenth percentile for height and weight on a standard growth chart.
   d. will eat only when the mother feeds her.

29. In postoperative clients with Cushing's syndrome, the nurse must take appropriate precautions to deal with which possible complication?
   a. Hyperglycemia.
   b. Hyperkalemia.
   c. Hypocalcemia.
   d. Hyponatremia.

30. A client with Parkinson's disease has been losing weight over the past two weeks. The client complains of increased difficulty in swallowing. The visiting nurse would suggest:
   a. fluids like juices and soups.
   b. a thick liquid diet.
   c. weighing the client weekly.
   d. maintaining a calorie count.

31. Following a craniotomy for an astrocytoma, a client is prescribed phenytoin (Dilantin) 100mg IV QID. To safely administer this drug, the nurse should:
   a. dilute the medication in 5% dextrose in water.
   b. administer at a rate no faster than 50mg per minute.
   c. administer by direct intravenous push.
   d. hold it if the client develops tonic-clonic seizures.

32. The nurse is doing discharge teaching with a client recovering from hepatitis A. What would be stressed to limit infection to family members?
   a. Eat all meals at home where care of food preparation can be assured.
   b. Stress good personal hygiene habits among all the family members.
   c. Serve only commercially bottled water for drinking purposes.
   d. Have all the family members undergo serologic screening.

33. A nurse is working with a client addicted to alcohol. The client states, "The reason I drink is because of my husband." The most therapeutic response by the nurse would be:
   a. "I find that hard to believe, your husband seems so nice."
   b. "Tell me more about your husband."
   c. "Let's talk about your husband's behavior."
   d. "Let's talk about your drinking."

34. Which is the best indication that the nurse has implemented nursing interventions to prevent paralytic ileus in a client who has undergone major abdominal surgery?
   a. On the first postoperative day, the client is taking pain medication every four hours.
   b. Two days after surgery, the client is ambulating in the halls.
   c. Three days after surgery, the client is taking and retaining clear liquids.
   d. On the fourth postoperative day, the abdomen is firm and distended.

35. The rehabilitation nurse is assigned a newly admitted client. As part of the assessment, the nurse should look for the client's present capacity for:
a. taking direction from the rehabilitation team.
b. reaching pre-injury status.
c. primary prevention of problems.
d. self-management and decision-making about care.

36. An 8-year-old child is admitted to the hospital and expected to have surgery early the next morning. How would the nurse expect this child to behave?
a. Acting scared when his roommate is there.
b. Ignoring that he will have the surgery.
c. Asking questions about what will happen.
d. Hiding under the bed.

37. A nurse is assessing a child with cystic fibrosis. The nurse would expect to find clinical manifestations caused by:
a. atrophic changes in the mucosal wall of the intestine.
b. hypoactivity of the autonomic nervous system.
c. mechanical obstruction of mucous gland secretions.
d. hyperactivity of sweat glands.

38. A nurse is teaching a group of clients about ranitidine (Zantac). The nurse would teach the clients that ranitidine (Zantac) works by:
a. blocking the production of acid in the stomach.
b. forming a coating of mucus over the stomach.
c. neutralizing the stomach acid.
d. causing mild sedation.

39. A client is about to be discharged with severe burns of the chest and arms. What should be included in the discharge-teaching plan?
a. Refrain from using lotions on the skin following a bath.
b. Report any new blisters to the physician.
c. Wear the pressurized garments continually.
d. Attempt to keep the arms in a dependent position as often as possible.

40. A client with hypokalemia is selecting foods. What group of foods would be best?
a. Bananas, oatmeal, chocolate.
b. Ginger ale, celery, shellfish.
c. Oranges, tomatoes, apricots.
d. Bananas, whole milk, potatoes.

41. A client is scheduled to have electrical physiological studies (EP). The nurse evaluates that the client has adequate understanding of the test when which statement is made?
a. "A catheter will be placed into my heart in an attempt to initiate dysrhythmias in a controlled environment."
b. "A catheter will be introduced into my heart and dye will be injected allowing visualization of the chambers."
c. "An internal cardiac defibrillator will be placed into my heart to counteract dysrhythmias."
d. "A monitor will be placed on my heart and hooked up with electrodes for a 24-hour period."

42. The nurse accompanies a new mother to the neonatal intensive care unit to visit her preterm baby. When the woman sees the baby she cries, "Oh, she's so small. I'll never be able to take care of her." The most appropriate reply by the nurse would be:
   a.   "Don't worry, your baby will grow."
   b.   "We can talk about how to take care of her."
   c.   "She's small because of the lung problems."
   d.   "How do you feel about the baby being small?"

43. Every time the nurse comes into a 29-year-old male client's room, the client makes a flirtatious remark or tries to grab the nurse. The nurse's response is based on the understanding that the client's behavior is an example of:
   a.   manipulation by guilt induction.
   b.   poor judgment.
   c.   sexual acting out.
   d.   sexual regression.

44. A nurse is making a home visit to a family with a child receiving chemotherapy for leukemia. What statement would indicate that the family is coping well with the child's illness?
   a.   "The other children are complaining that the sick child gets all the attention."
   b.   "Everything is just fine."
   c.   "We're doing everything so our child doesn't get sick again."
   d.   "Our child has improved since she has been home and it's nice to be a family again."

45. Which client statement is the best indication that the preoperative teaching about the patient controlled analgesia (PCA) infusion pump has been effective?
   a.   "I can't overdose on this machine."
   b.   "Clients usually use more medicine with the PCA pump than if they have to ask the nurse for it."
   c.   "I can get medication whenever I want it."
   d.   "I have to make sure to deep breathe and cough, since this method of pain control causes more sedation."

46. A client received a kidney transplant three days ago and is complaining of chills. The nurse notes: temperature 39.8°C (103.7°F), pulse 96, respirations 32, and blood pressure 126/84. The client's leukocyte count is 10,600/mm³. The client is receiving 500mg of cyclosporin (Sandimmune) p.o. BID. What would the nurse suspect?
   a.   Cyclosporin (Sandimmune) toxicity.
   b.   Septicemia.
   c.   Acute rejection.
   d.   Hemorrhage of the renal artery.

47. A client is receiving total parenteral nutrition (TPN). The nurse knows that this client is at increased risk for sepsis. This can be prevented by:
   a.   refrigerating the solution until two hours prior to administration.
   b.   changing the filter every 75 hours.
   c.   changing the dressing at the insertion site once each shift.
   d.   culturing the site, solution and tubing if infection is suspected.

48. A 24-year-old client is admitted to the hospital with a fractured femur sustained in an automobile accident. Twelve hours later, the client complains of a headache and is very restless. Further assessment yields difficulty following conversation, blood pressure 90/60, pulse 144 and respirations 32. The nurse would suspect what has developed?
   a.   Osteomyelitis.
   b.   Fat embolism.
   c.   Thromboembolism.
   d.   Delirium tremens.

49. A 6-year-old boy was diagnosed with a concussion after falling off his bicycle. He was not wearing a helmet. Which instruction should be given to the parents for the first 24 hours of home care?
   a. Do not permit the child to sleep.
   b. Give the child liquids only.
   c. Awaken the child every one to two hours.
   d. Do not give acetaminophen (Tylenol).

50. A client with a fractured hip is placed in traction while awaiting surgery. The nurse should plan to check the traction several times per day to ensure that the:
   a. unaffected foot is braced firmly against the bed.
   b. suspended weight is steadied against the bed frame.
   c. traction rope is free from the weight of the bed linen.
   d. rope knots are secured to the bed frame.

51. A client is admitted to the medical unit with rash and fever of unknown origin. The client has a dressing on the right buttock. The client stated that the home visiting skin care nurse told him not to remove the bandage until tomorrow. The client prefers that the nurse not touch it until then. The nurse should:
   a. let it alone and assess it in the morning.
   b. take off the dressing and assess it now.
   c. document the client's noncompliance.
   d. call the physician and ask for a prescription.

52. After an examination, the physician informs a woman that she is 10 weeks pregnant. The client has a history of Type 1 diabetes. She asks the nurse, "How should I regulate my sugar during my pregnancy?" The nurse responds:
   a. "It is important to try to maintain euglycemia during your pregnancy."
   b. "Hyperglycemia is the normal state during the last trimester of pregnancy to protect fetal brain cells."
   c. "It is important to maintain a hypoglycemic state to prevent macrosomia."
   d. "Ketosis is the normal state during pregnancy to allow balance between maternal and fetal catabolism."

53. While triaging an emergency department client with a lower leg cast, the nurse notes that the client has numbness, tingling, and burning in the toes of the affected foot. These are signs of which potential complication related to the cast?
   a. Disuse syndrome.
   b. Pressure ulcer.
   c. Peroneal nerve injury.
   d. Volkmann's contracture.

54. A nurse is working with a depressed client to decrease constant self-devaluation. To accomplish this the nurse should:
   a. engage the client in activities to distract from the thinking pattern.
   b. encourage the client to express positive thoughts.
   c. restrict the client to his room until the content of the conversation changes.
   d. teach relaxation techniques in an effort to change the feelings.

55. A client with spina bifida is placed on an intermittent catheterization schedule of every six hours. The client would need to change this schedule if which outcome occurred?
   a. Urine output of 800ml for two catheterizations in succession.
   b. Urine output of 450ml for two catheterizations in succession.
   c. Development of a urinary tract infection.
   d. Presence of cloudy urine with sediment.

56. A client was admitted with a cerebral vascular accident over two days ago. Her condition has stabilized. Strategies to prevent physical deformities and promote maximum restoration of function can best be accomplished through:
    a. providing passive and active range-of-motion while monitoring vital signs every two hours, observing for increased temperature, decreased pulse and respirations.
    b. meeting with the social worker, family, and physician to discuss arrangements for long-term care, based on the individual client needs, in a facility with a physical therapy department.
    c. working with the client, physical therapist, and physician to achieve the long-term goal of meeting immediate survival needs and preventing further brain damage, based on individual strengths and needs.
    d. working with the client, family, physician and other health care professionals to develop a plan of care, based on individual strengths and requirements.

57. A woman is scheduled to have a mastectomy. The nurse should address which nursing diagnosis when performing preoperative teaching?
    a. Impaired skin integrity.
    b. Activity intolerance.
    c. Altered comfort.
    d. Ineffective breathing pattern.

58. A group of four and five year olds are in a hospital playroom and are pretending they are nurses and doctors. The nurse encourages this behavior because it:
    a. allows expression of autonomy and control.
    b. helps them to think about others.
    c. provides guidelines for adult behavior.
    d. teaches children about stereotypes.

59. A client is brought to the emergency department after being struck by lightning. The client is alert and conscious. An expected finding would be:
    a. entry and exit wounds.
    b. a major fluid shift.
    c. sooty sputum.
    d. jugular vein distension.

60. The nurse would give which discharge instructions to a client with angina?
    a. Plan for regular activity programs, including isometric exercises.
    b. Take prescribed nitroglycerine (Nitrostat) prior to exercise if pain is expected.
    c. Sleep in a cool room to decrease cardiac workload.
    d. Report all episodes of angina to the physician.

STOP. You have now completed Practice Session: 12. Now take a few minutes and correct your answers. Calculate your accuracy rate by dividing the number of questions you completed correctly by the total number of questions you completed (60).

Correct answers ÷ total number of questions completed = accuracy rate.

_____ ÷ _____ = _____

ANSWERS AND RATIONALES
Practice Session 12

1. **The correct answer is a.** The question is asking whether the morphine sulfate (Morphine) prescribed should be questioned. The prescription is within normal limits for a client with chest pain, so the correct answer is to administer the medication while monitoring the client's blood pressure and respiratory rate. Pain causes anxiety and an increase in adrenaline, which increases myocardial oxygen consumption. Therefore, narcotics are administered (options b & c) but can also cause hypotension and lowered respirations and, therefore, must be given cautiously. Morphine sulfate is given intravenously for the quickest onset of action. The client may not ask for medication but the fact that the pain exists indicates a need for the medication (option d).
    Nursing Process: Implementation **Client Need:** Physiological Integrity

2. **The correct answer is c.** The question is asking when a couple can start having sexual relations after the woman has had a baby. Cessation of lochial flow and uterine involution varies from woman to woman, many couples resume sexual activity in three to four weeks if the mother's perineal tissues have adequately healed (options b & d). Sexual response in breastfeeding women is variable (option a). Some women are too fatigued while others notice no difference.
    Nursing Process: Implementation **Client Need:** Health Promotion & Maintenance

3. **The correct answer is d.** The question is asking how to give an intradermal injection. This is the preferred method for giving antigens to test for allergies. The antigen should be injected slowly and the needle left in place until a wheal develops. The needle is inserted with the bevel up at a 1 to 15 degree angle (option a). Massaging the whealed area can cause inaccurate results (option b). The needle is inserted into the epidermis (option c).
    Nursing Process: Implementation **Client Need:** Physiological Integrity

4. **The correct answer is c.** The question is asking what to do after administering a medication where the blood pressure (BP) needs to be monitored. The effects of hydralazine (Apresoline) need to be evaluated. It has already been determined that the aide can perform the task of taking the BP. The question stated that the aide originally took the BP and medication was given based on that report. When delegating tasks, it is necessary to be specific in your directions. Asking the aide to recheck the BP within the next hour is vague and global and does not require the aide to report the results to the nurse so that further action can be taken if necessary (option a). If the nurse personally rechecks the BP, it takes away from other necessary duties. The aide is capable of doing this (option b). The physician does not need to be notified yet. If, after giving the medication, the BP remains elevated, it would then be appropriate to call the physician (option d).
    Nursing Process: Evaluation **Client Need:** Safe, Effective Care Environment

5. **The correct answer is b.** The question is asking what test requires saving the urine for 24 hours. Urine for a creatinine clearance is collected over a 12 or 24-hour period, a 24-hour specimen is preferred. A serum creatinine (option c) may be taken through a blood (serum) sample at some point during the creatinine clearance urine test. A urea clearance (option d) is performed over several hours when the client empties the bladder, drinks two or more glasses of water, waits one hour and voids, then drinks more water and then voids a third time. Readings on the urine urea levels and the blood urea nitrogen (BUN) are taken for comparison. It is not believed to be as useful as the creatinine clearance test. Renal concentration tests, (option a) such as the Fishberg and Addis tests, involve urine collection of only 12 hours when specific gravity is tested.
    Nursing Process: Analysis **Client Need:** Physiological Integrity

6. **The correct answer is b.** The question is asking why lidocaine (Xylocaine) is given to clients in cardiac arrest. Lidocaine (Xylocaine) is given to stop ventricular dysrhythmias and raise the ventricular fibrillation threshold. Oxygen is given to treat hypoxemia (option a). Sodium bicarbonate is given to correct metabolic acidosis (option c). Lanoxin (Digoxin) will enhance the myocardial contractions (option d).
    Nursing Process: Evaluation **Client Need:** Physiological Integrity

7. **The correct answer is a.** The question is asking for analysis of the presenting data. The client's behaviors (lowering head and hiding eyes) are signs of withdrawal. They are corroborated by the symptoms shown prior to admission, that all point to the problem of depression. She has already shown other signs of withdrawal such as staying absent from her workplace. Behavior indicative of grieving (option b) would follow some type of loss which has not been indicated in this case. Delusions (option c) are a type of thought, which are fixed and false, without basis in fact. Since there is nothing in the situation which states any verbal communication is taking place, the nurse would be unable to infer these thought processes are occurring. Clients who are agitated (option d) show increased motor movement, pace and the inability to be still, which is not the case here.
Nursing Process: Analysis   **Client Need:** Health Promotion & Maintenance

8. **The correct answer is c.** The question is asking what is the appropriate treatment for a client with pediculosis or lice. The hair should be washed with lindane (Kwell). This drug produces seizures and death of the louse. Topical corticosteroids are used in the treatment of atopic dematitis (option a). Doxycycline is given to clients who have Lyme disease (option b). Burrows between the fingers and toes are found in clients who have scabies (option d).
Nursing Process: Analysis   **Client Need:** Physiological Integrity

9. **The correct answer is b.** The question is asking where the fundus would be in a woman who delivered a baby one hour ago. The uterine fundus should be easily palpated at the level of the umbilicus and remain firm immediately after delivery. If it is boggy and displaced to either side, this usually indicates bladder distention (options c & d). By the time the uterus has involuted to the level of the symphysis pubis, it cannot be detected by palpation (option a).
Nursing Process: Assessment   **Client Need:** Health Promotion & Maintenance

10. **The correct answer is c.** The question is asking for the best response for someone who is hearing voices. Asking, "who are they?" is a request for clarification. "Do you mean the voices?" requests clarification also but option (c) is a more open response that does not encompass an assumption (option a). The statements "I like you and want to help you." and "What makes you think that."(options b & d) do not ask for clarification. Option (b) does not address the client's comment. Option (d) allows for blame to be placed on an external source.
Nursing Process: Implementation   **Client Need:** Psychosocial Integrity

11. **The correct answer is c.** The question is asking what are the symptoms of carpal tunnel syndrome. Carpal tunnel syndrome occurs when the median nerve at the wrist is compressed causing pain, numbness, and paresthesia along the thumb, first and second fingers. Epicondylitis ("tennis elbow") is damage to the tendons of the medial or lateral, radial and ulnar epicondyles, resulting in pain, which radiates down the dorsal surface of the forearm (option a). A round firm cystic swelling near the wrist is a ganglion, which causes aching pain (option b). Numbness, tingling and color changes of white to blue skin then to red are indicative of Raynaud's phenomenon, which is a vasospasm in the vessels of the fingers (option d).
Nursing Process: Assessment   **Client Need:** Physiological Integrity

12. **The correct answer is d.** The question is asking how to respond to a client who denies she has a problem and is having a bronchoscopy. Option (d) focuses on the teaching-learning principles. The statement gathers information about the client's understanding of the situation and readiness to learn. The statement "Maybe you're right. I'll check the chart" agrees with the client and promotes denial (option a). Even when the nurse comes back and says the test has been prescribed, the client will just become upset since the client denies a problem exists. Option (b); "Remember what the physician told you this morning." confronts the client, which creates increased anxiety and distrust of the nurse. Option (c); "Tell me more about the problem..." is not specific to the immediate problem.
Nursing Process: Implementation   **Client Need:** Physiological Integrity

13. **The correct answer is a.** The question is asking what would be side effects from the contrast medium. Following an injection of iodinated radiopaque contrast, the client may experience a flushed face, salty taste, warmth at the injection site, and nausea. Bradycardia (option b),

hypotension (option c), blurred vision, and hand tremors (option d) are not related to the dye for CT scans.
Nursing Process: Assessment   **Client Need:** Physiological Integrity

14.   **The correct answer is b.** The question is asking which nurse should be sent to the emergency department to help. The nurse in option (b) has enough experience to help triage. This nurse's assignment does not have any critically ill clients and these clients would be easily reassigned. The nurse in option (a) has only two years experience, but more importantly, he is caring for a client with an abdominal aortic aneurysm. This is a potentially unstable client and would be difficult to reassign. Although the nurse in option (c) has much experience, she is also caring for two potentially critical clients. The new postoperative thyroidectomy client needs to be closely monitored for thyroid storm as well as airway obstruction. A client with a basilar skull fracture needs to be monitored for symptoms of increased intracranial pressure and meningitis. The nurse in option (d) also is very experienced, however, the client with a cardiac tamponade is critical and the client with compartment syndrome is potentially unstable. These clients would be difficult to reassign. The level of academic preparation is not relevant to this question.
Nursing Process: Planning   **Client Need:** Safe, Effective Care Environment

15.   **The correct answer is d.** The question is asking why clients with chronic renal failure tend to be anemic. Clients suffering with chronic renal failure do not produce adequate erythropoietin necessary for red blood cell maturation, thus leading to anemia. The inability of the kidneys to excrete potassium (option a) is unrelated to anemia, although it is associated with chronic renal failure. Defective hemoglobin molecules (option b) are not related to dialysis, but are related to clients suffering with sickle cell anemia. Clients undergoing chronic hemodialysis do lose blood (option c) into the dialyzer (artificial kidney); it is not generally the major cause of the anemia.
Nursing Process: Analysis   **Client Need:** Physiological Integrity

16.   **The correct answer is b.** The question is asking what is the most important assessment in an elderly client receiving steroid replacement therapy. The elderly client is more prone to the side effects of steroid replacement therapy. These include potassium and sodium alterations. Water retention also occurs. Intact skin and mucous membranes are achieved through meticulous skin care (option a). An increase in activity level is an expected outcome of the therapy (option c). The client's appetite usually increases with steroid therapy (option d).
Nursing Process: Evaluation   **Client Need:** Health Promotion & Maintenance

17.   **The correct answer is c.** The question is asking how to feel for the thyroid gland of a client who has low thyroid. Most times the thyroid may not be able to be seen or palpated at all (option d). The isthmus (area connecting the two lobes) may be felt as the client swallows. If the gland is enlarged, it should not be palpated at all. Pressing on the gland may release thyroid hormone. The proper procedure is to have the client sit upright. Ask the client to relax the muscles of the neck (option a) and flex the neck slightly forward (option b). As the client swallows, the isthmus can be felt. The right lobe may possibly be palpated as the client swallows again. The left lobe may be felt when displacing the trachea with the right hand.
Nursing Process: Assessment   **Client Need:** Physiological Integrity

18.   **The correct answer is a.** The question is asking which measure will relieve pain most effectively following an orchiectomy. Application of ice helps to reduce swelling and decrease pain. Diversional activities are helpful to control pain (option c), but in this case, ice is more effective. Scrotal supports should be used to elevate the surgical site (option d). Intermittent massage of the lower abdomen will not alleviate inguinal and scrotal pain (option d).
Nursing Process: Implementation   **Client Need:** Physiological Integrity

19.   **The correct answer is d.** The question is asking which postoperative instructions need to be reinforced. In other words, one of the options is incorrect information and three options are correct postoperative instructions. The incentive spirometer (IS) is a device designed to motivate the client to get more air into the lungs. The client is using the IS incorrectly. The IS should be used approximately 10 times every hour. The client is following postoperative instructions by

splinting the incision (option a), asking for pain medication when needed (option b) and turning every two hours (option c).
Nursing Process: Evaluation   **Client Need:** Safe, Effective Care Environment

20.   **The correct answer is a.** The question is asking what statement by the client would indicate that he understood the discharge instructions appropriate for a hernia repair. The client demonstrates that he understands the instruction to avoid strenuous activities such as driving. Signing the discharge instruction sheet (option b) does not ensure that the client has understood the instructions and will follow them. Lifting his 5-year-old grandson (option c) violates the instruction to avoid heavy lifting. Waiting to have the prescriptions filled (option d) clearly shows that he does not understand the importance of his medications.
Nursing Process: Evaluation   **Client Need:** Health Promotion & Maintenance

21.   **The correct answer is b.** The question is asking what the effects of smoking are during pregnancy. Smoking is consistently associated with infants who are an average of 0.5 lb (142g) smaller than infants born to mothers who do not smoke. There is no association between smoking and cardiac anomalies in the fetus, longer labor or Down's syndrome (options a, c & d).
Nursing Process: Implementation   **Client Need:** Health Promotion & Maintenance

22.   **The correct answers are a, and e.** The question is asking what the nurse would teach a client who has been diagnosed with bacterial conjunctivitis. Bacterial conjunctivitis, more commonly known as "pink eye" is most often caused by staphylococcus and haemophilus. Symptoms usually last for about a week (option a). Cool compresses will lessen any pain the client may have (option e). Patches are not indicated for conjunctivitis (option b). Mild soap (baby shampoo) and warm water is helpful in cleansing the eye (option c). The discharge is usually watery or purulent white not yellow (option d). Although the client may be photophobic, bacterial conjunctivitis is contagious and the client should not go outside until the eye is clear of drainage and returned to its previous state (option f).
Nursing Process: Implementation   **Client Need:** Safe, Effective Care Environment

23.   **The correct answer is c.** The question is asking which client condition will the pediatric nurse be most familiar with and, therefore, able to deliver safe care. Ketoacidosis occurs in children and adults. Renal failure (option a), myocardial infarction (option b), and CVA (option d) are more likely to occur in adults. The pediatric nurse is most likely to have experience with the client who has ketoacidosis.
Nursing Process: Implementation   **Client Need:** Safe, Effective Care Environment

24.   **The correct answer is c.** The question is asking what would be an abnormal finding for a woman in the second trimester of pregnancy. Swelling of the face is an abnormal sign in pregnancy and a symptom of pregnancy-induced hypertension, for which diabetics are at risk. Slight shortness of breath (option a), heartburn (option b) and epistaxis (option d) are considered to be normal health deviations, although these symptoms should be evaluated for a possible health problem.
Nursing Process: Assessment   **Client Need:** Physiological Integrity

25.   **The correct answer is c.** The question is asking the meaning of positive antibody for the AIDS virus. A positive test result would show antibodies in the blood of a client infected with the human immunodeficiency virus (HIV). The immune system produces these antibodies within one to fourteen months of exposure. These antibodies are ineffective in halting the HIV infection. A positive test does not necessarily mean the client has AIDS or will contract AIDS in the future (options a & b). A negative test may mean the client has been infected with the virus, but has not produced antibodies (option d).
Nursing Process: Analysis   **Client Need:** Physiological Integrity

26.   **The correct answer is d.** The question is asking what is the purpose of Alcoholics Anonymous (AA). AA is a self-help support group that believes individual members gives the person with alcoholism strength to abstain. Options (a) and (b) are denial of alcoholism and treatment. Option (c) is not the primary purpose of AA.

Nursing Process: Evaluation   **Client Need:** Psychosocial Integrity

27. **The correct answer is b.** The question is asking what causes the occurrence of pain. The ureter is composed of smooth muscle, which has a peristaltic action to move urine from the kidney to the bladder. The stone causes spasms, which result in acute severe pain. The location and the client's description of the pain can be significant diagnostic aids in determining where in the urinary tract the stone is located. There is no evidence of ureteral lacerations, nephron damage or bladder inflammation (options a, c & d).
Nursing Process: Analysis   **Client Need:** Physiological Integrity

28. **The correct answer is b.** The question is asking the definition of nonorganic failure to thrive (NFTT). NFTT is seen in children who do not grow due to an inability to obtain or use calories effectively. Very often, this is due to a lack of maternal attachment. Organic failure to thrive is often caused by some physical reason, such as malabsorption syndrome (option a). NFTT is diagnosed in children who are consistently below the third percentile for the child's age (option c). Children with new onset NFTT refuse feeding no matter who is doing the feeding (option d).
Nursing Process: Assessment   **Client Need:** Health Promotion & Maintenance

29. **The correct answer is a.** The question is asking what complication may occur with Cushing's syndrome. Unregulated secretion of cortisol causes increased gluconeogenesis and inhibits the ability of insulin to transport glucose into the cells. The mineralocorticoid actions of supraphysiologic levels of cortisone promote potassium excretion and sodium and water retention (options b & d). Protein catabolism leads to osteoporosis (option c).
Nursing Process: Planning   **Client Need:** Safe, Effective Care Environment

30. **The correct answer is b.** The question is asking what to do for a client with Parkinson's disease who is losing weight. A thick liquid or soft solid diet will assist the client to swallow more easily. Thin liquids (option a) such as juices or soups may cause aspiration since they are less easily controlled. Weighing the client weekly (option c) and maintaining a calorie count (option d) would serve no purpose. It has already been determined that weight loss is evident. Further weight loss and possible harm may occur if a plan is not instituted. Measurement of weight and calories might be appropriate once the new plan is begun.
Nursing Process: Implementation   **Client Need:** Physiological Integrity

31. **The correct answer is b.** The question is asking how to safely give phenytoin (Dilantin). Phenytoin (Dilantin) has the potential to cause cardiovascular problems, may also burn, and must be administered by slow IV push or infusion. This medication is incompatible with any other drug in solution, can only be given with physiologic saline (options a & c) and is used for tonic-clonic seizure activity. The dose may need to be increased rather than held (option d).
Nursing Process: Implementation   **Client Need:** Physiological Integrity

32. **The correct answer is b.** The question is asking what is the most important thing to teach the family about treatment for hepatitis A. Because hepatitis A transmission is by the fecal-oral route, good personal hygiene is important. Other measures may be appropriate to identify carriers (option d) or deal with specific sources of contamination (options a & c). Good personal hygiene, however, is always appropriate in controlling the spread of all types of viral infections.
Nursing Process: Planning   **Client Need:** Health Promotion & Maintenance

33. **The correct answer is d.** The question is asking how to respond to the client's statement that the drinking is not her fault. Gentle confrontation about the client's drinking and an open-ended question is the best response to use with persons addicted to alcohol. The denial of her drinking must be dealt with first. Option (a) is disagreeing with the client. Options (b) and (c) do not deal with the drinking issue but rather assist the client in denial and projection.
Nursing Process: Implementation   **Client Need:** Psychosocial Integrity

34. **The correct answer is c.** The question is asking for evaluation criteria on preventing paralytic ileus in a client with major abdominal surgery. Manipulation of the gastrointestinal (GI) tract

delays the return of peristalsis. GI function should return by the third postoperative day. Paralytic ileus is the absence of peristalsis beyond the third postoperative day and is evidenced by a feeling of fullness (option d). Ambulation in the hall and decreasing pain are measures taken to prevent paralytic ileus (options a & b).
Nursing Process: Evaluation   **Client Need:** Physiological Integrity

35.   **The correct answer is d.** The question is asking what should be assessed in a newly admitted rehabilitation client. The client should be assessed for the capacity for self-management and decision-making. Then plans can be made to further develop these abilities, since the client will need them once released from rehabilitation. The client should develop independence from, rather than dependence on, the team. The client should be a part of the team (option a). The ability to be flexible and adapt rather than be rigid should be fostered in the client. The client must also be willing to accept major lifestyle changes (option b). Problems that are related to rehabilitation deal with tertiary care rather than primary care (option c).
Nursing Process: Assessment   **Client Need:** Health Promotion & Maintenance

36.   **The correct answer is c.** The question is asking what would be a normal reaction for an 8-year-old who is about to have surgery. School-age children often try to gather information about what is happening to them. They will also try to act brave, especially in front of others (option a). Ignoring the upcoming surgery (option b) and hiding under the bed (option d) may be seen in preschool-age children.
Nursing Process: Assessment   **Client Need:** Health Promotion & Maintenance

37.   **The correct answer is c.** The question is asking the pathology of some of the symptoms seen in a child with cystic fibrosis. Secretions of the mucous glands of children with cystic fibrosis are abnormally viscous, sticky, and tenacious. They adhere to the walls of the glandular ducts and eventually obstruct them entirely. Obstruction causes fibrosis of the glands themselves. Atropic changes in the intestinal wall, hypoactivity of the autonomic nervous system, and hyperactivity of the sweat glands (options a, b & d) are not involved.
Nursing Process: Analysis   **Client Need:** Physiological Integrity

38.   **The correct answer is a.** The question is asking how ranitidine (Zantac) works. Ranitidine (Zantac) blocks the production of hydrochloric acid in the stomach. Burned clients are at risk for ulcer. Sucralfate (Carafate) produces a coating on the lining of the stomach (option b). Antacids neutralize acids (option c). Alprazolam (Xanax) is a tranquilizer, which has a sedative effect (option d).
Nursing Process: Analysis   **Client Need:** Physiological Integrity

39.   **The correct answer is c.** The question is asking what discharge instructions should be given to a client with burns. Pressurized garments should be worn continuously to decrease scar formation by compressing the burned collagen tissue. Lotions should be used on the skin to moisten, soften and aid in healing (option a). Some blistering is expected and does not need to be reported (option b). Keeping the arms in a dependent position will increase their discoloration. This problem can be alleviated by propping the arms on pillows during sleeping or placing elbows on a table while sitting (option d).
Nursing Process: Planning   **Client Need:** Health Promotion & Maintenance

40.   **The correct answer is c.** The question is asking what foods are high in potassium. Oranges, tomatoes and apricots have the highest amount of potassium. Potassium is a commonly occurring electrolyte and a normal diet usually supplies an adequate potassium intake. Bananas and potatoes are high in potassium; however, oatmeal, chocolate, whole milk, ginger ale, celery and shellfish are not (options a, b & d).
Nursing Process: Implementation   **Client Need:** Physiological Integrity

41.   **The correct answer is a.** The question is asking which statement is true about electrophysiology (EP) studies. EP studies are done to the heart in a controlled environment, as an attempt to induce ventricular dysrhythmias to determine the threshold of ventricular irritability. The statement, "A

catheter will be introduced into my heart…" is done with cardiac catheterization when blockage is suspected (option b). An internal cardiac defibrillator (option c) is a device that tests and terminates the life-threatening arrhythmias of ventricular tachycardia that cannot be controlled with medicine. A Holter monitor, which, is connected to the client with electrodes, gives a 24-hour readout of the heart's electrical activity (option d).
Nursing Process: Evaluation   **Client Need:** Physiological Integrity

42.   **The correct answer is b.** The question is asking how to respond to a mother's concern about her baby being so small. The statement "We can talk about how to take care of her" shows collaboration and reassures the mother that she is not alone but will have the necessary support. Option (a); "Don't worry you're baby will grow" belittles the complaint and asks the mother to do what she cannot do (stop worrying). Option (c); "She's small because of lung problems" gives false information. The infant's small size may be due to several reasons and a lung problem has not been evidenced in the question. Option (d); "How do you feel about the baby being so small" attempts to ascertain feelings but the mother has already told you her feelings.
Nursing Process: Implementation   **Client Need:** Health Promotion & Maintenance

43.   **The correct answer is c.** The question is asking what this behavior means. Sexual acting out is sexual/seductive behavior or action, which is what this client displays when he repeatedly touches the nurse inappropriately. Manipulation involves words rather than action and there is no evidence that the client is attempting to make the nurse feel guilty (option a). Although the client displays poor judgment in this situation (option b) sexual acting out is a descriptive explanation of his behavior. There is no evidence to support sexually regressive behavior (option d).
Nursing Process: Analysis   **Client Need:** Psychosocial Integrity

44.   **The correct answer is d.** The question is asking which statement shows constructive family coping. This is the only answer in which the nurse really does not have to continue with support and empathetic listening or refer the family for more psychological support. Option (b); "Everything is just fine." does not tell you enough. The statements "The other children are complaining…" and "We're doing everything so our child doesn't get sick again" (options a & c) show the nurse that there are definitely more problems.
Nursing Process: Evaluation   **Client Need:** Health Promotion & Maintenance

45.   **The correct answer is a.** The question is asking what is true regarding patient controlled analgesia (PCA). The PCA infusion pump has a security device that prevents the client from overdosing. The purpose is for the client to self-manage acute pain. The device is programmed to deliver a certain amount of medication within a specific time interval (option c). Clients generally use less pain medication, as they have some control over the process (option b) and, therefore, are less sedated (option d). Coughing and deep breathing are necessary for all post-surgical clients.
Nursing Process: Evaluation   **Client Need:** Health Promotion & Maintenance

46.   **The correct answer is b.** The question is asking what the symptoms given are indicative of in a kidney transplant client. The clinical manifestations of septicemia are chills, fever, tachycardia, tachypnea and either leukocytosis or leukopenia. Cyclosporin (Sandimmune) toxicity (option a) is manifested by hypertension, headache and seizures. Signs and symptoms of organ rejection (option c) include oliguria, hypertension, weight gain, malaise, leukopenia and fever. If the client were hemorrhaging, the blood pressure would drop as well as the temperature.
Nursing Process: Analysis   **Client Need:** Physiological Integrity

47.   **The correct answer is d.** The question is asking how to reduce the chance of systemic infection in a client receiving total parenteral nutrition. The solution should be refrigerated until one hour before administration (option a). The filter needs to be changed every 24 to 72 hours (option b). The dressing needs to be changed less frequently than every shift. Changing the dressing every shift would open it to contamination more often than it needs to be (option c). If the client exhibits signs and symptoms of a systemic infection, the catheter tip is usually suspect unless another cause can be found. The current bottle of total parenteral nutrition solution with tubing and filter should be cultured and replaced with an entirely new setup.

Nursing Process: Implementation   **Client Need:** Safe, Effective Care Environment

48.   **The correct answer is b.** The question is asking what these symptoms mean following a fracture. Fat emboli usually occur in young adults 12 to 72 hours after a traumatic accident or surgery; this client displayed many of the classic symptoms. The symptoms of memory loss, restlessness and confusion may be confused with the alcoholic's delirium tremens, but there is no evidence of alcoholism in this client (option d). Twelve hours after an accident is too early to diagnose osteomyelitis (option a). Thromboembolism could be considered, but due to the timing, age range and recent trauma, fat embolism is a more likely cause of the presenting symptoms (option c).
Nursing Process: Analysis   **Client Need:** Physiological Integrity

49.   **The correct answer is c.** The question is asking what should be taught for home care to the parents of a 6-year-old with a concussion during the first 24 hours post-injury. To determine whether there is deterioration in the level of consciousness, the client must be awakened regularly when asleep. A decrease in the level of consciousness could indicate a slowly growing hematoma. This, however, does not mean the client should not be permitted to rest and sleep (option a). Food is not restricted for children with concussions (option b). A mild analgesic such as acetaminophen (Tylenol) is often prescribed for the headache that usually accompanies a concussion (option d).
Nursing Process: Implementation   **Client Need:** Physiological Integrity

50.   **The correct answer is c.** The question is asking why the traction needs to be checked often. Traction ropes should hang free (option d). Weights should also hang free (option b). If a client's foot were braced against the bed, traction would be interrupted (option a).
Nursing Process: Planning   **Client Need:** Safe, Effective Care Environment

51.   **The correct answer is a.** The question is asking how to proceed when a newly admitted client asks the admitting nurse not to remove a dressing for assessment until the next day. The client has the right to refuse any procedure. When you touch the client against the client's will, it is battery (option b). The client's request should be respected and charted. The client stated the dressing may be removed the following day and assessment made at that time (option c). A home care nurse who would have assessed and documented the wound prior to hospital admission was also seeing the client. Calling the physician (option d) would not make a difference in terms of outcome. The physician would not over-ride the client's refusal, because he would then be a party to assault and battery.
Nursing Process: Assessment   **Client Need:** Physiological Integrity

52.   **The correct answer is a.** The question is asking what the glucose level should be in a pregnant diabetic client. Euglycemia (normal glucose level) is important to maintain during pregnancy. Maternal hyperglycemia (option b) early in pregnancy may even result in fetal abnormalities and fetal distress. Hypoglycemia and ketosis (options c & d) jeopardize fetal and maternal health.
Nursing Process: Implementation   **Client Need:** Health Promotion & Maintenance

53.   **The correct answer is c.** The question is asking for potential complications of a client in a leg cast. Numbness, tingling, and burning may be due to peroneal nerve injury from pressure at the head of the fibula. The cast would need to be loosened or removed to prevent permanent nerve damage leading to foot drop. Disuse syndrome/atrophy (option a) results from failure to contract the muscles surrounded by a cast. The client with a pressure ulcer (option b) has pain, tightness in the area, a warm area on the cast, drainage, and odor. Volkmann's contracture (option d) occurs in the hand and wrist as a result of compartment syndrome from an arm cast that is too tight.
Nursing Process: Analysis   **Client Need:** Physiological Integrity

54.   **The correct answer is a.** The question is asking the best way to keep a depressed client from ongoing self-depreciation. By engaging the client in activities, self-devaluation is limited and completion of activities will promote positive self-image. Option (b) blocks communication attempts. Negative thoughts should be limited, but some expression is necessary for ongoing assessment and intervention as well as the client's comfort. Option (c) promotes social

withdrawal, which should be avoided since it is a sign of depression. Option (d), relaxation, is effective for relieving the anxiety component of depression, but may not limit negative thinking.
Nursing Process: Implementation   **Client Need:** Psychosocial Integrity

55. **The correct answer is a.** The question is asking why a catheterization schedule would need to be changed. Over distension of the bladder can result in bladder damage and reflux into the kidney. The schedule will need to be shortened. The 450ml is an acceptable output per catheterization (option b). Development of a urinary track infection and/or presence of cloudy urine with sediment (options c & d) would not influence the catheterization schedule; however, further investigation is necessary.
Nursing Process: Evaluation   **Client Need:** Safe, Effective Care Environment

56. **The correct answer is d.** The question is asking how to best care for a client who had a cerebrovascular accident (CVA) two days ago. Using a multidisciplinary team approach is required to identify strengths and needs of the client, because one person does not have all the knowledge and skills for rehabilitation. Providing range-of-motion every two hours is a good intervention but monitoring vital signs every two hours is not required because the client has been stabilized (option a). Each individual client must be evaluated once maximal rehabilitation has been reached, as to whether the client needs the services of a nursing home or may return home (option b). Working with the client, physical therapist, and physician would be appropriate to achieve long-term goals. However, immediate survival needs and prevention of further brain damage are short-term goals based on frequent physical and neurological assessments and monitoring during the first 48 hours (option c).
Nursing Process: Planning   **Client Need:** Health Promotion & Maintenance

57. **The correct answer is d.** The question is asking what priority problem should be addressed for a mastectomy client. Teaching and learning principles emphasize the importance of prioritizing teaching content. Following a mastectomy, the maintenance of effective breathing patterns is most essential given the location of the surgical incision and the probability of pressure dressings applied to the chest immediately after surgery (options a, b & c).
Nursing Process: Planning   **Client Need:** Physiological Integrity

58. **The correct answer is a.** The question is asking why the nurse should encourage hospitalized children to play the roles of nurses and doctors. Role-playing assists the child in exerting autonomy and control and, thereby, decreases fear. The greatest number of real or imagined fears is present during the preschool years. The best way to help children overcome their fears is by actively involving them in finding practical methods to deal with experiences that frighten them. Role-playing will allow children to reconstruct painful experiences without directly involving themselves as vulnerable victims.
Nursing Process: Implementation   **Client Need:** Health Promotion & Maintenance

59. **The correct answer is a.** The question is asking which finding relates to an electrical burn. Electric burns, such as lightning strikes, have entry and exit wounds where the current passed through the body. A major fluid shift (option b) to extracellular tissue is found in all burns in the emergent phase. If the fluid shift back to the intravascular space is unable to be handled by the kidneys and heart, congestive heart failure and pulmonary edema may result, in which jugular vein distension is a symptom (option d). Sooty sputum (option c) is evident with respiratory burns.
Nursing Process: Assessment   **Client Need:** Physiological Integrity

60. **The correct answer is b.** The question is asking what discharge instructions you would give to a client with angina. A proper exercise program is important, so nitroglycerine (Nitrostat) should be taken if pain is anticipated. Isometric exercises place sudden demands on the heart, which cause increased venous return (option a). A cool room temperature will constrict blood vessels and increase cardiac workload (option c). Increased (not all) anginal pain should be reported to the physician (option d).
Nursing Process: Planning   **Client Need:** Health Promotion & Maintenance

PRACTICE SESSION: 13

> **Instructions: Allow yourself 60 minutes to complete the following 60 practice questions. Use a timer to notify yourself when 60 minutes are over so that you are not constantly looking at your watch while completing the questions.**

1. The nurse would suspect a client is developing age-related macular degeneration if he made which statement?
   a. "I have difficulty focusing both eyes on the same object."
   b. "It is getting harder to see things that are directly in front of me."
   c. "I feel like I have blinders on the sides of my face."
   d. "It seems like there is a curtain falling over my field of vision."

2. The nurse would pay special attention to the urine output of a client in shock because:
   a. acute tubular necrosis can occur as a result of inadequate blood supply.
   b. toxic levels of the BUN and creatinine occur with decreased urine output.
   c. decreased urine output is indicative of neurogenic shock.
   d. decreased urine output can lead to kidney failure.

3. A nurse caring for a client diagnosed with Addison's disease identifies a nursing diagnosis as: deficient knowledge related to lack of previous experience with new problem. An area of focus for this diagnosis will be to:
   a. pay attention to home care needs, so that the client/family can make appropriate plans.
   b. explain care to the client and family, so that no unexpected events occur.
   c. get the client out of bed and walk in the hall with him at least once every two hours.
   d. provide education in a verbal format exclusively.

4. A client with a spinal cord injury is placed in halo traction. What would be included in the teaching plan?
   a. "Clean the pin sites with hot soapy water every four hours."
   b. "If the vest becomes damp due to perspiration, use a blow dryer to dry it."
   c. "If you lose your balance, have a friend support the halo by holding on to the bars."
   d. "Do not loosen or remove the vest unless there is a cardiac or respiratory emergency."

5. A client comes to the outpatient center complaining of fatigue, shortness of breath, weight loss, malaise and fever. Further X-rays and tissue biopsy show sarcoidosis. Six months after treatment with corticosteroids is started, the nurse would evaluate an improvement occurred if the client had:
   a. gained weight.
   b. increased exercise tolerance.
   c. decreased pulmonary function tests.
   d. elevated glucose levels.

6. A client with surgery for an anorectal abscess and fistulectomy has returned to the unit. The nurse would examine the wound to determine:
   a. that granulating tissue is forming.
   b. if the gauze packing is in place.
   c. that the pouch is correctly attached.
   d. if hemorrhoids are released.

7. A nursing student is reviewing the plan of care for her status asthmaticus client with the assigned nurse. Which intervention would need to be corrected by the nurse?
   a. Keep flowers out of the room.
   b. Place a "no smoking" sign on her door.
   c. Check on her at least every two hours.
   d. Administer oxygen as prescribed.

8. Which activity may assist in promoting nutritional status in those suffering from AIDS?
   a. Administering systemic analgesics about 90 minutes prior to the meal to minimize mouth pain prior to eating.
   b. Planning for three meals per day as the client becomes very fatigued if feedings are more often than every five hours.
   c. Suggesting the client eat dry toast or crackers with some liquids about 30 minutes before meals to reduce nausea.
   d. Recommending a low-protein diet, since AIDS clients may also have liver and kidney involvement.

9. A client is admitted following a hip replacement. On the first postoperative day, what should be included in the client's plan of care?
   a. Keep the affected leg in adduction.
   b. Perform neurovascular checks once per shift.
   c. Teach the client to use incentive spirometry every four hours.
   d. Complete passive and active leg raising exercises.

10. A client diagnosed with laryngeal cancer undergoes a radical neck dissection. Which prescription is included in the plan for the first 24 postoperative hours?
    a. Keep the head of bed elevated at all times.
    b. Report drainage greater than 100ml.
    c. Assess the wound every three hours.
    d. Expect milky opaque drainage.

11. A nursing student is doing passive range-of-motion exercises on an unconscious client. Which student action would require intervention by the nurse?
    a. Hyperextending the wrist while flexing the fingers.
    b. Applying slow firm pressure to a contractured arm.
    c. Abducting and externally rotating the shoulder.
    d. Flexing and hyperextending the neck.

12. A nurse is inserting a nasogastric tube when the client begins to gasp, cough, and become cyanotic. The nurse should:
    a. pull back on the tube.
    b. notify the physician.
    c. quickly complete the tube insertion.
    d. assess the tube placement with a stethoscope.

13. An older adult client asks the nurse what the difference is between Medicare A and Medicare B. The nurse replies that Medicare B:
    a. is included in the cost of Medicare paid by the government.
    b. covers costs of hearing aids and glasses.
    c. protects against lost wages due to disability.
    d. pays for outpatient physical and speech therapies.

14. A nurse is giving discharge instructions to a woman who had a modified radical mastectomy. Which client statement would indicate that she understood the instructions?
    a. "I can't wait to get back home to finish working in my garden."
    b. "I've already called an agency to interview a temporary housekeeper to assist with the heavy chores at home."
    c. "Now that the surgery is over, I can get back to my regular routine."
    d. "My manicurist has offered to come to my home to do my nails as soon as I am discharged."

15. A client with a 10-year history of Type 1 diabetes was just admitted with a diagnosis of ketoacidosis. The nurse begins to develop a teaching plan. At this time, the most important initial strategy is to:
   a. explain to the client how diet influences blood glucose levels.
   b. teach the client self-monitoring of blood glucose and ketones.
   c. ask the client what she knows about diabetes.
   d. teach the client about ketoacidosis using visual aids.

16. A client receiving peritoneal dialysis is prescribed three exchanges of 1.5% dialysate to be followed by one exchange of 4.25% dialysate. The higher concentration of dextrose in the last exchange will cause:
   a. less weight to be lost during this exchange.
   b. a need for insulin to be added to the dialysate.
   c. the dwell time to be increased.
   d. more water to be removed with this exchange.

17. A client has been placed on a salt-restricted diet. Which meal, if selected, would indicate that the client is learning the diet?
   a. Low salt ham, boiled potato and biscuit.
   b. Kielbasa, baked potato and gelatin.
   c. Liver, mixed vegetables and ice cream.
   d. Broiled flounder, lima beans, and sherbet.

18. A female client is scheduled for a laparoscopic cholecystectomy. She asks the nurse, "What will my abdomen look like after the surgery?" The nurse tells the client that she can expect to have:
   a. a vertical incision on the right side.
   b. four small incisions or punctures.
   c. a 3cm to 4cm incision with a drain.
   d. two small puncture-like wounds.

19. The nurse knows that the husband of a pregnant woman understands his role as coach when he states that he will assist his wife with:
   a. relaxation and breathing techniques and supportive posturing.
   b. relaxation and breathing techniques and perineal care.
   c. positive reinforcement and watching the fetal monitor.
   d. timing contractions and distraction during contractions.

20. In caring for a client with schizophrenia, the nurse should be chiefly concerned with which goal?
   a. Assist the family to understand the client's needs.
   b. Increase social interaction.
   c. Reinforce and clarify reality.
   d. Develop a mutually trusting relationship.

21. The nurse in the rehabilitation unit is assisting a client to transfer from the bed to a wheelchair using a transfer board. The nurse would instruct a client to:
   a. use hands and arms for strength to move the buttocks onto the board to the wheelchair.
   b. face the wheelchair seat against the bed and lock the wheels.
   c. place one end of the transfer board on the bedrail and the other end on the wheelchair seat.
   d. ensure the transfer board has a dull finish to avoid sliding off the board.

22. A nurse is assessing a client for pregnancy induced hypertension (PIH). What would indicate severe progressive PIH?
   a. Epigastric pain.
   b. Burning on urination.
   c. Weight gain of 1.5 lb (595g) in one week.
   d. Small amounts of protein in the urine.

23. A nurse is teaching the parents of a child with tetralogy of Fallot. Which parent statement indicates that the teaching has been effective?
    a. "Clubbing of the fingers and toes should be expected as the child nears adolescence."
    b. "Cyanosis is unusual with this type of cardiac defect and should be reported to a physician."
    c. "Placing the child in a knee-chest position during a 'tet-spell' will facilitate relief.
    d. "The surgical repair will involve a single operative procedure."

24. A 60-year-old man has just been diagnosed with Alzheimer's disease. The man's family asks the nurse "What makes him behave this way?" The nurse understands that changes in the brain similar to Alzheimer's disease occur when there are insufficient amounts of:
    a. thiamine.
    b. aluminum.
    c. dopamine.
    d. acetylcholine.

25. A woman comes to the emergency department with a baby and shouts that the baby was playing by the washer; dumped a bottle of chlorine bleach over her head and it splashed in the baby's eyes. The baby is crying loudly and rubbing her eyes. The nurse would immediately:
    a. take the baby and begin to flush the eyes to rid them of the bleach.
    b. start an intravenous access and check for facial burns.
    c. obtain vital signs as a baseline for treatment.
    d. assess for signs and symptoms of aspiration.

26. The home health nurse is visiting a client with Parkinson's disease. The client is having difficulty responding to the nurse's questions. The client's wife states he has this trouble when he gets excited or tired. The nurse would:
    a. encourage short shallow breaths to help start speech.
    b. discourage other forms of communication to encourage speech.
    c. encourage facial muscle exercises.
    d. plan to discontinue speech therapy, since this is a progressive disease.

27. A client presents with cellulitis of the right forearm. What predisposing factor contributed to this problem?
    a. Recent trauma to that arm.
    b. Decreased skin turgor.
    c. A change in laundry detergents.
    d. Presence of hives.

28. The home care nurse is reviewing the care of a Hickman catheter with a client. The woman tells the nurse she is afraid that she will get air in the catheter and die. The nurse bases her explanation on the understanding that:
    a. clot formation is necessary to seal the catheter and prevent air leak.
    b. an air embolus can form if the catheter is unclamped when uncapping.
    c. air may enter the uncapped catheter through negative pressure from breathing.
    d. an air embolus is less likely to occur than is a thrombus.

29. A woman, who is 10 weeks pregnant, is admitted with a possible diagnosis of hydatiform mole. What would the nurse expect to be elevated?
    a. Blood pressure.
    b. Temperature.
    c. Pulse.
    d. Respirations.

30. The physician prescribes 1 Liter of lactated Ringer's solution to run intravenously over five hours. The drop factor is 15. The nurse would regulate the flow to deliver how many drops per minute?

    _____

31. A client who has been in the coronary critical care unit for the past five days is experiencing sensory overload. Which intervention would be most helpful?
    a. Reality orient the client by informing him of the day, time and place at least once per shift.
    b. Use touch when talking to the client.
    c. Medicate with triazolam (Halcion) to induce sleep as prescribed at 10:00PM.
    d. Move the electrocardiogram monitor out of view of the client.

32. In order to be therapeutic with a grieving client, the nurse should be guided by the principle that:
    a. nurses need to express personal feelings to clients about their dying in order to promote openness.
    b. the nurse must use confrontation to force the abandonment of denial.
    c. responses that are brief and succinct allow the client to maintain a necessary sense of hope for recovery.
    d. availability of the nurse will encourage the client to test the situation and ask for what she is ready to hear.

33. The nurse is working in an antepartum clinic. Which clients would be at increased risk for developing a placenta previa? Select all that apply.
    a. a 36 year old gravida 3 para2.
    b. a 28 year old who is carrying triplets.
    c. a 17 year old who is pregnant for the first time.
    d. a 23 year old who is gravida 2 para 1 and her first baby was born via cesarean section.
    e. a 32 year old who is Rh negative and gravida 2 para 1.

34. A nurse in the emergency department receives a call from a frantic mother that her 3-year-old son has taken a whole bottle of aspirin. The nurse asks the mother for her name, address and telephone number. What should the nurse do next?
    a. Ask the mother if she has ipecac on hand.
    b. Ask the mother the condition of the child.
    c. Ask the mother the time of ingestion, the amount ingested, and the age and weight of the child.
    d. Tell the mother to watch the child closely for the next four hours.

35. The nurse is conducting a group with high school students who witnessed another student shoot three of their friends in the cafeteria yesterday. One of the students states, "I don't understand why he had to shoot everyone." The nurse responds:
    a. "It's frightening when we don't understand why it happened."
    b. "I don't know, but we'll make sure it doesn't happen again."
    c. "Let's talk about how all of you are feeling."
    d. "He obviously had severe emotional problems."

36. A client has been admitted with hepatic encephalopathy. The nurse is documenting the assessment and would include which finding indicative of hepatic encephalopathy?
    a. Increased abdominal girth.
    b. Decreased output.
    c. Jaundiced sclera.
    d. Flapping tremor.

37. The nurse understands that a client's belief that her doctor is trying to spray her with a deadly gas is the result of a:
    a.   projection of the client's own feelings of self-worth.
    b.   misinterpretation of external stimuli.
    c.   false sensory perception without external stimuli.
    d.   loss experienced in early youth.

38. What would be a priority nursing diagnosis for a client with Meniere's disease?
    a.   Self-care deficit related to inner ear disturbance.
    b.   High risk for injury related to labyrinth dysfunction.
    c.   Anxiety related to diagnosis of Meniere's disease.
    d.   Fluid and electrolyte imbalance secondary to nausea and vomiting.

39. In the postoperative period following an anterior craniotomy, the nurse should change the client's position from:
    a.   side-to-side, with the head of the bed elevated 30 to 45 degrees and the head in neutral position.
    b.   supine-to-prone, with the head of the bed flat and the head turned to the right.
    c.   side-to-side, with the head of the bed elevated 30 to 45 degrees and the head flexed to the right.
    d.   left semi-prone to right semi-prone with the head of the bed flat and the head in neutral position.

40. A nurse is caring for a male client with a nursing diagnosis of urinary incontinence, related to decreased perception of need to void, secondary to cognitive impairment. In order to best promote urinary continence, what would the nurse do?
    a.   Restrict intake of fluids to 1,500ml/day.
    b.   Place a urinal and a call light within reach of the client.
    c.   Color code the bathroom door.
    d.   Assist the client to the bathroom every one to two hours.

41. The nurse working in the coronary care unit looks at the monitor and witnesses that the client is in sustained ventricular tachycardia. The priority action of the nurse would be to:
    a.   prepare the client for an immediate internal cardiac defibrillation.
    b.   stay with the client and decrease his anxiety.
    c.   prepare the client for placement of a pacemaker.
    d.   prepare the client for nonsynchronized cardioversion.

42. A truck driver had a laparoscopic cholecystectomy performed at 0800. The nurse in the same-day surgery unit is preparing to discharge him at 1700. Which statement should be included in the discharge instructions?
    a.   "Lie flat in bed for the next 24 hours to prevent a headache."
    b.   "If you develop right shoulder pain, apply a heating pad for 15 to 20 minutes."
    c.   "You may return to work tomorrow morning."
    d.   "Abdominal distention and a slight fever are a normal occurrence."

43. A woman with Type 1 diabetes is now 14 weeks pregnant. While teaching the client, the nurse should emphasize:
    a.   "Your insulin needs will stabilize during the pregnancy, because the fetus will also be producing insulin."
    b.   "Your insulin needs will increase during pregnancy, because of placental changes."
    c.   "You may now be able to start taking an oral diabetic agent, because insulin may hurt the fetus."
    d.   "Usually your insulin needs will decrease as the fetus makes its own insulin."

44. A client has just had a kidney stone removed with the use of extracorporeal shock wave lithotripsy (ESWL). Post-procedure, the nurse would expect the client to have:
    a. an increase in urine volume.
    b. pink-tinged urine.
    c. a decrease in urine volume.
    d. pain radiating in the back.

45. When caring for a client with hepatitis B, the nurse is especially careful when:
    a. disposing of the client's uneaten food.
    b. handling the client's feces.
    c. drawing blood.
    d. providing skin care to icteric skin.

46. A client comes to the campus clinic complaining of acute pharyngitis. It is determined that the client has a Group A streptococcal infection. Nursing actions would include:
    a. keeping the client NPO for the first 24 hours of antibiotic therapy.
    b. swabbing the pharynx and drawing blood samples as prescribed.
    c. having the client gargle with saline that has been warmed to 105° to 110°F (40.6° to 43.3°C).
    d. giving acyclovir (Zovirax) 200mg every four hours by mouth as prescribed.

47. A client with somatoform disorder has a nursing diagnosis of ineffective coping related to unresolved psychological issues. The outcomes for this client would include that the client will: Select all that apply.
    a. decrease level of social interaction away from family.
    b. verbalize decreased feelings of dependence.
    c. begin treatment for long ignored physical problems.
    d. focus on and discuss emotions.
    e. leave the sick role and quickly return to a healthy role.

48. A depressed client is scheduled to attend group therapy. He tells the nurse he does not want to go to group because he is too tired. The appropriate response would be to:
    a. allow the client to rest during group today.
    b. inform the client he will lose privileges for refusing to go to group therapy.
    c. walk with the client to group therapy.
    d. notify the physician that the client is probably over sedated.

49. A nurse is preparing a client for abdominal and thigh liposuction. Which client response indicates a lack of knowledge?
    a. "I am thrilled about having this surgery, because now I will be able to eat like I used to without having to look so fat."
    b. "Yes, you mentioned that I would have general anesthesia. I have not had anything by mouth since midnight, have arranged for a ride home and for someone to stay with me tonight."
    c. "I have lost 80 pounds already. I will be glad to have some of this fat removed that has been difficult to lose even with my weight loss."
    d. "I realize that I will need to wear a tight girdle type of garment for a number of weeks after this surgery."

50. Which client would be most prone to a nosocomial bacteremia? A client with:
    a. a radical neck dissection.
    b. an appendectomy.
    c. an abscessed tooth.
    d. a central venous pressure line.

51. A quadriplegic client asks the nurse if she will ever be able to have a baby. The nurse bases her response on the understanding that the menstrual cycle is under:
   a. the control of hormones.
   b. the control of the sacral segments.
   c. higher cortical control.
   d. higher brain stem control.

52. During a dressing change, the nurse notes drainage oozing from a small separation in the incision. The nurse understands that this wound site contains:
   a. a reservoir and a means of transmission.
   b. a reservoir and a portal of exit.
   c. a portal of entry and a means of transmission.
   d. microbes and a portal of entry.

53. The nurse has just returned from lunch. Which client should be cared for first? A client:
   a. with systemic lupus erethymatosus, who reports that her fingers are starting to turn blue.
   b. with a deep vein thrombosis, whose family reports he is very anxious and coughing a lot.
   c. admitted in the morning with infectious endocarditis, who now has blood in his urine.
   d. with pheochromocytoma, who has a postprandial blood glucose level of 270.

54. A client with gouty arthritis is prescribed colsalide (Colchicine) every two hours times four doses. The nurse would hold this medication if what occurred?
   a. Decreased serum uric acid levels.
   b. Flank pain and sweating.
   c. Decreased joint pain and swelling.
   d. Nausea, vomiting and diarrhea.

55. The nurse would best determine that a severely burned client is hypovolemic by monitoring:
   a. weight.
   b. urinary output.
   c. skin turgor.
   d. central venous pressure.

56. A nurse has been caring for a client with a respiratory infection for the past three days. Pneumonia was ruled out and, on the third day the nurse learns that the client has active tuberculosis (TB). The nurse undergoes diagnostic studies for possible diagnosis of TB. The nurse knows that:
   a. if she contracted TB from this client, the tuberculin skin test will be immediately positive.
   b. TB can only be positively diagnosed with positive findings on a chest X-ray study.
   c. a tuberculin skin test will not be necessary unless the nurse used poor hand washing techniques.
   d. a tuberculin skin test will need to be repeated in a period of 10 to 12 weeks.

57. A nurse employed in a dermatology office is asked to make a presentation on basal cell carcinoma at a local heath fair. Which comment by one of the participants indicates the need for more education?
   a. "This is the most deadly of skin cancers."
   b. "This is the most common skin malignancy occurring in light skinned individuals over the age of 40."
   c. "The appearance of a basal cell cancer is normally translucent with flesh to a pale pink color."
   d. "Treatment depends on the site and extent of the tumor."

58. A mother of a newborn infant is seen at home by the visiting nurse. The mother has a history of cocaine abuse and the infant is irritable and feeds poorly. What is the most important factor to assess in the mother?
   a. Attachment behaviors toward her infant daughter.
   b. Ability to cope with the infant's special needs.
   c. Knowledge regarding infant caretaking skills.
   d. Knowledge of family planning.

59. A client in the emergency department has been diagnosed as having a primary spontaneous pneumothorax. The nurse would expect to assess a (n):
   a. age of 28-years-old.
   b. arterial blood pH of 7.30.
   c. history of emphysema.
   d. penetrating chest wound.

60. A client is suspected of having glaucoma. The nurse would expect him to report which symptoms?
   a. Swollen, painful sac filled with pus.
   b. Lacrimation and purulent drainage.
   c. Flashes of light and floating particles in the eye.
   d. Haloes around lights and nausea with vomiting.

STOP. You have now completed Practice Session: 13. Now take a few minutes and correct your answers. Calculate your accuracy rate by dividing the number of questions you completed correctly by the total number of questions you completed (60).

Correct answers ÷ total number of questions completed = accuracy rate.

_____ ÷ _____ = _____

ANSWERS AND RATIONALES
Practice Session 13

1. **The correct answer is b.** The question is asking what subjective data indicates age-related macular degeneration. Damage or deterioration of photoreceptor cells in the area of the macula cause central vision loss. Age-related macular degeneration is the leading cause of severe vision loss in the 65 and older age group. A client who has difficulty focusing both eyes on the same object is experiencing strabismus (option a). People with glaucoma experience tunnel vision (option c). Clients with a retinal detachment will complain of a curtain falling over the field of vision (option d).
Nursing Process: Assessment   **Client Need:** Physiological Integrity

2. **The correct answer is a.** The question is asking why urine output is important when a client is in shock. When blood pressure falls dangerously low, blood is shunted away from the kidneys. The kidneys themselves may become ischemic, thus, leading to tubular necrosis and renal failure. Although the BUN and creatinine will rise (option b), they are not of immediate concern. Decreased urine output is indicative of any type of shock and is not unique to neurogenic shock (option c). Decreased urine output is a result of decreased blood flow to the kidneys, not the cause of it (option d).
Nursing Process: Analysis   **Client Need:** Physiological Integrity

3. **The correct answer is b.** The question is asking about the focus area of a nursing diagnosis for a client with Addison's disease. The key in Addison's disease is control of stress and conservation of energy. Addressing current needs at the time that the client is diagnosed is most helpful to the client and family. Although discharge planning is needed, conducting this activity too soon will lead to anxiety. Option (a) is incorrect as the present focus is on the newly diagnosed Addison's client's acute needs. Option (c) is incorrect, as this client should conserve energy. Option (d) is incorrect, as this client should not experience visual impairment. At this time, the client may be too ill to take part in education, verbal or otherwise.
Nursing Process: Implementation   **Client Need:** Safe, Effective Care Environment

4. **The correct answer is b.** The question is asking how to care for a client in halo traction. The halo vest may become damp from perspiration or even wet when washing the skin underneath. It should be dried with a blow dryer to prevent maceration of the skin. Pin sites should be cleaned with hydrogen peroxide or alcohol. Antibiotic cream may be prescribed to prevent infection to the pin sites (option a). If a client begins to fall or lose his balance, support should be provided under the arms. Grabbing the bars may alter the traction (option c). The halo vest may be loosened one side at a time to provide skin care (option d).
Nursing Process: Implementation   **Client Need:** Physiological Integrity

5. **The correct answer is b.** The question is asking for a sign of improvement in a client with sarcoidosis. Sarcoidosis is an inflammatory disease that may affect numerous body systems. About 90% of clients have lungs affected by the disease. The client does show respiratory involvement with the fatigue, shortness of breath and malaise. If the corticosteroids are effective, these symptoms will decrease. Better oxygen exchange takes place in the lungs and the client can tolerate activities, which require more oxygen. Therefore, the client will show an increased exercise tolerance. Although weight loss was a symptom, weight gain alone can be a side effect of the steroids and not indicate client improvement (option a). Decreased pulmonary function tests mean that there is a loss of lung capacity and a worsening condition (option c). Elevated glucose levels (option d) may be a side effect of the corticosteroid therapy.
Nursing Process: Evaluation   **Client Need:** Physiological Integrity

6. **The correct answer is b.** The question is asking what to assess in a postoperative client who had surgery for an anorectal abscess. The abscess is opened and drained and the fistula is laid open. The wound is packed with gauze and allowed to heal by granulation. However, granulating tissue would not be present immediately after surgery (option a). Drainage pouches are not used, (option

c) but may be present in colon surgery. Hemorrhoids may be present, but would be unrelated to this surgery (option d).
Nursing Process: Evaluation   **Client Need:** Physiological Integrity

7.   **The correct answer is c.** The question is asking which option is incorrect care and might be unsafe. Status asthmaticus is severe asthma that is unresponsive to medications and can lead to tiring and respiratory arrest. The nurse should continuously monitor the client. Checking every two hours is not often enough for a client this seriously ill. The room should be kept free of respiratory irritants like smoke, flowers and perfume (options a & b). Oxygen is used to treat hypoxia (option d).
Nursing Process: Planning   **Client Need:** Physiological Integrity

8.   **The correct answer is c.** The question is asking about activities to promote the nutritional status of AIDS clients. Pain control and energy conservation are important for the AIDS client. Nutrition is challenging and the choice to eat dry toast or crackers with some liquids about 30 minutes before meals to reduce nausea is the best intervention. Multiple small meals and local analgesics may help. One does not want to use systemic analgesics for a localized problem, as in the case of mouth pain (option a). The risks outweigh the benefits. The client should have small frequent meals to ensure nutritional status and maintain energy (option b). The client should have a high-protein diet to assist healing (option d).
Nursing Process: Implementation   **Client Need:** Physiological Integrity

9.   **The correct answer is d.** The question is asking how the nurse should care for a client who just had a hip replacement. Leg raising exercises prevent muscle atrophy and thromboembolism. The hip should be kept in abduction to prevent internal rotation and dislocation of the hip (option a). Neurovascular checks should be performed hourly on the first postoperative day (option b). Incentive spirometry is implemented every two hours to prevent pneumonia (option c).
Nursing Process: Planning   **Client Need:** Physiological Integrity

10.   **The correct answer is a.** The question is asking for the correct nursing strategy for a fresh postoperative radical neck dissection client. The head of the bed should stay elevated to decrease swelling and promote drainage with less danger of aspiration. Drainage of up to 120ml is considered normal for the first 24 hours (option b) and decreases to less than 50ml by the third day. The wound should be assessed every hour (option c) for signs of hematoma, emboli and carotid artery disruption. Another problem is salivary fistulas which delay wound healing. The fistulas are formed by saliva draining through skin breaks. The drainage from these fistulas is usually milky and opaque (option d).
Nursing Process: Planning   **Client Need:** Physiological Integrity

11.   **The correct answer is d.** The question is asking which option is wrong when doing passive range-of-motion. While flexing the neck is therapeutic, hyperextension could lead to spinal injury. Hyperextending the wrist, flexing the fingers (option a), applying slow firm pressure to contractures (option b), and abducting and externally rotating the shoulder (option c) are all indicated while doing passive range-of-motion.
Nursing Process: Evaluation   **Client Need:** Safe, Effective Care Environment

12.   **The correct answer is a.** The question is asking what to do when putting in a nasogastric tube and the client shows signs of respiratory distress. This would indicate that the tube might have passed into the trachea. The tube should be pulled back to remove it from that area. Notifying the physician (option b) may take too long and the necessary action for the client's safety is within the scope of nursing practice. Completing the tube insertion (option c) would create further respiratory distress. Assessing tube placement with a stethoscope (option d) is unnecessary based on the presenting symptoms.
Nursing Process: Implementation   **Client Need:** Safe, Effective Care Environment

13.   **The correct answer is d.** The question is asking what costs Medicare B covers. Medicare B covers physician's services, specified outpatient services and hospice. Medicare A covers

hospitalization and some long-term care facility and/or home-care services. Medicare B is a supplemental insurance to which persons must subscribe and pay for separately (option a). Neither Medicare A nor B covers the cost of hearing aids or glasses (option b). Persons may be able to purchase other types of supplemental insurance to help cover these costs. Disability insurance covers lost wages due to disabilities (option c).
Nursing Process: Implementation   **Client Need:** Health Promotion & Maintenance

14.   **The correct answer is b.** The question is asking which statement is correct about postoperative discharge instructions for a client who had a radical mastectomy. Following a mastectomy, careful attention must be given to limiting heavy lifting and physically exerting activity. Requesting help with such activities by family members or hired assistants should be encouraged (option c). Special attention should be given to the care of the affected extremity. Yard work and manicures (options a & d) may be done only with special precautions as they can lead to infections. A radical mastectomy includes removal of the regional lymph nodes, which increases the client's risk for developing an infection in that arm.
Nursing Process: Evaluation   **Client Need:** Health Promotion & Maintenance

15.   **The correct answer is c.** The question is asking what teaching strategy pertains particularly to this client. The nurse would identify the client's individual needs because different clients have different learning needs. The client has been a diabetic for 10 years and may be well informed on how to manage diabetes. It is up to the nurse to assess the knowledge of diabetes and identify any areas of need. An explanation of diet (option a), self-monitoring of blood glucose (option b), and the use of visual aids (option d) could be a waste of the nurse's valuable time and an insult to the client's knowledge, if the client was already well-informed and proficient in knowledge of ketoacidosis.
Nursing Process: Planning   **Client Need:** Health Promotion & Maintenance

16.   **The correct answer is d.** The question is asking why a higher concentration of dialysate is used in the last exchange of peritoneal dialysis. The higher concentration of dextrose will attract more water through the process of osmosis, and result in more rapid fluid removal. Thus, more weight loss will occur during this exchange (option a). Dwell time is prescribed by the physician and would not be increased due to the potential for a rapid shift, which could compromise the client (option c). Insulin added to the dialysate is usually not required, but may be added if specifically prescribed by the physician on an individualized basis (option b).
Nursing Process: Analysis   **Client Need:** Physiological Integrity

17.   **The correct answer is d.** The question is asking which option has the least sodium. So-called "low salt" ham (option a) is still high in sodium and should be avoided. Also biscuits are very high in sodium. Kielbasa, (option b) a processed food, and ice cream, a dairy food, both contain high amounts of sodium (option c). All of the other foods would be low in sodium.
Nursing Process: Evaluation   **Client Need:** Health Promotion & Maintenance

18.   **The correct answer is b.** The question is asking what the abdomen will look like after a laparoscopic cholecystectomy. This procedure typically involves four small incisions or punctures into the abdominal wall to allow for the introduction of air into the abdomen for visualization, the laparoscopic camera, a dissector and a retractor. Option (a) is the more traditional gallbladder surgery, option (c) is a minicholcystectomy, and option (d) does not allow for enough incisions for a laparoscopic cholecystectomy to be performed.
Nursing Process: Planning   **Client Need:** Physiological Integrity

19.   **The correct answer is a.** The question is asking for the coach's role during labor. A healthcare provider will perform fetal monitoring and perineal care (options b & c). In addition to coaching, breathing and relaxation, the husband may also time contractions but he should help his partner with concentration rather than distracting her (option d).
Nursing Process: Evaluation   **Client Need:** Health Promotion & Maintenance

20. **The correct answer is d.** The question is asking the most important goal for a client with schizophrenia. The primary goal with any suspicious client is the development of a trusting relationship. Options (a), (b) and (c) are appropriate goals but the primary goal is establishing trust. When this occurs, the other goals can be accomplished.
Nursing Process: Planning   **Client Need:** Psychosocial Integrity

21. **The correct answer is a.** The question is asking how to assist a client to use a transfer board. The client uses hands and arms to push against the bed surface, raise the buttocks and slide onto the board and over to the wheelchair. The wheelchair is placed with the seat facing parallel and toward the head of the bed with the wheels locked (option b). One end of the board is placed on the bed and the other end on the wheelchair (option c). Placing the board on the bedrail may cause it to move or collapse and be a safety hazard. The board surface should be polished (option d) to allow sliding rather than a dull board, which may cause scraping and skin irritation. The arm of the wheelchair should keep the client from sliding onto the floor.
Nursing Process: Implementation   **Client Need:** Physiological Integrity

22. **The correct answer is a.** The question is asking which is a sign of severe progressive pregnancy induced hypertension (PIH). Epigastric pain is a symptom of severe preeclampsia or PIH, which may soon progress to convulsions. Burning on urination (option b), a symptom of urinary tract infections is not associated with severe PIH. An excessive weight gain is associated with severe PIH; 1.5 lb (option c) is not excessive weight gain. Proteinuria of 3+ or 4+ is associated with severe PIH (option d).
Nursing Process: Assessment   **Client Need:** Physiological Integrity

23. **The correct answer is c.** The question is asking which is a true statement about tetralogy of Fallot, a cyanotic heart disease. For children with cyanotic heart disease, parents need instruction for hypercyanotic spells. Watching a child turn blue and have difficulty breathing is frightening, and parents should be prepared to assist the child. The child should be placed in a position of comfort and rest. The most therapeutic position is side lying with knees flexed and head and chest elevated. Flexing legs reduces venous return from the lower extremities and less blood enters the right ventricle. Blood shunted to the aorta has higher oxygen content. The child will become cyanotic due to the mixing of the blood (option b). Clubbing may occur earlier in development (option a). Correction may involve palliative and reparative surgeries (option d).
Nursing Process: Evaluation   **Client Need:** Health Promotion & Maintenance

24. **The correct answer is d.** The question is asking which substance is depleted in clients with Alzheimer's disease. Researchers have determined that many clients with Alzheimer's disease do not have the precursor enzymes necessary for acetylcholine production. Thiamine deficiency (option a) is related to amnestic syndrome. Aluminum deficiency (option b) is unrelated, however, some researchers believe an increase in aluminum in the brain is related to Alzheimer's disease. Dopamine deficiency (option c) is related to Parkinson's disease.
Nursing Process: Analysis   **Client Need:** Physiological Integrity

25. **The correct answer is a.** The question is asking what the immediate action should be if it is suspected that bleach has splashed into an eye. The eye should immediately be flushed in an effort to dilute and wash out any bleach that may have entered the baby's eyes. Starting an intravenous access and checking for facial burns (option b) would cause delay in flushing the baby's eyes and could result in further damage. Obtaining vital signs (option c) is important as a nursing function, but can be obtained once the more urgent need of flushing the eyes is performed. Assessing for signs of aspiration (option d) would be a priority, but the child is not coughing or choking, making care of the eyes the most immediate nursing action.
Nursing Process: Implementation   **Client Need:** Safe, Effective Care Environment

26. **The correct answer is c.** The question is asking what to do when a client with Parkinson's disease has difficulty talking. The nurse should encourage facial muscle exercises to increase strength for communicating. The client should take deep breaths (option a) before speaking to relax muscles. Short shallow breaths will increase muscle tension and rigidity. If the client has

problems with verbal speech, other forms of communication should be encouraged (option b) so the client can continue to participate in his care and other activities. A speech therapist (option d) will assist the client with better communication skills.

Nursing Process: Implementation   **Client Need:** Health Promotion & Maintenance

27.   **The correct answer is a.** The question is asking what would have contributed to the development of cellulites in this client. Cellulitis involves the inflammation of subcutaneous tissues and is often secondary to a break in the skin. Trauma is a common predisposing factor to skin infection and the causative agents are usually staphylococcus aureus and streptococci. Option (b) is an indication of dehydration and is not a predisposing factor to cellulitis. A change in laundry detergents (option c) might lead to contact dermatitis. Option (d) would be seen with an allergic reaction.

     Nursing Process: Analysis   **Client Need:** Physiological Integrity

28.   **The correct answer is c.** The question is asking how to respond to a client with a Hickman catheter who is afraid she will get an air embolus and die. The proper procedure includes clamping the catheter before uncapping so that air does not leak into the catheter (option b). Air is most likely to leak into the catheter due to the same negative pressure that causes breathing to occur. Clot formation (option a) is undesirable and can lead to a thromboembolus. Heparin flushes are routinely performed to decrease the amount of clot formation. Neither an air embolus nor a thrombus formation is likely to occur if proper procedure is followed (option d).

     Nursing Process: Analysis   **Client Need:** Physiological Integrity

29.   **The correct answer is a.** The question is asking what is elevated in a client with a hydatiform mole (molar pregnancy). Blood pressure is not normally elevated in early pregnancy, but with hydatiform mole, symptoms of true preeclampsia may occur before the twentieth week of pregnancy. An increase in temperature may indicate an infection, which is not a typical sign of molar pregnancy (option b). The pulse and respirations may be elevated in pregnancy or be a sign of hemorrhage (options c & d).

     Nursing Process: Analysis   **Client Need:** Physiological Integrity

30.   **The correct answer is 50.** The question is asking how many drops per minute the intravenous solution should infuse. First determine the hourly rate:

$$\frac{\text{amount to be infused}}{\text{number of hours for infusion}} = \frac{1{,}000ml}{5\ hrs} = \frac{200ml}{hr}$$

Next determine the drop rate:

$$\frac{\text{hourly rate x drop factor}}{60\ min} = \frac{200\ x\ 15}{60} = \frac{3{,}000}{60} = \frac{50gtts}{min}$$

     Nursing Process: Planning   **Client Need:** Physiological Integrity

31.   **The correct answer is d.** The question is asking for the best intervention for a client with sensory overload. The presence of continuous noises found in critical care units can cause increased anxiety in the client. Moving the cardiac monitor out of view decreases the sensory input. The client is not disoriented and orienting him every shift is not indicated (option a). Using touch when talking with the client demonstrates caring, however, it is not specific to this client (option b). Triazolam (Halcion) is a sedative and can interfere with rapid eye movement (REM) sleep. Normal sleep cycles should be maintained as much as possible (option c).

     Nursing Process: Implementation   **Client Need:** Psychosocial Integrity

32.   **The correct answer is d.** The question is asking which principle is true for grieving. The client recognizes the availability of the nurse, reality testing is normal and people ask for what they are willing to hear. Personal stories have nothing to do with therapeutic interaction (option a). Denial is normal during certain parts of the grieving process and information is shared gradually with honesty but without confrontation (option b). The nurse takes her cues from the client; brevity and succinctness are not principles of a therapeutic interaction (option c).

Nursing Process: Planning   **Client Need:** Health Promotion & Maintenance

33.   **The correct answers are a, b and d.** The question is asking which clients are at risk for developing placenta previa. The effects of age are the most important factor (option a). The majority of women experiencing placenta previa are multiparous (option c). Multiple gestations increase the risk of placenta previa (option b). Any surgery where the uterus was cut also increases the risk for placenta previa (option d). Rh factor does not influence the occurance of placenta previa (option e).

34.   **The correct answer is b.** The question is asking what would be the priority assessment data for this client. The management of poisoning over the telephone involves prioritizing gathered information as follows: 1. Name, address and telephone number of the caller; 2. Condition of the child; 3. Specific substance ingested, time of ingestion, amount ingested, age and weight of child; (option c) 4. Availability of ipecac; (option a) 5. Availability of transportation if a health facility is required (option d).
Nursing Process: Implementation   **Client Need:** Physiological Integrity

35.   **The correct answer is a.** The question is asking what to say to a group of adolescents who want to know why another student shot their friends. Stating, "It's frightening when we don't understand" reflects the feelings of the student and encourages further expression from this or other students. Saying that you will make sure it does not happen again is false reassurance (option b). Option (c) ignores the student's comment. Option (d) may be true but does not facilitate further discussion.
Nursing Process: Implementation   **Client Need:** Psychosocial Integrity

36.   **The correct answer is d.** The question is asking for a symptom of hepatic encephalopathy. Hepatic encephalopathy is characterized by disturbances in consciousness, changing neurological signs and flapping tremors. Increased abdominal girth (option a) and decreased output (option b) are found in fluid retention and ascites. Jaundiced sclera (option c) is a beginning sign of cirrhosis.
Nursing Process: Assessment   **Client Need:** Physiological Integrity

37.   **The correct answer is a.** The question is asking for the dynamics of the client's belief. The client's belief that her doctor is trying to spray her with a deadly gas is a delusion or fixed false belief that cannot be dispelled with logic or reasoning. Delusions usually result from a projection of the client's sense of self-worth. Misinterpretation of external stimuli is the definition of an illusion. False sensory perception without external stimuli is the definition of a hallucination (option c). Loss experienced in early youth is usually associated with depressed clients (option d).
Nursing Process: Analysis   **Client Need:** Psychosocial Integrity

38.   **The correct answer is b.** The question is asking the most important problem in a client with Meneire's syndrome. Because Meneire's syndrome causes dizziness and vertigo, this client is at high risk for injury secondary to falls. Preventing injury should be the first priority for this client. Options (a) and (c) would be appropriate but not the priority. Fluid and electrolyte imbalance (option d) has not been established.
Nursing Process: Analysis   **Client Need:** Physiological Integrity

39.   **The correct answer is a.** The question is asking for possible positions for a client who has had a craniotomy. Elevating the head of the bed facilitates venous drainage from the head as does maintaining the head in neutral position. Flexing the head will cause venous obstruction (option c). The veins in the head do not contain valves and pressure changes are reflected throughout the system. Promoting venous flow from the head will decrease venous congestion and help prevent cerebral edema and, therefore, help prevent increased intracranial pressure (option d). Option (b) is a particularly dangerous response. The supine position is a poor position for a client who is unresponsive because airway obstruction could occur. In addition, the flat head of the bed and flexed head contribute to increased intracranial pressure.
Nursing Process: Implementation   **Client Need:** Physiological Integrity

40.   **The correct answer is d.** The question is asking how to best help someone be continent of urine. Assisting a cognitively impaired client to the bathroom every one to two hours promotes habit training and, thus, improves continence. Restricting fluids should be avoided. Adults need two to three liters of fluid per day (option a). Placing a urinal and call light within reach would not improve continence of a client, who is unable to perceive the need to void (option b). Color-coding the bathroom door would be indicated for a client with Alzheimer's disease, who may have difficulty with memory (option c).
Nursing Process: Implementation   **Client Need:** Physiological Integrity

41.   **The correct answer is d.** The question is asking what to do for a client who shows ventricular tachycardia on a heart monitor. For witnessed ventricular tachycardia, the client should be prepared for immediate cardioversion. This is a medical emergency, which has to be corrected immediately with electric shock before the arrhythmia progresses into a more serious problem, such as ventricular fibrillation, which is life threatening and does not respond to medication. Although an internal cardiac defibrillator (ICD) is a device to terminate threatening episodes of ventricular tachycardia, it is not the treatment choice in an emergency situation (option a). It is always good to try to decrease a client's anxiety during an emergency situation; however, the client may die of a lethal arrhythmia if the client's condition is not immediately treated (option b). The ICD is usually placed into a client with unstable and repeated episodes of ventricular tachycardia, which are uncontrolled by medication while that client is stable. A pacemaker (option c) is not the treatment of choice for ventricular tachycardia but is often used with a second or third degree heart block.
Nursing Process: Implementation   **Client Need:** Safe, Effective Care Environment

42.   **The correct answer is b.** The question is asking what the nurse would teach a client who just had a laparoscopic cholecystectomy. Right shoulder pain may be caused by migration of CO_2 used to insufflate the abdomen and may be treated with application of heat, walking, and raising the upper torso while in bed. Option (a) is not necessary since the client did not have spinal anesthesia. Option (c) is incorrect since full activity and return to employment usually takes several days to a week. Abdominal distention and temperature elevation can be signs of intra-abdominal complications (option d).
Nursing Process: Planning   **Client Need:** Physiological Integrity

43.   **The correct answer is b.** The question is asking what will happen to the mother's insulin needs during pregnancy. Euglycemia is the goal during pregnancy, as complications are less likely to occur. Insulin needs will increase (possibly two or three times the usual dose) to achieve and maintain euglycemia. Oral hypoglycemic agents (option c) are never used in pregnancy because they are teratogenic. Even though the fetus produces insulin, it does not cross the placenta to help the mother (options a & d).
Nursing Process: Implementation   **Client Need:** Health Promotion & Maintenance

44.   **The correct answer is b.** The question is asking what should reasonably occur after an extracorporeal shock wave lithotripsy (ESWL). ESWL releases a pressure wave under water to crush or break the stone, which can then be easily voided. There will be slight bleeding due to trauma of instrumentation and manipulation. Changes in urine output (options a & c) are not expected and could indicate further renal damage. Pain radiating in the back (option d) may be a sign of further stones or part of a stone, which has lodged in the renal pelvis.
Nursing Process: Planning   **Client Need:** Safe, Effective Care Environment

45.   **The correct answer is c.** The question is asking what is the most important precaution in a client with hepatitis B. Hepatitis B is transmitted mainly through contact with contaminated blood. Contaminated food (option a) or feces (option b) are related to hepatitis A transmission. Feces would transmit hepatitis B only if gastrointestinal bleeding occurs. Icteric skin (option d) would be unrelated to hepatitis transmission.
Nursing Process: Planning   **Client Need:** Safe, Effective Care Environment

46. **The correct answer is c.** The question is asking how to assist a client with a sore throat. Warm saline gargles reduce spasm in the pharynx and relieve soreness by irrigating the throat. The saline should be warm enough to be effective (105°-110°F; 40.6-43.3°C). The client should be encouraged to drink as much as possible (option a). Swabbing the pharynx and drawing blood samples is not necessary at this time because it has already been determined that the client has a streptococcal infection (option b). Acyclovir (Zovirax) is an antiviral medication. A streptococcal infection is a bacterial infection; therefore, an antiviral medication would be ineffective (option d).
Nursing Process: Implementation   **Client Need:** Physiological Integrity

47. **The correct answers are b and d.** The question is asking how the nurse would know that a client with a somatization disorder is improving. Clients with somatization disorder must learn to decrease the focus on their physical symptoms (option c) and work to identify emotions and reactions to events (option d). Another important goal for the client is to gradually decrease feelings of dependence and the unconscious need to develop physical symptoms to meet those dependency needs (option b). The client's goal would be to increase social activity and experience success and increased self-esteem by being able to leave the home environment to expand experiences beyond the family (option a). Although the client eventually needs to leave the sick role to return to independent functioning, it is important that the nurse not have unrealistic expectations about the client's ability to leave or give up the sick role too quickly (option e). Clients need to take small steps toward independence of their sick role identity. If they believe their sick role identity, which is known and safe to them, is being threatened they may increase their focus on somatic complaints.
Nursing Process: Evaluation   **Client Need:** Psychosocial Integrity

48. **The correct answer is c.** The question is asking how to respond to a depressed client who is too tired to attend group session. Fatigue, lethargy and withdrawal are symptoms of the depression. The best way to assist the client is to offer support so that he can carry out expected activities, rather than to allow him to withdraw (option a). Threatening to take away privileges, in this case, will serve to increase the withdrawal (option b). The medication may cause some sedation (option d) but should not keep the client from supervised activities.
Nursing Process: Implementation   **Client Need:** Psychosocial Integrity

49. **The correct answer is a.** The question is asking about the client's knowledge of impending abdominal and thigh liposuction preoperatively. Having the thought pattern of using liposuction regularly is not prudent. The client will continue to gain weight if diet habits are not changed. Some liposuction requires general anesthesia and, in this case, the client had been told that is the plan and is aware of preoperative and postoperative routines associated with liposuction. The surgical candidate has lost 80 pounds and is close to an ideal weight, so she is a prime candidate for this surgery, due to the fact that she may have some areas that are difficult to correct via diet and exercise. A girdle type garment is standard post-procedure protocol and the length of time that a garment is required may vary based again on the individual needs. Clients do have general anesthesia and should not have had anything by mouth at midnight and have arranged for a ride home and for someone to stay with them at night (option b). Weight loss may cause loose skin and fat that is difficult to lose may remain in areas. Even those individuals of near ideal body weight can be troubled by this and can benefit from surgery (option c). A girdle is worn for a number of weeks after surgery and better results occur when clients are compliant (option d).
Nursing Process: Implementation   **Client Need:** Safe, Effective Care Environment

50. **The correct answer is d.** The question is asking which client would be most likely to get a systemic infection in the hospital. The client with a central venous pressure line has a direct access to the blood stream and is at higher risk for infection. The others are sites of possible local infection, which may then move into the blood stream to cause bacteremia (options a, b & c).
Nursing Process: Planning   **Client Need:** Safe, Effective Care Environment

51. **The correct answer is a.** The question is asking if she can have a baby. These areas are under the control of hormones, which are unaffected by the injury. The client will continue to ovulate and menstruate and can conceive and carry a baby to term, if there are no other medical problems.

There will be special care required due to her injury, because she will be prone to urinary tract infections, autonomic dysreflexia, and will not know when she has gone into labor. The other choices are not related to ovulation (options b, c & d).

Nursing Process: Analysis   **Client Need:** Health Promotion & Maintenance

52.   **The correct answer is d.** The question is asking what part of the chain of infection is represented by the findings. The wound serves as an opening or portal of entry. Since there is drainage it contains microbes. The dressing or the hands caring for the dressing are the mode of transmission, not the wound itself. The wound serves as a reservoir for growth of microorganisms (option a). A small break in the wound may become a portal of exit for these microorganisms (option b). The break in the wound would allow entry of microorganisms should unsafe technique be used in changing the dressing or should soiling of the wound and its dressing occur (option c).

     Nursing Process: Analysis   **Client Need:** Safe, Effective Care Environment

53.   **The correct answer is b.** The question is asking which client requires the nurse's immediate attention. A complication of deep vein thrombosis is pulmonary embolism. This is a life-threatening emergency, which requires immediate intervention. Symptoms of a pulmonary embolism include: anxiety, dyspnea, tachycardia, a frequent cough, which may be blood streaked, fever and crackles. The client is demonstrating early signs of pulmonary embolus. Cyanosis in the fingers is indicative of Raynaud's phenomenon, a complication of systemic lupus erythematosus. The fingers need to be rewarmed but this is not a priority (option a). A clinical manifestation of infective endocarditis is bloody urine. This is an expected finding, not a priority (option c). Pheochromocytoma, a tumor of the adrenal gland, may cause hyperglycemia. A glucose level of 270 is high and needs to be treated, however, it does not take precedence over the client with a possible pulmonary embolism (option d).

     Nursing Process: Analysis   **Client Need:** Safe, Effective Care Environment

54.   **The correct answer is d.** The question is asking what problem related to the medication should keep the client from receiving the drug. Nausea, vomiting and diarrhea are signs of gastrointestinal irritability and the drug is stopped temporarily. Decreased serum uric acid levels (option a) and decreased joint pain and swelling (option c) are therapeutic actions of the drug. Flank pain and sweating (option b) are signs of nephrolithiasis and are complications of gouty arthritis.

     Nursing Process: Evaluation   **Client Need:** Physiological Integrity

55.   **The correct answer is b.** The question is asking how to know when a client who has been burned has a low fluid volume. Urine volume should be between 30ml to 60ml/hr. This reflects how much blood is actually perfusing the kidney and, therefore, reflects the cardiac output. Option (a) is incorrect because weight would have to be continually assessed, which is impractical. Also, because of the third spacing of fluid, the client could maintain or gain weight even if he was hypovolemic. Skin turgor and central venous pressure are also measures of hydration but urinary output is the most objective (options c & d).

     Nursing Process: Assessment   **Client Need:** Physiological Integrity

56.   **The correct answer is d.** The question is asking what the nurse knows about the tuberculin skin test. Hypersensitivity to the tuberculin skin test results in a positive skin test. Hypersensitivity is the result of the body's immune response to the M. tuberculosis bacilli. It takes two to ten weeks for the body to develop a positive immune reaction after initial exposure, so the tuberculin test will need to be repeated in 10 to 12 weeks (option a). The skin test will not be immediately positive because the bacilli are slow growing and do not cause an immediate immune response. A tuberculin skin test is still indicated regardless of the hand washing technique used (option c) because the bacilli is spread via airborne droplet nuclei and can be inhaled, resulting in infection. TB cannot be positively diagnosed through X-ray study (option b). Other diseases can give the same results on an X-ray as TB. Bacteriological studies are the only method to establish a positive diagnosis of TB.

     Nursing Process: Evaluation   **Client Need:** Physiological Integrity

57. **The correct answer is a.** The question is asking to identify the statement, which indicates a need for additional education about basal cell carcinoma. Defining and understanding the type of skin cancer is the impetus of this question. Basal cell cancer is among the most treatable cancers. This is indeed the most common skin malignancy occurring in light skinned individuals over the age of 40 (option b). Basal cell cancer is indeed normally translucent with flesh to a pale pink color (option c). Treatment does depend on the site and extent of the tumor (option d).
Nursing Process: Planning   **Client Need:** Health Promotion & Maintenance

58. **The correct answer is a.** The question is asking what should be assessed in a mother who abused drugs and has an infant who feeds poorly and is irritable. The combination of the mother's history of drug abuse and her infant's irritable behavior place this mother and infant at risk for maladaptive attachment. Options (b) and (c) are also important but could be dealt with easily if the mother demonstrated positive bonding behaviors toward her infant. Option (d) is not an immediate priority. As long as the mother continues to use drugs, she places any future pregnancies at risk for a multitude of problems.
Nursing Process: Assessment   **Client Need:** Health Promotion & Maintenance

59. **The correct answer is a.** The question is asking the characteristic for a spontaneous pneumothorax. Primary spontaneous pneumothorax arises in otherwise healthy adults between the ages of 20 and 40 years. Arterial blood gases drawn to confirm a diagnosis of pneumothorax usually reveal a pH greater than 7.45, indicating respiratory alkalosis and hypoxemia (option b). Secondary spontaneous pneumothorax is usually the result of a disease that causes hyperinflation of the lungs, such as asthma or emphysema (option c). A penetrating chest wound may produce a traumatic pneumothorax as opposed to a spontaneous pneumothorax, where the chest wall remains intact (option d).
Nursing Process: Analysis   **Client Need:** Physiological Integrity

60. **The correct answer is d.** The question is asking for symptoms of glaucoma. Haloes around lights may occur because of the blurred vision. Nausea and vomiting may occur due to the increased intraocular pressure. A swollen painful sac filled with pus (option a) usually indicates a sty. Lacrimation and purulent drainage (option b) occur with conjunctivitis. Flashes of light and floating particles in the eye (option c) indicate a detached retina.
Nursing Process: Assessment   **Client Need:** Physiological Integrity

> **Instructions:** Allow yourself 60 minutes to complete the following 60 practice questions. Use a timer to notify yourself when 60 minutes are over so that you are not constantly looking at your watch while completing the questions.

1. A 32-year-old mother of three has just been diagnosed with endometriosis. The physician tells her that she probably had endometriosis before her first pregnancy. The woman asks the nurse why she did not notice any symptoms until now. The most appropriate response by the nurse would be:
   a. "Pregnancy often masks endometriosis."
   b. "The extra endometrial tissue is expelled with the placenta."
   c. "Increased sexual activity promotes endometrial growth."
   d. "Pregnancy and lactation tend to suppress endometriosis."

2. The nurse is caring for a client who had a kidney transplant two days ago. The client is prescribed tacrolimus (Prograf), co-trimoxazole (Bactrim), aluminum hydroxide (Mylanta), and nystatin (Mycostatin). Which finding would most concern the nurse?
   a. Redness at the central IV site.
   b. Blood pressure of 132/86.
   c. Creatinine level of 2mg/dL.
   d. Urine positive for occult blood.

3. The nurse should see which client first? A client with:
   a. a femur fracture, who has developed petechiae on the chest.
   b. asthma, who has an oxygen saturation of 92%.
   c. an abdominal aortic aneurysm, with a pressure that is 20 degrees higher in the arm than in the leg.
   d. tuberculosis, who has blood streaked sputum.

4. A 57-year-old man was referred to the geriatric clinic because he has been up at night wandering around. His wife reports that she had to go through the neighborhood earlier that week to find him. During the nurse's assessment what finding would be consistent with the physician's diagnosis of Alzheimer's disease?
   a. The client will understand the wandering behavior when it is explained to him.
   b. Both recent and remote memory are significantly impaired.
   c. Writing things down will help stimulate the memory.
   d. Decreased concentration is evident when performing tasks.

5. A family member is visiting her mother who has just had a cardiac catheterization using a femoral site. The family member asks the nurse if she could take the client to the lounge in a wheelchair. The most appropriate response would be:
   a. "After a catheterization, your mother must remain on bed rest to prevent a headache."
   b. "There's a chance your mother could have serious complications if we got her out of bed now."
   c. "She must remain on bed rest for 24 hours after the catheterization to prevent angina."
   d. "After a catheterization, we have to observe the needle site carefully and keep the leg straight, for several hours, to avoid bleeding."

6. A client is admitted to the emergency department with pulmonary edema. Morphine sulfate (Morphine) is prescribed. The nurse would expect what effect?
   a. Relaxed bronchospasm.
   b. Reduced pain and dyspnea.
   c. Vasoconstriction and venous pooling.
   d. Increased left ventricular output.

7. The nurse knows that a client with AIDS understands the goal of antiretroviral therapy when the client states:
   a. "It's okay to double up on my meds if I forget to take a dose."
   b. "These pills will lower my CD_4 count to 200."
   c. "A viral load of zero means the virus is gone."
   d. "These drugs will decrease my viral load."

8. The nurse is teaching a group of parents of children with diabetes. The nurse knows that the members can recognize hyperglycemia in their children when they observe:
   a. a rapid onset of shakiness, headache and weakness.
   b. urine reductions with negative glucose and ketones.
   c. blood glucose findings less than 60mg/100ml.
   d. a gradual onset of thirst, frequent urination and acetone breath.

9. A client's condition is improving and the medication is being switched from intravenous heparin sodium (Heparin) therapy to dicumarol (Coumadin). Dicumarol (Coumadin) 15mg p.o. at 6:00PM today is prescribed, but the heparin sodium (Heparin) is not discontinued. The nurse should:
   a. contact the physician and question the prescription.
   b. discontinue the intravenous heparin sodium (Heparin) at 6:00PM and administer the dicumarol (Coumadin).
   c. administer the prescribed amount of dicumarol (Coumadin) at 6:00PM then discontinue the heparin sodium (Heparin) at 9:00PM.
   d. continue the heparin sodium (Heparin) infusion at the current dose and administer the dicumarol (Coumadin) at 6:00PM.

10. The nurse plans to collect a new sputum specimen for culture and sensitivity (C & S) when she realizes the client:
    a. cleared his throat and spit without touching the inside of the container.
    b. rinsed his mouth and throat before obtaining the specimen.
    c. gave a first morning sputum.
    d. used a sterile container.

11. A nurse is planning teaching for parents of a child with a patent ductus arteriosis (PDA). Teaching would include that the blood is shunted from the:
    a. aorta to the pulmonary artery.
    b. left ventricle to the pulmonary artery.
    c. pulmonary artery to the aorta.
    d. right ventricle to the left atrium.

12. Proper postoperative care for a client who just had a thyroidectomy would include:
    a. laying the client flat to promote deep breathing.
    b. placing warm compresses on the operative site.
    c. asking the client to refrain from speaking.
    d. keeping tracheostomy equipment at the bedside.

13. A 67-year-old client with atherosclerosis is admitted with a pulse of 52, a temperature of 35.5°C, blood pressure of 106/80 and respirations of 10. The client is diagnosed with myxedema and medical treatment is started. What would be the priority intervention?
    a. Provide hot packs to help rewarm the client.
    b. Encourage increased intake of fluids.
    c. Draw arterial blood gases as prescribed.
    d. Report any confusion or agitation.

14. The nurse notes that a client with schizophrenia seems to be drinking large amounts of water throughout the day. She is concerned about the possibility of disordered water balance. The nursing interventions that would be necessary to prevent water intoxication would include: Select all that apply.
    a. assess for history of polydipsia and polyuria.
    b. observe the client for responses to temperature change.
    c. assist the client to develop self-monitoring skills.
    d. record daily weights.
    e. assess for possible substance abuse.

15. A woman is breastfeeding her newborn daughter and complains that she has pains similar to labor contractions. The nurse explains that this indicates:
    a. uterine atony.
    b. uterine involution.
    c. inadequate letdown reflex.
    d. incorrect breastfeeding technique.

16. The nurse is formulating a care plan for a client with a spinal cord injury. Which client goal would be most appropriate for recovery? The client will:
    a. accept the societal limitations imposed upon the disabled.
    b. demonstrate the ability to live within certain limitations.
    c. state she will complete educational pursuits.
    d. accept the cord injury.

17. A mother of two children has just been told by her physician that her ovarian cancer is terminal. The woman then tells the home care nurse that the doctor told her she is in remission and expected to recover. The nurse's response is based on the understanding that:
    a. the physician's report was probably misunderstood.
    b. the client is probably suicidal and should be hospitalized.
    c. this is a normal denial response in the grief process.
    d. the client is putting up a front for her children.

18. The charge nurse on a medical-surgical unit is making staffing assignments and must include an assignment for an agency nurse. She is unfamiliar with this nurse's background and experience. Which client assignment should the charge nurse assign to the agency nurse?
    a. A postoperative panniculectomy client, a client with a cardiovascular accident (CVA), a client with chronic obstructive pulmonary disease (COPD).
    b. A postoperative open cholecystectomy client, a client scheduled to receive peritoneal dialysis, a client with Type 1 diabetes.
    c. A client scheduled to receive chemotherapy, a client being admitted with pneumonia, a client with Crohn's disease.
    d. A client post-pacemaker insertion, a client with cystic fibrosis, a client with Addison's disease.

19. A client returns to his room at 2:00PM following an electroconvulsive therapy (ECT) treatment. What is true after ECT? The client:
    a. may go out to dinner with his wife, if he desires.
    b. should not have visitors until he regains his memory.
    c. should be restrained due to an unsteady gait.
    d. may complain of a headache later that evening.

20. The nurse is working with a client who has chronic urinary tract infections. Which outcome would indicate the client has learned how to prevent urinary infections? The client states she will:
    a. drink citrus juices three times each day.
    b. drink cranberry, grape and apple juice liberally.
    c. call her doctor if her urine pH indicates acidity.
    d. maintain urinary output at 1,500ml to 2,000ml per day.

21. A client in skeletal traction must remain on bed rest for several days. The nurse should teach this client to avoid foods high in:
    a. iron.
    b. calcium.
    c. protein.
    d. vitamin C.

22. A client is scheduled to have an ureterostomy. The client angrily tells the nurse, "How do you expect me to live with this. I'll never be normal again." The most appropriate response by the nurse at this time would be:
    a. "Of course you'll be normal, many people live with ostomies."
    b. "I will have experts from the Ostomy Society come to talk with you."
    c. "I can see that you are upset, I'd be upset if this were happening to me."
    d. "Your concerns are normal. Tell me what concerns you the most."

23. The physician prescribes morphine sulfate 2mg intravenously. The vial available contains 10mg in 2mls. How many milliliters should the nurse administer?

    _____

24. The nurse is teaching prenatal class techniques that will be of benefit antepartally and postpartally? Select all that apply.
    a. Kegel's exercises.
    b. Pelvic tilting.
    c. Relaxation exercises.
    d. Cleansing breaths.
    e. Tailor sit.

25. The nurse evaluates that a client on a low-cholesterol, low-sodium diet understands this diet when he chooses:
    a. macaroni and cheese, green beans, lettuce salad.
    b. chicken noodle soup, bagel, peanut butter.
    c. baked chicken leg, corn, gelatin salad with fruit.
    d. broiled ham slice, asparagus, applesauce.

26. In a client with dyspnea, fatigue and a cough productive of frothy sputum, the nurse suspects:
    a. right-sided heart failure.
    b. pulmonary embolism.
    c. left-sided heart failure.
    d. endocarditis.

27. A nurse is notified that a new admission is coming to the unit. The nurse should:
    a. ask the aide to finish this client's bath and then attend to the newly admitted client.
    b. finish the morning care of the other assigned clients before attending to the new client.
    c. ask the unit secretary to escort the client to a room, and then notify the physician of the client's arrival.
    d. direct the aide to take the vital signs, orient the client to the room and fill out the clothing form.

28. Following an exacerbation of her multiple sclerosis, a woman is prescribed methylprednisolone (Solumedrol). Which client statement would indicate that teaching about this drug has been effective?
   a. "This drug will make it easier for me to urinate."
   b. "If I get a fever, I should immediately stop taking the drug."
   c. "This drug may cause me to grow more hair on my body."
   d. "It's alright to take acetaminophen (Tylenol) as long as it's not an elixir with alcohol."

29. The nurse is teaching a mother specific guidelines to follow for her 7-month-old infant. The infant has been diagnosed with nonorganic failure to thrive (NFTT). The nurse evaluates that teaching is effective when the mother:
   a. plays soft music while feeding the baby.
   b. establishes a routine feeding time of 30 minutes.
   c. force feeds at least four ounces of formula per feeding.
   d. maintains eye contact, but does not talk to the baby during feeding.

30. A pregnant woman comes to the clinic with cough, fever and night sweats. She is found to have tuberculosis. The physician prescribes isoniazid (INH). The nurse should:
   a. question the prescription.
   b. wait for the sputum culture report.
   c. give vitamin B complex with the drug.
   d. administer the drug.

31. A client with a pneumothorax has been prescribed the following medications to control pain and facilitate coughing and deep breathing. The nurse should question the appropriateness of which medication?
   a. Acetaminophen with codeine #2 (Tylenol with Codeine #2).
   b. Meperidene hydrochloride (Demerol).
   c. Oxycodone hydrochloride (Percodan).
   d. Propoxyphene napsylate (Darvon).

32. A client has an eye removed for severe pain from glaucoma. Nursing care includes:
   a. administering medication for severe pain.
   b. teaching about care of the prosthesis.
   c. observing the skin graft for signs of infection.
   d. monitoring sutures for absorption.

33. A client is admitted to the intensive care unit with a pneumothorax. The nurse would stay alert for which early symptom of empyema?
   a. Rales and rhonchi.
   b. Straw-colored chest tube drainage.
   c. Temperature of 101°F (40.5°C).
   d. Unusual chest movement.

34. A client is sent to the emergency department with pain on deep inspiration. The physician suspects a possible pulmonary embolus. What assessment will support this diagnosis?
   a. Significant decrease in platelet count.
   b. Recent diagnosis of pneumonia.
   c. Recent repair of hip fracture.
   d. History of coronary artery disease.

35. A 16-month-old child admitted for congestive heart failure, is being treated with furosemide (Lasix) IV in conjunction with lanoxin (Digoxin). What nursing measure is appropriate?
   a. Offering broth and crackers to the client.
   b. Offering the client bananas and oatmeal with brown sugar.
   c. Placing the client on a low-salt diet.
   d. Increasing the client's activity.

36. A client on a psychiatric unit refuses to take his risperidone (Risperdol) when offered by the nurse. The nurse's initial response is to:
    a. wait 15 minutes and offer it again.
    b. offer the alternative of an intramuscular injection.
    c. chart it as refused and offer the medication at the next scheduled time.
    d. mix the liquid form of the medication with his orange juice and place it on his next meal tray.

37. A client comes to the emergency department with complaints of abdominal pain and a throbbing sensation. Blood work shows decreased hematocrit and hemoglobin. Ultrasound shows an abdominal aortic aneurysm of approximately 6cm. Surgery is anticipated. Prior to surgery, the nurse should plan to:
    a. measure urine output for signs of diabetes insipidus.
    b. look for signs of fluid volume overload.
    c. check peripheral pulses and circulation below the aneurysm.
    d. discuss risks and potential complications of surgery.

38. A nurse is working with a client with left hemiparesis. An appropriate short-term goal is that the client will:
    a. position her left arm safely.
    b. dress herself independently.
    c. bathe herself independently.
    d. ambulate safely with a quad cane.

39. The nurse is helping a woman with cirrhosis plan her daily diet. The nurse would encourage her to choose foods that are high in:
    a. fats.
    b. proteins.
    c. carbohydrates.
    d. amino acids.

40. The nurse is assessing a client with suspected hepatitis A. What type of information in the history should the nurse elicit that would be significant to the diagnosis? He:
    a. obtained a tatoo when he was in the Army.
    b. frequently visits a friend on hemodialysis
    c. frequently eats shellfish.
    d. has a habit of heavy alcohol use.

41. A client is admitted with a descending colostomy. The nurse would expect the stool to be of what consistency?
    a. Liquid.
    b. Semi-liquid.
    c. Mushy.
    d. Formed.

42. In a problem-solving group, one client tries to bring her problems up every week and give her solutions to others' problems. She discourages others from speaking and many group members no longer try to participate. The nurse leader should:
    a. make an observation describing the group members' behaviors.
    b. wait for the group to resolve the issue themselves.
    c. tell a story about conflict and resistance in groups.
    d. ask the disturbing group member to leave the group.

43. A nurse is giving a child a feeding through a gastrostomy tube by gravity. During this procedure, the feeding stops flowing. The nurse should:
   a. clamp the gastrostomy tube and assess the child for distress.
   b. gently milk the gastrostomy tube to advance food to the stomach.
   c. lower the gastrostomy tube and allow the formula to drain out.
   d. using a plunger, gently tap the food forward in the syringe.

44. A camp nurse is called to help a child who was bitten by a poisonous snake. What should the nurse do first?
   a. Apply ice to the wound.
   b. Splint the extremity.
   c. Assess range-of-motion of the extremity.
   d. Irrigate the wound with normal saline.

45. A woman begins premature labor and is prescribed ritodrine hydrochloride (Yutopar) 10mg every four hours. During administration, the nurse would especially assess:
   a. changes in temperature.
   b. increase in pulse.
   c. decrease in respirations.
   d. patellar reflexes.

46. When completing the assessment of a client receiving glucocorticosteroid therapy, the nurse will observe for:
   a. nervousness and palpitations.
   b. dehydration and hypertension.
   c. fat deposits in all extremities.
   d. moon face and a buffalo hump.

47. A client with full thickness burns of both arms has just returned from surgery for skin grafts. The nurse determines that the client complies with preoperative teaching when the client:
   a. moves the arms through passive range-of-motion exercises.
   b. keeps the arms down flat on the bed and immobile.
   c. moves legs using active range-of-motion.
   d. keeps well hydrated through fluid intake.

48. Which statement by a client with rheumatoid arthritis indicates that she is ready to care for herself at home?
   a. "I will push doors closed with my hand."
   b. "I will always use a hand bag."
   c. "I will grasp a coffee mug by its handle."
   d. "I will push bowls along the counter."

49. A nurse and client on a psychiatric unit are having a one-to-one interaction. During the session, the client sits very close to the nurse and frequently places his hand on her knee. The appropriate intervention by the nurse would be to say:
   a. "I wish you wouldn't sit so close."
   b. "I am uncomfortable when you touch me, please stop."
   c. "This is inappropriate behavior, we will continue our meeting later."
   d. "It is against the rules to behave like this."

50. When assessing a client, the nurse notes decreased pedal pulses, pallor of the feet and coolness to touch. The nurse would suspect:
   a. varicose veins.
   b. acute femoral artery occlusion.
   c. venous insufficiency.
   d. arterial insufficiency.

51. The nurse realizes that a client with chronic obstructive pulmonary disease (COPD) needs more information when stating that the illness is related to:
   a. gender.
   b. air pollution.
   c. genetic predisposition.
   d. alcohol intake.

52. When planning care for a client with myasthenia gravis, the nurse would especially monitor:
   a. gastrointestinal function.
   b. pulmonary status.
   c. nutritional intake.
   d. activity and sleep patterns.

53. After returning from break, which client should the nurse assess first? A client:
   a. who is ready to go to surgery and needs a preoperative medication before leaving the floor.
   b. who has just expelled two large blood clots into his stoma bag.
   c. with pneumonia, who is scheduled to receive an albuterol (Ventolin) treatment.
   d. with cholecystitis who just vomited 300ml and is complaining of shoulder pain.

54. Appropriate nursing care for a client with an arteriovenous fistula would include:
   a. auscultating for the presence of a bruit.
   b. taking blood pressures on the affected arm.
   c. keeping the fistula covered with a sterile dressing.
   d. observing for separated blood within the fistula.

55. The physician prescribes 15 grams of sodium polystyrene sulfate (Kayexalate) p.o. for a client. The nurse evaluates that this drug has been effective when it:
   a. corrects the client's metabolic acidosis.
   b. enhances vitamin D absorption.
   c. removes excess potassium from the body.
   d. binds excess phosphates in the gastrointestinal tract.

56. The home care nurse is visiting a woman who just had a baby two days ago. Both parents are asking several questions about the care of their new baby. The nurse would facilitate bonding by:
   a. accepting positive emotional parental behaviors and discouraging negative behaviors.
   b. serving as an expert role model in caring for and handling the infant.
   c. observing and pointing out infant behaviors and assisting parents to interpret the meaning of the behaviors.
   d. providing as much care as possible for the infant and encouraging the parents to observe the nurse.

57. In planning care for a client with anorexia nervosa, the nurse understands that the client often fears that:
   a. everyone is against her.
   b. she will never marry or have children.
   c. her family will not love her if she is not perfect.
   d. life is meant to demonstrate success through material possessions.

58. Following an intravenous pyelogram, it is determined that there is a 4ml kidney stone in the lower third of the left ureter. Based on the location of the stone, the nurse realizes that the resulting damage will be:
   a. limited to the left ureter and area above the stone.
   b. localized to the area around the stone.
   c. to the bladder.
   d. to both kidneys.

59. A woman who is addicted to cocaine comes to an outpatient detoxification center for treatment. The client becomes increasingly agitated, paranoid and violent with persecutory delusions. The nurse would:
   a. administer methadone hydrochloride (Methadone).
   b. ask the physician to admit her to a hospital.
   c. talk to her about the consequences of using cocaine.
   d. suggest a warm bath or shower.

60. The nurse is evaluating the plan of care of a client with systemic lupus erythematosus. This evaluation should include:
   a. fatigue and stress assessment.
   b. observation of musculoskeletal function.
   c. bone marrow biopsies.
   d. examination of cranial nerves.

> **STOP. You have now completed Practice Session: 14. Now take a few minutes and correct your answers. Calculate your accuracy rate by dividing the number of questions you completed correctly by the total number of questions you completed (60).**

Correct answers ÷ total number of questions completed = accuracy rate.

_____ ÷ _____ = _____

ANSWERS AND RATIONALES
Practice Session 14

1.   **The correct answer is d.** The question is asking why endometriosis symptoms stop during pregnancy. Pregnancy and lactation suppress menstruation, which decreases endometrial growth. Endometrial implants often shrink over time. Endometriosis usually does not occur for up to five years after the last pregnancy. Pregnancy does not mask the endometriosis (option a). The extra endometrial tissue decreases in size rather than being expelled after pregnancy (option b). Sexual activity does not promote endometrial growth. However, painful intercourse (dyspareunia) may signal the presence of previously undiagnosed endometriosis (option c).
     Nursing Process: Implementation   **Client Need:** Physiological Integrity

2.   **The correct answer is a.** The question is asking which clinical assessment would indicate that the client is having a problem. Tacrolimus (Prograf) is an immunosuppressant used to prevent rejection of the transplanted kidney. The client needs to be closely monitored for possible infections. Redness at the IV site may indicate a local infection. Since it is at a central line site, it can lead to a systemic infection. A blood pressure of 132/86 is slightly elevated, however, this would be expected two days after a kidney transplant (option b). An elevated creatinine level and occult blood in the urine would also be expected findings two days post-kidney transplant (options c & d).
     Nursing Process: Analysis   **Client Need:** Physiological Integrity

3.   **The correct answer is a.** The question is asking the nurse to prioritize care. A complication of a femur fracture is a fat embolism. Petechiae, a symptom of a fat embolism, occur because intravascular thromboses result from decreased tissue oxygenation. An oxygen saturation of 92% is low; however, this would be expected in a client with asthma (option b). The abdominal aorta perfuses the lower extremities; therefore, when there is an aneurysm in this major artery, the pressure would be lower in the legs than in the arms (option c). Bloody sputum is a clinical manifestation of advanced tuberculosis (option d). Although this client should be assessed, he would not take precedence over a client with a fat embolism.
     Nursing Process: Planning   **Client Need:** Safe, Effective Care Environment

4.   **The correct answer is b.** The question is asking what symptoms relate to Alzheimer's disease. Both recent and remote memory is significantly impaired in a client with Alzheimer's disease. This is due to the structural changes, which take place in the brain and interfere with nerve pathways. Understanding behavior (option a) or insight will not diminish as a part of the normal aging process. Clients with Alzheimer's disease may not have insight into behavioral changes, although they may realize that changes in behavior have occurred. Writing things down will stimulate memory in normal aging (option c) but nothing has been successfully demonstrated to stimulate memory in clients with Alzheimer's disease. They also may lose the ability to write (agraphia). Decreased concentration (option d) occurs in normal aging as opposed to the inability to concentrate in clients with Alzheimer's disease.
     Nursing Process: Assessment   **Client Need:** Physiological Integrity

5.   **The correct answer is d.** The question is asking if a client can be up in a wheelchair after a cardiac catheterization using a femoral site. After a catheterization, the needle site must be observed for several hours for bleeding or hematoma formation. Pulses distal to the site must be frequently assessed. Prevention of headaches (option a) is a rationale for bed rest after a spinal tap. Talking about serious complications (option b) may be true, but would be too alarming if said to a client or family member. Angina (option c) may occur, but is not the primary reason for the bed rest.
     Nursing Process: Analysis   **Client Need:** Physiological Integrity

6.   **The correct answer is b.** The question is asking the role of morphine sulfate (Morphine) in treating pulmonary edema. Morphine sulfate (Morphine) reduces pain, anxiety and dyspnea, and decreases peripheral resistance so blood is transferred from pulmonary to peripheral circulation.

Theophylline ethylenediamine (Aminophylline) relaxes bronchospasm if the client is wheezing (option a). Morphine sulfate (Morphine) causes vasodilation or decreased peripheral resistance rather than vasoconstriction (option c). Digitalis preparations may be prescribed to increase heart contractility, which will increase left ventricular output (option d).
Nursing Process: Analysis   **Client Need:** Physiological Integrity

7.   **The correct answer is d.** The question is asking which statement is correct regarding antiretroviral therapy. The goal of this therapy is to decrease the amount of viral load in the blood. Even at an undetectable level (option c), the virus is still present in the lymph nodes and organs. The progression of HIV infection is monitored by a CD_4 count. The goal is to maintain or raise the level to greater than 200 (option b). Adherence to drug regimens is always important. A dose can lead to viral mutations that allow HIV to become resistant to the drug (option a).
Nursing Process: Evaluation   **Client Need:** Physiological Integrity

8.   **The correct answer is d.** The question is asking the signs of hyperglycemia in children. With an increased blood glucose level, a hyperosmolar state exists; fluid would be pulled into the bloodstream from the intracellular compartment resulting in dehydration and thirst. Frequent urination would occur because of the spillage of glucose into the urine and, subsequently, increased urine output; a metabolic acidosis would result in acetone breath. Option (a) indicates hypoglycemia. Option (b) indicates euglycemia or possibly hypoglycemia. Glucose and possible ketones would be present in hyperglycemia. Option (c) indicates hypoglycemia; a blood glucose that is more than 180 to 200mg/100ml would indicate hyperglycemia.
Nursing Process: Evaluation   **Client Need:** Health Promotion & Maintenance

9.   **The correct answer is d.** The question is asking how best to proceed with the physician's prescription. Dicumarol (Coumadin) takes about three to five days to exert an anticoagulant effect; therefore, it is usually initially given in conjunction with heparin sodium (Heparin). The usual initial dose of dicumarol (Coumadin) is 15 to 25mg with a daily dose of 5mg after that. There is no need to question the prescription (option a). Discontinuing the heparin sodium (Heparin) would leave the client vulnerable to clot formation (options b & c).
Nursing Process: Implementation   **Client Need:** Physiological Integrity

10.   **The correct answer is a.** The question is asking which option is wrong when obtaining a sputum specimen. The client should be instructed not to clear his throat and spit, but to breathe deep and cough using his diaphragm. It is correct to advise the client to rinse first (option b), as this may decrease some of the contaminants of the mouth. The sputum collected should be the first of the morning (option c) and should be collected in a sterile container (option d).
Nursing Process: Planning   **Client Need:** Safe, Effective Care Environment

11.   **The correct answer is a.** The question is asking how the blood circulates with this heart defect. In fetal life, the ductus arteriosis connects the pulmonary artery to the aorta, which shunts oxygenated blood directly into the systemic circulation bypassing the lungs. A patent ductus arteriosis (PDA) is present when the normal fetal structure fails to completely close after birth. A PDA causes the blood to shunt from the aorta to the pulmonary artery (option c). Additional blood is recirculated through the lungs. In a ventricular septal defect (VSD), there is an opening between the left and right ventricles. Blood is shunted from the left to right ventricle and the mixed oxygenated blood is sent to the pulmonary artery (option b). In normal cardiac physiology, blood comes into the heart via the vena cava to the right atrium. It then travels to the right ventricle and to the pulmonary artery to be oxygenated by the lungs. Once oxygenated, it travels to the left atrium then to the left ventricle and is pumped out to the body via the aorta (option d).
Nursing Process: Planning   **Client Need:** Physiological Integrity

12.   **The correct answer is d.** The question is asking for the correct action for a client who has had the thyroid removed. The thyroid is in the neck and postoperative swelling or hemorrhage could occur which can press against the trachea and obstruct breathing. For safety, tracheostomy and suctioning equipment are kept at the bedside. The client should be placed in semi-Fowler's position postoperatively to reduce swelling (option a). An ice collar is also used to decrease

swelling. Heat will dilate the vessels and cause increased edema (option b). The client's ability to speak should be tested every two hours. If voice quality worsens, swelling or laryngeal nerve damage is present and should be reported to the physician immediately (option c).
Nursing Process: Implementation   **Client Need:** Safe, Effective Care Environment

13.   **The correct answer is c.** The question is asking what would be the first thing a nurse would do if a client were admitted with severe hypothyroidism. Myxedema is a severe complication of hypothyroidism that most often occurs in clients over 50. Myxedema, left untreated, can result in coma, shock, organ damage and death. A client who has respirations of 10 is demonstrating abnormal respiratory function. Arterial blood gases will provide a baseline assessment of oxygenation so that appropriate treatment can be initiated. Although the client should be rewarmed, hot packs are contraindicated as they may lead to peripheral vasodilation and vascular collapse (option a). Fluids are necessary to help decrease the effects of constipation caused by the lowered metabolism; however, this is not the priority (option b). Confusion or agitation may result from myxedema coma, although it would be more important to obtain arterial blood gases so that any decrease in oxygenation can be treated early. Therefore, confusion and agitation could be prevented (option d).
Nursing Process: Implementation   **Client Need:** Physiological Integrity

14.   **The correct answers are a, c and d.** The question is asking what the nurse can do to prevent water intoxication. Nursing interventions for clients with disordered water balance (which can lead to water intoxication) include assessing the client for a history of polydipsia and polyuria and current fluid intake and output (option a). The nurse would teach the client self-monitoring (option c). Clients can learn to measure specific gravity, record daily weight (option d) and to develop control over their own fluid intake. Substance abuse, while considered a behavioral co-morbidity to schizophrenia, is not associated with disordered water balance (option e). Observing responses to temperature change (option b) would be associated with assessment for disturbed temperature regulation, which is also associated with schizophrenia.
Nursing Process: Planning   **Client Need:** Psychosocial Integrity

15.   **The correct answer is b.** The question is asking what the pains are from in a woman who is breastfeeding soon after delivery. The letdown reflex stimulates the release of oxytocin from the posterior pituitary gland. Oxytocin also affects the smooth muscle of the uterus, causing contractions. Uterine atony (option a), inadequate letdown reflex (option c), and incorrect breastfeeding technique (option d) are less likely to cause the release of oxytocin and, thus, less likely to cause cramping.
Nursing Process: Implementation   **Client Need:** Health Promotion & Maintenance

16.   **The correct answer is b.** The question is asking how to assist a client with a spinal cord injury. Acceptance of life within certain limitations is the most comprehensive goal and shows that the client can cope with a variety of problems, which may be encountered. The client will probably need to challenge societal limitations many times in order to live within the limitations of the injury (option a). The client would have to accept the ability to live within certain limitations in order to finish educational pursuits (option c). The spinal cord injured client is frequently faced with situations that challenge acceptance of the injury (option d).
Nursing Process: Planning   **Client Need:** Physiological Integrity

17.   **The correct answer is c.** The question is asking how to analyze the client's response to learning of terminal illness. The first phase of the grief process in most models is that of shock, disbelief, denial and disorganization. A client needs time and support to assimilate the new information and mobilize reality-based coping skills. Denial can be healthy until the person can start to face the reality of death. The client then usually progresses toward constructive action. There is no evidence to support options (a), (b) or (d).
Nursing Process: Analysis   **Client Need:** Health Promotion & Maintenance

18.   **The correct answer is a.** The question is asking which assignment a charge nurse would give to

an agency nurse with whom she is unfamiliar. The charge nurse must assess each client's particular needs and determine which staff members have the appropriate education and skill to deliver safe, quality care. A greater risk is involved in delegating complex care, such as, clients receiving peritoneal dialysis (option b) or chemotherapy (option c). Additionally, when predictable outcomes are fairly certain, for example, the clients with abdominal surgery, CVA and COPD, safe delegation is more likely. A client post-pacemaker insertion (option d) has unpredictable cardiac rhythms; therefore, this assignment would not be the best option.

Nursing Process: Analysis   **Client Need:** Safe, Effective Care Environment

19. **The correct answer is d.** The question is asking what is true for electroconvulsive therapy (ECT). Due to the nature of the treatment, the client may have a headache, which is easily relieved. Clients usually remain on the unit for observation of complications and treatment effectiveness (option a). The client should have memory loss only for the time of the treatment, but it should not continue unless complications have arisen (option b). Restraints are unnecessary unless a demonstrated problem, such as agitation, has occurred (option c).

Nursing Process: Planning   **Client Need:** Safe, Effective Care Environment

20. **The correct answer is b.** The question is asking which would be true to keep a client from having continuous urinary tract infections. Cranberry, grape and apple juices leave an acid ash that discourages bacterial growth. Citrus juices produce an alkaline residue and servings should be limited to one per day (option a). Urine is normally acidic. Acid urine discourages bacterial growth and is desirable; intervention is not required (option c). A urine output of about 3,000ml per day ensures adequate dilution, which, helps prevent infection (option d).

Nursing Process: Evaluation   **Client Need:** Health Promotion & Maintenance

21. **The correct answer is b.** The question is asking what food substance the immobile client should avoid to prevent complications. A diet high in calcium for the immobile client could lead to the development of renal stones. It is important intake for bone repair, but not to excess. Iron is necessary for cellular oxidation (option a). Protein is essential to replace the extensive use of proteins during the period of illness in order to maintain the nitrogen balance (option c). Vitamin C is vital for wound healing, bone and dentin formation (option d).

Nursing Process: Implementation   **Client Need:** Physiological Integrity

22. **The correct answer is d.** The question is asking how to respond to the client's statement. The statement demonstrates the nurse's empathy and collaboration with the client to address specific concerns. Option (a) minimizes the client's feelings and belittles the client. Option (b) does not address the problem expressed by the client. Option (c) is inappropriate self-disclosure by the nurse. The nurse focused on her feelings, which should not be the focus of the therapeutic relationship.

Nursing Process: Implementation   **Client Need:** Psychosocial Integrity

23. **The correct answer is 0.4.** The question is asking the correct dose to give this client.

$$\frac{\text{dose desired}}{\text{dose on hand}} \times \text{quantity} = \frac{2mg}{10mg} \times \frac{2ml}{1} = \frac{4}{10} = 0.4ml$$

Nursing Process: Planning   **Client Need:** Physiological Integrity

24. **The correct answers are a and c.** The question is asking what exercises would benefit women both before and after birth. Antepartally, Kegel's exercises relieve discomfort of pelvic engorgement and strengthen bladder control muscles. Postpartally, Kegel's exercises promote healing, comfort and reestablishment of perineal muscle tone. Relaxation techniques are of benefit during labor, and throughout pregnancy to facilitate rest and oxygenation of the mother. Postpartally, relaxation techniques help the mother deal with perineal discomfort and aid in breastfeeding. Cleansing breaths (option d) are specific to labor and delivery. Pelvic tilting and the tailor sit (options b & e) relieve low back discomfort through positioning and stretching exercises. These techniques would be used antepartally.

Nursing Process: Implementation   **Client Need:** Health Promotion & Maintenance

25. **The correct answer is c.** The question is asking what foods are low in cholesterol and low in sodium. All of the foods in option (c) are low in both cholesterol and sodium. Macaroni and cheese (option a) contains cholesterol and sodium in the cheese. Canned soups or soups with a dehydrated bullion base contain high sodium content (option b). Most ham contains sodium as a preservative (option d).
Nursing Process: Evaluation   **Client Need:** Health Promotion & Maintenance

26. **The correct answer is c.** The question is asking the meaning of the symptoms: difficulty breathing, tiredness and cough with air laden sputum. In left-sided heart failure, fluid backs up into the lungs resulting in cough and dyspnea. The lowering of cardiac output results in fatigue. Right-sided heart failure (option a) is characterized by edema, weight gain and other symptoms of systemic fluid overload. Pulmonary embolism (option b) presents with sudden onset of chest pain, dyspnea and cyanosis. Endocarditis (option d) is an infection and presents with fever, chills, sweats and cough.
Nursing Process: Analysis   **Client Need:** Physiological Integrity

27. **The correct answer is a.** The question is asking what the nurse should do when engaged in morning care and a newly admitted client is assigned. The aide can finish a client's bath because it is within the scope of practice for an aide. The newly admitted client should be assessed as soon as possible so proper care priorities can be established (option b). Asking the unit secretary to take the client to a room and call the physician (option c) delays assessment, particularly if the physician requests data, which has not yet been gathered. The aide can perform all of the tasks in option (d) but the nurse should assess a client as quickly as possible to detect and prioritize problems.
Nursing Process: Implementation   **Client Need:** Safe, Effective Care Environment

28. **The correct answer is c.** The question is asking which is correct about methylprednisolone (Solumedrol). One side effect of this drug is hirsutism. Steroids are used for their anti-inflammatory response and do not have a direct effect on bladder control (option a). Steroids should never be abruptly discontinued (option b) because it can cause adrenal gland atrophy and lead to adrenal insufficiency. Acetaminophen (Tylenol) and alcohol are both contraindicated when taking methylprednisolone (Solumedrol) (option d). Acetaminophen increases the risk of hepatotoxicity and alcohol increases the risk of a gastrointestinal hemorrage.
Nursing Process: Evaluation   **Client Need:** Health Promotion & Maintenance

29. **The correct answer is b.** The question is asking what would be a correct intervention for a baby diagnosed with nonorganic failure to thrive (NFTT). The parent should develop a structured routine with an established length of time. Thirty minutes is the recommended amount of time. Feedings should take place in a nonstimulating atmosphere to decrease the child's distractibility (option a). Feedings should never be forced (option c). Not only should eye contact be maintained, but also directions about eating should be given while feeding (option d).
Nursing Process: Evaluation   **Client Need:** Health Promotion & Maintenance

30. **The correct answer is d.** The question is asking what to do when isoniazid (INH) is ordered for a pregnant client with newly diagnosed tuberculosis. Isoniazid (INH) is not prohibited in pregnant clients, as are other antituberculin drugs. Therefore, the prescription does not need to be questioned (option a). The client is already diagnosed and the drug prescribed. Waiting for further reports (option b) is unwarranted. Pyroxidine (vitamin B_6), not vitamin B complex, is generally given to prevent the neurological side effects of INH. In any event, the medication must be prescribed by the physician (option c).
Nursing Process: Analysis   **Client Need:** Health Promotion & Maintenance

31. **The correct answer is b.** The question is asking which drug may be questionable in a client with pneumothorax, who needs pain control but also needs the ability to cough and deep breath for lung expansion and to prevent pneumonia. A major hazard of meperidine hydrochloride (Demerol) is respiratory depression. Acetaminophen with codeine #2 (Tylenol with Codeine #2) contains 15mg of codeine and 300mg of acetaminophen (Tylenol). This amount of codeine would not usually

cause respiratory depression (option a). Oxycodone hydrochloride (Percodan) (option c) and propoxyphene napsylate (Darvon) (option d) do not depress respiratory function.
Nursing Process: Analysis   **Client Need:** Physiological Integrity

32.   **The correct answer is b.** The question is asking the postoperative care of a client who has had an enucleation. Post-enucleation for glaucoma, a temporary prosthesis is placed in the eye socket then a pressure dressing is applied to prevent bleeding. The client should be monitored for bleeding. Creams to decrease inflammation and prevent infection may be applied in the cavity. On or about three weeks, a permanent prosthesis is inserted. The client needs to learn how to manipulate and clean the prosthesis. The client usually experiences great pain relief once the eye is removed and should feel little pain afterwards (option a). The physician should be notified if severe pain develops. Skin grafts may be a part of exenteration, which is removal of everything in the area including the optic nerve, which is usually due to cancer (option c). No sutures are needed (option d).
Nursing Process: Implementation   **Client Need:** Physiological Integrity

33.   **The correct answer is c.** The question is asking for an early sign of empyema, which is an infection. An elevated temperature may be an early sign of empyema. Rales and rhonchi (option a) are symptoms of pulmonary edema. Straw-colored drainage (option b) indicates pleural effusion. Unusual chest movement (option d) may signify a new air leak or incomplete air evacuation or be due to an accumulation of purulent fluid, which is a late sign of empyema.
Nursing Process: Evaluation   **Client Need:** Physiological Integrity

34.   **The correct answer is c.** The question is asking which symptom relates to a pulmonary embolus. Clients suffering with long bone injuries or trauma, such as hip or pelvic fractures, are predisposed to pulmonary emboli, because these conditions slow venous return, which can cause emboli. Other risk factors include: surgery, pregnancy, oral contraceptive use, myocardial infarction, immobilization, obesity and malignancy. A rise in platelets may occur due to release of tissue thromboplastin after injury (option a). Recent diagnosis of pneumonia may cause the client to present with signs of shortness of breath; however, it is not related to pulmonary embolism (option b). Coronary artery disease (option d) causes narrowing of the arteries but does not usually result in pulmonary embolus.
Nursing Process: Assessment   **Client Need:** Physiological Integrity

35.   **The correct answer is b.** The question is asking what to do with an infant on lanoxin (Digoxin) and furosemide (Lasix). Furosemide (Lasix) causes the body to lose potassium, which is necessary for proper heart functioning. The client also needs a diet high in potassium because lanoxin (Digoxin) toxicity occurs rapidly in the presence of a low serum potassium level. Bananas, oatmeal and brown sugar are all foods the child might eat and are high in potassium. Congestive heart failure generally includes an excess of fluid. Salty foods, such as broth and crackers, (option a) will not help the child rid the body of extra fluids. However, infants are rarely placed on low-salt diets (option c) because they may refuse to eat all together. Increasing the child's activity (option d) will rapidly deplete the child of oxygen when the child needs to conserve oxygen.
Nursing Process: Implementation   **Client Need:** Physiological Integrity

36.   **The correct answer is a.** The question is asking how to respond when a psychotic client will not take medication. The client should be given time to think about it and another opportunity to accept the medication. A client should not be threatened with the alternative intramuscular injection (option b) just for refusal of medication. Clients have the right to refuse treatment. Option (c) is an inadequate intervention and assists the client with noncompliance. Option (d) is unethical and illegal.
Nursing Process: Implementation   **Client Need:** Physiological Integrity

37.   **The correct answer is c.** The question is asking for a preoperative plan of care for a client with an abdominal aortic aneurysm. Circulation below the aneurysm may be compromised since the aneurysm is bleeding and blood is pooling and being lost in that area. Oxygen and other nutrients

are not getting to the area below the aneurysm, which may result in ischemic areas. Due to blood and fluid loss, a fluid volume deficit often occurs with resultant dehydration and decreased urinary output unrelated to hormones (options a & b). Discussing risks and benefits of surgery is the physician's responsibility (option d).
Nursing Process: Planning   **Client Need:** Physiological Integrity

38.   **The correct answer is a.** The question is asking for a reality based short-term goal for the client with left-sided paralysis. The client has unilateral neglect, which means that she denies the left side of her body. She would tend to ignore the position of her left arm, making the potential for injury to this arm great. Options (b), (c) and (d) are long-range goals and not appropriate at this time. First, the client must learn to acknowledge the left side of her body and will need assistance to learn to do this.
Nursing Process: Planning   **Client Need:** Physiological Integrity

39.   **The correct answer is c.** The question is asking what foods would be recommended for a client who has problems with the liver. Think about what the liver does in relation to these food substances. Carbohydrates are necessary because the liver cannot synthesize or store glucose. The liver is responsible for the metabolism of fat. A diseased liver would have difficulty metabolizing a high fat diet (option a). The protein is less likely to be tolerated in a client with liver problems because protein breaks down to nitrogenous wastes (ammonia), which cannot be detoxified by the liver. The ammonia increases and results in nausea and anorexia. Increasing ammonia can lead to confusion and coma, if allowed to accumulate (option b). Amino acids are the building blocks for protein (option d).
Nursing Process: Analysis   **Client Need:** Physiological Integrity

40.   **The correct answer is c.** The question is asking which data is related to hepatitis A. Outbreaks of hepatitis A occur in environments with good sanitation when the causative virus contaminates water, milk or food. Of special concern are individuals who eat raw or steamed shellfish. Hepatitis B is contacted primarily through the serum of an infected person, as in tattooing or hemodialysis (options a & b). Heavy alcohol ingestion (option d) is the cause of alcoholic hepatitis, an inflammation of the liver.
Nursing Process: Assessment   **Client Need:** Physiological Integrity

41.   **The correct answer is d.** The question is asking what type of stool to expect from a descending colostomy. The normal character of stool passed from a descending colostomy is formed. Liquid and semi-liquid stool (options a & b) are from an ascending colostomy, depending on position. Mushy stool (option c) comes from a transverse colostomy.
Nursing Process: Analysis   **Client Need:** Physiological Integrity

42.   **The correct answer is a.** The question is asking how to handle a group situation when one member monopolizes the discussion and the other members do not respond. The nurse leader's role is to facilitate group process. Therefore, making an observation of the group's behavior allows the group to see and respond differently by discussing the matter in an open forum. This allows for feedback from others, self-reflection and trying new behaviors in a safe place, which is the point of group support. The group has responded by allowing the monopolizer to continue and becoming silent themselves. This maladaptive behavior needs to cease or the group will become dysfunctional (option b). Conflict should be addressed directly, not through stories (option c). Asking the monopolizer to leave the group may be a last resort if the behavior continues and intimidates others (option d).
Nursing Process: Implementation   **Client Need:** Health Promotion & Maintenance

43.   **The correct answer is b.** The question is asking what to do when the feeding stops flowing in by gravity. Gentle milking of the tube may promote movement by gravity. For gastrostomy tube feedings, the tube should be raised about 12 inches. The formula should be allowed to flow by gravity (option c). Pressure is never applied and could force the formula into the esophagus (option d). Air should be introduced through the gastrostomy tube and never forced through the esophagus. Thus, clamping the tube is contraindicated. Also, clamping may promote

regurgitation and place pressure on the suture line. Open-air passage via the tube allows regurgitation through the tube. There is no indication that distress is present or that the feeding should be interrupted (option a).

Nursing Process: Implementation   **Client Need:** Physiological Integrity

44. **The correct answer is b.** The question is asking what should be done first when a poisonous snake bites a person. Actions need to be taken to prevent the spread of the venom. The affected extremity should be immobilized and splinted. Applying ice can cause the tissue to necrose, so it should be avoided (option a). Some snake bites are neurotoxic and can cause parasthesias, but assessing range-of-motion would be contraindicated as it could help spread the venom to other parts of the body (option c). Irrigating the wound will not remove the toxin (option d), since this is a puncture wound.

Nursing Process: Implementation   **Client Need:** Physiological Integrity

45. **The correct answer is b.** The question is asking what is essential to assess when a client is receiving ritodrine hydrochloride (Yutopar). This medication increases the heart rate and exerts preferential effect on beta-receptors. It does not affect body temperature (option b). It may cause pulmonary edema, thus, an increase in respirations (option c). Patellar reflexes (option d) are not altered with ritodrine hydrochloride (Yutopar), but may be altered with magnesium sulfate.

Nursing Process: Evaluation   **Client Need:** Physiological Integrity

46. **The correct answer is d.** The question is asking what was important to look for in a client on glucocorticoid (steroid) therapy. Moon face and a buffalo hump appearance result from altered fat metabolism, causing abnormal deposits of fat in the face and intracapsular areas. Most clients experience an increase in appetite. The arms and legs are thin as a result of muscle wasting from altered protein catabolism (option c). Clients are prone to fluid overload, not depletion as seen in dehydration (option b). Hypertension, nervousness and palpitations (option a) are signs of pheochromocytoma.

Nursing Process: Assessment   **Client Need:** Physiological Integrity

47. **The correct answer is c.** The question is asking which action shows understanding of preoperative teaching on skin grafts. The client should perform active range-of-motion exercises to uninvolved areas to promote circulation and prevent thrombus formation. The arms should remain immobile. Physical therapy is suspended for several days while the grafts begin to heal, and then movement is permitted (option a). Arms with grafts are often in splints to immobilize them and should be positioned so that edema does not occur (option b). Proper fluid balance is always important, not just during grafting (option d).

Nursing Process: Evaluation   **Client Need:** Physiological Integrity

48. **The correct answer is d.** The question is asking which would be true for a client with rheumatoid arthritis. The client should slide objects rather than lifting them. She should also push doors open with her shoulders, not the hand (option a). Backpacks or fanny packs are suggested rather than a handbag (option b). Coffee mugs should be grasped by the mug and not just the handle (option c). It should be stressed to use the strongest joint for all activities. Joints should be used in their best positions.

Nursing Process: Implementation   **Client Need:** Health Promotion & Maintenance

49. **The correct answer is b.** The question is asking what the nurse should do about the client's behavior. The first step in intervening with unacceptable sexual behavior from clients is a matter of fact statement that sets limits without being punitive. The nurse needs to use clear and definitive language that simply states what behavior she expects. Options (a) and (d) are unclear messages to the client and option (c) is punishing rather than therapeutic.

Nursing Process: Implementation   **Client Need:** Psychosocial Integrity

50. **The correct answer is d.** The question is asking what is probably wrong with this client. The nurse should suspect arterial insufficiency. Atherosclerosis is the cause of chronic arterial occlusive disease and results in weakened or absent peripheral pulses, cyanosis, or paleness of

color and coolness of extremities as a result of a lack of blood supply below the occlusion. Acute femoral artery occlusion (option b) would result in sudden onset of lack of pulses and a cold foot that became progressively cyanotic. In venous insufficiency (option c), blood can enter the leg but has difficulty returning; therefore, there is edema and often rubor and warmth of the extremity. Varicose veins (option a) would not interfere with arterial circulation.
Nursing Process: Assessment   **Client Need:** Physiological Integrity

51.   **The correct answer is d.** The question is asking which factor would not predispose the client to chronic obstructive pulmonary disease (COPD). Studies show that COPD is both genetic (option c) and environmental (option b). Cigarette smoking and air pollution are both known contributors. Men develop COPD more frequently than women (option a).
Nursing Process: Analysis   **Client Need:** Physiological Integrity

52.   **The correct answer is b.** The question is asking for the most important area to address in a client with myasthenia gravis. Maintaining optimal respiratory status is of primary concern because weakness and fatigue of respiratory muscles can lead to respiratory depression and arrest. Swallowing may also be impaired, which is a gastrointestinal dysfunction (option a) and poor nutritional intake, (option c) as well as risk for aspiration. Fatigue (option d) is also a problem and sufficient rest must occur or the client will have difficulty engaging in any activities.
Nursing Process: Planning   **Client Need:** Physiological Integrity

53.   **The correct answer is b.** The question is asking which client is most in need of help from the nurse. A stoma should produce stool. Two large clots are an indication of gastrointestinal bleeding, which left untreated, could lead to hypovolemic shock and death. The client, who is ready to go to surgery, is not in any apparent danger and can wait until the nurse provides care for the client who is bleeding (option a). Albuterol (Ventolin) is a bronchodilator that is used to help the client with pneumonia breath more easily. However, this client is not demonstrating signs of respiratory distress and, therefore, would not take precedence over the client who is bleeding (option c). Vomiting and shoulder pain are expected clinical manifestations of cholecystitis and would not require the nurse's immediate attention.
Nursing Process: Analysis   **Client Need:** Safe, Effective Care Environment

54.   **The correct answer is a.** The question is asking how to care for an arteriovenous (AV) fistula. A fistula uses the client's blood vessels as an internal access. The only way to check functioning is through assessment of a bruit or thrill, which can be heard and felt at the site. A shunt has external structures, which provide access. A shunt needs protection by wrapping with gauze (option c). The shunt should also be checked for separated blood and for a thrill or bruit (option d). Blood pressure to the affected extremity is contraindicated as it cuts off blood flow and may precipitate clot formation (option b).
Nursing Process: Implementation   **Client Need:** Physiological Integrity

55.   **The correct answer is c.** The question is asking for the action of the drug. Kayexalate is a cation exchange resin used to treat hyperkalemia. It removes potassium from the body by exchanging one milliequivalent of sodium for each milliequivalent of potassium removed. Sodium bicarbonate is used to correct acidosis (option a). Vitamin D (option b) is given to enhance absorption of calcium. Calcium carbonate may be given to bind to phosphorous and lower phosphate levels (option d).
Nursing Process: Evaluation   **Client Need:** Physiological Integrity

56.   **The correct answer is c.** The question is asking how best to help parents bond to their newborn infant. One of the major blocks to positive parent-infant attachment is that parents do not know how to interpret infant behaviors and to respond appropriately. With this knowledge, they will feel much better equipped to deal with their newborn. The other options (a, b & d) only serve to emphasize the parents' feeling of inadequacy in understanding their infant.
Nursing Process: Implementation   **Client Need:** Health Promotion & Maintenance

57. **The correct answer is c.** The question is asking what the client with anorexia nervosa is most concerned about or what the underlying dynamics are of the disease. Rather than rebel, perfection is sought. Although unattainable, approval and love are sought by trying harder to be perfect. Fear of imperfection means loss of family love and approval. Thinking everyone is against you (option a) is a type of persecutory delusion seen in schizophrenia. Fear of never marrying or having children (option b) is not usually true since one theory of the disease is that persons with anorexia do not wish to progress past puberty so would not want to marry or have children. Material possessions exclusively (option d) may relate to antisocial personality disorder.
Nursing Process: Analysis   **Client Need:** Psychosocial Integrity

58. **The correct answer is a.** The question is asking where the damage will be based on location of the stone. When there is an obstruction to the normal flow of urine, the damage is to areas above the point of obstruction (options b & c). If the stone is located in the left ureter, the damage will be to the left ureter, left renal pelvis, and left renal parenchyma (option d).
Nursing Process: Analysis   **Client Need:** Physiological Integrity

59. **The correct answer is b.** The question is asking what should be done for a client having a psychotic reaction to cocaine. With cocaine withdrawal, the person may exhibit psychotic symptoms and is often admitted to the hospital for treatment. Methadone hydrochloride (Methadone) is used for heroin withdrawal (option a). Talking to the client about consequences would be difficult when the client is not reality based (psychotic) (option c). A warm bath or shower may calm the client but will not reduce psychotic symptoms (option d).
Nursing Process: Planning   **Client Need:** Physiological Integrity

60. **The correct answer is a.** The question is asking what to assess in a client with systemic lupus erythematosus (SLE). To maintain the remission, it is important to have regular sleep, food and exercise, without developing fatigue. A variety of stressful events place the client in jeopardy. Observation of musculoskeletal function (option b) might be helpful in general, but not in particular. Bone marrow biopsies (option c) are not routinely performed on clients with SLE. Cranial nerve assessment (option d) would not yield significant data related to the effects of SLE.
Nursing Process: Evaluation   **Client Need:** Health Promotion & Maintenance

PRACTICE SESSION: 15

> **Instructions: Allow yourself 60 minutes to complete the following 60 practice questions. Use a timer to notify yourself when 60 minutes are over so that you are not constantly looking at your watch while completing the questions**

1. An emergency department nurse is triaging clients during a busy weekend night. Which client should be seen first?
   a. A man who was involved in motorcycle accident. He was talking when he came in but is now snoring loudly.
   b. An 8-year-old female who may have been molested by a relative. She is quiet and is clinging to her mother.
   c. A man with a suspected transient ischemic attack. He is talking with his daughter, saying he is feeling well and wants to go home.
   d. A client with diabetes complaining of having difficulty walking because a sore on the bottom of her foot is beginning to bleed.

2. A client is diagnosed at the clinic with iron deficiency anemia. The nurse would expect what complaints by the client?
   a. Weakness, dizziness and shortness of breath.
   b. Nausea, vomiting and diarrhea.
   c. Pain, dyspnea and loss of consciousness.
   d. Amenorrhea, lanugo and weight loss.

3. A client is admitted with hypoparathyroidism. The nurse would assess for:
   a. polyuria.
   b. fatigue.
   c. leg cramping.
   d. low urine specific gravity.

4. During peptic ulcer healing, the nurse would teach the client to:
   a. eat several small meals per day.
   b. consume mainly bland foods.
   c. use milk and cream products.
   d. season with black pepper but no salt.

5. What would be included when teaching a client who has been diagnosed with Addison's disease? Select all that apply.
   a. Techniques for stress management.
   b. Need for lifelong corticosteroid replacement therapy.
   c. Low-sodium diet.
   d. Frequent blood glucose monitoring.
   e. Need to avoid the sun.
   f. Self-administration of IM injections.

6. A diabetic client questions why she must take the insulin by injection, "Don't they have pills that are the same?" The best reply by the nurse would be that regular insulin taken orally would:
   a. be absorbed more slowly than the parenteral route.
   b. not be given in sufficient quantity to meet the metabolic needs.
   c. cause nausea and vomiting.
   d. be destroyed by the gastric contents.

7. A client is admitted after hitting his chest on the steering wheel during a motor vehicle accident. The client's blood pressure is falling, neck veins are distended and heart sounds are muffled. The nurse should suspect:
   a. subcutaneous emphysema.
   b. pulmonary contusion.
   c. hypovolemic shock.
   d. cardiac tamponade.

8. A female client is concerned about her ability to become pregnant. In discussing this with her, the nurse understands that the best indicator of fertility is:
   a. an early onset of menarche.
   b. galactorrhea.
   c. monthly menstruation with premenstrual symptoms.
   d. that the client is younger than 35 years of age.

9. A client diagnosed with pulmonary tuberculosis is started on isoniazid (INH). The nurse would teach the client to:
   a. wear glasses instead of contacts.
   b. take the medication with milk or food.
   c. have liver enzyme levels drawn monthly.
   d. report any changes in hearing immediately.

10. A client with an implanted prosthetic device of the arm complains of severe pain at the insertion site and loosening of the prosthesis six months after insertion. The white blood count and sedimentation rate are elevated. A diagnosis of osteomyelitis is made. After surgical removal of the prosthesis, the client is admitted to the orthopedic unit for intravenous antibiotics. The nursing care plan would include:
    a. visual imagery and a low-protein diet.
    b. muscle strengthening exercises and a low-calorie diet.
    c. range-of-motion exercises and monitoring for side effects of antibiotics.
    d. weight bearing on the affected arm and a diet high in vitamins A and C.

11. A client comes to the emergency department after a head injury. The client is unconscious and has signs of increased intracranial pressure. The client is admitted and an osmotic diuretic is prescribed. The priority nursing diagnosis would be:
    a. fluid volume excess.
    b. altered cerebral tissue perfusion.
    c. impaired breathing pattern.
    d. altered thought processes.

12. A client on oxygen therapy needs arterial blood gases to be drawn. The nurse teaches that the purpose of the test is to:
    a. evaluate functional capacity.
    b. identify lung defects.
    c. assess if oxygen therapy is adequate.
    d. differentiate between types of perfusion defects.

13. A 79-year-old man is admitted with periods of confusion, weight loss and delusional thinking. He is diagnosed with dementia. The priority nursing assessment for this client would be:
    a. memory impairment.
    b. social alterations.
    c. impaired reality testing.
    d. impaired judgment.

14. A new nurse asks the charge nurse for some guidance. She relates that she did not know how to intervene with a 4-year-old that just kicked her. The charge nurse offers the following suggestion. Tell/Ask the child:
    a. "Are you angry with me? Let's talk about it."
    b. "If you kick me again, you will not get to go to the playroom."
    c. "It is not nice to hurt other people, and you need to say you are sorry."
    d. "It is hard to be sick, but let's talk about how you can handle your feelings differently."

15. A hypertensive client is about to be discharged. The client has been noncompliant with diet and exercise leading to hospitalization. To increase compliance, the nurse would:
    a. explain dietary changes and refer to a dietician.
    b. teach the client how to take and record blood pressure.
    c. identify how high blood pressure led to hospitalization.
    d. discuss how changes can fit with daily lifestyle practices.

16. Which assessment parameter should be checked for a nursing diagnosis of fluid volume deficit?
    a. Urine specific gravity.
    b. White blood cell count.
    c. Food intake at meals.
    d. Range-of-motion.

17. A client needs a bone marrow aspiration. The nurse should prepare the client by:
    a. explaining how to deal with the pain of aspiration.
    b. telling the client that the test will be performed under general anesthesia.
    c. starting a preoperative checklist to be completed in the morning.
    d. teaching that he will remain flat for eight hours.

18. The nurse validates that an adolescent has learned how to administer NPH and regular insulins when he:
    a. gives the NPH and regular insulins in two separate syringes.
    b. gives the NPH and regular insulins together, withdrawing the regular insulin first, then the NPH insulin.
    c. gives NPH and regular insulins together; withdrawing the NPH insulin first, then the regular insulin.
    d. gives the regular insulin in the morning and the NPH insulin in the afternoon.

19. A client with a malignant lung tumor is scheduled to begin chemotherapy tomorrow. The initial action of the nurse at this time would be to:
    a. assure the client that chemotherapy, if successful, will eradicate the tumor.
    b. administer an antiemetic to minimize nausea and vomiting.
    c. inform the client about chemotherapy and its expected side effects.
    d. place the client in strict isolation before chemotherapy begins.

20. A client is diagnosed with chronic suppurative otitis media. A myringotomy is scheduled. The client asks how this will help. The nurse states, "It will:
    a. repair the hole in the tympanic membrane."
    b. remove the cyst and graft skin to the area."
    c. equalize pressure between the middle and external ear."
    d. involve insertion of an electrostimulation device."

21. The priority nursing action for a client with magnesium sulfate toxicity is to:
    a. administer calcium gluconate.
    b. stop the infusion of magnesium sulfate.
    c. immediately call the attending physician.
    d. administer oxygen.

22. A sliding hiatal hernia was diagnosed in a female client. The assessment data, which supports this diagnosis, is:
    a. weight loss and persistent cough.
    b. pain in mouth and pharynx.
    c. dysphagia and fever following vomiting.
    d. regurgitation and heartburn.

23. The nurse is teaching a client about home intravenous therapy. The client demonstrates the procedure for the nurse. Which return demonstration would the nurse document as correct?
    a. Stating, "The tubing will be changed every 48 hours."
    b. Attaching the filter before purging the tubing.
    c. Flushing the site with sterile water.
    d. Increasing the rate when the solution slows or stops.

24. A child, who recently had surgery to correct a cleft palate, has now developed otitis media. Cleft palate is associated with otitis media because of:
    a. plugging of the eustachian tube with food particles.
    b. lowered resistance due to poor nutritional status.
    c. inefficient function of eustachian tubes and improper middle ear drainage.
    d. coexisting defects of the middle ear and eustachian tube related to eardrum deficiencies.

25. A client suffered a stroke several days ago. The nurse is encouraging the client to perform morning care independently. The client's brother enters the room and says, "You should be doing that. My brother's too ill." The best reply of the nurse would be:
    a. "It's difficult to see your brother so ill, isn't it?"
    b. "I was evaluating his ability to do this for himself."
    c. "This helps him exercise his arm and feel independent."
    d. "You aren't helping your brother recover this way."

26. A client with an ileostomy complains of blockage. Dietary foods that should be limited in this client would be:
    a. spicy foods, red wine and green beans.
    b. corn, Chinese vegetables and wild rice.
    c. applesauce, creamy peanut butter and tea.
    d. eggs, fish and cheddar cheese.

27. A 4-year-old child with a hearing impairment is admitted to the pediatric unit. The best way to communicate would be to:
    a. write messages on a chalkboard.
    b. speak slightly slower than usual.
    c. refrain from visual aids.
    d. give complete and detailed explanations.

28. After coming out of shift report, a nurse on a medical-surgical unit would assess which client first?
    a. A woman with congestive heart failure, who just started receiving her first unit of packed RBCs and is asking for pain medication for a "side ache."
    b. A man who had a small bowel resection two days ago. His NG tube drained 400ml of green fluid on the previous shift. He is complaining of difficulty swallowing and nausea.
    c. A woman who recently arrived to the floor from the post-anesthesia care unit (PACU) in stable condition with a patient controlled analgesia (PCA) pump. She is complaining of a headache and a dry mouth.
    d. A man who had hemodialysis in which 2.4L of fluid was removed. He had been complaining of shortness of breath before the procedure. He is asking for ginger ale and something to eat.

29. A nurse is teaching a client about her newly prescribed prednisone (Deltasone) therapy. What should be included?
    a. Extra prednisone (Deltasone) may be needed with increased stress.
    b. Blood pressure should be checked regularly.
    c. Take prednisone (Deltasone) on an empty stomach.
    d. Store prednisone (Deltasone) in the refrigerator.

30. The charge nurse returns from break and is approached by several personnel who relate the following information. Which situation should the nurse address first?
    a. A physician is waiting to give a verbal order for a STAT dose of promethazine (Phenergan).
    b. The emergency department is on the telephone to give report on a new admission.
    c. A maintenance worker is laying on the ground next to a ladder.
    d. An aide is reporting that a client's blood transfusion is complete.

31. A client is diagnosed with amyotrophic lateral sclerosis (ALS). The client asks how long it will take to cure it. The nurse replies:
    a. "Muscle relaxants will reduce spasticity until it disappears."
    b. "Once the tracheostomy is in, your problem will be relieved."
    c. "Physical therapy will assist with weak muscles."
    d. "Supportive therapy helps, but the disease is progressive."

32. The nurse has collected a stool specimen for ova and parasites. The nurse should then:
    a. refrigerate it until it is taken to the lab.
    b. ask the aide to take it to the lab.
    c. place it in the utility room until lab personnel pick it up.
    d. place it in a formaldehyde solution.

33. While taking the history of a newly diagnosed 6-year-old with Type 1 diabetes, the nurse would expect to find that:
    a. children with diabetes often manifest few symptoms prior to an episode of acute ketoacidosis.
    b. children with diabetes do not experience the typical hunger symptoms seen in adults.
    c. children with diabetes usually will experience bedwetting and tiredness as the initial manifestations.
    d. parents of diabetic children usually experience a period of denial in which they believe the symptoms mean nothing and no treatment is sought.

34. A client on a psychiatric unit calls the local variety store and orders over 1,000 dollars of party supplies to be delivered to her in the hospital. The manager calls to confirm the order. When the nurse questions the client, she tells her that she is planning a big surprise party for everyone. The nurse should:
    a. ask the client how she intends to pay for the party.
    b. tell the client that the party has been cancelled.
    c. tell the client she can help the other clients who are planning a small unit party.
    d. tell the client that the party must be postponed until she is feeling better.

35. A student nurse is caring for a client with chronic bronchitis. The student shows understanding of medication use, when stating the primary action of aminophylline (Theophylline) in this client, is to:
    a. liquefy tenacious sputum.
    b. ease the coughing up of secretions.
    c. relax the bronchial smooth muscle.
    d. block beta-receptors in the lungs.

36. On the cardiac monitor, the nurse notes the rhythm shows no P wave and no PR interval. The nurse would analyze this as:
   a. atrial fibrillation.
   b. premature ventricular contractions.
   c. ventricular tachycardia.
   d. ventricular asystole.

37. A client with pancreatitis is admitted to the medical unit in severe pain. Which data would show that the pancreatitis would be severe?
   a. Over age 55 years.
   b. White blood cell count 12,000.
   c. Serum glucose of 120.
   d. Pale stools.

38. In the immediate postoperative period, a client awakens and complains of discomfort. The appropriate nursing action would be to:
   a. assess the lungs.
   b. reposition the client.
   c. check the drains.
   d. administer an analgesic.

39. When teaching a woman about oral contraceptives, the nurse should instruct her to be alert for an increase in:
   a. iron-deficiency anemia.
   b. ectopic pregnancy.
   c. pelvic inflammatory disease.
   d. blood pressure.

40. The nurse is interviewing a client on admission to the ambulatory surgery center. The client tells the nurse that she's part of a research project on renal disease, but does not know if she wants to continue. The nurse determines that the client signed a consent form. The nurse's reply is based on the knowledge that consent in research studies:
   a. legally binds the client to continue in the research.
   b. provides certain conditions under which a client may leave the study.
   c. expects clients to leave the study only if a medical condition warrants it.
   d. protects the rights of clients to leave the study, if desired.

41. A client is admitted with an acute episode of sickle cell disease. The primary goal of treatment at this time is:
   a. relieving pain.
   b. finding factors that precipitate episodes.
   c. preventing infection.
   d. educating about altered sexuality patterns.

42. A client is prescribed 2,200ml of D$_5$ 1/2 NSS over 24 hours. The drop factor is 12gtts per milliliter. How many drops per minute should the nurse plan to administer?

   _____

43. A client with myasthenia gravis calls the nurse at night stating she is having a lot of difficulty swallowing and "got something caught" in her throat. The client's husband kept her from choking. The nurse should direct the client to:
   a. drink some fluids to moisten the esophagus.
   b. sleep sitting up that night.
   c. rest and call the physician in the morning.
   d. go to the emergency department now.

44. During a routine physical, a client tells the nurse that she is having difficulty sleeping at night and asks what to do. The best nursing response would be for this client to:
    a. maintain a regular daily schedule.
    b. take a sleeping medication to establish a pattern.
    c. nap during the day to obtain sleep whenever possible.
    d. stress that this is a lifetime problem.

45. A client is admitted to the post-surgical unit after a pedicle flap graft to an area where a pressure ulcer had been located. The most important nursing diagnosis would be:
    a. impaired tissue integrity related to surgical procedure.
    b. alteration in comfort because of pain related to break in skin integrity.
    c. alteration in body image related to grafting.
    d. risk for complications related to immobility.

46. A client who had a prostatectomy earlier that day complains of abdominal pain. The initial action of the nurse is to:
    a. listen for bowel sounds.
    b. check patency of the catheter.
    c. give an analgesic, as prescribed.
    d. take vital signs.

47. The nurse at a senior citizen's center notes an increased incidence of constipation among a number of clients. The nurse provides a program on the problem. What information should be included?
    a. Use laxatives to maintain normal peristalsis modeling.
    b. Drink fruit juices rather than water.
    c. Get daily exercise, even brief walks.
    d. Decrease fiber, which adds bulk.

48. A 16-year-old client has just delivered her first baby by cesarean section. The nurse observes the client falling asleep while holding her baby. What is the best nursing action?
    a. Awaken the client and encourage her to interact with her infant.
    b. Document on the nursing notes the lack of bonding behavior.
    c. Recognize that this is usual behavior and take the infant back to the nursery.
    d. Refer the mother to social services for potential lack of bonding.

49. A client suspected of having glaucoma says to the nurse, "I can't see very well. Am I going to go blind?" The nurse answers the question knowing that:
    a. some peripheral vision that is already lost will not return, but the condition can be controlled by medication.
    b. treatment will slow the process of vision loss, but most clients eventually lose all sight.
    c. although the field of vision may initially be narrowed, sight may return after appropriate medical treatment.
    d. after surgery, the visual loss previously experienced will be reversed with often dramatic effects.

50. A client with liver disease is prescribed neomycin sulfate (Neomycin). The client asks the nurse why he is taking an antibiotic. The nurse tells the client the antibiotic is prescribed to:
    a. repel pathogens in the urinary bladder.
    b. absorb ammonia in the colon.
    c. prevent upper respiratory infection.
    d. reduce the normal flora in the bowel.

51. The major nursing diagnosis for a client with a hip fracture is:
   a. impaired physical mobility.
   b. ineffective management of therapeutic regimen.
   c. risk for infection.
   d. anxiety.

52. The charge nurse hears another nurse who is giving medications tell a client that she is unsure of the new medication's action. The charge nurse should:
   a. tell the client what the medicine's action is.
   b. ask the nurse to look up the new medicine.
   c. suggest to the nurse not to tell a client when not knowing a drug action.
   d. restrict the nurse from giving medicines for the remainder of the shift.

53. A delusional client has been making progress and relating to the nurse on a one-to-one basis. The next appropriate goal would be that the client would:
   a. participate in a group discussion on medications.
   b. observe a volleyball game.
   c. play a card game with one other client.
   d. meet with the nurse on a daily basis.

54. A nurse is performing a neurological exam on a client and notes rapid jerky movements when she gazes laterally. This would be documented as:
   a. lateral strabismus.
   b. normal extraocular movements.
   c. bounding esophoria.
   d. nystagmus.

55. A client returns to the unit after a radical nephrectomy due to cancer. A priority assessment should be:
   a. fluid and electrolyte status.
   b. level of anxiety from diagnosis.
   c. patency of drainage tubes.
   d. bowel elimination.

56. A client has been hospitalized with renal calculi. Tests showed it to be cystine calculi. The client understands teaching about this type of calculi when stating:
   a. "I will drink plenty of fluids during the day."
   b. "I will eat legumes and fruits every day."
   c. "I will call the doctor if I have pain again."
   d. "I will restrict milk and calcium."

57. A 10-month-old infant is brought to the pediatrician's office. The parent states the child was up crying at night and feels warm. The nurse observes the infant sucking the thumb and pulling at the right ear. The nurse teaches the parent to suspect:
   a. allergic rhinitis.
   b. hearing loss.
   c. ear infection.
   d. sinusitis.

58. A nurse is observing a mother with her newborn baby. The mother is stimulating her infant by cooing and talking when the infant is withdrawing and turning away from the mother. The nurse understands this situation as:
   a. synchrony between the mother and the infant.
   b. an obvious lack of bonding between the mother and her infant.
   c. a lack of reciprocity in the mother-infant interaction.
   d. effective use of infant stimulation behaviors.

59. A client fractures the right humerus. The physician prescribes a sling. The nurse explains to the client that the sling is used for:
    a. fixation.
    b. immobilization.
    c. traction.
    d. reduction.

60. A nurse is performing a neurovascular assessment. The best way to assess grip strength is to:
    a. ask the client to squeeze your hand as hard as possible.
    b. attempt to pull index and middle fingers from the client's grasp.
    c. push the client's fingers toward each other while the client opposes.
    d. hold down the client's arm while the client resists.

STOP. You have now completed Practice Session: 15. Now take a few minutes and correct your answers. Calculate your accuracy rate by dividing the number of questions you completed correctly by the total number of questions you completed (60).

Correct answers ÷ total number of questions completed = accuracy rate.

_____ ÷ _____ = _____

ANSWERS AND RATIONALES
Practice Session 15

1. **The correct answer is a.** The question is asking about the nurse's priority setting for clients to be seen in an emergency department. The man, who was riding a motorcycle may have suffered a head injury, is at potential risk and in need of further assessment and intervention. The fact that he was talking when he came in but is now sleeping soundly and snoring, is a critical indicator that his level of consciousness may be changing due to brain swelling and neurological injury. The other clients listed obviously need attention. But again, thinking about Maslow's hierarchy of needs tells one that the physiological condition of this client is worsening and there is a profound need for intervention. The child who may have been molested by a relative is a serious situation, however, issues of "life and limb" are more demanding (option b). A diagnosis of transient ischemic attack (TIA) is not critical and the client appears to be doing well (option c). The client with diabetes is in no acute distress (option d).
   Nursing Process: Evaluation   **Client Need:** Physiological Integrity

2. **The correct answer is a.** The question is asking the signs of iron deficiency anemia. They include weakness, fatigue, dizziness and shortness of breath related to the lack of oxygen getting to the tissues. Nausea, vomiting and diarrhea are gastrointestinal complaints seen with many disorders like the flu (option b). Pain, dyspnea and loss of consciousness may be true for myocardial infarction (option c). Amenorrhea, lanugo and weight loss are seen in anorexia nervosa (option d).
   Nursing Process: Assessment   **Client Need:** Physiological Integrity

3. **The correct answer is c.** The question is asking for symptoms of hypoparathyroidism. They would relate primarily to decreased calcium in the body. Symptoms include: leg cramps and tingling or numbness. Polyuria, fatigue and low urine specific gravity are all signs of hyperparathyroidism (options a, b & d).
   Nursing Process: Assessment   **Client Need:** Physiological Integrity

4. **The correct answer is a.** The question is asking which option would be correct to teach a client with a peptic ulcer. Several small meals per day are preferable because smaller levels of acid production occur. Most foods will neutralize acid production. Large meals increase gastric motor activity to a greater extent than smaller meals. Bland foods have not been proven to help in healing and may be nutritionally incomplete (option b). Milk and cream products may buffer the gastric mucosa and have been found to increase gastrin production due to other components such as protein and fat (option c). Black pepper tends to produce lesions in the stomach (option d).
   Nursing Process: Implementation   **Client Need:** Physiological Integrity

5. **The correct answers are a, b, c and f.** The question is asking which client teaching would be appropriate for someone diagnosed with Addison's disease. Addison's disease is a form of adrenal hypofunction whereby the adrenal corticosteroids are reduced (option b). The mainstay of treatment for adrenocortical insufficiency is lifelong replacement therapy. Due to the fact that corticosteroids cannot be produced, the client cannot tolerate physical or emotional stress without additional exogenous corticosteroids. The client needs to recognize the need for extra medication and stress management (option a). The client should carry an emergency kit with IM hydrocortisone and syringes in case replacement therapy cannot be taken orally (option f). Adequate sodium is needed in the diet (option c). Blood glucose monitoring (option d) would only be necessary if the client has diabetes mellitus. There is no need to avoid the sun (option e).
   Nursing Process: Implementation   **Client Need:** Health Promotion & Maintenance

6. **The correct answer is d.** The question is asking why a client cannot take insulin orally. Insulin must be administered parenterally to avoid enzymatic digestion of it in the intestines. Different injection sites will absorb the insulin at slightly different rates and this must be considered when giving it and teaching the client (option a). The oral insulin would be destroyed in the stomach, no amount would be sufficient and it would serve no purpose to give it this way (option b). Side

effects are mostly the effect of insulin level, namely hypoglycemia or hyperglycemia (option c).
Nursing Process: Implementation   **Client Need:** Physiological Integrity

7.   **The correct answer is d.** The question is asking the meaning of the client's symptoms: falling blood pressure, distended neck veins and muffled heart sounds. These are signs of cardiac tamponade. Due to the trauma, the pericardial sac fills with fluid. Crackling tissues and misshapen skin are signs of subcutaneous emphysema (option a). Tachypnea and pleuritic chest pain are signs of pulmonary contusion (option b). Distended neck veins are a sign of fluid volume excess, which rules out hypovolemic shock (option c).
Nursing Process: Analysis   **Client Need:** Physiological Integrity

8.   **The correct answer is c.** The question is asking which finding is most likely to indicate ability to get pregnant. Regular cycles with premenstrual symptoms indicate ovulation in 95 to 98% of women, thus making it the most likely indicator of fertility. Early onset of menarche is not an indicator of fertility (option a). Galactorrhea may be a sign of androgen excess, which would cause problems with ovulation (option b). Women are more likely to be fertile at younger ages, but age in and of itself is not an indicator of fertility (option d).
Nursing Process: Analysis   **Client Need:** Physiological Integrity

9.   **The correct answer is c.** The question is asking what information is needed when a client is taking isoniazid (INH). An adverse effect of INH is hepatotoxicity; therefore, liver enzyme levels need regular monitoring. Glasses, not contact lenses, should be worn by clients with tuberculosis who are taking rifampin (RMP), as the contact lenses can become discolored (option a). Isoniazid (INH) should be taken on an empty stomach (option b). Hearing can be affected when a client is taking streptomycin for tuberculosis (option d).
Nursing Process: Implementation   **Client Need:** Physiological Integrity

10.   **The correct answer is c.** The question is asking for nursing care for a client with osteomyelitis of the arm. The client will be on bed rest while recuperating. Range-of-motion exercises will help promote joint flexibility. The client will be on long-term intravenous antibiotic therapy plus pain medication and should be monitored for side effects of these drugs. Visual imagery will help with decreasing pain, but the client will need added protein to help with healing (option a). Muscle strengthening exercises, such as isotonic and isometric exercises, are usually prescribed, but the client may need nutritional supplements and vitamins A, B and C for healing (options b & d). The arm should not carry weight and may even be placed in a sling for support (option d).
Nursing Process: Planning   **Client Need:** Physiological Integrity

11.   **The correct answer is b.** The question is asking the most essential nursing diagnosis for a client with a head injury and increased intracranial pressure. The priority would be altered cerebral tissue perfusion. The client has fluid around the brain, which creates pressure on the brain tissue, altered circulation and decreased oxygen to that tissue. If the intracranial pressure rises, altered breathing patterns may occur from pressure to that area of the brain (option c). If pressure is placed on the medulla, a Cushing's syndrome may occur creating fluid volume excess (option a). At present there is extra fluid in the brain but not elsewhere in the body system so fluid volume excess would not apply. Altered thought process is not evident in an unconscious client (option d). If the problem of altered cerebral tissue perfusion is addressed, the other problems may never occur, as they are consequences of altered tissue perfusion.
Nursing Process: Analysis   **Client Need:** Physiological Integrity

12.   **The correct answer is c.** The question is asking why a client on oxygen is prescribed arterial blood gases. This is a way to check if the oxygen is working properly or if more is needed. A stress test evaluates functional capacity (option a). Vital capacity will help identify lung defects (option b). Perfusion defects may be differentiated through a residual volume (option d).
Nursing Process: Evaluation   **Client Need:** Physiological Integrity

13.   **The correct answer is d.** The question is asking what would be the most important problem for a client with dementia. Safety is always key. Impaired judgment may be the most detrimental to

the client and safety measures would need to be taken so that problems would not occur. Impaired reality testing would be a second priority, especially since the client shows problems in this area, such as, confusion and delusional thinking (option c). Social alterations would deal with the client's and significant others' ability to continually adapt to the degenerative process and would need assessment but not as the first priority (option b). Memory impairment may be anxiety producing for the client and add to impaired judgment but would not be the priority (option a).
Nursing Process: Assessment   **Client Need:** Safe, Effective Care Environment

14.   **The correct answer is b.** The question is asking what the nurse should do when a 4-year-old child kicks her. This violent behavior towards the nurse should be addressed immediately. It is important for the nurse to establish appropriate limits as soon as there is an infraction. Delaying limit setting will only minimize the inappropriate act. Providing the consequences of the behavior allows the child to experience the results of their misbehavior. When using consequences, the choice should be given only once and then acted upon. The nurse should avoid trying to reason with preschool children because they are often egocentric and are not cognitively able to see how they might be hurting the other person (options, a, c & d). Some children will use reasoning as a way of gaining attention. The nurse would not want to reinforce this negative behavior. Reasoning would be appropriate with an older child.
Nursing Process: Implementation   **Client Need:** Health Promotion & Maintenance

15.   **The correct answer is d.** The question is asking how to assist the client to adhere to the treatment regimen. The client has been treated for hypertension in the past. Although teaching in diet (option a) and blood pressure monitoring (option b) are important, how these changes will affect lifestyle often leads to noncompliance. The client knows why hospitalization occurred (option c). Promoting self-care through active participation in planning best leads to success.
Nursing Process: Implementation   **Client Need:** Health Promotion & Maintenance

16.   **The correct answer is a.** The question is asking what to look for in a nursing diagnosis of fluid volume deficit. Fluid volume, in most cases, can be checked with the urine specific gravity. This assesses the concentration level of the urine. A high specific gravity means concentrated urine, often a sign of fluid volume deficit. White blood cell count (option b) relates to risk for infection. Food intake (option c) relates to altered nutrition. Range-of-motion (option d) relates to immobility and skin integrity.
Nursing Process: Analysis   **Client Need:** Physiological Integrity

17.   **The correct answer is a.** The question is asking which option is true for a bone marrow aspiration. The procedure is relatively painless except for the time of aspiration when brief pain is felt. Clients should be informed and told how to take deep breaths to tolerate the procedure. The procedure is done under local anesthesia where the needle will pierce the skin (option b). Therefore, a preoperative checklist is unnecessary (option c). Pressure is placed on the site for a few minutes, but the client does not have to remain flat for eight hours (option d).
Nursing Process: Implementation   **Client Need:** Physiological Integrity

18.   **The correct answer is b.** The question is asking what is the correct procedure for administering NPH and regular insulins. The two insulins can be given together. Regular insulin is clear and it is withdrawn first. NPH, the modified insulin, is drawn up second. This method is recommended to avoid contaminating the regular insulin with the intermediate acting NPH insulin (options a, c & d).
Nursing Process: Evaluation   **Client Need:** Safe, Effective Care Environment

19.   **The correct answer is c.** The question is asking for the plan for a client about to have chemotherapy. The nurse should inform the client about why chemotherapy is the choice of treatment for lung cancer and about the expected side effects. Tumor eradication by chemotherapy is not considered possible. The goal is to eradicate enough of the tumor so that the body's immune system can destroy the remaining cells (option a). Administering an antiemetic to decrease or eliminate nausea and vomiting may be needed, but teaching about this before it occurs would be the priority (option b). Strict isolation is not necessary unless severe bone marrow

depression is present (option d).
Nursing Process: Implementation   **Client Need:** Safe, Effective Care Environment

20.   **The correct answer is c.** The question is asking how a myringotomy would help the client with chronic suppurative ear infection. The infection is in the middle ear. Extra fluid and pus increases the pressure. A myringotomy relieves the pressure buildup and drains the fluid. Holes in the tympanic membrane may result from infection, but usually heal spontaneously (option a). Otitis media does not include cyst formation or skin grafting (option b). An electrostimulation device is used to treat tinnitus (option d).
Nursing Process: Implementation   **Client Need:** Physiological Integrity

21.   **The correct answer is b.** The question is asking what to do if magnesium sulfate toxicity is evident. The nurse should immediately stop the drug from infusing any more. Secondly, the nurse would have someone call the physician (option c) while she stayed with this client. Calcium gluconate (option a) is the antidote for magnesium sulfate but the nurse must wait for the physician to prescribe it. Although oxygen would be helpful, it would not be the first nursing measure (option d) because you must first stop the medication from causing further toxicity.
Nursing Process: Implementation   **Client Need:** Safe, Effective Care Environment

22.   **The correct answer is d.** The question is asking what symptoms are associated with a sliding hiatal hernia. Due to the partial obstruction that occurs, heartburn and regurgitation may occur. A persistent cough and weight loss are signs of esophageal cancer (option a). Pain in the mouth and pharynx are signs of the chemical burn, related to undigested medicines caught in the esophagus (option b). Dysphagia and fever after vomiting are signs of esophageal perforation (option c).
Nursing Process: Assessment   **Client Need:** Physiological Integrity

23.   **The correct answer is a.** The question is asking what information is true about IV therapy. Tubing should be changed every 48 to 72 hours to decrease the chance of infection. The tube should be flushed with heparin sodium (Heparin) to maintain patency (option c). If heparin sodium (Heparin) is contraindicated, sterile saline should be used as it approximates body fluid. Tubing should be purged before attaching the filter so air does not get trapped in the filter (option b). If the rate slows or stops, the intravenous site may be occluded and should not be forced (option d).
Nursing Process: Evaluation   **Client Need:** Physiological Integrity

24.   **The correct answer is c.** The question is asking the relationship between cleft palate and otitis media. Children with cleft lip and palate have a greater tendency to get ear infections due to the greater opening between the ear, nose and mouth. In general, all children have inefficient function of eustachian tubes causing improper middle ear drainage due to their ear anatomies. The eustachian tubes are short and straight. Additionally, surgery is an invasive procedure and can cause infection. Nutritional needs should be monitored but can easily be met with special feeding techniques (option b). Food particles do not end up in the eustachian tubes (option a). There are no defects of the eardrum mentioned in this situation (option d).
Nursing Process: Analysis   **Client Need:** Physiological Integrity

25.   **The correct answer is c.** The question is asking why a client should perform his own self-care as soon as possible after a stroke. This encourages the client to stay independent, promotes positive self-esteem and prevents complications of immobility. Family members may have problems watching someone struggle with these tasks (option a), but teaching about the reasons helps them to understand and also encourage their brother. The nurse may be evaluating abilities, (option b) but the primary reason is independence and exercise. Option (d) promotes guilty feelings and defensiveness. This will not promote the client's welfare.
Nursing Process: Implementation   **Client Need:** Physiological Integrity

26.   **The correct answer is b.** The question is asking what foods might cause a blockage in an ileostomy. Corn and Chinese vegetables do so, as well as, fresh vegetables, nuts and dried fruits. Spicy foods, red wine and green beans may cause diarrhea in an ostomy client (option a).

Applesauce, peanut butter and tea can be used to treat diarrhea (option c). Eggs, fish and cheddar cheese may cause odor but will not obstruct an ostomy (option d).
Nursing Process: Planning   **Client Need:** Health Promotion & Maintenance

27.   **The correct answer is b.** The question is asking how to communicate with a hearing-impaired child. Face the child and get full attention. Speak clearly but slightly slower so the client has a chance to perceive the message. The child is too young for written messages (option a). Visual aids help in perception (option c) for all clients. Detailed explanations (option d) would be difficult for a child of this age.
Nursing Process: Planning   **Client Need:** Health Promotion & Maintenance

28.   **The correct answer is a.** The question is asking about priority setting for the nurse and which client needs to be assessed first. The client in option (a) may be having a transfusion reaction and the nurse must note any chills, diaphoresis, complaints of back pain, urticaria, etc. Also, with a history of CHF and receiving extra fluids, the client needs to be assessed for circulatory overload. The client in option (b) is uncomfortable from the placement of the NG tube; however, this would not be a priority. It would be appropriate to send in the nurse's aide to offer support, elevate the head of the bed for easier swallowing, and encourage diversional activities until the nurse can get there to check on him. The client in option (c) needs additional education on use of the PCA pump, but is not a high priority. The aide can offer mouth care to her. The aide can give ginger ale to the client in option (d) after noting any fluid restrictions.
Nursing Process: Planning   **Client Need:** Safe, Effective Care Environment

29.   **The correct answer is b.** The question is asking what is true about this medication. Prednisone (Deltasone) may cause hypertension, because fluid is pulled into the system and retained. Therefore, the client should have her blood pressure checked on a regular basis. Extra doses of prednisone (Deltasone) are never to be taken (option a). Only the physician alters the medication dosage. This medication should be taken with meals to avoid gastrointestinal distress (option c). There is no need to store the medication in the refrigerator, but it should be stored in a light resistant tightly closed container (option d).
Nursing Process: Implementation   **Client Need:** Physiological Integrity

30.   **The correct answer is c.** The question is asking which of four scenarios should be addressed first. Recognition of life-threatening illness or injury is one of the most important aspects of nursing care. Before a diagnosis can be made, recognition of dangerous clinical symptoms with initiation of interventions to reverse or prevent a crisis is essential. The nurse must first complete an initial assessment of the maintenance worker to determine the presence of actual or potential threats to life and then initiate appropriate interventions for his condition. Options (a), (b) and (d), which are not emergencies, would not be the nurse's first priority.
Nursing Process: Analysis   **Client Need:** Safe, Effective Care Environment

31.   **The correct answer is d.** The question is asking if amyotrophic lateral sclerosis can be cured. The disease is chronic and muscle weakness continues until death. Supportive therapies, such as muscle relaxants, tracheostomy and physical therapy, as described in the other options (a, b & c) are implemented to keep the client as functional and comfortable as possible.
Nursing Process: Implementation   **Client Need:** Physiological Integrity

32.   **The correct answer is b.** The question is asking what to do with a stool specimen for ova and parasites. The sample should be kept warm (option a) to detect the parasites. Specimens should be taken directly to the lab if possible (option c). Other solutions (option d) may contaminate and destroy the specimen's usefulness.
Nursing Process: Implementation   **Client Need:** Physiological Integrity

33.   **The correct answer is c.** The question is asking what would occur in a child with newly diagnosed Type 1 diabetes. Bedwetting and tiredness are commonly the chief complaints that prompt parents to take their children to a physician. Bedwetting, grouchiness, feeling overly tired, abdominal discomfort, and weight loss are examples of symptoms, which may be manifested by

children prior to an episode of ketoacidosis (option a). Children will experience the same three "polys" as adults do including: polyphagia (hunger), polydypsia (thirst), and polyuria (frequent urination) (option b). Periods of denial may occur with some parents, it is not experienced by most (option d).
Nursing Process: Assessment   **Client Need:** Physiological Integrity

34.   **The correct answer is c.** The question is asking how to intervene in a client experiencing grandiose behavior. When setting limits on a client's manic behavior, alternative suggestions assist the client to take part in an activity that is more appropriate. Clients in a manic state often fear loss of control; setting limits helps the client gain security in the surroundings. Asking the client how she intends to pay for the party is confrontational (option a). Clients with mania do not have a sense of financial responsibility and often believe they can pay debts that are incurred. Telling the client the party is cancelled (option b) does set limits but does not help the client understand appropriate behavior. The client may have lowered self-esteem and become angry. Telling the client that the party must be postponed until she is feeling better (option d) avoids the issue. Also, the client in a manic state would dispute your reasoning for postponing the party.
Nursing Process: Implementation   **Client Need:** Psychosocial Integrity

35.   **The correct answer is c.** The question is asking what this drug does for the client with chronic bronchitis. Aminophylline (Theophylline) relaxes the bronchial smooth muscle and acts directly on these muscles, thus producing bronchodilation. Different aerosol therapies are provided to liquefy secretions (option a). Easing the coughing-up of secretions is primarily achieved through chest physiotherapy (option b). Blocking beta-receptors would increase the degree of bronchospasm and agents such as isoproterenol (Isuprel) may be used to act as beta agonists (option d).
Nursing Process: Evaluation   **Client Need:** Physiological Integrity

36.   **The correct answer is a.** The question is asking which rhythm would have no P wave and no PR interval. The P wave comes from the atria of the heart. Without a P wave there cannot be a PR interval. In atrial fibrillation the atria contract so fast that they do not show the contraction because depolarization is ill-defined. If P waves show atrial function, the ventricular dysrhythmias would not be depicted. Ventricular problems show in the QT interval where repolarization occurs (options b, c & d).
Nursing Process: Analysis   **Client Need:** Physiological Integrity

37.   **The correct answer is a.** The question is asking what sign would designate this case as severe pancreatitis. Adults, over age 55 years, are prone to more severe cases of pancreatitis. A white blood cell count of 12,000 is expected in a client with pancreatitis (option b). Glucose of 200 or greater is a sign of danger in pancreatitis (option c). A sign of pancreatitis is pale stools (option d).
Nursing Process: Analysis   **Client Need:** Physiological Integrity

38.   **The correct answer is a.** The question is asking what to do when a postoperative client complained of discomfort. Postoperative discomfort is commonly due to alterations in ventilation and incisional pain. For validation of the cause and to ensure the adequacy of respiratory function, lung sounds should be assessed first. Respiratory function should also be assessed before analgesics are given because many analgesics depress respiratory function. If the lungs are adequately ventilated, the nurse should reposition the client (option b), check the dressing (option c), and medicate with an analgesic (option d).
Nursing Process: Implementation   **Client Need:** Physiological Integrity

39.   **The correct answer is d.** The question is asking how to caution a woman taking oral contraceptives. Women using oral contraceptives have a higher incidence of increased blood pressure and it is contraindicated in people who already have hypertension. Because of decreased menstrual flow, there is usually a decrease in the incidence of iron deficiency anemia (option a). There is also a reduction in the incidence of ectopic pregnancy and pelvic inflammatory disease while using oral contraceptives (options b & c).

Nursing Process: Implementation   **Client Need:** Health Promotion & Maintenance

40.   **The correct answer is d.** The question is asking if a client has the right to leave a research study. All clients have the right to decide if they want to participate and if they want to decline to participate at any point in the research project (option a). Clients may leave the study for any reason without penalty (options b & c).
Nursing Process: Analysis   **Client Need:** Health Promotion & Maintenance

41.   **The correct answer is a.** The question is asking what goal best describes acute care. Pain is the most difficult to address during the acute phase. It comes from small thrombi, which restrict oxygen to cells. Preventing infection would be included in teaching about precipitating factors (option b). Infection could precipitate an episode of sickle cell crisis, which the client already is experiencing (option c). Although it is important to educate the client about precipitating factors and altered sexuality patterns related to the disease, teaching is less effective when the client is in pain (option d).
Nursing Process: Planning   **Client Need:** Physiological Integrity

42.   **The correct answer is 18.** The question is asking for the rate of the intravenous in drops (gtts) per minute.

$$\frac{2,200ml}{24\ hr} \times \frac{1\ hr}{60min} \times \frac{12gtts}{ml} = \frac{26,400gtts}{1,440min} = 18.3gtts \text{ or } 18\ min$$

Nursing Process: Planning   **Client Need:** Safe, Effective Care Environment

43.   **The correct answer is d.** The question is asking what to do when a client with myasthenia gravis states she has choked and something is still caught in her throat. The client is having increased problems swallowing and had an episode of choking. Aspiration may have already occurred. The client's condition has worsened and she should be checked for respiratory problems. Drinking fluids should be contraindicated, because the client's swallowing and respiratory muscles have shown signs of weakening and compromise (option a). The client is, therefore, predisposed to further episodes of aspiration. Sleeping sitting up would not necessarily prevent aspiration or other respiratory compromise (option b). The client should be checked and monitored. Calling the physician in the morning may compromise the client's safety (option d).
Nursing Process: Implementation   **Client Need:** Safe, Effective Care Environment

44.   **The correct answer is a.** The question is asking how the nurse should instruct the client who is having trouble sleeping at night. Maintaining a schedule for sleep assists the mind and body to become familiar with a set routine rather than constantly adjusting to a new schedule. Telling the client to take sleeping medication (option b) is outside the scope of nursing practice and alternate means should be tried first before resorting to medications. Daytime naps (option c) promote the reversal of day and night patterns and often is frustrating to the client and family. Insomnia does not have to be a lifelong problem if treated (option d).
Nursing Process: Implementation   **Client Need:** Health Promotion & Maintenance

45.   **The correct answer is a.** The question is asking for the priority problem after a flap graft. Impaired tissue integrity is most important because compromised circulation will cause graft failure, possible infection and necrosis to the area. Pain (option b) will cause discomfort but will not keep the graft from repairing the ulcer site. Altered body image (option c) is a concern, but will become worse if the ulcer is not healed. Immobility (option d) should be addressed as well, although care must be taken that exercises not interfere with circulation.
Nursing Process: Assessment   **Client Need:** Physiological Integrity

46.   **The correct answer is b.** The question is asking what to do first when a client complains of abdominal pain after surgery to the prostate gland. First, the nurse should examine the tube for patency. If the tube is blocked, tension to the operative area and bladder could result in hemorrhage. Giving an analgesic (option c) would mask problems. It may be administered after checking the catheter. Bowel sounds and vital signs would be checked after tube patency assessment (options a & d).

Nursing Process: Implementation   **Client Need:** Physiological Integrity

47.   **The correct answer is c.** The question is asking what to tell older adults to relieve or prevent constipation. Exercise assists with normal motility and peristalsis through the intestines. Immobility is a definite cause of constipation in older adults. Laxatives should only be used if constipation does not respond to dietary methods. Laxatives should not be used on a regular basis (option a) or normal peristalsis will slow or stop. At least eight glasses of water should be taken daily to maintain proper hydration and decrease the chance of constipation (option b). Increased fiber triggers peristalsis due to irritation of the intestinal mucosa (option d).
Nursing Process: Implementation   **Client Need:** Health Promotion & Maintenance

48.   **The correct answer is c.** The question is asking how to respond to a post-cesarean section client who has fallen asleep holding her baby. A mother who is only 24 hours post-cesarean section is exhausted. Her physical needs are a higher priority than attachment issues (options a, b & d).
Nursing Process: Implementation   **Client Need:** Health Promotion & Maintenance

49.   **The correct answer is a.** The question is asking what is true about eyesight loss with glaucoma. Peripheral vision is lost when increased intraocular pressure causes ischemia to the nervous tissue. This vision loss, often known as tunnel vision, cannot be reversed and blindness will result if the condition is not treated. Medical treatment will control the condition by decreasing intraocular pressure, so that further damage may not occur and blindness is averted (option b). The treatment will not restore lost sight (option c). Surgical treatment may produce better vision, but it does not restore vision already lost from nerve tissue destruction (option d).
Nursing Process: Analysis   **Client Need:** Physiological Integrity

50.   **The correct answer is d.** The question is asking why the antibiotic neomycin sulfate (Neomycin) is given to a client with liver disease. Ammonia is produced in the intestine due to normal body flora. The ammonia causes hepatic encephalopathy in the client with liver disease. The expected outcome is to reduce normal flora, therefore, reducing ammonia levels in the blood. This antibiotic does not target pathogens in the urinary bladder or lung (options a & c). The drug prevents ammonia from being formed rather than absorbing it (option b).
Nursing Process: Implementation   **Client Need:** Physiological Integrity

51.   **The correct answer is a.** The question is asking for the main nursing diagnosis for a client who has a fracture of the hip. The main problem would be impaired mobility. The client is confined for a time, whether it be while the hip is healing or because of a hip replacement. He must learn how to move differently, accomplish familiar tasks differently and to accept help. There is no evidence to support ineffective management (option b). There would be a risk for infection, since there is a break in the usual integrity of the body (option c) as well as anxiety about the new situation and changes as a result (option d), however, these would not be the priority.
Nursing Process: Analysis   **Client Need:** Physiological Integrity

52.   **The correct answer is b.** The question is asking how the charge nurse should intervene when another nurse giving medications tells the client she does not know the drug action. The charge nurse should stop the nurse from giving the medication. The nurse should know the action and purpose of the drug. She should also know contraindications in case this client should not be receiving the medication and the side effects to look for. Telling the client what the drug is for (option a) will help place the client at ease, but still endanger the client because the nurse is giving an unknown drug. The nurse probably should not announce the drug action is unknown, (option c) but this is not the best action as the client is in danger if adverse effects occur. Restricting the nurse from giving medications (option d) only places more burden on other staff members.
Nursing Process: Implementation   **Client Need:** Safe, Effective Care Environment

53.   **The correct answer is c.** The question is asking the next goal for a client after relating to the nurse. The next appropriate step in increasing the relationships and trust would be for the client to relate to a second person. This allows the client to practice new skills in a less threatening way with a concrete activity. The nurse acts as a support person, assisting the client with feedback

about the interaction. Group activities such as observing a volleyball game (option b) and participating in the group discussion (option a) may be too threatening and overwhelming for the client. The client is already meeting with the nurse on a daily basis; therefore, this goal has already been accomplished (option d).
Nursing Process: Planning   **Client Need:** Psychosocial Integrity

54.   **The correct answer is d.** The question is asking the name of the eye problem. Bouncing, rapid and jerky movements of the eye are called nystagmus, which frequently accompanies disorders of the inner ear and certain neurologic tumors (option b). Strabismus and esophoria are forms of crossed eyes or squint eyes and were not described in the assessment (options a & c).
Nursing Process: Assessment   **Client Need:** Physiological Integrity

55.   **The correct answer is a.** The question is asking for the most important assessment area when a client has a kidney removed. During a radical nephrectomy, a great deal of fluid and blood is lost and fluid volume deficit is a problem. Assessing areas such as intake and output, urine specific gravity and vital signs are important to monitor the need for added fluids to prevent dehydration and shock. Anxiety from the cancer diagnosis may be of concern (option b) but should be addressed when the client's status is hemodynamically stable. Drainage tubes should be assessed, (option c) but they are only a part of fluid balance. Bowel elimination will be important later in the recovery period (option d).
Nursing Process: Assessment   **Client Need:** Physiological Integrity

56.   **The correct answer is b.** The question is asking what would be correct information about cystine calculi. The goal is to increase alkalinity of the urine. This is accomplished by eating foods such as legumes, green vegetables and fruits. All clients with renal calculi should increase fluids (option a) and call the physician if pain occurs (option c). Calcium sources would be restricted for calcium rich calculi (option d).
Nursing Process: Evaluation   **Client Need:** Health Promotion & Maintenance

57.   **The correct answer is c.** The question is asking the meaning of the child's symptoms. These are signs of otitis media, an ear infection. Allergic rhinitis symptoms include nasal congestion, sneezing, and dry lips (option a). Hearing loss may occur as a result of otitis media (option b). Sinusitis symptoms include fever, nasal congestion, headache, halitosis and cough (option d).
Nursing Process: Analysis   **Client Need:** Physiological Integrity

58.   **The correct answer is c.** The question is asking the nurse to analyze the mother-infant interaction. A reciprocal relationship between the mother and infant is one in which the mother responds to the infant's cues. Such cues indicate when the infant is ready to be stimulated and what kind of stimulation the infant can respond to. In this example, the mother is not responding appropriately (options a & d). If this continues there may be serious problems in bonding (option b).
Nursing Process: Assessment   **Client Need:** Health Promotion & Maintenance

59.   **The correct answer is b.** The question is asking the purpose of a sling for a fractured humerus. The sling immobilizes the fracture, allowing it to heal and preventing further tissue injury. Fixation (option a) occurs when fusing the ends of a break together with pins or plates. Traction (option c) is when the limb is immobilized with weights. Reduction (option d) is when the fractured ends are approximated.
Nursing Process: Implementation   **Client Need:** Physiological Integrity

60.   **The correct answer is b.** The question is asking how to check grip strength in a client. Pulling out the first two (index and middle) fingers, while the client is grasping, tests the muscle strength of that area. Squeezing the hand is not as reliable (option a). Strength to put fingers together against an opposing force comes from the wrist and finger muscles (option c). Holding down an arm against resistance relates to the deltoid muscles (option d).
Nursing Process: Assessment   **Client Need:** Physiological Integrity

PRACTICE SESSION: 16

> **Instructions: Allow yourself 75 minutes to complete the following 75 practice questions. Use a timer to notify yourself when 75 minutes are over so that you are not constantly looking at your watch while completing the questions.**

1. The nurse is teaching an adolescent who has recently been diagnosed with Type 1 diabetes. The nurse realizes the adolescent understands that he is most likely to become hyperglycemic when he states:
   a. "I take too much insulin."
   b. "I exercise without eating."
   c. "I get an infection."
   d. "I eat too rapidly."

2. A client is receiving glucocorticosteroid therapy at home for his Addison's disease. After the teaching, the nurse would expect the client to state that the physician should immediately be called if there is:
   a. a decrease in weight of two pounds over one week.
   b. a negative urine glucose.
   c. evidence of mood swings.
   d. a slight temperature increase.

3. Which client should the nurse on a rehabilitation unit see first?
   a. A 48-year-old male who has pneumonia, whose IV antibiotic is not running in as it should.
   b. A 23-year-old male who has a spinal cord injury who is complaining of a bad headache.
   c. A 78-year-old female who has had a stroke and is becoming increasingly agitated.
   d. A 36-year-old male who is in sickle cell crisis and needs to be medicated for pain.

4. The physician prescribes 2,700ml of D_5 1/4 NSS to infuse over 24 hours. The drop factor is 15 drops per ml. How many milliliters will be given during an eight-hour shift?

   _____

5. Following delivery of a healthy baby boy, the nurse assesses the new mother's temperature is 100°F (37.8°C). The increase in temperature is probably due to the mother:
   a. experiencing subinvolution of the uterus.
   b. developing a uterine infection.
   c. developing a breast infection.
   d. experiencing dehydration.

6. A client is admitted to the intensive care unit due to massive hematemasis secondary to esophageal varices. The nurse inserts the prescribed Sengstaken-Blakemore tube in order to:
   a. apply direct pressure to the esophageal varices.
   b. suction blood and gastric contents from the lungs.
   c. administer sterile iced water lavages.
   d. prevent gastric aspiration into the lungs.

7. During surgery for a ruptured appendix, a penrose drain is inserted. The nurse understands that the primary purpose for the drain is to:
   a. promote drainage of body fluids.
   b. assess for infection.
   c. prevent tension on the abdominal suture line.
   d. decompress the bowel.

8. The nurse is creating a teaching pamphlet for clients diagnosed with gastroesophageal reflux disease (GERD). Indicate what should be included in the teaching. Select all that apply.
   a. Eat small, frequent meals.
   b. Avoid coffee, tea, chocolate and peppermint.
   c. Drink plenty of fluids with meals.
   d. Regurgitation of hot, bitter liquid into the mouth should be reported to the physician.
   e. Avoid milk products.

9. A client with coronary artery disease is returned to the hospital room after a percutaneous transluminal coronary angioplasty (PTCA) with stent deployment. The care plan includes:
   a. monitoring for signs of bleeding from the insertion site.
   b. teaching on follow-up care for laser plaque removal.
   c. instructions related to post-myocardial infarction care.
   d. observing for vasospasms related to medication dosage.

10. A client, newly diagnosed with systemic lupus erythematosus, is explaining the disease to her teenage children. The nurse evaluates that the client is explaining it correctly when she states:
    a. "It is a disease of exacerbation and remission."
    b. "Teenagers are no more likely to get it than their friends."
    c. "The disease gradually and steadily worsens."
    d. "The medication used to treat the disease causes involuntary muscle movements."

11. A client, who is having her insulin and diet regulated, is placed on Humulin N and Humulin R insulins BID. After three days of treatment, the client tells the nurse, "Every afternoon around 3:30PM, I begin to feel shaky, weak and lightheaded." The daily pattern most likely contributing to these symptoms is that the client:
    a. checks her blood glucose level at 7:00AM and 4:00PM.
    b. eats three meals a day at 8:00AM, 12:00 noon, and 5:00PM and a bedtime snack at 9:30PM.
    c. administers her morning insulin at 7:30AM.
    d. exercises for one half hour in the morning and evening.

12. A nurse is performing a neurological assessment using the Glasgow Coma Scale (GCS). Using the GCS, the nurse would measure:
    a. eye opening, verbal response, motor response.
    b. vital signs, pupillary response, motor response.
    c. verbal response, pupillary response, cranial nerve assessment.
    d. eye opening, motor response, cranial nerve assessment.

13. A client with AIDS calls to report the following symptoms. Which symptom would most concern the nurse?
    a. A productive cough.
    b. Blurred vision.
    c. Painful urination.
    d. Vaginal discharge.

14. A client had a radical neck dissection and is resting in the intensive care unit. The client indicates pain and discomfort in the epigastric region. The nurse notes carotid artery bleeding. The initial action of the nurse would be to:
    a. apply direct pressure to the artery.
    b. immediately go to get help.
    c. elevate the head of the bed.
    d. notify the physician for surgery.

15. A client scheduled for a barium enema appears anxious and tells the nurse he is concerned because of what his friend told him about the procedure. The nurse should prepare him first by:
   a. encouraging him to consult his physician.
   b. reinforcing that the procedure is relatively painless.
   c. asking him to verbalize what he has heard.
   d. providing him with a pamphlet about the procedure.

16. Improper positioning following an above the knee amputation may produce a (n):
   a. flexion contracture at the hip of the unaffected limb.
   b. abduction of the stump toward the midline of the body.
   c. flexion contracture at the hip of the amputated limb.
   d. external rotation of the unaffected leg at the hip.

17. While caring for a client on a ventilator, the client develops the need for positive end expiratory pressure (PEEP). The nurse knows that the major indication of PEEP is:
   a. to allow an increase of oxygen delivered by the ventilator.
   b. a severe gas exchange disturbance not corrected with high flow oxygen.
   c. to provide temporary ventilator support while the alveolar pressure gradually returns to zero.
   d. to decrease the possibility of a pneumothorax while the client is ventilator dependent.

18. A client with a spinal cord injury is getting up for the first time. What nursing measure would prevent associated postural hypotension?
   a. Quickly place the client in an upright position.
   b. Apply an abdominal binder and elastic support hose.
   c. Ask family to be present during the event.
   d. Administer trimethobenzanide (Tigan) before the client gets up.

19. A man who practices Hinduism has been diagnosed with terminal lung cancer. When planning his psychological needs what would the nurse consider?
   a. He cannot eat a meal in which dairy and beef products are served together.
   b. He may have an increase in rituals to be pure with a higher existence.
   c. The client may blame himself for the illness.
   d. Readings from the Koran are important at this time.

20. The nurse is charting on a client with a cardiac disorder. Which documentation would be written as a normal electrocardiogram (EKG)? There is a:
   a. PQRST wave with a rate of 108.
   b. PQRSTU wave with a rate of 88.
   c. PQRST wave without ectopy with a rate of 88.
   d. PQRS wave without ectopy with a rate of 88.

21. A nurse is conducting a support group for parents of children with spastic cerebral palsy. A new member asks what exactly the disorder is. The nurse evaluates the group members' understanding when one member states, "It is:
   a. a congenital disease transmitted by recessive genes."
   b. a permanent loss of sensation from a birth injury."
   c. a condition in which there is difficulty in controlling voluntary muscles."
   d. muscle weakness, uncoordination, and permanent loss of sensation brought on by mental retardation."

22. The parents of a child with a tetralogy of Fallot ask the nurse why the baby gets so blue. The nurse's response would be based on the knowledge that the cyanosis is caused by:
   a. a constricted aorta.
   b. a hypoplastic left ventricle.
   c. mitral valve stenosis.
   d. pulmonary artery stenosis.

23. A 14-year-old girl's father passed away while at war. Since her father's death, her mother has noted drastic behavior changes in her daughter. While all need to be addressed, which symptom would be the priority? She is:
   a. refusing to go to school.
   b. afraid something very bad will happen to her mom.
   c. lashing out.
   d. sleeping 14 hours a day.

24. A client with Parkinson's disease might have which nursing diagnosis?
   a. Self-esteem disturbance.
   b. Chronic confusion.
   c. Altered tissue perfusion.
   d. Impaired gas exchange.

25. During a prenatal visit, a woman in the last trimester tells the nurse that a friend of hers almost bled to death after she had her baby. The nurse bases her response on the knowledge that the most common cause of postpartum hemorrhage is:
   a. perineal and/or cervical lacerations.
   b. prolonged labors.
   c. retained placental fragments.
   d. uterine atony.

26. A newborn is having some respiratory distress following delivery. The nurse suspects that the client has:
   a. inadequate alveolar ventilation and pulmonary vasodilation.
   b. overproduction of surfactant and uninflatable alveoli.
   c. decreased pulmonary resistance and underdeveloped alveoli.
   d. inadequate surfactant production and underdeveloped alveoli.

27. A 5-year-old child, who has just undergone a cardiac catheterization, has a blood pressure of 72/44. The initial action by the nurse would be to:
   a. assess the catheter site pressure dressing.
   b. assess the client's peripheral pulses.
   c. compare this pressure to the precatheterization pressure.
   d. notify the physician at once.

28. A client with asthma is learning how to use his peak flow meter. Which statement indicates a need for further teaching?
   a. "I should stand up when I use it."
   b. "I will measure every morning after I take my daily medication."
   c. "I will take my albuterol (Ventolin) if my peak flow is less than 80% of my personal best."
   d. "I should blow as hard and fast as I possibly can."

29. There has been a train derailment and many people need to be admitted to the local hospital. In order to make room for the new clients, which client would the charge nurse suggest be discharged?
   a. A client with sickle cell crisis who was taken off a PCA pump this morning.
   b. A client admitted yesterday with nephrotic syndrome secondary to syphilis.
   c. A woman admitted three days ago with a femur fracture secondary to a skiing accident.
   d. A client with myasthenia gravis who is being treated for an upper respiratory infection.

30. A client with a cardiac disorder has been ordered intravenous potassium to correct a deficit. The nurse plans to give the potassium slowly because:
    a. it is irritating to the vein and will cause discomfort.
    b. rapid replacement of potassium can cause cardiac arrest.
    c. levels must continuously be monitored during administration.
    d. it results in hypotension if administered too rapidly.

31. After several sessions with a client, the nurse has conducted a complete sexual assessment but, at this point, feels unprepared to continue working with the client. The nurse should:
    a. consult with the mental health clinic treatment team about an appropriate referral for the client.
    b. consult with her colleagues about how to proceed in her sessions with the client.
    c. refer the client to a support group for individuals with sexual identity issues.
    d. refer the client to social service department for marriage counseling.

32. For clients receiving dicumarol (Coumadin) preoperatively, the nurse should be most concerned with the medication's potential for:
    a. clotting abnormalities.
    b. decreasing intraoperative blood pressure.
    c. altering the effects of the anesthetic agent.
    d. creating potassium depletion.

33. The nurse tells a woman with tuberculosis that she would like to spend some time planning for discharge and health teaching tomorrow. The client tells the nurse that she is a lesbian and asks if her partner can come in to hear this too. The nurse responds by saying:
    a. "I really don't know if I'll have time to go over this with both of you."
    b. "I will make sure that I give you printed materials to share with her."
    c. "We usually only do teaching with immediate family members."
    d. "Tell her to be here at 10:00AM."

34. A client with hypertension is placed on a low-sodium diet. Which lunch choice would indicate an understanding of this diet?
    a. Baked chicken, canned green beans, cookie.
    b. Baked fish, frozen peas, glazed strawberries.
    c. Roast beef, baked potato, sherbet.
    d. Baked chicken, biscuit, buttermilk.

35. In the operating room, the circulating nurse's scrub top becomes wet when irrigation solution is inadvertently spilled. The circulating nurse should:
    a. place a scrub gown over the wet scrub top.
    b. dry the area with a hand dryer.
    c. wash the area first then dry it.
    d. change the scrub top.

36. The laboratory informs the nurse that the client's calcium level is 7. The nurse should further assess for:
    a. numbness, twitching and positive Chvostek's sign.
    b. nausea, vomiting and anorexia.
    c. muscle weakness numbness and tented T waves on ECG.
    d. headache, blurred vision and convulsions.

37. A 14-year-old client in diabetic ketoacidosis is attached to a cardiac monitor after being admitted to the intensive care unit (ICU) with a blood glucose of 500mg/100ml. The child becomes frightened and asks, "Am I having a heart attack?" The nurse would base the response on the understanding that:
    a. myocardial infarctions are very likely at this time due to the physical stress response.
    b. cardiac monitoring is necessary to detect problems from changing potassium levels caused by decreased insulin.
    c. elevated glucose levels may precipitate a cardiac arrest, which can be detected early through cardiac monitoring.
    d. all clients admitted to the ICU are monitored routinely for potential life-threatening problems.

38. The nurse is assisting a client to ambulate postoperatively in the hall for the first time. The client becomes dizzy and starts to fall. The best action by the nurse would be to:
    a. place the client against the wall.
    b. immediately go and get help.
    c. allow the client to fall slowly to the floor.
    d. assist the client to the floor.

39. The aide tells the nurse that a 77-year-old disoriented client's side rail is loose. The nurse calls maintenance to check the faulty side rail. Even though the nurse told maintenance the side rail would not lock, maintenance insisted it was fixed. The next action of the nurse should be to:
    a. ask the supervisor to talk to maintenance.
    b. tell the client to be careful of the side rail.
    c. call maintenance again to fix the side rail.
    d. move the client to a new bed.

40. A nurse is assessing a client with a spinal cord injury for deep vein thrombosis. What would be most appropriate?
    a. Dorsiflex the foot and ask if there is pain in the calf.
    b. Observe for redness, warmth and swelling along the calf and thigh.
    c. Compress the calves and observe for discomfort.
    d. Observe for elevated temperature.

41. The community health nurse visits a client one-week post-hospital discharge. The nurse finds the client very upset that her 24-year-old daughter is moving back home but will not discuss financial arrangements and household responsibilities. The best action of the nurse is based on the understanding that 24-year-old adults:
    a. should provide for their parents' needs without being asked.
    b. cannot understand why the parent would be upset about this issue.
    c. may not fully understand the situation until older.
    d. understand the parental viewpoint with assistance.

42. On admission to a psychiatric unit a client is tearful, stares at his hands and refuses to speak. The client's wife states he has lost 10 pounds in one month. At home, he either stays in bed or sits in a chair and stares at the television. The priority assessment for this client is:
    a. alteration in nutrition.
    b. risk for self harm.
    c. altered self-concept.
    d. altered thought processes.

43. The nurse notes that a client receiving tube feedings has developed diarrhea. To decrease the diarrhea, the nurse would expect the physician to:
    a. change the feeding schedule to intermittent.
    b. increase the rate of infusion.
    c. decrease the concentration of the formula.
    d. order 10ml of normal saline solution every hour.

44. When planning care for a child with cystic fibrosis, what would be indicated?
   a. Give prescribed medication, provide foods that are liked, and maintain isolation.
   b. Provide rest periods, nutritional foods that are liked, and teach how to prevent pulmonary infections.
   c. Teach good hygiene, encourage fluids, and maintain respiratory isolation.
   d. Regulate the child's diet, force fluids, and prevent any new infections.

45. A client is given a preliminary diagnosis of possible colon cancer. Based on the diagnosis, the nurse would expect this client to complain of:
   a. hemoptysis and dyspepsia.
   b. liquid tarry diarrhea.
   c. fat intolerance and steatorrhea.
   d. blood streaked pencil-thin stool.

46. A client with a disability moves into a new community. The nurse is trying to make the client aware of resources in the community. The nurse would:
   a. suggest the client call different resources.
   b. tell the client resources are easy to locate.
   c. refer the client to a self-help group.
   d. only suggest resources if the client asks.

47. A client, diagnosed with pernicious anemia, asks why she has to take these injections when her friend, who has anemia, is taking pills. The best reply of the nurse is:
   a. "The physician will change you to oral preparation after your blood count increases sufficiently."
   b. "These injections are a different medicine than your friend is taking for her anemia."
   c. "When you go home the physician will prescribe folacin (Folic Acid) by mouth which you can buy in the drug store."
   d. "The injection will prevent you from having a blood transfusion to treat the anemia."

48. An elderly client is to be transferred to a nursing home following acute care for a cerebrovascular accident (CVA). The client tells the nurse, "I don't want to go to that horrible place." Based on this information, the nursing care plan should include:
   a. an orientation to the facility where he is to be transferred.
   b. convincing him of the merits of the facility where he is to go.
   c. spending more time with him.
   d. the risk of elopement.

49. Which medication would a nurse expect the physician to prescribe in order to close a patent ductus arteriosus (PDA)?
   a. Erythromycin (E-Mycin).
   b. Indomethacin (Indocin).
   c. Albuterol (Proventil).
   d. Prednisone (Deltasone).

50. A client is scheduled to have an electromyography (EMG) and asks about the test. The nurse's teaching should include:
   a. "This is a painless procedure that measures the electrical activity of the brain."
   b. "You will experience a mild shock when the nerve that is being tested is electrically stimulated."
   c. "Needles are placed in selected muscles and electrical activity is recorded."
   d. "You will be given a muscle relaxant prior to the procedure to decrease any pain."

51. The nurse is reinforcing diet teaching in a client with hepatic encephalopathy. The client understands the teaching if he chooses:
   a. a T-bone steak.
   b. fried chicken.
   c. macaroni.
   d. a protein supplement.

52. A client is admitted to the hospital with syndrome of inappropriate antidiuretic hormone (SIADH). The nurse would plan for which potential problem?
   a. The need for insulin temporarily.
   b. Excessive weight loss.
   c. Diarrhea.
   d. Fluid and electrolyte imbalance.

53. A client, admitted with major depression, is nearing discharge. Which client statement indicates progress?
   a. "I'm going to ask the doctor to decrease my medicine."
   b. "Your suggestion sounds a lot better than mine does."
   c. "I understand that I'll sometimes make mistakes."
   d. "I'm sure I can go back to work without any trouble."

54. A family is anxiously waiting for their mother to return from coronary artery bypass graft surgery (CABG). Upon seeing her mother, the daughter asks the nurse why her mother has wires coming out of her chest. The nurse replies:
   a. "These wires are used to connect to the EKG monitor for more accurate monitoring."
   b. "These wires are attached to the heart and, if she should arrest, will be attached to a defibrillator."
   c. "These wires are attached to the heart and to a pacemaker that will fire should the heart rate drop below a set rate."
   d. "These wires will be attached to a Swan Ganz catheter to measure pressures in the heart."

55. On the day before surgery for a coronary artery bypass graft (CABG), the client says to the nurse, "The doctor said I would have an incision in my leg. I don't understand why." The nurse explains:
   a. "During surgery, the doctors will remove part of the femoral artery in your leg and graft it to your heart."
   b. "Why don't you ask the doctor to explain it to you when he comes in later?"
   c. "During the surgery, the doctors will remove part of the saphenous vein from the leg and graft it to your heart."
   d. "That's where you will be attached to the heart-lung machine."

56. While performing an assessment on a client with acquired immunodeficiency syndrome (AIDS), the nurse notes a rash with reddish-brown and bluish spots on the legs. This finding is probably related to:
   a. pernicious anemia.
   b. pneumocyctis carinii.
   c. Kaposi's sarcoma.
   d. lymphocytic leukemia.

57. Following treatment for two days with magnesium sulfate (Magnesium) a woman delivered a preterm male weighing 1.8 kg (4 lbs). Since the mother has received magnesium sulfate (Magnesium), the baby should be monitored by the nurse for:
   a. bradycardia.
   b. respiratory depression.
   c. tachycardia.
   d. hypocalcemia.

58. A newborn is diagnosed with developmental dysplasia of the hip (DDH). An abducter harness is prescribed. The nurse teaches the parents to:
    a. place the baby's diaper over the harness straps.
    b. adjust the harness every two hours.
    c. apply lotion or powder underneath the straps.
    d. pad the shoulder straps.

59. A woman calls the nurse at the emergency department because she fell and believes she injured her Hickman catheter. The appropriate nursing action would be to:
    a. tell the woman to come to the emergency department for catheter repair.
    b. call the physician immediately.
    c. send an ambulance crew to replace the catheter.
    d. ask the woman to make an appointment with her physician.

60. A client with rib fractures is visited by several family members. After the visit, the nurse finds the client anxious, slightly tachypneic, diaphoretic and holding her side. She states, "I'm fine, my mother just got me upset." The nurse should:
    a. notify the physician immediately.
    b. ask the client if she would like to talk about what upset her.
    c. suggest that she restrict her visitors until she is feeling better.
    d. allow her to calm down and check her in 15 minutes.

61. The priority nursing assessment of a client who has overdosed on cocaine is to:
    a. take vital signs.
    b. determine support systems.
    c. establish seizure precautions.
    d. check for cyanosis.

62. A newly admitted client is irritable and uncommunicative during the assessment process, giving one-word answers. The client is pale, looks fatigued and asks not to be physically examined. The client admits being in pain, but does not want anything for it. The best reply of the nurse would be:
    a. "What concerns you most about taking pain medication?"
    b. "You're probably right to wait until later."
    c. "You're worried you'll become addicted?"
    d. "The doctor wanted you to have pain medication."

63. A client with Alzheimer's disease is found staring at his breakfast. When the nurse asks him what is wrong, he replies, "Oh, I'm so hungry," and bows his head into his hands. The nurse should respond by:
    a. asking what he would prefer to eat.
    b. suggesting he pick up his fork and take a bite.
    c. having a nursing assistant feed him.
    d. obtaining packaged foods to eat.

64. A client is scheduled for an echocardiogram. The nurse would include what in the teaching plan?
    a. The client must have written consent.
    b. An intravenous lock is inserted prior to the test.
    c. The procedure is noninvasive and may be done at the bedside.
    d. Some risk of bleeding is possible.

65. After interviewing a client and reviewing the nurse's assessment, the physician diagnoses a client with borderline personality disorder. The documentation by the nurse that supported this diagnosis was:
   a. preoccupation with fantasies of success, exhibitionism and indifference toward others.
   b. persistent lying, manipulative behavior and history of juvenile delinquency.
   c. overly dramatic behavior, angry outbursts and seductive behavior.
   d. intense anger, self-mutilation and fear of abandonment.

66. A client in labor is placed on a continuous electronic fetal monitor. Nursing care for this client includes:
   a. assessment of the client's knowledge of the monitor.
   b. keeping the client on her left side.
   c. positioning the monitor over the baby's heart and keeping it in place.
   d. maintaining the client in a supine position, raising and lowering the head only.

67. A client comes to the emergency department with wheezing, inspiratory stridor and apprehension. The client has a history of asthma but the wheezing did not respond to inhalers. The client is very fatigued, has difficulty concentrating and appears drowsy. The best analysis by nursing diagnosis is:
   a. impaired gas exchange related to tenacious sputum.
   b. ineffective airway clearance related partially blocked airway.
   c. ineffective breathing pattern related to hypoventilation.
   d. fluid volume deficit related to dehydration.

68. A one-day postpartal client is prescribed methylergonovine maleate (Methergine). The nurse teaches the client that: "This medication
   a. stimulates your uterus to contract, which minimizes bleeding."
   b. is used to facilitate the formation of clots, thereby reducing bleeding."
   c. relaxes the uterus to prevent further contractions."
   d. is used to promote healing of your reproductive tract."

69. When the school nurse realizes that a student has rubella, she reports it to the:
   a. county health officer.
   b. state health officer.
   c. child's physician.
   d. center for disease control.

70. An appropriate nursing measure to initiate voiding in a client with a spinal cord transection at C_7 would be to:
   a. tap the suprapubic area, brush the inner thighs or stroke the abdomen with ice.
   b. instruct the client to perform the Valsalva maneuver.
   c. employ the Credé maneuver.
   d. leave the water running in the bathroom.

71. A nurse is introducing a work sponsored health fitness program to personnel at a local business. One client asked how to build endurance for climbing stairs. The nurse would suggest:
   a. strength exercises.
   b. stretching.
   c. weight lifting.
   d. bicycling.

72. During a prenatal assessment, the nurse realizes a client is at increased risk for abruptio placenta due to a history of:
   a. hypertension.
   b. low weight gain.
   c. Asian descent.
   d. cesarean section.

73. A postoperative mastectomy client is encouraged by the nurses to perform self-care. While combing her hair, the client states she cannot lift her arm without help. The appropriate intervention by the nurse would be to:
   a.   assist the client to lift her affected arm.
   b.   encourage the client to use the unaffected arm.
   c.   explain to the client the importance of complying with the therapies.
   d.   complete the hair care for the client.

74. The nurse should utilize which approach when formulating a therapeutic relationship with a client with acquired immunodeficiency syndrome (AIDS)?
   a.   Focus on the health that remains rather than discussing declining health status.
   b.   Always give the client a sense of protection by having available answers to client questions.
   c.   Admit to uncertainty or discomfort, forming an honest relationship.
   d.   Reassure the client about the future even though you know it is uncertain.

75. During the diuretic phase of a client's acute renal failure, the nurse notes the presence of dry mucous membranes, hypotension, and tachycardia. The most appropriate nursing diagnosis for this client would be:
   a.   fluid volume excess related to renal dysfunction.
   b.   fluid volume depletion related to excessive urinary output.
   c.   electrolyte imbalance related to retained toxins.
   d.   anemia related to lack of erythropoietin production.

STOP. You have now completed Practice Session: 16. Now take a few minutes and correct your answers. Calculate your accuracy rate by dividing the number of questions you completed correctly by the total number of questions you completed (75).

Correct answers ÷ total number of questions completed = accuracy rate.

_____ ÷ _____ = _____

ANSWERS AND RATIONALES
Practice Session 16

1. **The correct answer is c.** The question is asking what type of problem causes the blood sugar to be elevated. Stress of any kind initiates a glucocorticoid response and the release of glucose into the blood stream by the liver. Too much insulin will lead to hypoglycemia; too little insulin leads to hyperglycemia (option a). Increased exercise without increased food intake leads to hypoglycemia. Insulin will move into cells without glucose during exercise, thereby diminishing blood glucose levels (option b). Skipping meals may lead to hypoglycemia; rapid eating has no effect (option d).
   Nursing Process: Evaluation   **Client Need:** Health Promotion & Maintenance

2. **The correct answer is d.** The question is asking when the client should call the physician. Excess cortisol contributes to an altered inflammatory and immune response resulting in decreased resistance to infection. Temperature increase is a sign of infection. Negative glucose in the urine and decreased weight are desirable outcomes (options a & b). Cortisol excess results in emotional instability (option c) but this manifestation does not require immediate treatment.
   Nursing Process: Assessment   **Client Need:** Safe, Effective Care Environment

3. **The correct answer is b.** The question is asking for priority setting on a rehabilitation unit for clients who need to be assessed after report. Thinking about Maslow's hierarchy of needs, the man who has a spinal cord injury who is complaining of a severe headache is telling us something that could be critical based on his diagnosis. A severe headache is a symptom of autonomic dysreflexia, a complication of a spinal cord injury. Although the other issues are important, this client requires immediate intervention to avoid potentially life-threatening complications. Option (a) is incorrect as this client who has pneumonia and whose IV antibiotic is not running as it should is not the highest priority. Option (c) is incorrect as this confused client who had a stroke is not the highest priority. Option (d) is incorrect as this paraplegic who would like better food is not a priority. For priority setting, think "life and limb" when answering these questions.
   Nursing Process: Implementation   **Client Need:** Physiological Integrity

4. **The correct answer is 900.** The question is asking how many milliliters of fluid should infuse over one shift or eight hours.
   $$\frac{2{,}700 \text{ ml}}{24 \text{ hr}} = \frac{112.5 \text{ml}}{\text{hr}} \times 8 \text{ hr} = 900\text{ml}$$
   Nursing Process: Planning   **Client Need:** Physiological Integrity

5. **The correct answer is d.** The question is asking why the mother's temperature was slightly elevated after delivery. Temperature elevations may be a sign of infection and must be carefully monitored. The normal process of wound healing, as well as dehydration and breast engorgement, may also increase body temperature. Temperature elevation less than 100.4°F (38°C) from normal processes should last for only a few days and should not be associated with other clinical signs of infection (options a, b, & c).
   Nursing Process: Analysis   **Client Need:** Physiological Integrity

6. **The correct answer is a.** The question is asking the purpose of the tube. The Sengstaken-Blakemore tube has three lumens. Lumen one applies direct pressure to esophageal varices. Lumen two keeps the tube in place. Lumen three is to suction blood and gastric contents from the stomach. Suctioning blood and gastric contents from the lungs (option b) is incorrect because the material would be suctioned from the stomach and not the lungs. Administering sterile iced water lavages (option c) is incorrect because the nurse would use isotonic normal saline and not water. Preventing gastric aspiration into the lungs (option d) is incorrect because aspiration is a complication of the Sengstaken-Blakemore tube and the client must be observed for this complication.
   Nursing Process: Analysis   **Client Need:** Safe, Effective Care Environment

7. **The correct answer is a.** The question is asking why a penrose drain is in the body after an appendectomy. The drain facilitates the movement of body fluids that collect in a partially closed wound. If the wound is partially closed and drains are in place, the nurse must continue to assess. The incision is observed for suture integrity and signs and symptoms of wound inflammation and infection (option b). Drainage tubes may be placed into the wound or along the incision to promote drainage of fluids, which may otherwise impair healing (option c). A nasogastric tube is used to decompress the bowel if needed (option d).
Nursing Process: Analysis **Client Need:** Physiological Integrity

8. **The correct answers are a, b and e.** The question is asking which client teaching would be appropriate for a client diagnosed with gastroesophageal reflux disease (GERD). One of the primary factors in GERD is an incompetent lower esophageal sphincter (LES). Gastric contents move from an area of higher pressure (stomach) to an area of lower pressure (esophagus) when in a supine position. The head of the bed should be elevated on 4 to 6 inch blocks. Small, frequent meals are advised to prevent over distention of the stomach (option a). Decreased LES pressure can result from foods containing caffeine and peppermint; therefore, they should be avoided (option b). Fluids should be taken between rather than with meals to reduce gastric distention (option c). Regurgitation of food or gastric contents from the stomach into the esophagus or mouth is a common manifestation of GERD and need not be reported to the physician (option d). Milk products increase gastric acid secretion and should be avoided (option e).
Nursing Process: Implementation **Client Need:** Health Promotion & Maintenance

9. **The correct answer is a.** The question is asking how you would take care of a client who has had a percutaneous transluminal coronary angioplasty (PTCA). The procedure for insertion of the catheter to perform the angioplasty is similar to cardiac catheterization. The catheter is passed through to the coronary artery. Bleeding can occur at the insertion site or from rupture or puncture of the vessel, which could require emergency surgery. Laser plaque removal may occur if the plaque is hard and does not respond to PTCA treatment (option b). There is no evidence to suggest that a myocardial infarction has occurred (option c). Vasospasm may occur during the procedure due to manipulation of the vessel (option d). It may resolve itself or require calcium channel blocker medication.
Nursing Process: Planning **Client Need:** Physiological Integrity

10. **The correct answer is a.** The question is asking for correct information about systemic lupus erythematosus (SLE). SLE is a disease of exacerbation and remission. It is unpredictable in its course ranging from a mild disorder to a rapidly progressive one (option c). A familiar tendency makes it possible for the disease to be transmitted genetically (option b). The medication for SLE does not cause involuntary movements, as do other medications such as antipsychotic drugs (option d).
Nursing Process: Evaluation **Client Need:** Physiological Integrity

11. **The correct answer is b.** The question is asking for the reason a client would have a reaction to the insulins. Humulin N insulin peaks 8 to 12 hours after administration. Without a scheduled afternoon snack, a glucose deficiency will exist during the peak period and symptoms of hypoglycemia will result. Checking blood glucose levels with a glucometer will not alter them (option a). Morning insulin is administered approximately one half hour before breakfast (option c). Morning and evening exercise will have little effect on the afternoon glucose level (option d).
Nursing Process: Analysis **Client Need:** Physiological Integrity

12. **The correct answer is a.** The question is asking what this scale measures. The Glasgow Coma Scale assesses eye opening, best verbal response and best motor response. Vital signs, pupillary response and selected cranial nerve assessment would provide additional vital data, but these assessments are not considered to be components of the GCS (options b, c & d).
Nursing Process: Assessment **Client Need:** Physiological Integrity

13. **The correct answer is b.** The question is asking which symptom in a client with AIDS is most concerning. A client with AIDS who complains of blurred vision may be developing

cytomegalovirus retinitis. This type of ocular disease usually will only appear when the client is severely immunosuppressed. If it is not treated, it can lead to blindness. A productive cough (option a), painful urination (option c) and vaginal discharge (option d) are all symptoms that should be reported within 24 hours as they indicate the client may have an infection. However, these symptoms do not take precedence over the potential permanent loss of vision.
Nursing Process: Analysis   **Client Need:** Physiological Integrity

14. **The correct answer is a.** The question is asking what the nurse should do when a client is hemorrhaging. The first action is to apply pressure to try and control the bleeding. Otherwise, the client could have a severe hemorrhage, shock and death. The nurse should ask another person (option b) to elevate the head of the bed to assist with airway maintenance (option c). The physician should be notified. Immediate surgery is needed for repair of the artery (option d).
Nursing Process: Implementation   **Client Need:** Safe, Effective Care Environment

15. **The correct answer is c.** The question is asking how to begin teaching an anxious client. Before initiating teaching or providing the client with any literature (option d), the nurse should validate his fears and concerns through questioning. This intervention is within the nurse's scope of practice and should not be given to the physician (option a). The procedure may be uncomfortable and misleading to the client, thus, providing false reassurance (option b).
Nursing Process: Implementation   **Client Need:** Safe, Effective Care Environment

16. **The correct answer is c.** The question is asking what would happen if the limb is not placed in the proper position postoperatively. The affected limb should be in proper alignment using rolled towels or sand bags to prevent contractures. Placing the client on the abdomen for short periods can prevent further problems. Improper positioning should not produce problems for the unaffected limb (options a & d). Abduction of the stump would be away from, not toward (option b) the midline of the body.
Nursing Process: Planning   **Client Need:** Physiological Integrity

17. **The correct answer is b.** The question is asking why PEEP is used on a ventilator. The major indication for positive end expiratory pressure (PEEP) is a severe gas exchange disturbance not corrected with regular ventilator settings. By using PEEP, alveolar collapse is reversed, resulting in improved arterial oxygenation. PEEP is needed to hold the alveoli open during expiration; this is done by gradually increasing the expiratory pressure. PEEP is normally instituted to decrease the amount of oxygen required by a ventilator client (option a). When using PEEP, a lower amount of oxygen is required because it causes a continuous positive pressure in the lungs, which improves oxygenation to the tissues. The expiratory pressure should not return to zero because this places the client at risk for atelectasis due to alveolar collapse (option c). Clients placed on PEEP are at increased risk for pneumothorax due to the increased positive pressure exerted on the lungs (option d).
Nursing Process: Planning   **Client Need:** Physiological Integrity

18. **The correct answer is b.** The question is asking how to prevent postural hypotension in a spinal cord injured client, who is getting up for the first time. An abdominal binder and elastic support hose help prevent venous pooling and increase venous return. These measures will help to prevent or decrease postural hypotension. The client will probably faint if he is immediately placed in an upright position (option a) for even a short period of time. Family support is essential for the cord-injured client (option c) but hypotension will occur whether the family is there or not. A common side effect of trimethobenzanide (Tigan) and most antiemetics is postural hypotension. This intervention (option d) would aggravate the problem.
Nursing Process: Implementation   **Client Need:** Physiological Integrity

19. **The correct answer is c.** The question is asking what psychological needs should be addressed when caring for someone of the Hindu faith. Clients of this faith believe illness is a result of misuse of their bodies or sins in their past life. Orthodox Jewish people believe that dairy products and meat products should not be eaten together (option a). Buddhists believe that pure

prayer will give them a stronger connection with a higher existence (option b). The Koran is the religious guide for Muslims (option d).
Nursing Process: Planning   **Client Need:** Psychosocial Integrity

20.   **The correct answer is c.** The question is asking for a description of a normal electrocardiogram (EKG). A normal EKG would be a PQRST wave without ectopy with a rate of 88. The P wave represents atrial depolarization, the QRS complex represents ventricular depolarization, and the T wave represents repolarization (option d). A U wave (option b) usually indicates hypokalemia. Ectopy refers to abnormal beats that arise from "ectopic" sites. The normal heart rate is between 60 to 100 beats per minute (option a).
Nursing Process: Analysis   **Client Need:** Physiological Integrity

21.   **The correct answer is c.** The question is asking the definition of spastic cerebral palsy. Cerebral palsy is a term that indicates motor function impairment and is a static nonprogressive neurological condition resulting from some antecedent insult to the central nervous system. It is a condition in which control of voluntary muscles is lost. The cause has not yet been determined in this child (options a, b & d).
Nursing Process: Implementation   **Client Need:** Physiological Integrity

22.   **The correct answer is d.** The question is asking why a baby with tetralogy of Fallot (TOF) turns blue. Cyanosis is evident, as blood cannot oxygenate adequately due to the pulmonary atresia associated with TOF. Newborns, however, do not always demonstrate cyanosis until the pulmonic stenosis worsens. Constricted aorta, hypoplastic left ventricle and mitral valve stenosis are not associated with TOF (options a, b & c).
Nursing Process: Analysis   **Client Need:** Physiological Integrity

23.   **The correct answer is d.** The question is asking which symptom should be the priority in a grieving child. Sleeping 14 hours per day would be a red flag for depression. Refusing to go to school (option a) and fear of doom (option b) are symptoms of separation-anxiety. Lashing out (option c) is a symptom of an anxiety disorder and while all need to be addressed once depression is controlled, the other symptoms may dissipate on their own.
Nursing Process: Analysis   **Client Need:** Psychosocial Integrity

24.   **The correct answer is a.** The question is asking which is a problem related to Parkinson's disease. Parkinson's disease is often accompanied by tremors, problems with gait, difficulty with speech and other self-care problems, which decrease the person's sense of well-being and ability to function leading to poor self-esteem. Chronic confusion (option b) may relate to dementias such as Alzheimer's disease. Altered tissue perfusion (option c) would occur with circulatory impairment, such as with immobility related to lumbar disk herniation. Parkinson's disease is a defect in the neurotransmitters or a neurological disorder. Impaired gas exchange (option d) is more likely to occur with seizures.
Nursing Process: Analysis   **Client Need:** Physiological Integrity

25.   **The correct answer is d.** The question is asking what the usual reason for hemorrhage is in a woman after delivery of the baby. Uterine atony leads to hemorrhage. Perineal and cervical lacerations, prolonged labors, and retained placental fragments (options a, b, & c) may cause uterine atony, but the uterine atony causes hemorrhage.
Nursing Process: Implementation   **Client Need:** Physiological Integrity

26.   **The correct answer is d.** The question is asking what would cause respiratory distress syndrome (RDS) in a newborn. Neonatal RDS is manifested by the presence of hyaline material in the alveoli and alveolar ducts, which prevents aeration. The cause of this hyaline membrane formation is unknown, but three theories have been postulated; this answer is based on one of those theories. The remaining two theories involve pulmonary hypoperfusion and alteration in the enzyme system of the lung leading to proliferation of fibrin exudate (options a, b & c).
Nursing Process: Analysis   **Client Need:** Physiological Integrity

27. **The correct answer is a.** The question is asking how the nurse should respond when a 5-year-old child's blood pressure is 72/44. First ask if this is normal. The most important post-catheter nursing procedure is observation. Blood pressure should be monitored, especially for hypotension, which may indicate hemorrhage from the cardiac perforation, or bleeding at the site of the initial catheterization. The nurse should identify this as a low blood pressure for a 5-year-old child (normal: 101/57) and immediately assess the site of cardiac catheterization (option c). Peripheral pulses should be assessed (option b) for circulation post-catheterization, but assessing for hemorrhage would be more important. The physician should be notified after assessment (option d) since the nurse can take some action such as pressure to the site, if bleeding is found.
Nursing Process: Implementation   **Client Need:** Safe, Effective Care Environment

28. **The correct answer is b.** The question is asking how the nurse would know that a client does not completely understand how to use a peak flow meter. A peak flow meter is used to help clients with asthma determine how well the asthma is being controlled. A client in good control will have a peak flow rate between 80 and 100% of their personal best peak flow number. In order to determine the peak flow number, the client should measure every morning before taking scheduled medications. The client should either sit up straight or stand when measuring (option a). If the peak flow is less than 80%, medication should be taken (option c). The client should blow as hard and fast as possible (option d).
Nursing Process: Implementation   **Client Need:** Health Promotion & Maintenance

29. **The correct answer is b.** The question is asking which client could be safely discharged to make room for more critically ill clients. The client with nephrotic syndrome is treated symptomatically. The client's edema is treated with low-sodium, low to moderate protein diet, nonsteroidal anti-inflammatory drugs and antihypertensives. The syphilis is treated with antibiotics. This can be done at home. Decreased pain and discontinuation of a patient controlled analgesia pump is indicative of improvement in a client with sickle cell crisis. However, this client is not yet ready for discharge as the client is still experiencing pain and more studies are needed to determine if oxygen is still required and tissue damage has halted (option a). A fat embolism can complicate a femur fracture. This can occur within 48 to 72 hours of the fracture. Femur fractures are most often treated with skeletal traction for 8 to 12 weeks (option c). A client with myasthenia gravis and an upper respiratory infection needs to be hospitalized so that adequate ventilation can be provided (option d).
Nursing Process: Analysis   **Client Need:** Safe, Effective Care Environment

30. **The correct answer is b.** The question is asking why potassium should be given slowly. Rapid replacement of potassium can cause cardiac arrest. Cardiac cell depolarization depends on the lower concentrations of potassium outside of the cell; therefore, rapid replacement can alter this. Intravenous potassium is irritating (option a) to the vein, but the life-threatening cardiac arrest is the priority. Potassium levels are usually rechecked one hour after administration, not continuously (option c). If hypotension occurs, it will be the result of cardiac arrest, not potassium administration (option d).
Nursing Process: Planning   **Client Need:** Physiological Integrity

31. **The correct answer is a.** The question is asking what the nurse should do when the client's case seems beyond the scope of practice or skill level. The appropriate action for the nurse generalist after completing a sexual assessment is to consult with the clinic's psychiatrist and treatment team about an appropriate referral. Although the nurse may make suggestions to the treatment team it is their responsibility to refer the client to the appropriate resource. The nurse has recognized that she is not prepared to conduct sexual counseling with the client and is aware of her limitations (option b). At this point, support groups and marriage counseling would be premature referrals (options c & d).
Nursing Process: Planning   **Client Need:** Health Promotion & Maintenance

32. **The correct answer is a.** The question is asking what problems can occur if a client takes a medication that affects clotting factors. The anticoagulant has the specific potential for producing clotting disorders. Prescription and over the counter medications may increase operative risk and

interact unfavorably with the anesthetic agents (option c). Tranquilizers may lower the intra-operative blood pressure and thiazide diuretics may cause potassium depletion (options b & d).
Nursing Process: Analysis   **Client Need:** Safe, Effective Care Environment

33.   **The correct answer is d.** The question is asking what to say to a lesbian client who wants to have her partner present during discharge planning and health teaching. The nurse should encourage the presence and assistance of significant others (option a). This helps provide appropriate support for the client. The client will then be able to assume greater responsibility for her care. Options (a) and (b) are subtly judgmental as they avoid the issue presented by the client by implying that the partner's presence is not a priority. Providing printed materials often enhances discharge teaching but this should not replace the client's desire to have her partner with her (option b). Option (c) is judgmental; the lesbian client's partner is an immediate family member to her and should be treated as such.
Nursing Process: Planning   **Client Need:** Physiological Integrity

34.   **The correct answer is c.** The question is asking what foods would be on a low-sodium diet. Roast beef, baked potato and sherbet are all acceptable on a 2g low-sodium diet. Canned vegetables, glazed strawberries, biscuit, buttermilk and commercially prepared cookies are all high in sodium (options a, b & d).
Nursing Process: Evaluation   **Client Need:** Physiological Integrity

35.   **The correct answer is d.** The question is asking what to do when a scrub top gets wet. In a sterile environment, this means it is contaminated. Wet clothes should be changed to minimize the chance of spreading infection. A dry gown over a wet one will probably result in that gown becoming wet as well (option a). Washing and drying the garment can introduce new germs to the area (options b & c).
Nursing Process: Implementation   **Client Need:** Safe, Effective Care Environment

36.   **The correct answer is a.** The question is asking what to look for in a client with a calcium level of 7. Normal calcium levels are 9 to 11mg/dL and the client will show signs of hypocalcemia. A Chvostek's sign is noted when the nurse brushes the client's cheek and the facial muscles twitch in response to low calcium levels. Numbness is also a symptom of hypocalcemia. Nausea, vomiting and anorexia are signs of hypokalemia or hypercalcemia (option b). Muscle weakness and numbness (option c) refers to signs of hyperkalemia, while headache, blurred vision and convulsions are signs of hyponatremia (option d).
Nursing Process: Analysis   **Client Need:** Physiological Integrity

37.   **The correct answer is b.** The question is asking why someone in diabetic ketoacidosis is also on a cardiac monitor. Hypokalemia may not be evident in serum potassium levels due to fluid volume deficit. Changes in potassium levels can be detected by the presence of a wave after the T wave on the cardiac monitor. There is no relationship between acute ketoacidosis and myocardial infarction (option a). Elevated glucose levels will not precipitate a cardiac arrest. A rare instance of cardiac arrest would be related to complications of sustained elevated glucose levels, such as hypokalemia; metabolic acidosis; etc. (option c). While most clients admitted to the ICU are monitored, the rationale is not "for routine purposes" (option d).
Nursing Process: Analysis   **Client Need:** Physiological Integrity

38.   **The correct answer is d.** The question is asking what to do when a client walking in the hall starts to fall. The client should be assisted to the floor by supporting and lowering the client and using good body mechanics. Allowing the client to fall unassisted (option c) may cause injury to the client. Placing the client against the wall (option a) would be difficult to do after the client starts to fall. If the client were dizzy, the potential to fall would be great. The client should not be left alone (option d) when in distress. The nurse should stay with the client and call for help.
Nursing Process: Implementation   **Client Need:** Safe, Effective Care Environment

39.   **The correct answer is d.** The question is asking what to do if the bed is broken and maintenance insists it is fixed. The main focus here is the client's safety. Regardless of the problem between

the nurse and maintenance, the client must be placed in a safe bed. If the equipment is faulty in any way, it should not be used. Telling the client to be careful of the side rail (option b) admits equipment failure and does nothing to actually protect the client. The client is disoriented and may not understand the instruction. Calling maintenance (option c) is an option, but the priority concern is the client's safety. Passing information on to the supervisor (option a) is proper; however, the equipment should not be used at all as the client would be in continued danger.
Nursing Process: Implementation   **Client Need:** Safe, Effective Care Environment

40.   **The correct answer is b.** The question is asking how to look for a clot in the leg of a client who does not have sensation in the legs. Deep vein thrombophlebitis may obstruct venous return and cause edema, which would be reflected in calf size. Redness and warmth may accompany deep vein thrombophlebitis. The client cannot tell you if he has pain in his calves because of the spinal cord injury (options a & c). An elevated temperature (option d) may occur, but could also be indicative of other problems and not specific to the thrombophlebitis.
Nursing Process: Assessment   **Client Need:** Physiological Integrity

41.   **The correct answer is d.** The question is asking how the nurse can intervene based on the developmental level of the daughter. Young adults are usually confirming their independence at this point and their viewpoint deals mainly with setting up their own life goals toward independence (option a). However, when the situation is explained to them, young adults can usually relate to the parental point of view and a compromise can be worked out (options b & c). The nurse is in a position to do this with an understanding of normal growth and development. The parents can also be assisted to understand why the young adult is acting in this manner, so that further discussions can take place without the intervention of the nurse.
Nursing Process: Analysis   **Client Need:** Health Promotion & Maintenance

42.   **The correct answer is b.** The question is asking for an analysis of the data presented. When a client is severely depressed, the potential for suicide should always be assessed. Suicidal ideation occurs in about 74% of very depressed clients and is a safety issue, where the client may need protection from his self-destructive impulses. Alteration in nutrition (option a) would be a concern but a 10-pound weight loss in one month does not constitute a life-threatening condition, compared to suicide. Altered self-concept (option c) and alteration in thought processes (option d) would also be assessed, but would not be the priority.
Nursing Process: Assessment   **Client Need:** Safe, Effective Care Environment

43.   **The correct answer is c.** The question is asking what to do when a client who is on a continuous tube feeding develops diarrhea. If diarrhea occurs with a continuous tube feeding, the causes may be feeding too fast or at too high a concentration. The formula should be stopped and then reintroduced gradually from a quarter to a half of full strength, as tolerated. Notify the physician for a change in formula and discard the old formula. Change the tubing every 24 hours, changing from a continuous to intermittent feeding schedule and increasing flow rate or administering normal saline solution will not decrease or eliminate the diarrhea (options a, b & d).
Nursing Process: Implementation   **Client Need:** Physiological Integrity

44.   **The correct answer is b.** The question is asking how to care for a child with cystic fibrosis. Adequate rest is one of the key factors in cystic fibrosis clients as well as the nutritional foods. However, the clients must like the foods or they will not be eaten. Avoiding people with upper respiratory infections is important, but complete isolation is not necessary. Cleanliness (option c) is important but not essential. Preventing dehydration and giving her medications (options a & d) are essential, but were part of wrong answers.
Nursing Process: Planning   **Client Need:** Health Promotion & Maintenance

45.   **The correct answer is d.** The question is asking which symptom shown by the client relates to colon cancer. Alterations in the shape of the stool may be a direct result of a tumor partially obstructing the colon. Since the stool is in this region of the upper gastrointestinal tract, any bloody discharge in this aspect of the bowel will be red and appear blood streaked. Hemoptysis

would be seen with lung problems (option a). Liquid tarry diarrhea is seen with a GI bleed (option b). Fat intolerance and steatorrhea would be seen with gallbladder problems (option c).

Nursing Process: Assessment   **Client Need:** Physiological Integrity

46.   **The correct answer is c.** The question is asking how to assist a new client in the community who is looking for specific resources for a handicap. Self-help groups are quite beneficial because these are people who have already found and probably used many of the community's resources for a particular handicap. They can often advise the client with much practical knowledge. Often the nurse should make initial contacts with agencies (option a). Searching for and contacting resources can be very discouraging (option b). The nurse can avoid these problems for the client, gather information about different resources, make valuable community contacts and make informed appropriate referrals. The client might not know what types of resources are available and may not think to ask.

        Nursing Process: Implementation   **Client Need:** Health Promotion & Maintenance

47.   **The correct answer is b.** The question is asking why a client with pernicious anemia cannot have pills instead of injections. Vitamin B_{12} is a necessary lifetime replacement for the treatment of pernicious anemia. With pernicious anemia, there is faulty absorption from the gastrointestinal tract due to the lack of intrinsic factor necessary for gastrointestinal absorption of vitamin B_{12}. Iron replacement is necessary for iron deficiency anemia and is an oral preparation (option a). Iron deficiency anemia is usually associated with iron loss during bleeding, such as during menstruation. Folic acid (option c) may be given in conjunction with vitamin B_{12} if nutritional problems are found. Blood transfusions (option d) should be the treatment of choice for aplastic anemia. Aplastic anemia is caused by a decrease in precursor cells in the bone marrow.

        Nursing Process: Implementation   **Client Need:** Physiological Integrity

48.   **The correct answer is a.** The question is asking how to plan care for a client reluctant to transfer to a nursing home. An orientation to the facility may decrease anxiety and misinformation about the nursing home. Giving information about the new facility assists the client to feel less powerless by knowing what to expect. Explaining the merits of the facility may help (option b), but convincing a client implies a lack of empathy on the nurse's part. Spending more time with the client (option c) may help, but it may also increase his desire to stay where he is. There is insufficient data to support risk of elopement (option d).

        Nursing Process: Planning   **Client Need:** Psychosocial Integrity

49.   **The correct answer is b.** The question is asking the medication used for this heart anomaly. Medical management of the ductus may be attempted with indomethacin (Indocin), which is a prostaglandin inhibitor. It has been successful in constricting the ductus in premature infants. Surgical ligation may be necessary. Erythromycin (E-Mycin), an antibiotic, may be used to treat rheumatic fever (option a). Albuterol (Proventil) is a bronchodilator, often used in asthma (option c). Prednisone (Deltasone) is a corticosteroid, which may be used with leukemia (option d).

        Nursing Process: Planning   **Client Need:** Physiological Integrity

50.   **The correct answer is c.** The question is asking which option best describes an electromyography (EMG). An EMG records the electrical activity of selected muscles during voluntary contraction and at rest. This test is done by placing needle electrodes into the muscle. The electrical activity is then recorded when the client contracts the muscle and it is then compared to the electrical activity of that muscle at rest. An electroencephalogram (EEG) is the painless procedure that measures the electrical activity of the brain by placing electrodes on different areas of the head (option a). As part of the EMG, nerve conduction studies measure the speed of conduction along the nerve by electrically stimulating the nerve (option b); however, the client does not usually feel the shock. Muscle relaxants are contraindicated in EMGs, as they alter the activity in the myoneural junction (option d).

        Nursing Process: Implementation   **Client Need:** Health Promotion & Maintenance

51.   **The correct answer is c.** The question is asking what a client with liver problems must be concerned about with their diet. When hepatic encephalopathy is present, protein is temporarily

eliminated from the diet and foods high in carbohydrate are administered. Steak and chicken have protein, as would a protein supplement (options a, b & d). Macaroni has no protein and is high in carbohydrates.

Nursing Process: Implementation   **Client Need:** Physiological Integrity

52.   **The correct answer is d.** The question is asking what problems would occur in a client with syndrome of inappropriate antidiuretic hormone (SIADH). There is excessive loss of water and electrolytes due to an inappropriate amount of antidiuretic hormone. Therefore, the client must be on strict intake and output and have electrolytes checked, regularly. Insulin need is seen in clients diagnosed with type 1 diabetes (option a). With SIADH the client retains fluid; therefore, there is weight gain, not loss (option b). Diarrhea is usually associated with some type of irritable bowel syndrome (option c).

     Nursing Process: Planning   **Client Need:** Physiological Integrity

53.   **The correct answer is c.** The question is asking which statement made by the client shows readiness for discharge. In other words, look for the option that shows no sign of depression. "I'll sometimes make mistakes" denotes a realistic sense of self rather than unrealistic perfection or self-devaluation. "Asking the physician to decrease medication" (option a) implies that he does not realize the role of medication in treatment. "Your suggestion is better than mine…." suggests devaluation of his contributions, which is a continued sign of depression (option b). "I'm sure I can go back to work without trouble," suggests unrealistic goal setting where the client is set up for possible failure (option d).

     Nursing Process: Evaluation   **Client Need:** Health Promotion & Maintenance

54.   **The correct answer is c.** The question is asking why wires should be coming from the heart after cardiac surgery. These wires are attached to the heart and to a pacemaker that will fire should the heart rate drop below 60. The pacemaker wires are unrelated to the EKG monitoring, defibrillator or Swan Ganz catheter (options a, b & d).

     Nursing Process: Analysis   **Client Need:** Physiological Integrity

55.   **The correct answer is c.** The question is asking why someone having heart surgery would have an incision on the leg. Part of the saphenous vein will be removed from the leg and grafted to the heart. Part of this vein will be attached to the blocked artery. Veins are used instead of arteries because they are less muscular and provide better blood flow. The cardiopulmonary bypass machine (option d) is attached through the vena cava and aorta. Removing part of the femoral artery (option a) would compromise the blood flow to the leg. It is within the nurse's scope of practice to teach this rather than telling the client to ask the physician (option b).

     Nursing Process: Implementation   **Client Need:** Safe, Effective Care Environment

56.   **The correct answer is c.** The question is asking what these spots mean. Kaposi's sarcoma is a rare cancer characterized by reddish-brown or bluish spots on the individual. It is most often manifested in clients who have AIDS. Pernicious anemia (option a) is caused by a vitamin B_{12} deficiency. This is related to an absence of the intrinsic factor in the stomach mucosa and unrelated to AIDS. Pneumocystis carinii (option b) may be present in AIDS clients as a pulmonary infection. Lymphocytic leukemia (option d) is caused by a proliferation of B-lymphocytes and is unrelated to AIDS.

     Nursing Process: Analysis   **Client Need:** Physiological Integrity

57.   **The correct answer is b.** The question is asking what problems may occur in the neonate when the mother received magnesium sulfate (Magnesium) during labor. Neonatal respiratory depression and hypotonus should be evaluated. Bradycardia (option a) may be a symptom of impending cardiac dysfunction in the mother. Tachycardia (option c) is associated in the mother with the drug, ritodrine (Yutopar). Hypoglycemia (option d) is associated in the neonate with ritodrine (Yutopar).

     Nursing Process: Assessment   **Client Need:** Physiological Integrity

58. **The correct answer is d.** The question is asking what is the appropriate care for a newborn that must wear an abducter harness for developmental dysplasia of the hip (DDH). Shoulder straps should be padded to prevent pressure sores to the underlying skin. The diaper should be placed under the straps (option a). The harness is worn continuously and should be adjusted only with the supervision of a health care professional (option b). Lotions and powders often irritate the skin and should not be used (option c).
Nursing Process: Implementation   **Client Need:** Health Promotion & Maintenance

59. **The correct answer is a.** The question is asking what to do when a client states the Hickman catheter may be injured. If the client reports any injury (or possible injury) to the catheter, the client should be instructed to clamp the catheter between the body and the injured portion of the catheter and to go to the emergency department for repair. Calling the physician, sending an ambulance crew to replace the catheter, or making an appointment with the physician (options b, c & d) would delay necessary treatment and may be unsafe.
Nursing Process: Implementation   **Client Need:** Safe, Effective Care Environment

60. **The correct answer is a.** The question is asking what to do when the client shows signs that either could be due to anxiety or a complication of the rib fracture. The physician should be notified as the client might be showing signs of pneumothorax including: pain on inspiration, tachypnea, diaphoresis and tachycardia. Although her symptoms may be a result of anxiety, further assessment is required. Asking the client to talk about it, restricting visitors and checking back with the client in 15 minutes (options b, c & d) neglect the fact that she is at high risk for a pneumothorax. The potential for pneumothorax is a medical priority, which requires prompt treatment.
Nursing Process: Implementation   **Client Need:** Physiological Integrity

61. **The correct answer is a.** The question is asking what to assess when a client has taken too much cocaine. A physical assessment must be done first to determine if any symptoms are life threatening. These life-threatening symptoms would be indicated in vital signs. Determining support systems (option b) is a psychological assessment. Establishing seizure precautions (option c) is an action and not an assessment. Cyanosis (option d) should be monitored since the client is often oxygen deficient, but the priority is vital signs for total assessment.
Nursing Process: Assessment   **Client Need:** Physiological Integrity

62. **The correct answer is a.** The question is asking how to address the problem of pain when the client refuses pain medication, even if the pain is severe. The nurse should explore the client's perception of pain and pain medication to assist in educating the client. Waiting until later (option b) may cause the pain to become too severe. Pain medication has less effect if muscles are tightened. Some clients may be concerned about addiction, but this was an assumption and does not allow the client to describe the problem (option c). Allowing the client to decide when to take pain medication decreases a sense of powerlessness (option d).
Nursing Process: Implementation   **Client Need:** Physiological Integrity

63. **The correct answer is b.** The question is asking how to encourage the client to eat. Direct communication works best. Clients who have Alzheimer's disease may have difficulty remembering what to do and in making decisions. A suggestion by the nurse relieves the client by meeting the immediate need. Asking the client about food preferences (option a) is unnecessary since there does not appear to be a dislike of the food. Feeding the client (option c) is inappropriate at this time; since it has not been determined that he cannot feed himself. Obtaining packaged food (option d) is not necessary since there are no problems with persecutory delusions.
Nursing Process: Implementation   **Client Need:** Physiological Integrity

64. **The correct answer is c.** The question is asking what would be included in the teaching plan for a client receiving an echocardiogram. An echocardiogram is a noninvasive ultrasound test used to examine the size, shape and motion of cardiac structures. Providing written consent, inserting an intravenous lock and explaining the risk of bleeding options (a, b & d) are incorrect because the procedure is noninvasive.

Nursing Process: Planning   **Client Need:** Physiological Integrity

65.   **The correct answer is d.** The question is asking which option shows signs of borderline personality disorder. The classic characteristics of this disorder include: intense anger or rage, self-mutilation, fear of abandonment, splitting, poor reality testing and projection. Preoccupation with fantasies of success (option a) is characteristic of narcissistic personality disorder. Persistent lying and manipulative behavior (option b) is characteristic of antisocial personality disorder. Overly dramatic behavior, angry outbursts and seductive behavior (option c) are characteristic of dependent personality disorder.
Nursing Process: Assessment   **Client Need:** Psychosocial Integrity

66.   **The correct answer is a.** The question is asking how to care for a client who has an electronic fetal monitor. It is important to assess what the client knows, then to reinforce that knowledge and add the needed information. The client is able to move from side-to-side and can assume any position of comfort. There are no restrictions in position of the client while monitoring her labor. Some monitoring systems allow the client to ambulate (options b & d). The monitor should be moved frequently as the baby moves (option c).
Nursing Process: Implementation   **Client Need:** Health Promotion & Maintenance

67.   **The correct answer is b.** The question is asking for an analysis of the situation. During asthma attacks, the airway is partially compromised due to bronchospasm. Wheezing confirms the blocked airway. Ineffective airway clearance is defined as blocked passage but oxygen can diffuse well if it gets to the alveoli. Impaired gas exchange (option a) occurs when the problem is oxygen diffusion within the alveoli. Tenacious sputum is generally not found with asthma, but may be true for cystic fibrosis or chronic obstructive pulmonary disease. Ineffective breathing pattern occurs when the client's breathing is insufficient in bringing in enough oxygen for the lungs to diffuse oxygen. Hypoventilation would not occur, but hyperventilation would because the decreased oxygen supply will trigger increased respirations to replace needed oxygen (option c). Fluid volume deficit (option d) is incorrect because there is no evidence to support it. The dehydration would be the result of fluid volume deficit (fluid loss) not the cause of it.
Nursing Process: Analysis   **Client Need:** Physiological Integrity

68.   **The correct answer is a.** The question is asking the purpose of this medication. Methylergonovine maleate (Methergine) works directly on the smooth muscle of the uterus to cause it to contract, thus decreasing bleeding from the placental site. The medication is not used to facilitate the formation of clots and does not promote healing of the reproductive tract (options b & d). Ritodrine hydrochloride (Yutopar) relaxes the uterus to prevent further complications (option c).
Nursing Process: Implementation   **Client Need:** Physiological Integrity

69.   **The correct answer is a.** The question is asking to whom the rubella should be reported. Reportable communicable diseases are reported to the county health officer, not to the child's physician (option c). The county health officer then reports it to the state health department (option b) who then reports the incidence to the U.S. Public Health Service Center for Disease Control (option d).
Nursing Process: Implementation   **Client Need:** Safe, Effective Care Environment

70.   **The correct answer is a.** The question is asking how to assist a client to void if the client has a spinal cord injury and lacks full sensation. The client will have an upper motor neuron (reflex) bladder since the sacral segments are intact. This type of bladder may respond to external stimulation. The client cannot perform the Valsalva maneuver because of the level of injury (option b). The Credé maneuver (option c) may cause autonomic dysreflexia and is of more use with the lower motor neuron bladder type. Running the water (option d) is not effective as there is no nervous system connection between higher cortical centers and the bladder.
Nursing Process: Implementation   **Client Need:** Health Promotion & Maintenance

71. **The correct answer is d.** The question is asking which exercise helps build endurance. Endurance comes from an increased ability to provide oxygenated blood to the body system allowing it to function longer and at a better capacity. Aerobic exercises, such as, bicycling and jogging would be recommended. Weight lifting (option c) is a type of strength building exercise (option a). This helps to increase muscle mass and improve appearance. Flexibility exercises, such as stretching, (option b) help the body move more easily and decrease chance of injury. They should be used prior to other types of exercise.
Nursing Process: Implementation   **Client Need:** Health Promotion & Maintenance

72. **The correct answer is a.** The question is asking which option relates to abruptio placenta. Pregnancy induced hypertension would increase the risk of abruptio placenta. Low birth weight (option b) and nationality or race (option c) are not significant factors in abruptio placenta. Possible scarring of the uterus by a cesarean section may be a factor in placenta previa (option d).
Nursing Process: Assessment   **Client Need:** Physiological Integrity

73. **The correct answer is a.** The question is asking how to address the client's problem of lifting her arm. First, is this an abnormal finding? It is not unusual for a client following a mastectomy to complain of difficulty lifting the affected extremity. To facilitate care and to assist with the required range-of-motion activities, assisting the client to lift her arm would be most appropriate. Wall climbing and pulleys will also assist the arm in exercises. Using the unaffected arm will not assist in range-of-motion of the affected parts, which is needed for strengthening and good drainage (option b). The client is not showing noncompliance. The surgery may limit easy motion at first due to pain and tissue removal (option c). Completing hair care for the client does not help with needed exercises and may decrease the client's self-esteem (option d).
Nursing Process: Implementation   **Client Need:** Physiological Integrity

74. **The correct answer is c.** The question is asking how best to maintain a therapeutic relationship with a client diagnosed with acquired immunodeficiency syndrome (AIDS). Establishing rapport through honesty, trust, respect, genuineness and empathy are important for any therapeutic relationship, regardless of the client. Option (a) is incorrect because the client does not guide the discussion. Option (b) is incorrect because clients do not usually expect the nurse to have all of the answers. Option (d) is incorrect because it is not honest and gives false reassurance.
Nursing Process: Implementation   **Client Need:** Psychosocial Integrity

75. **The correct answer is b.** The question is asking what type of problem is shown by the symptoms. Keep in mind that this is the diuretic phase and that the client is losing fluid. The signs indicate fluid deficit, which is a common problem during this phase (option a). Both options (c), electrolyte imbalance related to retained toxins and (d), anemia related to lack of erythropoietin may be existing problems but they are not indicated by these assessment data.
Nursing Process: Analysis   **Client Need:** Physiological Integrity

> **Instructions: Allow yourself 75 minutes to complete the following 75 practice questions. Use a timer to notify yourself when 75 minutes are over so that you are not constantly looking at your watch while completing the questions.**

1. The nurse anticipates which type of diet will be prescribed for a client prior to her colectomy?
   a. High-calorie and high-residue.
   b. High-calorie and low-residue.
   c. Low-calorie and high-residue.
   d. Low-calorie and low-residue.

2. A client, who is taking prednisone (Deltasone) to keep him from rejecting his newly transplanted liver, demonstrates that he understands his medication regimen when he states:
   a. "I will take my medication when I feel weak, dizzy and nauseated."
   b. "I will decrease my dosage when exposed to increased stressors."
   c. "I will wear a medic alert band at all times."
   d. "I will omit a dose if I feel edematous."

3. A client returns from the post-anesthesia care unit after a laparoscopic cholecystectomy. Which physician's prescription, should the nurse question?
   a. Place client in Sims' position.
   b. Ondansetron (Zofran) 4mg IV every four hours p.r.n. for nausea and vomiting.
   c. Morphine 2mg IV every four hours for pain.
   d. Remove bandages and bathe or shower tomorrow.

4. A client with alcohol dependence is admitted. In planning the client's care, the nurse knows that the chief aim in a therapeutic relationship is to:
   a. assist the client to develop independent behaviors.
   b. alleviate the client's anxiety and depression.
   c. improve the client's self-esteem.
   d. assist the client in learning new coping mechanisms.

5. A client complains of difficulty falling asleep at night. The nurse suggests:
   a. naps during the day.
   b. a warm cup of tea at bedtime.
   c. relaxation techniques.
   d. falling asleep with the television or radio on.

6. An 87-year-old male is scheduled for an emergency exploratory laparotomy. Before signing the consent form for surgery, the client states, "I don't understand what is going to happen to me." Which is the most appropriate action for the nurse to take?
   a. Ask the client's daughter to sign for the procedure.
   b. Contact the physician to clarify the information for the client.
   c. Have the client sign the consent form and then contact the physician to clarify the information.
   d. Explain the procedure and then have the client sign the consent form.

7. A client with myasthenia gravis is being discharged to home. One goal for treatment at home would be that the client will:
   a. maintain a clear airway.
   b. be absent of seizures.
   c. maintain joint mobility.
   d. use adaptive devices.

8. The nurse assesses that a couple is bonding appropriately with their newborn son when which behavior is observed?
   a. The parents are conversing with each other; father is holding the baby.
   b. Father is holding the baby; mother says that the baby looks like the father.
   c. Mother is holding the baby; father reports what has been going on at home.
   d. The parents discuss plans for leaving the hospital; the baby is in a bassinet nearby.

9. A newly-diagnosed client with Type 2 diabetes tells his nurse, "My friend just went blind from diabetes; I don't want to go blind." What is the nurse's best response?
   a. "Let the doctor know if you begin to have blurred vision."
   b. "If you lose weight, blindness will not be an issue."
   c. "Control of your blood glucose will help prevent blindness."
   d. "Regular eye exams will prevent blindness from occurring."

10. A client, who uses rationalization about a speech he made, would probably tell the nurse:
    a. "I lost my voice and wasn't able to do the speech."
    b. "You would never believe it, I forgot the right day for the speech."
    c. "The speech went well, don't you think?"
    d. "The light at the podium was too low to see my notes clearly."

11. The physician is treating a client with a pneumothorax by inserting a chest tube and connecting it to a water seal drainage system. When the nurse attaches it to suction as prescribed, a continuous bubbling and fluctuation in the water seal chamber is observed. The nurse's initial response is to:
    a. alert the physician of the observation.
    b. apply Vaseline gauze at the chest tube insertion site.
    c. wait to see if the pressure stabilizes before proceeding.
    d. proceed with turning on the suction.

12. The physician prescribes an indwelling urinary catheter for a client with a bleeding ulcer who also has a NG tube. The nurse understands that the primary purpose for the catheter is that it:
    a. permits urinary drainage since having a nasogastric tube would make it awkward to go to the bathroom.
    b. carries out policy of most institutions that clients receiving nasogastric suction also have an indwelling catheter.
    c. provides an additional measurement of fluid balance to indicate potential shock.
    d. provides easy access to the client's urine for ongoing diagnostic studies.

13. A newly admitted client with mental retardation is found in the community room masturbating in front of other clients. The most appropriate initial action by the nurse would be to:
    a. stop the behavior and restrict all privileges.
    b. encourage the client to talk about how he is feeling.
    c. ignore the behavior; the client is working through his feelings.
    d. matter-or-factly tell the client to either stop the behavior or go to his room.

14. What must be reported and documented immediately in a postoperative thyroidectomy client?
    a. Discomfort around the incision site.
    b. Sensation of the dressing being too tight but relieved by loosening the dressing.
    c. Tingling sensation around the mouth.
    d. Hoarseness.

15. A 72-year-old woman comes to the outpatient clinic for a routine check up. During the visit the woman pulls the nurse aside and says, "My husband wants to have sex, but it is very uncomfortable. What can I do?" The most appropriate response would be:
    a. "Have you talked to your husband about this?"
    b. "How often are you having sex?"
    c. "Using water soluble lubricant may decrease the discomfort."
    d. "Are you saying your desire is not the same as your husband?"

16. On her second postpartal day, a client complains of perineal discomfort from her episiotomy. Following assessment of the site, the nurse would intervene by:
    a. applying ice to the perineum.
    b. providing a warm sitz bath.
    c. utilizing a heat lamp to the site.
    d. placing a hot water bottle on the site.

17. A postoperative coronary bypass graft client is on a continuous lidocaine (Xylocard) infusion. The client's wife asks why her husband needs this medicine. The nurse understands that lidocaine is given to this client to:
    a. prophylactically treat angina.
    b. reduce the preload of the heart.
    c. reduce the afterload of the heart.
    d. prevent ventricular arrhythmias and irritability.

18. A client is admitted to the emergency department with complaints of angina, which awakens the client during the night while sleeping. The nurse would assess the client for which additional symptoms?
    a. Relief of pain when the client is sitting upright.
    b. Pain, which occurs with physical exertion.
    c. Severe incapacitating angina that occurs at any time during the day.
    d. Pain associated with coronary artery spasm.

19. A client awaiting liver transplantation has an ammonia level of 110mcg/dL. To prevent further exacerbation of this problem, the nurse would:
    a. give salt poor albumin as prescribed to decrease ascites.
    b. give octreotide (Sandostatin) as prescribed to prevent bleeding from esophageal varices.
    c. monitor the serum creatinine and BUN daily for early indications of hepatorenal syndrome.
    d. encourage foods high in Vitamin B-6 to prevent peripheral neuropathy.

20. A 42-year-old woman comes to the clinic for a routine physical. The client tells the nurse she has been having hot flashes and asks what she can do about them. The nurse would suggest:
    a. decreasing caffeine intake.
    b. wearing tight fitting clothing.
    c. increasing intake of dietary calcium and vitamin D.
    d. having a FSH level drawn before any measures are instituted.

21. The nurse is reviewing a client's blood gas results. The client has a medical diagnosis of pneumonia with a history of chronic obstructive pulmonary disease. The blood gases are pH 7.37, $PaCO_2$ 50, PaO_2 65 and HCO_3 29. The nurse notes that the client is experiencing:
    a. respiratory acidosis.
    b. respiratory alkalosis.
    c. compensated respiratory acidosis.
    d. compensated respiratory alkalosis.

22. A child is brought to the clinic stating that a squirrel that she was trying to feed bit her. The bite broke the skin, but was washed with soap and water right after it occurred. What should the nurse do next?
    a. Instruct the parents to clean the wound with antiseptic daily.
    b. File a report with the animal rescue league so that the animal can be captured and checked for rabies.
    c. Give human rabies immune globulin followed by a course of antibiotics, as prescribed.
    d. Give rabies immune globulin and follow with a series of six rabies vaccine injections, as prescribed.

23. A client has just returned from a liver biopsy. Place the nursing interventions in the order in which they should be performed.
   a. Draw blood for hematocrit and hemoglobin, as prescribed.
   b. Take vital signs.
   c. Place the client on her right side.
   d. Notify the radiology department that a portable chest X-ray was prescribed.

24. A child is brought to the pediatrician's office with rash, low-grade fever and itching. The child is diagnosed with chickenpox. It would be most important for the nurse to assess:
   a. for symptoms of heart problems.
   b. for symptoms of neuritis.
   c. if brothers and sisters have had chickenpox.
   d. whether or not the parents have had chickenpox.

25. A woman who is three months pregnant asks the nurse about the brownish marks around her face that have appeared during this pregnancy. The nurse explains that this is:
   a. rarely seen in pregnant women.
   b. due to underlying pathology and needs to be watched carefully.
   c. due to hormonal changes from the fetus.
   d. due to stimulation of pigment cells and will fade after delivery.

26. A client with Type 1 diabetes is admitted because she is in ketoacidosis. The nurse would assess for which symptom that would indicate that the condition is worsening?
   a. Acetone breath odor.
   b. Slow shallow respirations.
   c. Absence of glucose and ketones in urine.
   d. Peripheral edema.

27. The nurse evaluates that the victim of a rape from three months ago needs to continue counseling when she:
   a. continues to talk about the perpetrator.
   b. still feels some guilt and anger over the event.
   c. has difficulty falling asleep and wakens at night.
   d. is trying to understand some altered self-perceptions.

28. In order to prevent hepatic coma with end-stage cirrhosis, the nurse would anticipate the physician would prescribe which diet?
   a. Low-carbohydrate.
   b. Low-fat.
   c. High in vitamin A.
   d. Low-protein.

29. A bedridden client has been hospitalized for two weeks and the nurse is preparing to wash the client's hair. The nurse should:
   a. lightly rub the client's head with shampoo.
   b. place cotton in the client's ears.
   c. refrain from applying conditioner.
   d. dry the wet hair by rubbing with a linen saver pad.

30. When caring for a client in skeletal traction, it is important for the nurse to:
   a. prevent countertraction.
   b. inspect the pin sites two to three times a week.
   c. remove the weights when pulling the client up in bed.
   d. assess the extremities for circulatory impairment.

31. A client is recovering from a ruptured appendix of two days ago. He has been walking in his room, and tolerating a full-liquid diet. The nurse notes that his blood pressure is 190/110. The nurse should:
   a. notify the physician immediately.
   b. medicate the client with the p.r.n. pain medication he has been receiving.
   c. inform the client that his blood pressure is elevated and tell him to relax.
   d. recheck the blood pressure and other vital signs.

32. A 38-year-old woman is prescribed warfain sodium (Coumadin). Which statement indicates that the client understands the instructions given by the nurse?
   a. "I will increase the amount of green leafy vegetables in my diet."
   b. "I should use mineral oil to prevent constipation and bleeding."
   c. "I should expect that I would have some bleeding between menstrual periods."
   d. "I will get a night light for when I have to use the bathroom at night."

33. A client is placed on medication to be taken three times per day. What is the best method of instructing the client so that the client remembers when to take the medication?
   a. Tell the client to take the medicine upon awakening, one hour before dinner and at bedtime.
   b. After talking to the client, give a written record stating times the medication is due.
   c. Write for the client to take the medicine at 8:00AM, 4:00PM and 12:00AM.
   d. Suggest the client take the medication when certain television programs are on.

34. A male client, who had abdominal surgery, has difficulty voiding after urinary catheter removal. A bedside sonogram shows 800ml of urine in the bladder. The nurse obtains a prescription to catheterize the client, but has problems passing the catheter. The nurse should:
   a. pull the catheter out, allow the client to rest and try reinserting the catheter later.
   b. ask the client to relax the muscles around the lower abdomen for easier catheter passage.
   c. remove the catheter and contact the physician for further instructions.
   d. suggest that another nurse try inserting the catheter.

35. A nursing student has been caring for a child who was hit by a car. Later that day, it is determined that the boy also has scabies. The student admits that he did not wear gloves while giving the child a bath. The student goes to the employee health department and is instructed to:
   a. take a hot shower and wash with antibacterial soap.
   b. apply a thin layer of 1% lindane (Kwell) ointment as prescribed.
   c. report any allergies he might have to an immunoglobulin injection.
   d. submit a urine sample for testing and diagnosis.

36. A nurse is assessing a client with gouty arthritis. Which symptom would be expected?
   a. Hyponatremia.
   b. Hyperuricemia.
   c. Hypoproteinuria.
   d. Ketonuria.

37. The charge nurse is making assignments. Which client should be assigned to the LPN?
   a. A client with a bleeding gastric ulcer who is prescribed a unit of fresh frozen plasma.
   b. A woman who is being admitted with urolithiasis.
   c. A client with terminal cancer who will need G-tube feedings throughout the shift.
   d. A man with congestive heart failure who is prescribed lanoxin (Digoxin) and IV furosemide (Lasix).

38. The nurse is conducting an infant parenting class related to feeding. What should be included?
   a. Fortified rice cereal can be added to the nighttime bottle to promote sleeping through the night for infants over six months of age.
   b. Cow's milk can be introduced after the baby is nine months of age.
   c. When solid foods are introduced, the formula should be reduced to 500ml (16.7 oz) per day.
   d. Introduce foods one at a time with five to seven days between each introduction.

39. A charge nurse comes on duty to the medical unit at change of shift and finds the unit personnel involved in an emergency situation with a client. The nurse should:
   a. relieve a nurse at the emergency situation.
   b. make assessment rounds on the other unit clients.
   c. answer the telephone at the nurses' station.
   d. ask one of the unit personnel for report.

40. An elderly obese male is recovering from total hip replacement surgery three days ago. He complains to the nurse that his left calf hurts and he would prefer sitting up in a chair. The nurse should:
   a. help the client get into his chair.
   b. massage the calf and assist him with range-of-motion exercises.
   c. apply moist heat to the area.
   d. tell the client that the physician will have to look at his calf and he should remain in bed.

41. The nursing assistant reports to the nurse that a client with dementia has been wandering the halls and walking into other clients' rooms insisting that he lives there. The best instructions the nurse can give to the nursing assistant is to:
   a. have the client repeat his room number several times so he remembers it.
   b. confine the client to his room so he becomes familiar with it.
   c. print the client's name clearly in large letters so he can identify it.
   d. place an object on the door so the client can find the location of his room.

42. What must be considered when a nurse is evaluating a child for suicide potential?
   a. Depression and other moods.
   b. Suicidal thoughts.
   c. Motivation for suicide.
   d. Concept of suicide and death.

43. Several hours after heparin sodium (Heparin) therapy is initiated, the nurse is reviewing a client's partial thromboplastin time (PTT). A therapeutic level has been reached when the baseline PTT is 30 and the current PTT is how many seconds?
   a. 55.
   b. 75.
   c. 85.
   d. 90.

44. A client is admitted following an emergency colon resection for a malignant tumor. The nurse assesses the vital signs as: blood pressure 140/90, pulse 84, and respirations 20 and regular. A short time later, the nurse notes that the blood pressure is 90/60, the pulse is 120 and the respirations are 28. The initial action of the nurse should be:
   a. place her in Trendelenburg position immediately.
   b. notify the physician immediately.
   c. elevate her legs 20 degrees and slightly elevate her head.
   d. place her in reverse Trendelenburg position.

45. A client with methicillin resistant staphylococcus aureus (MRSA) is placed in isolation to:
    a. provide a mechanism by which the reservoir of the infectious agent is eliminated.
    b. prevent the transmission of the infectious agent from a source to another person.
    c. provide for proper disposal of infected materials.
    d. allow time for antimicrobial agents to treat the infected person.

46. An adolescent has been admitted to a psychiatric unit with a diagnosis of conduct disorder. He is unwilling to comply with unit rules and his treatment plan. He does not make his bed in the morning and is consistently late for group meetings. The most appropriate approach would be to:
    a. present reality in a here and now focus.
    b. matter of factly state unit rules and expectations.
    c. ask the client to identify positive attributes about himself.
    d. discuss the client's perceptions of unit rules and expectations.

47. Nursing care for a client who just had a renal biopsy would include:
    a. positioning him on his left side for the first four hours.
    b. teaching the client to cough and deep breathe.
    c. calling the physician if hematuria is noted.
    d. reporting any complaints of shoulder pain.

48. An 83-year-old woman is brought to the hospital by her daughter for evaluation. The woman awakens at night because she believes people are breaking into her house and taking her things. Her daughter states that although she has checked numerous times, she has not seen any evidence of someone breaking into the home or found anything missing. The woman refuses to talk to her daughter. She is diagnosed with dementia. An appropriate nursing diagnosis would be:
    a. alteration in thought processes related to cognitive impairment.
    b. impaired communication related to aphasia.
    c. alteration in family processes related to loss of maternal role.
    d. impaired home health maintenance management related to fatigue.

49. The nurse covers a client's new colostomy with an appliance. This is done to:
    a. begin the process of bowel retraining.
    b. promote the passage of formed stool.
    c. assist the client with the acceptance of the stoma.
    d. protect the abdominal incision from stool contamination.

50. A client is scheduled for an outpatient bronchoscopy tomorrow. The nurse is giving the client instructions over the telephone. Which statement by the client would indicate a need for further teaching?
    a. "I will not eat or drink anything after midnight tonight."
    b. "I may feel like I am choking when they put in the tube."
    c. "I will be asleep during the procedure."
    d. "The anesthetic will taste bitter."

51. A client with hyperthyroidism is given antithyroid medication prior to surgery. Which documented evidence would best demonstrate a euthyroid state?
    a. Temperature 98.6° F (37°C); pulse 110; respirations 20.
    b. Weight loss of two pounds since diagnosis; no complaints of diminished appetite.
    c. Rested and relaxed, sleeping without difficulty.
    d. Absence of exophthalmos.

52. The nurse is reviewing lab results on a bulimic client. Which lab result would be common with this disorder?
    a. K=2.9mEq/L.
    b. WBC=3,000.
    c. Na=128mEq/L.
    d. Platelets=40,000.

53. A 70 kg (175 lbs) client is prescribed 5mg of midazolam hydrochloride (Versed) intramuscularly and 50mg of meperidine hydrochloride (Demerol) intramuscularly one hour prior to surgery. Which nursing action is appropriate?
   a. Teach coughing and deep breathing exercises immediately prior to giving the midazolam hydrochloride (Versed).
   b. Draw the medications up in two separate syringes and give two injections.
   c. Give the midazolam hydrochloride (Versed) and hold the meperidine hydrochloride (Demerol) until after notifying the physician.
   d. Check vital signs within 15 minutes of medication administration.

54. The nursing supervisor calls the unit to inform the nurses that a client with kidney stones is being admitted within the next hour. All of the nurses complain that they "couldn't possibly take care of one more person." Based on the information provided, which nurse would be ineligible to receive the new client?
   a. A pregnant nurse in her third trimester caring for a client with a cerebrovascular accident, a woman with pelvic inflammatory disease and an 18-year-old with a fractured femur.
   b. A nurse with six months experience caring for a client with Type 1 diabetes, a client with chronic obstructive pulmonary disease, and a client with a cerebrovascular accident.
   c. A 58-year-old nurse caring for clients with chronic renal failure, multiple sclerosis, and Guillian Barré syndrome.
   d. A 31-year-old nurse caring for a newly postoperative client with a cardiac artery bypass graft, a client with tuberculosis and a client awaiting results of a needle biopsy for breast cancer.

55. A woman who has recently been diagnosed with primary epilepsy is concerned that she will have to stay in her house and live like an invalid. The most appropriate response by the nurse would be:
   a. "Once you are taking medications regularly, you can return to your previous lifestyle."
   b. "Usually you need to wait one seizure-free year before you are eligible to drive."
   c. "You will need to always avoid swimming and operating machinery."
   d. "Alcohol should be used only in moderation."

56. A 38-year-old gravida III para II client is admitted to the labor suite at term pregnancy. The client tells the nurse she had some bleeding that morning. The first nursing action should be to:
   a. assess amount and type of bleeding.
   b. examine for abruptio placenta.
   c. notify the physician of the condition.
   d. obtain the client's vital signs.

57. A nurse is working with a client diagnosed with a delusional disorder with persecutory delusions. What are appropriate interventions? Select all that apply.
   a. Schedule a time each day to discuss the delusion.
   b. Help the client to change the content of the delusion.
   c. Evaluate the meaning of the delusion for the client.
   d. Assess the client's safety on an ongoing basis.
   e. Teach the client social skills to decrease social isolation.

58. A client on a clear-liquid diet has selected the following beverages from a menu. Which beverage would the nurse remove from the tray?
   a. Cranberry juice cocktail.
   b. Orange juice.
   c. Ginger ale.
   d. Iced tea.

59. A mother with four small children is severely injured in a car accident. It is evident that the mother will need extensive rehabilitation. The father says to the nurse, "Who will do all of the housework and look after the children?" The nurse realizes the problem is related to:
   a.   poor communication.
   b.   religious beliefs.
   c.   power distribution.
   d.   rigid division of labor.

60. A 40-year-old woman is suspected of having breast cancer. The client asks the nurse which test will most definitely assess the nature of the tumor. The nurse tells the woman it is:
   a.   bilateral mammography.
   b.   transillumination of the breasts.
   c.   biopsy and histologic classification.
   d.   thermography of the breasts.

61. A 19-year-old with anorexia nervosa is 86 pounds. If the client looks into the mirror, the nurse would expect to hear which statement?
   a.   "I have a wonderful body."
   b.   "I'm overweight."
   c.   "I am too thin."
   d.   "My weight is normal."

62. A 6-week-old infant is admitted with possible pyloric stenosis. Which assessment data, collected by the nurse, would assist the physician in ruling out pyloric stenosis?
   a.   Blood-tinged emesis.
   b.   Increased urine specific gravity.
   c.   Frequent watery stools.
   d.   Peristaltic waves.

63. A client on the orthopedic unit is scheduled for replacement arthroplasty of the left knee. Preoperative management would include:
   a.   avoiding vitamins with iron and discontinuing steroids which interfere with recovery.
   b.   evaluating the client's ability to keep the left leg and foot immobile for the first 24 hours after surgery.
   c.   evaluating the client's ability to manipulate crutches or a walker.
   d.   informing the client that total knee replacement rehabilitation is longer than other joint surgeries.

64. The nurse would assess that a newly burned client is hypovolemic if his lab values were:
   a.   CVP 7, hematocrit 27, sodium 140.
   b.   CVP 3, hematocrit 27, potassium 3.2.
   c.   CVP 3, hematocrit 48, potassium 5.
   d.   CVP 7, hematocrit 48, sodium 120.

65. A postoperative client has been NPO with a nasogastric tube for 10 days. Salivary gland swelling becomes apparent and the client is diagnosed with parotitis. This could have been prevented by:
   a.   good oral hygiene.
   b.   decreasing fluids.
   c.   restricting child visitors.
   d.   giving antacids.

66. A nurse is caring for a woman with a cerebrovascular accident. The family tells the nurse that they plan to convert the living room into a "hospital room." The nurse's response should be based on the understanding that:
   a.   emphasizing the family's abilities decreases stress.
   b.   supporting the husband's decision decreases caregiver burden.
   c.   changing life patterns quickly minimizes strain.
   d.   maintaining usual life patterns minimizes stress.

67. On a very hot day, a client comes to the emergency department with abdominal cramping and profuse sweating. Which additional finding is of most concern to the nurse?
   a.   Thirst.
   b.   Diarrhea.
   c.   Headache.
   d.   Confusion.

68. A client with a bleeding gastric ulcer has stabilized and the nurse is teaching symptoms of perforation. The nurse would teach the client to notify the physician if experiencing:
   a.   guaiac positive stools.
   b.   dizziness.
   c.   lower abdominal pain.
   d.   increased appetite.

69. A client is beginning treatment for an acute attack of gouty arthritis and wants to attend his daughter's wedding tomorrow. When giving instructions, the nurse would include:
   a.   limiting fluid intake.
   b.   avoiding foods such as citrus fruits.
   c.   using crutches.
   d.   using moist heat applications to reduce swelling.

70. What would be the appropriate nursing intervention to prevent pulmonary complications following thoracic surgery?
   a.   Ambulate after the second postoperative day.
   b.   Cough, turn, and deep breathe every hour.
   c.   Splint the incision with a pillow when moving and coughing.
   d.   Medicate the client for pain, as prescribed.

71. A newborn baby is being evaluated for possible tracheoesophageal fistula (TEF). Which symptom would indicate that the baby has something other than TEF?
   a.   Projectile vomiting.
   b.   Increased sneezing.
   c.   Mouth drooling.
   d.   Intermittent cyanosis.

72. A nursing student is reviewing interventions to reduce nausea in a new postoperative client. Which intervention would be included in the plan?
   a.   If nausea occurs, place the client on the side.
   b.   Ask the client to sip fluids such as ginger ale.
   c.   Encourage the client to take short shallow breaths.
   d.   Remove the nasogastric tube 24 hours after surgery.

73. A 28-year-old man sustained a T_4 spinal cord injury and is to be discharged. The client's father tells the nurse that he is remodeling his home for wheelchair access. He later tells the nurse his plans for his son when he can walk again. The nurse understands that the client's father:
   a.   does not understand the extent of his son's injury.
   b.   is still hoping for complete recovery.
   c.   is still experiencing periods of denial.
   d.   is having difficulty with his memory.

74. A 51-year-old woman with terminal cancer asks the nurse about palliative care at a hospice. The nurse teaches the client that this involves:
   a. no cure and no code.
   b. no treatment of the effects of the disease.
   c. active euthanasia provided when necessary.
   d. only clients with legal living wills.

75. A visiting nurse is called for referral as part of a discharge plan to follow a 1-year-old child after admission for croup. At the home, the nurse finds that both parents work and the children are being cared for by the grandmother. Besides the 1-year-old child, the grandmother is also watching three other children under the age of five. The woman looks upset and tired. The nurse should:
   a. check all of the children for problems.
   b. confine her visit to care of the 1-year-old child.
   c. call the physician and request referral for the other children.
   d. talk with the grandmother about her ability to cope with the situation.

STOP. You have now completed Practice Session: 17. Now take a few minutes and correct your answers. Calculate your accuracy rate by dividing the number of questions you completed correctly by the total number of questions you completed (75).

Correct answers ÷ total number of questions completed = accuracy rate.

_____ ÷ _____ = _____

ANSWERS AND RATIONALES
Practice Session 17

1. **The correct answer is b.** The question is asking what type of diet would most benefit a client before colon surgery. If time permits before colon surgery, a diet high in calories and low in residue is generally prescribed. This is done to ensure the nutritional state of the client while also reducing the bulk of the stool in the bowel (options a, c & d).
Nursing Process: Planning   **Client Need:** Physiological Integrity

2. **The correct answer is c.** The question is asking which statement is correct for discharge teaching in this client. The medic alert band should always be worn and include condition, drugs and dosages, name and phone number of physician. Medication should be taken regularly, (options a & d) as prescribed. Dosages should be maintained or increased, not decreased (option b) in response to increased stressors.
Nursing Process: Evaluation   **Client Need:** Physiological Integrity

3. **The correct answer is c.** The question is asking which prescription would be questioned for a client post-laparoscopic cholecystectomy. Morphine is not administered because it can cause spasms of the sphincter of Oddi and increase pain. A common postoperative problem is referred pain to the shoulder, because the carbon dioxide used during surgery irritates the phrenic nerve and the diaphragm. Placing the client in Sims' position (option a) helps move the gas pocket away from the diaphragm. Antiemetics (option b) may be necessary for episodes of postoperative nausea and vomiting. Clients may remove bandages and bathe or shower the day after surgery (option d).
Nursing Process: Implementation   **Client Need:** Physiological Integrity

4. **The correct answer is d.** The question is asking the most important goal within the therapeutic relationship. Developing independent behaviors, alleviating anxiety and depression, and improving self-esteem (options a, b, & c) are all-important. However, the major and primary goal of working with substance abuse clients is helping them learn new coping mechanisms, since the present coping skill (alcohol) is not constructive.
Nursing Process: Planning   **Client Need:** Psychosocial Integrity

5. **The correct answer is c.** The question is asking how to help a client sleep. Relaxation techniques put the body in a restful state so sleep comes more easily. A nap during the day (option a) may decrease the ability to fall asleep at night. Tea contains caffeine, a stimulant (option b). Falling asleep with a radio or television on (option d) may help initiate sleep, but later in the night during periods of light sleep the sounds may actually awaken the client.
Nursing Process: Implementation   **Client Need:** Health Promotion & Maintenance

6. **The correct answer is b.** The question is asking what to do when a client says he does not understand the procedure before the consent is signed. The nurse is the client's advocate in ensuring that the consent for surgery is truly voluntary and informed. The nurse should determine that the client fully understands the information. If any confusion or doubt exists regarding this information, the nurse should ask the physician to explain or clarify the information (option d). Having the client sign the consent form before he understands the information would not be acting as an advocate for the client (option c). There is no evidence to suggest that the client is confused, therefore, he can sign his own consent (option a).
Nursing Process: Implementation   **Client Need:** Safe, Effective Care Environment

7. **The correct answer is a.** The question is asking what option would be the priority for home care of the client. Respiratory muscles may also be involved with myasthenia gravis and the client may have more difficulty breathing, swallowing and clearing the throat. This makes the client prone to aspiration. The main goal would be to maintain respiratory function. Clients with myasthenia gravis are not particularly prone to seizures (option b). Joint mobility (option c) is unaffected, but

muscles may be fatigued. Adaptive devices (option d) may not be necessary with this disease, but may be used with multiple sclerosis.
Nursing Process: Planning   **Client Need:** Physiological Integrity

8.   **The correct answer is b.** The question is asking for the usual behavior for bonding. Option (b) is the best example of parent-child affiliation. In options (a) and (d), the baby is not actively involved or a part of the affiliation with the parents. In option (c) conversation is not related to parent-child affiliation and could take place without the child.
Nursing Process: Assessment   **Client Need:** Health Promotion & Maintenance

9.   **The correct answer is c.** The question is asking which response made by the nurse is an accurate statement regarding the diabetic complication of blindness. Diabetic retinopathy, the major cause of blindness among clients with diabetes, refers to the process of microvascular damage to the retina as a result of chronic hyperglycemia. Consistent and tight glycemic control may be able to prevent or stop microvascular changes that lead to diabetic retinopathy. Although any alteration in vision should be reported, the client should be taught how to prevent visual problems (option a). Weight loss assists in achieving glucose, lipid and blood pressure goals, but does not resolve diabetes (option b). Clients with diabetes must have regular eye examinations by an ophthalmologist for early detection and treatment of diabetic retinopathy; however, the exams do not prevent the condition from occurring (option d).
Nursing Process: Implementation   **Client Need:** Health Promotion & Maintenance

10.   **The correct answer is d.** The question is asking for an analysis of the dynamics. The client is offering an excuse for why the speech did not go as planned, which is rationalization. Losing your voice is converting the psychological problem of anxiety to a physical problem and is called conversion (option a). Forgetting the date of the speech is unconsciously excluding a painful event from awareness, which is repression (option b). Stating that the speech went well is avoidance of the issue that the speech probably did not go well, which is denial (option c).
Nursing Process: Analysis   **Client Need:** Psychosocial Integrity

11.   **The correct answer is d.** The question is asking what the nurse should do when the water seal chamber of the chest tube shows evidence of continued air bubbling as soon as it is attached to suction. For a client with a pneumothorax, air has collected in the intrapleural space. Upon insertion of a chest tube, air rushes out through the tube and bubbling in the water seal chamber is evident. Fluctuation in the water seal chamber indicates that there is effective communication between the pleural cavity and the chamber, and that it corresponds to the client's respiratory cycle. Options (a) and (c) would be unnecessary because the nurse's observations are expected in this situation. Option (b) might be implemented at the end of the procedure when the nurse applied a chest tube dressing, but it would not be an initial action.
Nursing Process: Implementation   **Client Need:** Physiological Integrity

12.   **The correct answer is c.** The question is asking why this client would need a urinary catheter when he does not have any urinary problems. As the intravascular volume decreases due to hemorrhage, urine output decreases. The hourly calculation of urinary output is an excellent parameter in assessing shock. An indwelling urinary catheter would not be used merely for convenience or as a matter of policy because of the risk of infection (options a, b & d).
Nursing Process: Planning   **Client Need:** Safe, Effective Care Environment

13.   **The correct answer is d.** The question is asking what to do when a client is masturbating publicly. A client with mental retardation may act out through physically self-stimulating behaviors to alleviate anxiety. Behaviors that are destructive or socially unacceptable need to be modified. The initial action by the nurse is to identify the problem in a nonjudgmental way. It is socially unacceptable to masturbate in front of other clients; however, the client is given the option to go to his room. If the client continues the behavior, privileges may need to be restricted (option a). Behavior modification is the treatment of choice as many clients who are mentally retarded are not able to discuss their feelings or needs in a one-on-one interaction (option b). Although the client is working through his behavior, it should not be ignored (option c).

14. **The correct answer is c.** The question is asking what constitutes a problem in a client post-thyroid surgery. Tingling sensation around the mouth or in the fingers may be an early sign of tetany, resulting from accidental injury or removal of the parathyroid during surgery. Discomfort is common around the incisional site. The client is usually medicated with meperidine (Demerol) or morphine sulfate (Morphine) (option a). If loosening the dressing relieves the tightening sensation, this is normal. It may be life-threatening if loosening the dressing does not relieve the sensation. A tracheostomy set should be kept near the client (option b). Hoarseness and voice weakness may occur if there has been unilateral injury of the recurrent laryngeal nerve during surgery. This condition is usually temporary (option d).
Nursing Process: Evaluation   **Client Need:** Safe, Effective Care Environment

15. **The correct answer is c.** The question is asking what to do for a woman who is having discomfort during sex. Aging does not alter sexual functioning, but there is a decrease in vaginal lubrication because of a diminished blood flow to the vagina secondary to reduced estrogen levels. Providing a synthetic form of lubrication is helpful. Option (a) does not answer the question; rather it avoids the concern of being uncomfortable. Option (b) is a judgmental response. Option (d) introduces an unrelated topic.
Nursing Process: Implementation   **Client Need:** Health Promotion & Maintenance

16. **The correct answer is b.** The question is asking what to do when a second day postpartal client complains of pain from the episiotomy site. Warm moist heat, provided by the sitz bath, is most appropriate for the client on her second postpartal day. Warm, moist heat decreases discomfort and promotes healing by increasing circulation to the area. Ice is appropriate for the first 24 hours to decrease edema and provide some anesthesia (option a). A hot water bottle or heat lamp might provide some relief, but could also burn the client. Moist heat is preferable (options c & d).
Nursing Process: Implementation   **Client Need:** Health Promotion & Maintenance

17. **The correct answer is d.** The question is asking why a client post-heart surgery would be prescribed lidocaine (Xylocard). This drug is used as a means of reducing ventricular irritability and arrhythmias. It has a calming effect on damaged myocardial tissue. Preload refers to the tension in the left ventricle at the end of the diastole or the pressure in the heart at rest. Preload is lowered by vasodilators, such as nitroglycerine (Nitro-Bid), which pool blood in the periphery. Afterload is the pressure in the arteries that the heart must pump against. Afterload is lowered by arterial vasodilators, such as hydralazine (Apresoline). Neither preload nor afterload is affected by lidocaine (Xylocard) (options b & c). It is not used to prevent angina (option a).
Nursing Process: Analysis   **Client Need:** Physiological Integrity

18. **The correct answer is a.** The question is asking what other symptoms should be addressed when a person complains of nighttime angina. Angina is pain and pressure, which usually is related to inadequate blood flow to the coronary artery. This results in decreased oxygenation to the heart muscle creating pain from ischemia. Angina decubitus occurs when the client is lying down and can be lessened by sitting up. Angina pectoris, which is stable, occurs during periods of exertion and is most often relieved by rest (option b). Severe incapacitating angina is pain, which is present much of the time, not allowing the person to function (option c). Prinzmetal's angina occurs due to spasm of the coronary artery, is accompanied by ST segment elevation, and may occur during activity or at rest (option d).
Nursing Process: Assessment   **Client Need:** Physiological Integrity

19. **The correct answer is b.** The question is asking how the nurse could prevent the ammonia level from increasing. A major cause of increased ammonia in clients with liver failure is due to enzymatic and bacterial digestion of blood proteins in the gastrointestinal tract. The major source is gastrointestinal bleeding. Octreotide (Sandostatin) decreases bleeding associated with esophageal varices. Salt poor albumin will decrease ascites by creating a fluid shift from the extravascular space to the intravascular space; however, this will not decrease ammonia levels (option a). Monitoring the creatinine and BUN will alert the nurse to impending renal damage but

does nothing to decrease the ammonia level (option c). A client with liver failure may experience vitamin deficiencies; however increasing dietary intake of Vitamin B-6 will not lower ammonia levels (option d).
Nursing Process: Implementation   **Client Need:** Physiological Integrity

20. **The correct answer is a.** The question is asking what the nurse would suggest for a woman who is experiencing hot flashes. Caffeine increases heat production and should be reduced or eliminated. This will combat the hot flashes caused by vasomotor instability in the menopausal woman. Tight fitting clothing, retain heat and should be avoided (option b). Calcium and vitamin D are encouraged to decrease the risk of osteoporosis in menopausal women (option c). Vitamin E has been used to decrease the hot flashes. FSH levels are not reliable because of the hormonal fluctuations that occur before menopause (option d).
Nursing Process: Implementation   **Client Need:** Physiological Integrity

21. **The correct answer is c.** The question is asking the nurse to analyze these arterial blood gases. Arterial blood gases reflect the adequacy of oxygenation and ventilation, respectively. In COPD with pneumonia, there is poor gas exchange and an accumulation of CO_2 occurs, causing respiratory acidosis. Over a period of time, the kidneys respond by retaining HCO_3 to bring the pH to a more normal level, causing compensated respiratory acidosis with a normal pH, but still having an elevated $PaCO_2$ and HCO_3.
Nursing Process: Analysis   **Client Need:** Physiological Integrity

22. **The correct answer is d.** The question is asking what treatment is essential after a wild squirrel bites a child. If any wild animal bites a human, prophylactic treatment for rabies is instituted. Rabies is a fatal disease, if contracted. Once symptoms are noted, treatment has not been effective in most cases. So, even if there is only a slight possibility for rabies, treatment takes place. Treatment consists of an initial injection of human rabies immune globulin followed by a series of human diploid cell rabies vaccine (option c). Initial dose of the vaccine is given at the time of the incident. Follow-up injections are given at days 3, 7, 14, 28 and 90. The wound should be kept clean to prevent infection but rabies treatment is essential (option a). The animal is wild and probably unidentifiable, so could not easily be captured (option b).
Nursing Process: Implementation   **Client Need:** Physiological Integrity

23. **The correct order of answers is c, b, a, d.** The question is asking for the correct order in which the tasks should be performed after a client has undergone a liver biopsy. The client should be placed on her right side first to stop any bleeding that might occur from the biopsy site (option c). The vital signs should be taken next to assess for any changes that might result from bleeding (option b). Since bleeding is the most common complication of a liver biopsy, the hematocrit and hemoglobin levels can then be drawn and sent to the lab (option a). While waiting for the results of the hematocrit and hemoglobin, the portable chest X-ray can be arranged to assure that the biopsy needle did not puncture the lung (option d).
Nursing Process: Planning   **Client Need:** Physiological Integrity

24. **The correct answer is d.** The question is asking what is most important to check when a child is diagnosed with chickenpox (varicella). Chickenpox is the product of a virus, which is communicable unless immunity has been built up through contact with the disease or by vaccine. Varicella zoster is usually benign in children; however, there may be serious complications in adults. Other children in the family may contract the disease, (option c) but it is more dangerous for the adults. Children should be kept away from the sick child until the disease is no longer communicable. Neuritis (option b) and myocarditis (option a) are not associated with chickenpox, but may be complications of diphtheria.
Nursing Process: Assessment   **Client Need:** Physiological Integrity

25. **The correct answer is d.** The question is asking the definition of chloasma. These brownish spots are called chloasma or the "mask of pregnancy." It is thought to be due to changes in the mother's hormone levels during pregnancy (options b & c). The pigmentation usually fades post-

delivery when hormone levels return to normal. Chloasma occurs more frequently in age extreme pregnancies (option a) and may also be seen as a side effect of estrogen therapy.
Nursing Process: Implementation   **Client Need:** Health Promotion & Maintenance

26.   **The correct answer is a.** The question is asking how the nurse can tell when a client with too much glucose in the blood is getting worse. Acetone breath indicates the respiratory system's attempt to eliminate excess carbonic acid from the body to compensate for metabolic acidosis. Kussmaul respirations are characteristic; they are rapid deep breaths (option b). Increased severity would be characterized by increased levels of glucose and ketones in urine (option c). There is dehydration with ketoacidosis and fluid volume deficit (option d).
Nursing Process: Assessment   **Client Need:** Physiological Integrity

27.   **The correct answer is c.** The question is asking which symptom would be abnormal three months after a traumatic incident. Sleep disturbances indicate a problem with anxiety. Talking about the perpetrator; (option a), feelings of guilt, anger and shame; (option b) and continued self-exploration; (option d), are normal goals in the resolution phase.
Nursing Process: Evaluation   **Client Need:** Psychosocial Integrity

28.   **The correct answer is d.** The question is asking what foods need to be avoided when preventing hepatic coma. How does a client with cirrhosis get hepatic coma? Dietary protein is broken down into ammonia. A low-protein diet is the diet of choice because the goal is to reduce the ammonia level. When a high protein diet is permitted, the protein cannot be metabolized by the liver, which results in high levels of ammonia. The ammonia crosses the blood brain barrier and causes hepatic encephalopathy. A low-carbohydrate diet (option a) is incorrect because these clients need more carbohydrates to compensate for the lack of proteins to prevent malnutrition. A low-fat diet (option b) is unrelated to cirrhosis, but may be indicated in clients with cardiac or gallbladder problems.
Nursing Process: Planning   **Client Need:** Physiological Integrity

29.   **The correct answer is b.** The question is asking the proper way to wash a bedridden client's hair. Part of the preparation is to place cotton in the client's ears to keep water from getting into the ear canal. The hair and scalp should be rubbed vigorously to stimulate the scalp and relax the client. Massaging the scalp also helps break up the hair oils and prevent scalp problems (option a). Conditioner can be used to keep hair from tangling and pulling (option c). Rub the hair with a towel to dry (option d). The linen saver pad is placed under the head to keep the bed dry.
Nursing Process: Implementation   **Client Need:** Safe, Effective Care Environment

30.   **The correct answer is d.** The question is asking what to do for a client in skeletal traction. Neurovascular checks should be done hourly for the first 48 to 72 hours post-trauma after that, at least every shift. Skeletal traction is always continuous once applied and is not intermittent as with some other forms of traction (option c). Countertraction is important in all types of traction (option a). Pin sites should be inspected daily, preferably every shift, for signs of infection (option b).
Nursing Process: Implementation   **Client Need:** Physiological Integrity

31.   **The correct answer is d.** The question is asking what to do when a client has a very elevated blood pressure at one reading. Recheck the blood pressure and other vital signs to complete the assessment of the client and to insure that the reading is correct. The client was not complaining of pain, so should not be medicated (option b). Telling the client his blood pressure is elevated and to relax (option c) may make him more anxious and create an abnormal reading. The physician will want to know all of the vital signs and verification of the elevated reading (option a).
Nursing Process: Implementation   **Client Need:** Physiological Integrity

32.   **The correct answer is d.** The question is asking how the nurse would know that teaching about warfarin sodium (Coumadin) has been effective. Wafarin sodium (Coumadin) is an anticoagulant that can increase bleeding. The client should be taught how to prevent injury that can lead to

hemorrhage. A nightlight may keep the client from bumping into things in the middle of the night. Green leafy vegetables are high in vitamin K, which would increase clotting, thus decreasing the effectiveness of the warfarin sodium (Coumadin) (option a). Mineral oil is also contraindicated, as it decreases the absorption of the warfarin sodium (Coumadin) (option b). Bleeding between menstrual periods may indicate hemorrhage and should be reported immediately (option c).
Nursing Process: Planning   **Client Need:** Physiological Integrity

33.   **The correct answer is b.** The question is asking how to teach clients when to take their medication in order to increase compliance. A written record of instruction allows the client to review information. Although option (c) also says written instructions, it does not account for the client's schedule so option (b) is better. Option (a) does not account for the client's schedule. No information exists about when the client awakens, eats meals or retires. These times may not be appropriate medications times. Option (d) would be incorrect because not all television programs are consistently on every day of the week.
      Nursing Process: Implementation   **Client Need:** Health Promotion & Maintenance

34.   **The correct answer is c.** The question is asking what to do when a urinary catheter cannot be inserted into a male client. This may indicate swelling and blockage in the prostate area from a variety of problems. The catheter should not be forced nor should the area be irritated by further attempts to insert the catheter (options a & d). Relaxing abdominal muscles will not relieve the blockage (option b). The physician should be notified so that the problem can be treated.
      Nursing Process: Implementation   **Client Need:** Physiological Integrity

35.   **The correct answer is b.** The question is asking for the appropriate treatment for someone who has come in contact with a person who has scabies. Scabies occurs following infestation of the itch mite into the epidermis. This causes very small lesions that are difficult to detect, but cause extreme pruritis. Although prolonged contact is usually necessary for infestation to occur, all people who are in close contact with the child should be treated. This is because it can take 60 days from the time of infestation for symptoms to appear. The treatment of choice is lindane (Kwell) ointment applied to cool dry skin (option a). Immunoglobulins are not effective (option c). Diagnosis is made through scrapings of the burrow the mite has made (option d).
      Nursing Process: Implementation   **Client Need:** Physiological Integrity

36.   **The correct answer is b.** The question is asking what would be seen in a client with gout. Lab studies in gout would indicate an elevated serum uric acid. Hypoproteinuria (option c) may be found in clients with severe liver disease or severe burns. Hyponatremia and ketonuria (options a & d) are usually found in uncontrolled diabetics.
      Nursing Process: Assessment   **Client Need:** Physiological Integrity

37.   **The correct answer is c.** The question is asking about the role of the licensed practical nurse (LPN). An appropriate assignment for a LPN would include a client who is stable and does not require care that is not within the scope of practice of a LPN. Clients who have terminal cancer require comfort measures and palliative care. The LPN can provide this. It is within the scope of LPN practice to administer feedings via a G tube. The client in option (a) is hemorrhaging and, therefore, is not stable. Further he requires blood products. This is not in the LPN's scope of practice. The client in option (b) requires an initial assessment. A nurse should do this. The client in option (d) requires IV medications. The nurse should give these.
      Nursing Process: Planning   **Client Need:** Safe, Effective Care Environment

38.   **The correct answer is d.** The question is asking what the nurse should teach the parents about feeding their infant. Foods should be introduced one at a time with five to seven days between each introduction to detect any allergies. Feeding infants solids before four months of age predisposes them to possible protein allergies. Furthermore, the GI tract may have difficulty digesting them properly (option a). Cow's milk should not be introduced until after the child is 1-year-old, as it is not digested well; it carries increased risk of contamination; and does not contain all of the nutrients required for adequate growth (option b). At six months of age, when solid foods are introduced, the amount of formula should be reduced to 900ml (option c). Reducing

fluids to 500ml could lead to dehydration, a potentially life-threatening problem for infants.
Nursing Process: Implementation   **Client Need:** Health Promotion & Maintenance

39.   **The correct answer is b.** The question is asking what the responsibility is of the oncoming nurse when other unit personnel are involved in an emergency. In an emergency situation, the personnel involved should stay with the case for continuity (option a). Often other clients may be concerned and may need attention. The safest course of action would be to assess the remaining clients on the unit and attend to their needs. Answering the telephone at the nurses' station might be correct once the other clients have been checked (option c). Asking unit personnel for report may take them away from the emergency and jeopardize client safety (option d).
Nursing Process: Implementation   **Client Need:** Safe, Effective Care Environment

40.   **The correct answer is d.** The question is asking how to assist a postoperative client who has calf pain. Tell the client that the physician will have to look at his calf. Older, obese, bedridden individuals are at high risk for thrombus formation. Thrombus is characterized by pain in the calf, heat, and redness to the area. Swelling may also be present. Massaging the area (option b) or allowing the client out of bed (option a) is contraindicated because it could dislodge a thrombus into an emboli. Applying heat (option c) would require a physician's prescription. A further assessment would be to check for Homan's sign, which is increased pain in the calf when the foot is dorsiflexed.
Nursing Process: Implementation   **Client Need:** Physiological Integrity

41.   **The correct answer is d.** The question is asking what to tell the nursing assistant about how to deal with a client who is wandering and disoriented. Placing a familiar object on the door will better assist the client to locate the room than his name, (option c) because objects or symbols are easier to remember. Confining the client to his room (option b) will not insure familiarity, especially since many hospital rooms look alike. Repeating the room number several times (option a) will probably not improve memory since recent memory is often impaired in the client with dementia.
Nursing Process: Implementation   **Client Need:** Health Promotion & Maintenance

42.   **The correct answer is d.** The question is asking what information the nurse must additionally ask when assessing a child for potential suicide. A child's concept of suicide and death can be distorted because of their lack of understanding. Depression (option a), suicide thoughts (option b), motivation for suicide (option c) are all used in evaluating anyone with a suicide potential regardless of age.
Nursing Process: Assessment   **Client Need:** Psychosocial Integrity

43.   **The correct answer is b.** The question is asking what is the therapeutic partial thromboplastin time (PTT) when a client is receiving heparin sodium (Heparin) for anticoagulation. Heparin sodium (Heparin) therapy is usually aimed at maintaining the PTT at two to two and one half times the baseline time; therefore, it should be between 60 and 75 seconds. Fifty-five seconds would be too low and would indicate that the dosage needs to be increased (option a). The other values suggest that the dosage needs to be decreased (options c & d).
Nursing Process: Evaluation   **Client Need:** Physiological Integrity

44.   **The correct answer is c.** The question is asking what the change in vital signs indicates and what should be done about it. These findings are indicative of shock. The best action at this time is to elevate the legs and the head slightly. This is done to promote cerebral perfusion. It is thought that the Trendelenberg position (option a) should be avoided as it causes the abdominal organs to put pressure on the diaphragm, thus, interfering with adequate ventilation. The physician should be notified (option b), but action to improve cerebral perfusion should be taken first. Reverse Trendelenberg (option d) would be contraindicated, as this would pool blood peripherally and decrease blood pressure.
Nursing Process: Implementation   **Client Need:** Physiological Integrity

45. **The correct answer is b.** The question is asking why an infected client is placed in isolation. The aim of isolation precautions is to prevent the movement or transmission of pathogens from their source to other places and/or persons. Isolation precautions contain, but do not eliminate, the reservoir as suggested in option (a). The proper disposal of waste is a safety concern whether infection is involved or not; therefore, option (c) is not acceptable. Option (d) is a possible answer (e.g., care of client with tuberculosis) but certainly applies to only a limited number of situations, thus, the better answer is option (b).
Nursing Process: Implementation   **Client Need:** Safe, Effective Care Environment

46. **The correct answer is b.** The question is asking how to approach an adolescent who does not want to follow the rules. Stating limits and rules in a matter of fact and consistent manner is the best approach for the client's noncompliance with unit rules and routines. There is no evidence that the client is not able to correctly interpret reality at this time (option a). Identifying positive attributes (option c) would be more appropriate for a depressed client. Obtaining perceptions about hospital rules would not alter the fact that he is not complying with them and does not address the noncompliant behavior (option d).
Nursing Process: Planning   **Client Need:** Psychosocial Integrity

47. **The correct answer is d.** The question is asking for the nursing implications for a client who has had a renal biopsy. Shoulder pain is an indication of hemorrhage. The escaped blood causes irritation to the diaphragmatic nerve, which leads to shoulder pain. The client should be placed in a supine position to apply direct pressure to the kidney (option a). The client should avoid coughing for the first 24 hours post-procedure to decrease strain on the kidney and chances of hemorrhage (option b). Hematuria (option c) is normal for the first 24 hours after a kidney biopsy is performed.
Nursing Process: Implementation   **Client Need:** Physiological Integrity

48. **The correct answer is a.** The question is asking which nursing diagnosis is appropriate for this client. The client has an alteration in thought processes, related to the cognitive impairments manifested by confusion and delusional thinking. Impaired communication (option b), alteration in family processes (option c) and impaired mobility (option d) may be implied in this condition, but are not supported by the assessment data.
Nursing Process: Assessment   **Client Need:** Safe, Effective Care Environment

49. **The correct answer is d.** The question is asking why the ostomy has to be covered. Any abdominal wound needs to be protected from outside contamination, such as stool, from a stoma opening. Bowel training cannot be achieved by covering the stoma (option a). Regardless of the consistency of the stool, the appliance is attached so the stool is emptied into it. It does not promote formed stool (option b). The client begins to accept the stoma when he begins to look at it and completes the grieving process over the lost body part (option c).
Nursing Process: Analysis   **Client Need:** Physiological Integrity

50. **The correct answer is c.** The question is asking which option is wrong about a bronchoscopy. The client will not be asleep during the procedure. Most bronchoscopies are performed under local anesthetic and the client may be given diazepam (Valium) as a sedative. The client should remain NPO 6 to 12 hours prior to the procedure to decrease the risk of aspiration (option a). Many clients do complain of a choking sensation when the tube is introduced and should be warned of the possibility (option b). The local anesthetic placed on the back of the throat often tastes bitter (option d).
Nursing Process: Planning   **Client Need:** Physiological Integrity

51. **The correct answer is c.** The question is asking how to tell if the medication is working. In other words, what would be the signs of a person without any thyroid problems? These data indicate an absence of the hyperactivity present in hyperthyroidism. Pulse rate of 110 indicates tachycardia, often seen in hyperthyroidism (option a). The client should gain weight with decreased metabolism (option b). Exophthalmos does not necessarily regress with treatment (option d).
Nursing Process: Evaluation   **Client Need:** Physiological Integrity

52. **The correct answer is a.** The question is asking which lab result is common in bulimia. Hypokalemia (option a) is common in a bulimic client from purging and abuse of diuretics. This can be life threatening. Angranulocytosis (option b) is common with clients on clozapine (Clozaril) and carbamazepine (Tegretol). Hyponatremia (option c) is common in Addison's disease as well as carbamazepine (Tegretol) use. Thrombocytopenia (option d) is common in clients using some psychiatric medications such as clozapine (Clozaril).
Nursing Process: Analysis   **Client Need:** Physiological Integrity

53. **The correct answer is d.** The question is asking what precautions need to be taken when administering meperidine (Demerol) and midazolam (Versed). Respiratory status, heart rate and blood pressure should be monitored as both drugs can cause respiratory depression and changes in heart rate and blood pressure. Onset of action of these drugs is within 15 minutes after intramuscular injection. Preoperative teaching should not be done immediately prior to administration of midazolam (Versed) (option a). Midazolam (Versed) has an amnestic effect and recall of information taught may be lost. Meperidine (Demerol) and midazolam (Versed) are compatible and can be given in the same syringe (option b). Both dosages are correct for this client. There is no need to hold the meperidine (Demerol) or notify the physician (option c).
Nursing Process: Implementation   **Client Need:** Physiological Integrity

54. **The correct answer is d.** The question is asking which nurse should not have the new client. The nurse in option (d) is caring for a client who just had coronary artery bypass graft surgery and will need to monitor this client closely for complications such as myocardial infarction, dysrhythmias and hemorrhage. This nurse will also need to be available to the client awaiting biopsy results to provide support in case the results are positive for cancer. Even though in option (b) the nurse has only six months experience, none of the clients are so critically ill as to require that she be ineligible to care for a client with kidney stones. The nurse caring for the clients with chronic renal failure, multiple sclerosis and Guillian Barré syndrome is also eligible to accept the new admission. Her age is not relevant (option c). Even though the nurse in option (a) is pregnant, this should not affect her ability to accept the new admission, either is her current assignment, as stated, too critical for her to be deemed ineligible to receive the new client.
Nursing Process: Analysis   **Client Need:** Safe, Effective Care Environment

55. **The correct answer is b.** The question is asking how to address the client's concern that she will have to stay at home as an invalid. Waiting one seizure-free year before driving is recommended despite medication, and is the law in most states. The client should be free of seizures while on the medication for a while before hazardous activities are resumed (option a). This includes swimming and operating machinery (option c). Alcohol should be avoided because it lowers the seizure threshold (option d).
Nursing Process: Analysis   **Client Need:** Health Promotion & Maintenance

56. **The correct answer is a.** The question is asking how to assess a pregnant woman who states she had bleeding this morning. If the "bleeding" is actually bloody show, there is no need for alarm. If the amount is excessive and bright in color, this could indicate placental abnormalities, such as placenta previa or abruptio placenta. The most important thing to assess at this point is the amount and type of bleeding (options b, c & d).
Nursing Process: Implementation   **Client Need:** Health Promotion & Maintenance

57. **The correct answers are c, d and e.** The question is asking what interventions the nurse should utilize when caring for a client with delusional disorder. Delusions are beliefs held by the client that are false and cannot be changed by reasonable arguments. The nurse should not try to change the client's delusional beliefs or focus on the content of the delusions during their daily interactions (options a & b). It is important for the nurse to assess the client's safety, as well as the safety of the other clients, on a regular basis especially, if the client believes that someone is out to get him (option d). Although the nurse does not want to dwell on the delusions, she does want to understand the meaning of the delusional belief to the client in order to respond to the feelings associated with the delusions instead of the specific content (option c). Clients with

delusional disorders are often socially isolated and need social skills training geared toward their specific problems in order to help them improve their interactions with others (option e).
Nursing Process: Implementation   **Client Need:** Psychosocial Integrity

58.   **The correct answer is b.** The question is asking which food is not clear liquid. Clear liquids are those that will not provide a residue during or following digestion (options a, c & d). Juices should be clear. Orange juice contains pulp and, therefore, would not be allowed on this diet.
Nursing Process: Planning   **Client Need:** Physiological Integrity

59.   **The correct answer is d.** The question is asking why the father said, "Who will do all of the housework and look after the children?" The father is having difficulty conceiving of a plan to alter family roles. This is a sign of rigid division of household labor. Rigid definition of roles creates more stress when a crisis happens and family members cannot fulfill their usual roles. There is no evidence of communication problems (option a), since the father is talking about his problems to the nurse and there are no data on any other communication patterns in the family. No religious beliefs (option b) have been stated. A problem with power (option c) is not evident here. The person in power in the immediate situation is talking to the nurse.
Nursing Process: Analysis   **Client Need:** Psychosocial Integrity

60.   **The correct answer is c.** The question is asking which test would definitively show whether the client had cancer. While mammography, transillumination and thermography (options a, b & d) are techniques commonly used to evaluate the character of the soft tissues of the breast, only the use of a biopsy and classification of tissue leads to the final diagnosis.
Nursing Process: Implementation   **Client Need:** Physiological Integrity

61.   **The correct answer is b.** The question is asking what a client with anorexia nervosa would believe about the body. Body image distortion is reflected in constant overestimation of the size of the body. Although the client is actually underweight (options c & d), she does not see herself this way. Therefore, the ongoing need and desire of the client is to be beautifully thin by losing more and more weight. She does not see herself as beautiful, only overweight (option a).
Nursing Process: Analysis   **Client Need:** Psychosocial Integrity

62.   **The correct answer is c.** The question is asking how to rule out pyloric stenosis by examining the assessment data. Because of the decreased intake and dehydration, water is absorbed from the stool leaving the infant constipated. A small amount of blood in the emesis is due to irritation and inflammation of the hypertrophic pylorus occluding the lumen (option a). Urine specific gravity tends to increase with concentrated urine for the dehydrated infant (option b). Peristalsis increases in the epigastrium to force formula down into the duodenum (option d).
Nursing Process: Analysis   **Client Need:** Physiological Integrity

63.   **The correct answer is c.** The question is asking for the appropriate preoperative care for clients who will a have a knee replacement. Evaluation of arms and shoulders is needed to assess a client's ability to properly use a walker or crutches. Iron supplements may be given preoperatively to prevent anemia. Clients on corticosteroid therapy need to be monitored carefully for postoperative problems such as shock, but are still permitted to take the drug (option a). Flexion of the foot is encouraged to prevent thromboembolism, peroneal nerve palsy and infection (option b). Rehabilitation from shoulder and elbow surgery is longer than other joint surgeries (option d).
Nursing Process: Planning   **Client Need:** Physiological Integrity

64.   **The correct answer is c.** The question is asking what lab values would indicate that a burned client is hypovolemic. In the early post-burn phase, the client is at great risk for hypovolemic shock for two reasons: evaporation of fluids due to the loss of skin; and fluids leaking out of the blood vessels into the tissues because of damage to the capillaries. There is an increased hematocrit because fluid leaks out of the blood vessels leaving red blood cells behind (options a & b). A normal hematocrit is 40 to 50%. CVP measures the amount of fluid being maintained in the intravascular compartment. A normal CVP is 5 to 10. A CVP of 3 indicates low systemic fluid

volume. A low CVP indicates hypovolemia and 7 is normal (options a & d). Hyperkalemia occurs because potassium is released when cells are damaged. Normal potassium is 3.5 to 5.0 (option b). Sodium also leaks out of the vascular system leading to edema. Normal sodium is 135 to 145 (option a).
Nursing Process: Assessment   **Client Need:** Physiological Integrity

65.   **The correct answer is a.** The question is asking how to prevent parotitis in a postoperative client. Clients who are NPO have decreased activity in the salivary glands. The glands do not produce saliva, may become inflamed and oral bacteria can cause infection. Good oral hygiene, which cleans the mouth, decreases bacteria and stimulates the salivary glands, thus decreasing the chance of inflammation and infection. Increasing hydration (option b) is a way to prevent infection. Although another name for postoperative parotitis is surgical mumps, it is not contracted from children exposed to mumps (option c). Antacids are unrelated to parotitis (option d) but may be helpful with dysphagia from an esophageal disorder.
Nursing Process: Evaluation   **Client Need:** Physiological Integrity

66.   **The correct answer is d.** The question is asking how to respond when a family states they are making plans, which change a great deal about their environment for when the client comes home. Previous life patterns should be disrupted as little as possible. Although some changes may need to occur, they should be approached with thought and negotiated with family members. Keeping things normal at home assists the recovering client to maximize strengths and minimize disability. It also minimizes guilt the client may feel about causing such changes to occur (options a, b & c).
Nursing Process: Analysis   **Client Need:** Health Promotion & Maintenance

67.   **The correct answer is b.** The question is asking what client symptom will pose a greater problem or danger to the client. The client already has symptoms of fluid volume deficit. Further loss through diarrhea would be dangerous. Thirst and headache are signs of fluid loss (options a & c). Confusion, a change of consciousness, is an advanced sign of dehydration (option d). Although this shows a present danger, diarrhea will cause further fluid loss which would worsen the condition.
Nursing Process: Analysis   **Client Need:** Physiological Integrity

68.   **The correct answer is b.** The question is asking which is a sign of perforation of a gastric ulcer. Symptoms of perforation derive from bleeding into the peritoneal cavity and the resulting loss of circulating blood. Fluid loss leads to hypotension and dizziness. Definitive treatment would have to be undertaken immediately to save the individual. The client was admitted with a bleeding ulcer; therefore, guaiac positive stools would be expected (option a). Upper abdominal pain would be more likely for gastric ulcer disease (option c). Due to bleeding and stomach upset, decreased (not increased) appetite would occur (option d).
Nursing Process: Assessment   **Client Need:** Physiological Integrity

69.   **The correct answer is c.** The question is asking what instructions would be given to a client who has gout. Weight bearing should be avoided or the attack will recur. Fluid should be encouraged and maintained with at least 2,000ml per day to decrease uric acid levels and prevent nephrolithiasis (option a). An alkaline-ash diet with foods such as milk, potatoes and citrus fruits are necessary to promote alkaline urine and discourage urate crystal formation (option b). Cold applications will help reduce inflammation; heat may exacerbate the inflammation (option d).
Nursing Process: Implementation   **Client Need:** Health Promotion & Maintenance

70.   **The correct answer is b.** The question is asking how to prevent lung and breathing problems after chest surgery. Following anesthesia, lung volumes are decreased, leading to collapse of alveoli and eventually atelectasis. In addition, airway secretions are retained because of a decrease in mucociliary transport, a diminished cough reflex, and drying of the airways by preoperative medication and anesthetic gases. Thus, asking clients to cough, deep breathe and turn takes the place of what the body should normally be doing as a defense. Ambulation should begin on day one, even with chest tubes in place (option a). Splinting does help relieve pain on moving and

coughing, but does not prevent airway collapse (option c). Although medicating for pain is appropriate, this will not prevent airway collapse (option d).
Nursing Process: Implementation   **Client Need:** Physiological Integrity

71.   **The correct answer is a.** The question is asking which symptom would not go with tracheoesophageal fistula (TEF). Projectile vomiting is not associated with TEF, it is associated with pyloric stenosis. Presence of TEF is suspected in an infant with excessive mucous in the nasopharynx. Frothing, drooling, sneezing and choking can all be observed (options b & c). Laryngospasm creates cyanosis in an attempt to prevent aspiration of excess mucous into the tracheobronchial tree. When the mucous is aspirated, breathing becomes easier and cyanosis subsides. As secretions in the nasopharynx accumulate, cyanosis returns (option d). Continuous cyanosis may indicate another pathological process and should be investigated (option d).
Nursing Process: Assessment   **Client Need:** Physiological Integrity

72.   **The correct answer is a.** The question is asking what to do for nausea in a client who just returned from surgery. Placing the client on the side is prudent to prevent aspiration from vomiting, should it occur. Sipping fluids (option b) before peristalsis has fully returned is a common cause of nausea and vomiting postoperatively. Hypoventilation and swallowing air occur when taking short shallow breaths (option c) and is also believed to be a cause of nausea. Peristalsis may not adequately return for up to 48 hours after anesthesia. Removing the nasogastric tube may precipitate nausea and vomiting (option d).
Nursing Process: Planning   **Client Need:** Physiological Integrity

73.   **The correct answer is c.** The question is asking an analysis of the dynamics of the situation. The family of the client who has a spinal cord injury experiences the same adjustment process as the client. It is not unusual for the family or client to waver between stages of adjustment. This does not mean that the client's father does not understand the extent of the injury (option a) because he is planning to make the house wheelchair accessible. Hope (option b) is usually expressed in terms of the reality, "I know what the doctors have said but I can hope, can't I?" There is no indication of memory loss (option d).
Nursing Process: Analysis   **Client Need:** Psychosocial Integrity

74.   **The correct answer is a.** The question is asking what palliative care at a hospice would include. Palliation does not mean no treatment of symptoms (option b), use of euthanasia (option c), or mandating living wills (option d). The basis of care is that the client is terminal without hope of cure, and does not wish to be resuscitated.
Nursing Process: Analysis   **Client Need:** Health Promotion & Maintenance

75.   **The correct answer is d.** The question is asking what action the nurse should take in this situation. The grandmother's ability to cope with the situation will have an impact on her health as well as the health of all of the children, including the identified client. The nurse should be concerned about the health of all people in the family. In this case, however, there is no reason to suspect problems with the other children at first (options a & c). However, the grandmother is showing problematic signs and should be assessed (option b).
Nursing Process: Implementation   **Client Need:** Health Promotion & Maintenance

PRACTICE SESSION: 18

> **Instructions: Allow yourself 75 minutes to complete the following 75 practice questions. Use a timer to notify yourself when 75 minutes are over so that you are not constantly looking at your watch while completing the questions.**

1. To prevent skin breakdown from alkaline encrustations around the ileal conduit stoma, the nurse should teach the client to include which in the daily diet?
   a. Cranberry juice.
   b. Milk.
   c. Orange juice.
   d. Water.

2. The nurse is monitoring a client with severe pregnancy induced hypertension (PIH) who is receiving magnesium sulfate. The nurse would need to be alert for which early sign of hypermagnesemia?
   a. Respiratory paralysis.
   b. Circulatory collapse.
   c. CNS depression.
   d. Depression of reflexes.

3. The nurse knows that teaching has been effective when the client with congestive heart failure makes which statement about the purpose of receiving digoxin (Lanoxin)?
   a. "It decreases the amount of blood my heart has to pump with each contraction."
   b. "It will suppress any irregular beats that my heart will make."
   c. "It keeps my heart from beating too fast."
   d. "It makes the muscle contraction stronger so more blood can be pumped out."

4. A nurse becomes ill during your shift. Reassignment of tasks is necessary. It is appropriate to delegate which tasks to the licensed practical nurse?
   a. Obtain vital signs, and check urine for acetone.
   b. Admit a client to the unit.
   c. Give discharge instructions to a client with an appendectomy.
   d. Hang a blood transfusion.

5. A 13-year-old child with scoliosis is treated surgically with spinal fusion and rod insertion. The client understands discharge teaching when which statement is made?
   a. "I can water ski if I use proper posture."
   b. "My dad can't make me mow the lawn."
   c. "I can use roller blades but not a skateboard."
   d. "Riding a bicycle will help me gain strength."

6. A client has a Queckenstedt test done. Results are positive. The nurse should:
   a. be alert for signs of increased intracranial pressure.
   b. keep the client flat in bed for 36 hours.
   c. place the client prone for as long as tolerated, then supine for six hours.
   d. check for other signs of hypertension, such as headache.

7. The nurse would suspect thrombophlebitis in a postoperative client who was noted to have:
   a. decreased capillary refill.
   b. a reddened line along the vein.
   c. diminished pedal pulses.
   d. decreased temperature of the extremity.

8. What would the nurse teach a client who was just diagnosed with pregnancy induced hypertension (PIH)?
   a. Bed rest at home.
   b. Moderate exercise.
   c. Low-salt diet and mild weight reduction.
   d. Regular daily activities and urine monitoring.

9. A client is admitted following the insertion of a Greenfield filter for peripheral vascular disease. He is on heparin sulfate (Heparin), total parenteral nutrition (TPN), digoxin (Lanoxin) and IV fluids. The heart monitor reveals rapid atrial fibrillation with heart rate 138. The client is diaphoretic and breathless when answering questions. The cardiac monitor is also demonstrating several short runs of ventricular tachycardia and asystole. What should the nurse do? Select all that apply.
   a. Consult with other nurses regarding rhythm strip interpretation.
   b. Obtain a set of vital signs.
   c. Initiate a transfer to the CCU.
   d. Notify the cardiologist of change in rhythm strip.
   e. Stop the heparin sulfate (Heparin) infusion.

10. While the nurse is conducting the admission interview, a client has an emesis of 100ml coffee ground fluid. The nurse plans care with the understanding that this type of emesis most likely indicates origin in the:
    a. lungs.
    b. stomach.
    c. esophagus.
    d. colon.

11. A postpartum client asks the nurse, "How long will I have this discharge?" The nurse responds that lochia usually lasts:
    a. about three weeks.
    b. about four weeks.
    c. about six weeks.
    d. until menstruation resumes.

12. A woman comes to the Family Practice Clinic with recurrent endometriosis. What findings would possibly indicate endometriosis?
    a. Dyspareunia and diarrhea.
    b. Pain and excoriation.
    c. Itching and drainage.
    d. Chills and hand rash.

13. The nurse believes a spinal cord injured client has developed a paralytic ileus when she assesses:
    a. nausea and absence of bowel movement for 24 hours.
    b. vomiting, abdominal distention and absence of bowel sounds.
    c. abdominal pain and seepage of bowel movement.
    d. anorexia, abdominal pain and hyperactive bowel sounds.

14. The nurse has returned from dinner and is receiving report from the nurse who was covering for her. Which client needs to be assessed first?
    a. A woman with a right hip fracture who is scheduled for surgery tomorrow. The surgical checklist needs to be completed and preoperative blood work needs to be drawn. Buck's traction of 7 lbs. is in place. The client is requesting to be repositioned.
    b. A man with diabetes and a gangrenous stump. He had a debridement yesterday. The dressing is saturated and needs to be changed. The antibiotic that was due this morning has just arrived from the pharmacy and needs to be hung as soon as possible.
    c. A woman who was admitted from the emergency department with dizziness and tinnitus. She came to the floor at the beginning of the shift with a potassium level of 3 and is resting in bed.
    d. A man who has received a new permanent tracheostomy two days ago. The surgeon was in during the nurse's dinner break and has "down-sized" the client's tracheostomy tube to a size #6. The client is sitting upright in bed and is receiving oxygen.

15. A woman addicted to drugs has delivered an infant who is now going through withdrawal. The woman asks the nurse if there is anything that can be done to calm down her fussy baby. The nurse's response would be:
    a. "We can get a prescription for phenobarbitol (Luminol). That sometimes is very effective for infants who are withdrawing from drugs."
    b. "Frequently babies who are irritable do best when the environment is quiet and dark."
    c. "Did you bubble her? Gas is a frequent cause of irritation in infants."
    d. "Let me hold her and see if I can comfort her for you."

16. A client has a Ca^{++} level of 11.5 and is prescribed 1,000ml NSS to run at 200ml per hour. The nurse should:
    a. administer the fluid as prescribed.
    b. call the physician and question the prescription.
    c. ask the physician to add potassium.
    d. offer the client milk or ice cream.

17. A 28-year-old man was brought to the hospital by the police after reports of domestic violence. During the initial interview with the nurse, the client states, "My wife starts an argument and I hit her just to keep her quiet." The defense mechanism being used by this man is:
    a. rationalization.
    b. denial.
    c. displacement.
    d. projection.

18. A woman is suspected of having systemic lupus erythematosus when the nurse notes a rash that is:
    a. scaly, maculopapular and malar.
    b. maculopapular in the lumbar area.
    c. generalized with red splotches on the trunk.
    d. ulcerative on sun-exposed areas of the body.

19. While educating a 20-year-old client with bipolar disorder who has been prescribed carbamazepine (Tegretol), which statement indicates further teaching is necessary?
    a. "I will still be able to drive to work."
    b. "I will continue to use birth control pills."
    c. "I will take my medicine with food."
    d. "I may be dizzy and have tremors, but they will go away."

20. The typical pattern of chronic fatigue syndrome necessitates a (n):
    a.   sedentary occupation.
    b.   strong support system.
    c.   aerobic exercise program.
    d.   fat-controlled diet.

21. A 12-month-old is brought to the hospital with persistent crying; foul smelling stools and signs of malnutrition. Celiac's disease is diagnosed. The goal for the parents would be that they will:
    a.   understand the reasons for antacids and antibiotics.
    b.   list the reasons for corrective surgery and/or transplant.
    c.   demonstrate how to position the infant for feeding.
    d.   state the importance of maintaining the child's diet.

22. A homeless man, with a history of schizophrenia, is being discharged after losing a finger to frostbite. The priority of the nurse should be to:
    a.   help him explore possible benefits through the Veteran's Association or Social Security.
    b.   give information on shelters that provide food and clothing.
    c.   explain the importance of medication compliance.
    d.   direct the client to a mental health support group.

23. A client comes to the emergency department complaining of racing heart and dizziness. The nurse observes sweating and fast respirations. The heart monitor shows paroxysmal supraventricular tachycardia. Vagus nerve stimulation is unsuccessful. The nurse would prepare to:
    a.   administer verapamil (Calan) by mouth.
    b.   infuse atropine sulfate (Atopine) intravenously.
    c.   give adenosine (Adenocard) intravenous push.
    d.   assist with synchronized cardioversion.

24. A newly admitted client with schizophrenia is noticeably agitated and hostile for the first few days. The primary goal for the nurse during this time would be to:
    a.   approach the client frequently for brief periods of time.
    b.   allow the client to approach the nurse to initiate conversation when she is ready.
    c.   set limits on the client's behavior by setting up a daily interaction time with the nurse.
    d.   ascertain the client's suicide potential.

25. A new mother is bottle-feeding her infant and expresses some uncertainty over her decision to bottle-feed. What is the nurse's responsibility to the client in this situation?
    a.   Regardless of the client's choice, the nurse should support the decision.
    b.   The nurse should give a personal opinion but, ultimately, support the decision of the client.
    c.   The nurse should give the client the facts about breastfeeding so she can change her mind.
    d.   The nurse should provide the client with literature, which supports one method over another.

26. In the immediate postoperative period, the nurse would instruct a mastectomy client to perform which exercises?
    a.   Hand to shoulder.
    b.   Arm above head.
    c.   Elbow and neck.
    d.   Shoulders and neck.

27. When interacting with a client experiencing a panic attack, the nurse would:
    a.   use touch in order to minimize the client's anxiety level.
    b.   give detailed explanations of treatments.
    c.   speak to the client in simple terms and in brief intervals.
    d.   encourage the client to give up coping mechanisms that are not effective.

28. The nurse would observe an 18-month-old child in the playroom doing which age appropriate activity?
   a. Building a tower of eight cubes.
   b. Playing hide and seek.
   c. Pulling a toy in movement.
   d. Unscrewing a jar lid.

29. A client comes to the outpatient clinic complaining of dull eye pain that kept him up last night, tearing and blurred vision. After examination, the physician diagnoses uveitis and prescribes various eye drops. The nurse does discharge teaching for home care. The teaching plan includes:
   a. how to massage lid margins.
   b. importance of documenting allergic responses.
   c. reasons to avoid bending and lifting.
   d. avoiding kissing others while infected.

30. A nurse on a psychiatric unit comes out after shift report and finds four clients asking for attention. Which client should be seen first? A client on:
   a. haloperidol (Haldol), complaining of stiff muscles, no fever.
   b. olanzapine (Zyprexa), with an inability to sit still.
   c. paroxetine (Paxil), asking about blurred vision.
   d. phenelzine (Nardil), requesting headache medicine.

31. A client requests pain medication following hip replacement surgery. The client is prescribed oxycodone (Percocet) one or two tablets every four hours as needed for pain. The graduate nurse assigned to care for this client asks, "Should I give one or two tablets?" The best response that would help the graduate nurse make a decision would be:
   a. "How much did the client receive for pain the last time?"
   b. "Give two tablets, this is a very painful procedure."
   c. "Does the client look like he is in pain?"
   d. "Ask the client to rate the pain on a scale of 1 to 10."

32. During a routine antepartal visit, a client complains to the nurse that she is experiencing leg cramps during the night. The nurse asks further questions regarding the client's intake of:
   a. fruits and yellow vegetables.
   b. dairy products.
   c. whole grain breads and cereals.
   d. red meat and green leafy vegetables.

33. The nurse is caring for a client who is in chronic rejection following a liver transplant. He begins to experience pallor, petechiae, tachypnea, dyspnea, oliguria and abdominal pain. Lab results reveal elevated PT, PTT and decreased platelet levels. The nurse would expect which drug to be prescribed?
   a. Vitamin K.
   b. Menadiol sodium diphosphate (Synkavite).
   c. Heparin sodium (Heparin).
   d. Albumin.

34. A client's nephrostomy tube is accidentally dislodged. The appropriate initial nursing action would be to:
   a. notify the physician.
   b. cover the site with a sterile dressing.
   c. replace the tube with a new one.
   d. obtain the client's vital signs.

35. A client calls the medical clinic and tells the nurse that the family is going on vacation to the Pocono Mountains. The client asks how to prevent Lyme disease. The nurse replies:
   a. "The doctor can give an antibiotic prescription prophylactically."
   b. "Wear sunscreen and reapply every few hours after swimming."
   c. "Wear long sleeved clothing and long pants when hiking in the woods."
   d. "Shower and shampoo hair with antibacterial soap after being in wooded areas."

36. A woman is brought to the emergency department by the police due to an alleged sexual assault. The woman is very quiet, has tears in her eyes and does not make eye contact. The client asks if she can just wash up a bit. The nurse should:
   a. take her to a private room with a wash basin, clean towels and hospital gown.
   b. ask her to place her clothes in a paper bag before washing herself.
   c. give her a towel, washcloth and soap and take her to the shower area.
   d. ask her to wait to wash until after the physician examines her.

37. A 5-week-old infant has had a ventriculoperitoneal shunt placed to treat her hydrocephalus. During the first few days after surgery, the nurse should:
   a. leave the infant in the crib at all times to prevent suture strain.
   b. provide crib toys for distraction.
   c. plan to hold and cuddle the infant more than usual.
   d. keep the infant heavily sedated.

38. A client diagnosed with gonorrhea comes to the clinic for a checkup. The nurse is doing teaching on how to prevent further infection. Based on teaching-learning principles, the nurse would:
   a. use a visual diagram to explain how the disease occurs.
   b. suggest the client ask the physician for more information.
   c. ask the client what is known about tests for gonorrhea.
   d. give the client a pamphlet to read at leisure and call later for questions.

39. A family member reports to the nurse that his brother's chest tube disconnected from the drainage system. Upon entering the room, the nurse would expect the client to display:
   a. dyspnea and restlessness.
   b. tachypnea and numbness.
   c. dysphagia and gastric reflux.
   d. a precordial friction rub and fever.

40. A client is scheduled for a proximal vagotomy for treatment of peptic ulcer disease. The nurse teaches that the purpose of the procedure is to:
   a. decrease food transit in the stomach.
   b. regenerate gastric mucosa.
   c. decrease Helicobacter pylori organisms.
   d. reduce the stimulus of the parietal cells.

41. A severely burned client is admitted. The physician prescribes a large amount of fluid to be infused. The most important nursing measure is:
   a. assessing vital signs.
   b. auscultating the lungs.
   c. evaluating urine output.
   d. checking the level of consciousness.

42. Cerebral palsy was just diagnosed in a 7-month-old. The parents ask why it was not detected at birth. The nurse responds:
    a. "The joint deformities associated with cerebral palsy only appear after six months."
    b. "The health care personnel in the clinic did not want to alarm you until it was necessary."
    c. "The neurological lesions responsible for your child's condition may have changed as he matured, which would have affected the diagnosis."
    d. "Early diagnosis of cerebral palsy is difficult in infants until they develop control of voluntary movements."

43. In obtaining the history of a client with peptic ulcer disease, the nurse would rule out which piece of information as being a significant contributor to the illness?
    a. Drinks several cups of coffee daily.
    b. Takes a prescribed thiazide diuretic daily for hypertension.
    c. "Fairly heavy" alcoholic intake in social situations.
    d. Heavy aspirin use when stressed.

44. The nurse is caring for a client who was just admitted with a ruptured cerebral aneurysm. Which finding would be of most concern to the nurse?
    a. The client has not had a bowel movement during the last three days.
    b. The client complains of severe photophobia.
    c. A lumbar puncture performed in the emergency department revealed blood in the CSF.
    d. The client complains of a headache and rates it 7 of 10 with 10 being the most severe.

45. A client was diagnosed with tuberculosis. The nurse expects that the client will be treated with the primary drug of choice for tubercle bacillus, which is:
    a. nystatin (Mycostatin).
    b. cycloserine (Seromycin).
    c. isoniazide (INH).
    d. ethionamide (Treactor-SC).

46. A client is admitted in diabetic ketoacidosis with a glucose level of 640mg/dL and a serum pH of 7.19. The physician orders 300 units of regular insulin to be added to 1,000ml of D_5W to be given at a rate of 1ml/minute. The infusion set delivers 60gtts/ml. The nurse should regulate the infusion to run at how many drops per minute?

_____

47. In order to meet the developmental needs of a 5-month-old infant with rumination, it would be most important for the nurse to teach the parent to:
    a. play a musical wind-up mobile.
    b. prop her bottle to assist with feeding.
    c. maintain eye contact with the infant at each feeding.
    d. weigh the infant daily and document fluctuations.

48. During a routine gynecological visit, a 30-year-old woman tells the nurse, "I eventually want children, but not now. What birth control method should I use?" The nurse makes a recommendation after teaching that which method might cause fertility problems later?
    a. Intrauterine device (IUD).
    b. Oral contraceptive.
    c. Cervical cap.
    d. Abstinence.

49. The nurse is giving discharge instructions to a man who had an inguinal herniorrhaphy. Which statement would indicate that the client is ready for discharge?
   a. "My doctor said that I can resume normal activities in about three days."
   b. "I may have problems with urination but this is normal and they will subside."
   c. "I should call the doctor even for a little bit of drainage."
   d. "I shouldn't push on the area or I could split the incision."

50. The nurse evaluates that a suspicious client is ready for discharge when the client:
   a. relates to others when rewarded.
   b. communicates in a clear manner when relating to others.
   c. speaks to others when they speak.
   d. does not report any paranoid ideation.

51. A client on a psychiatric unit tells the nurse, "I'm no good, and I wish I was dead." The nurse's response would be to:
   a. place the client in seclusion and institute suicide precautions.
   b. ignore the client's remark because it is manipulation.
   c. encourage the client to play volleyball with the other clients.
   d. sit with the client in the dayroom and quietly talk with him.

52. What would be included in the nursing care plan for a client with tuberculosis? Select all that apply.
   a. Provide a HEPA-filtered respirator for anyone who enters the client's room.
   b. Wear gloves when taking vital signs.
   c. Ensure that the client uses disposable eating utensils.
   d. Place a mask on the client when transporting to other departments.
   e. Teach the client to cough into tissues.
   f. Place the client in a negative airflow room.

53. A woman has just delivered her first child. During the postpartal assessment, the nurse notices that the woman's fundus is markedly deviated to the left side of her abdomen. The nurse's initial action would be to:
   a. administer fundal massage.
   b. check the client's perineal pad for bleeding.
   c. ask the client when she last voided.
   d. get a prescription for an oxytocic drug.

54. The nurse is teaching a client's daughter how to change the wet-to-dry dressing on her mother's decubitus ulcer. The daughter needs a review of the procedure when she tells the nurse:
   a. "I should wring the dressing tightly before applying it to the wound."
   b. "I should wrap it with a plastic cling wrap when I am done."
   c. "I should remove the dressing while it is dry."
   d. "I should wear sterile gloves when I put the new one on."

55. A 3-year-old child is admitted with a history of vomiting six times in the past four hours. The parents state that the child has vomited all food and fluids given. The priority nursing diagnosis is:
   a. altered home health maintenance related to knowledge deficit of diet therapy.
   b. altered nutrition: less than body requirements related to nausea and vomiting.
   c. risk for fluid volume deficit related to vomiting.
   d. altered comfort related to vomiting.

56. An African-American client of brown skin is admitted to the hospital with breathing problems. The nurse would assess for cyanosis:
    a.   through skin temperature.
    b.   in the nail beds.
    c.   over gluteal folds.
    d.   on the inner aspect of the forearm.

57. A client is admitted with suspected cholera. What assessment finding would be most helpful in confirming this diagnosis?
    a.   He grows his own vegetables on the roof of his apartment building.
    b.   He reports being sexually active with his partner within the past 24 hours.
    c.   He went out to dinner with friends the night before.
    d.   He flew over 12 hours on a crowded airplane two days ago.

58. A client is scheduled for a peripheral venography to rule out venous thrombosis. The nurse will explain to the client that:
    a.   a sandbag will be placed over the arterial site post-venography.
    b.   radiographic dye will be injected into a dorsal foot vein.
    c.   the procedure is used to confirm a diagnosis of occlusive arterial disease.
    d.   the client will be NPO after midnight prior to the procedure.

59. In caring for a preoperative client with Cushing's syndrome, the nurse should be chiefly concerned with which nursing diagnosis?
    a.   Altered thought processes related to mood swings.
    b.   Body image disturbance related to physical changes.
    c.   Self-care deficit related to fatigue and/or muscle wasting.
    d.   Risk for infection related to altered immune response.

60. A client with ritual behavior becomes upset in the dayroom and hurries to the bathroom to wash her hands. After completing the ritual, she turns to leave and sees the nurse standing there. The client says, "I'm sorry, I know this behavior seems silly to you." The nurse responds based on the knowledge that the client is:
    a.   trying to manipulate the nurse.
    b.   attempting to problem solve.
    c.   demonstrating obsessive thinking.
    d.   expressing her embarrassment.

61. A woman comes to the emergency department with a fractured arm. After a long assessment, it is found that her husband is abusing her. The nurse should:
    a.   discuss with the physician the possibility of an overnight admission.
    b.   refer the client and her spouse to couples counseling.
    c.   offer information on support groups.
    d.   suggest ways in which she can leave her husband as soon as possible.

62. A client comes to the mental health clinic and tells the nurse that he's not sure if he wants to deal with the fact that he might be a homosexual. "I don't know if I can live with the idea that I'm sick." The nurse's response would be:
    a.   "Homosexuality is not an illness."
    b.   "Many people have homosexual thoughts at various points in their lives."
    c.   "What have you read about homosexuality?"
    d.   "What does being homosexual mean to you?"

63. A client requests information on how to decrease the risk of lung cancer. His father died of lung cancer last month. Which dietary adjustment should be discussed with the client?
   a. Decreased vitamin C.
   b. Decreased fiber.
   c. Increased protein.
   d. Increased vitamin A.

64. A 23-year-old woman is admitted to the labor suite at term pregnancy. Her mother and two small children have accompanied her to the hospital. When the client's mother attempts to leave the labor room to go get the children, the client becomes upset and begs her not to leave. The best way for the nurse to respond to this situation is to:
   a. ask social service to provide caretaking for the children.
   b. give them privacy to deal with the situation themselves.
   c. bring the children into the labor room so they are supervised.
   d. enter the room and talk with the client about her concerns of the labor experience.

65. A client comes back to the unit after a colonoscopy and needs to use the bathroom. Some rectal bleeding is evident and the client complains of abdominal pain. The nurse should:
   a. call the physician.
   b. ask the client to stay in bed.
   c. obtain vital signs.
   d. administer an analgesic.

66. The nurse is reviewing the treatment plan for premenstrual syndrome (PMS) with a newly diagnosed 18-year-old client. Which instruction is appropriate?
   a. Avoid diuretics and laxatives.
   b. Exercise at least 30 minutes per day.
   c. Increase the caffeine in your diet.
   d. Take acetaminophen (Tylenol) to relieve pain.

67. A nurse is working with a client with chronic paranoid schizophrenia. He has become increasingly suspicious. He avoids other clients, appears tense and constantly scans the room as if he is guarding himself. The nurse should plan a schedule that:
   a. is routine like the other clients' schedules.
   b. is flexible and can be changed daily.
   c. eases him into group activities slowly.
   d. provides a variety of interpersonal contacts.

68. A nurse is conducting a course, to a group of adolescent females, on human sexuality and the spread of sexually transmitted diseases. Which statement by the participants would indicate an understanding of safer sex?
   a. "I will get tested at least once a year for HIV."
   b. "If we don't have anal intercourse, we don't have to worry about getting AIDS."
   c. "I can keep a latex condom in my purse in case my boyfriend doesn't have one."
   d. "We should use a petroleum lubricant with a condom to protect me from tearing my skin inside."

69. What is the best way to feed a child with cleft lip and palate prior to surgery?
   a. Keeping the child in a near horizontal position during feeding.
   b. Continuous feeding via a gastric tube.
   c. Bolus feedings via a NG tube.
   d. Providing for sucking needs while using a syringe.

70. Which client is at highest risk for peripheral vascular disease? A client with:
    a.   job stress that walks one mile each day on the treadmill.
    b.   obesity on a low-cholesterol weight reduction diet.
    c.   cigarette smoking history who joined a smoking cessation group.
    d.   diabetes who takes hypertension medication diligently.

71. The nurse is providing client teaching for urinary incontinence to a 45-year-old female with stress incontinence. What will help reduce factors contributing to the problem?
    a.   Decreasing fluid intake to 1,000ml/day.
    b.   Decreasing dietary fiber.
    c.   Eliminating aerobic exercise.
    d.   Using stool softeners.

72. A client with diabetes asks the nurse about the relationship among diet, exercise and insulin requirements. The nurse teaches the client that when exercising:
    a.   less than usual, the client should decrease dietary intake and decrease insulin dosage.
    b.   less than usual, the client should increase dietary intake and increase insulin dosage.
    c.   more than usual, the client should either decrease dietary intake or increase insulin dosage.
    d.   more than usual, the client should either increase dietary intake or decrease insulin dosage.

73. A client with abruptio placenta is in active labor. The nurse would be alert for which symptom of concealed abruptio placenta during labor?
    a.   Regular contractions with increasing rest periods.
    b.   Board-like uterus.
    c.   Increasing relaxation of the contraction stage.
    d.   Uterine atony.

74. The nurse should consider which factor when planning an individualized management program for a newly diagnosed 8-year-old with Type 1 diabetes?
    a.   The needed discipline of the parents in changing their dietary patterns to adhere to the strict requirements of the diabetic diet.
    b.   The restriction of school activities to prevent episodes of hypoglycemia.
    c.   A flexible program, which considers the 24-hour insulin coverage in relation to the child's present lifestyle.
    d.   The family finances to cover the cost of expected and repeated hospitalizations.

75. A client with a migraine headache comes to the emergency department. The physician prescribes sumatriptan (Imitrex). The nurse should ask which assessment question?
    a.   "Did you have an aura?"
    b.   "Do you have photophobia?"
    c.   "Have you been vomiting?"
    d.   "Do you have hypertension?"

STOP. You have now completed Practice Session: 18. Now take a few minutes and correct your answers. Calculate your accuracy rate by dividing the number of questions you completed correctly by the total number of questions you completed (75).

Correct answers ÷ total number of questions completed = accuracy rate.

_____ ÷ _____ = _____

ANSWERS AND RATIONALES
Practice Session 18

1.   **The correct answer is a.** The question is asking which dietary measure will help to prevent alkaline encrustations. Cranberry juice causes acid urine and helps to prevent these encrustations. Milk and orange juice make the urine more basic and should be avoided or limited in amount (options b & c). Water dilutes, but does not acidify, the urine (option d).
     Nursing Process: Implementation   **Client Need:** Physiological Integrity

2.   **The correct answer is d.** The question is asking which is an early sign of increased magnesium. Magnesium sulfate (Magnesium) is given to decrease the contractions. Therefore, it would make sense for it to decrease contractility in other muscles as well. Depression of reflexes is an early sign of hypermagnesemia. Respiratory paralysis, circulatory collapse and CNS depression (options a, b & c) are serious signs of late hypermagnesemia.
     Nursing Process: Evaluation   **Client Need:** Physiological Integrity

3.   **The correct answer is d.** The question is asking for lanoxin's (Digoxin's) action. Strengthening the heart muscle and the force of contraction is the primary reason to use lanoxin (Digoxin) in most clients with congestive heart failure. Although the medication also suppresses arrhythmias and slows the heart rate (options b & c), the usual objective is to improve cardiac output by increasing the strength of the heart's contraction. Preload, (option a) is decreased by reducing fluid volume.
     Nursing Process: Evaluation   **Client Need:** Physiological Integrity

4.   **The correct answer is a.** The question is asking for the appropriate task to delegate to the LPN. LPNs can obtain vital signs and check urine for acetone. They cannot perform admission assessments (option b); do planned teaching unless using a standard care plan (option c), or hang blood transfusions (option d). Only a registered nurse can perform those functions.
     Nursing Process: Implementation   **Client Need:** Safe, Effective Care Environment

5.   **The correct answer is b.** The question is asking which statement shows the child understands discharge teaching about the spinal surgery and rod insertion. The client cannot do anything that might disrupt the healing process. Therefore, the child can do none of the activities listed: mow the lawn, water ski (option a), roller blade, skateboard, (option c) or ride a bicycle (option d), therefore, the father cannot allow the child to mow the lawn.
     Nursing Process: Evaluation   **Client Need:** Physiological Integrity

6.   **The correct answer is a.** The question is asking what to check in a client with positive results for the Queckenstedt's test. This test result means the subarachnoid space is blocked. This will lead to increased intracranial pressure. Leaving the client flat when increased intracranial pressure is present may lead to further problems (option b). Immobility problems may arise if in bed and flat for 36 hours. A client may be prone for one hour and supine for six hours following a lumbar puncture (option c). Hypertension is not the problem (option d), increased intracranial pressure is.
     Nursing Process: Planning   **Client Need:** Physiological Integrity

7.   **The correct answer is b.** The question is asking which sign relates to thrombophlebitis in a postoperative client. Capillary refill time is increased, the strength of the pedal pulses is decreased and the temperature of the extremities decreases in arterial insufficiency, not venous insufficiency (options a, c & d). Signs of a thrombophlebitis include positive Homan's sign, pain, local tenderness, and a reddened line, which feels firm on palpation, may be apparent.
     Nursing Process: Assessment   **Client Need:** Physiological Integrity

8.   **The correct answer is a.** The question is asking the intervention that will benefit the client the best who has pregnancy induced hypertension (PIH). Bed rest is the most important treatment in early PIH. Mild exercise such as range-of-motion and stretching can be performed, however, moderate exercise is not recommended when the client is at risk for altered tissue perfusion (option b). Research has identified that a low-salt diet and weight reduction (option c) are not

354

therapeutic and may limit protein, which may be a factor in the cause of PIH. Although it may be helpful for the client to monitor her urinary output (option d) and protein, rest is the priority.
Nursing Process: Implementation   **Client Need:** Health Promotion & Maintenance

9.   **The correct answers are a, b and d.** The question is asking what the nurse should do when a client who just had a Greenfield filter inserted begins to have several dysrhythmias. It is important to clarify the dysrhythmias with other staff (option a). Vital signs are important as a baseline assessment (option b). The physician should be notified of changes in cardiac status (option d). Option (c) is incorrect because the nurse cannot initiate client transfers. The physician would have to prescribe the transfer. The client still needs to be anti-coagulated due to the new Greenfield filter and history of PVD (option e).
Nursing Process: Implementation   **Client Need:** Physiological Integrity

10.   **The correct answer is b.** The question is asking the origin of coffee ground emesis. It signifies old blood, which has come in contact with the gastric acids. Fluid from the lungs (option a) would be frothy. If it were from the esophagus, (option c) it would show recent red bleeding. Emesis from the colon (option d) may be green if from the duodenum or brown if from the large intestine.
Nursing Process: Analysis   **Client Need:** Physiological Integrity

11.   **The correct answer is a.** The question is asking how long lochial discharge occurs. The lochia progresses through three stages. The first stage is rubra, which is deep red and lasts about one or two days. The second stage is serosa, which is pinkish fluid and lasts about three to ten days. The third stage is alba, which is a creamy or yellowish discharge and lasts between one and two weeks. Generally this process is completed in about three weeks (options b, c & d).
Nursing Process: Implementation   **Client Need:** Health Promotion & Maintenance

12.   **The correct answer is a.** The question is asking what would be present in endometriosis. Dyspareunia (painful intercourse) and diarrhea may be present due to prostaglandin sloughing from endometrial tissues. Also occurring is a dull pain and heaviness. Excoriation, itching and drainage relate to vaginal infection (options b & c). Chills and hand rash are symptoms of toxic shock syndrome (option d).
Nursing Process: Assessment   **Client Need:** Physiological Integrity

13.   **The correct answer is b.** The question is asking what are the symptoms of paralytic ileus in a client with a spinal cord injury. Lack of gastrointestinal motility will cause distention of the abdomen. Lack of bowel sounds that arise from gastrointestinal movement and vomiting frequently occur. Lack of bowel movement with resulting nausea (option a) may be a result of the effect of spinal shock on emptying of the rectum and lack of physical mobility. This may occur with ileus but the data in option (b) would need to be confirmed. The client may not be able to experience abdominal pain due to the level of the injury. Seepage of bowel movement is more indicative of fecal impaction (option c). Hyperactive bowel sounds are not indicative of ileus, but may occur with obstruction (option d).
Nursing Process: Evaluation   **Client Need:** Physiological Integrity

14.   **The correct answer is d.** The question is asking about who needs to be assessed first. The client in option (d) has had stimulation to the new tracheostomy site, which will cause increased mucous production and coughing. The client is at risk for aspiration, may be in need of comfort measures to decrease anxiety, and the pulse oximeter needs to be rechecked. It is expected that a client with Buck's traction and a hip fracture (option a) will need to be repositioned and possibly given pain medication, but it is not the highest priority. The diagnostic work-up and recheck of the potassium level (option c) can wait, as it is not as important as the potential airway problem. The dressing needs to be changed and the antibiotic needs to be hung, these too can also wait (option b).
Nursing Process: Analysis   **Client Need:** Safe, Effective Care Environment

15.   **The correct answer is b.** The question is asking for the best way to calm a baby who is withdrawing from drugs. Infants who are irritable due to their mother's drug use frequently

respond well to decreasing environmental stimulation. When that does not work, then sometimes drugs such as phenobarbital (Luminol) are used (option a). Bubbling the infant (option c) does not address the true cause for the irritability. Separating the mother and infant (option d) makes the mother feel inadequate. The nurse's job is to enhance the relationship between the two of them and help the mother learn how to care for her infant.
Nursing Process: Implementation   **Client Need:** Health Promotion & Maintenance

16.   **The correct answer is a.** The question is asking what to do when a physician prescribes an intravenous infusion of 1,000ml NSS at 200ml per hour for a client with too much calcium. A normal calcium level is 8.5 to 10.5. Hypercalcemia causes problems with cardiac rhythm. Treatment is to give intravenous normal saline quickly to increase fluid to the system and decrease calcium levels. Often a diuretic is prescribed as needed to prevent fluid volume overload and promote calcium excretion. Then the cause of the hypercalcemia is determined and treated. Questioning the prescription (option a) would be inappropriate. Adding potassium (option c) would be of no value except to possibly overload the system with potassium. Milk and ice cream (option d) are rich in calcium and would place the client in danger.
Nursing Process: Implementation   **Client Need:** Physiological Integrity

17.   **The correct answer is a.** The question is asking what dynamic this client is using. The client is using the defense mechanism of rationalization, which is attempting to justify or make acceptable otherwise unacceptable feelings or behaviors. Denial (option b) is avoiding or ignoring disagreeable realities. Displacement (option c) is the shift of an emotion from the person towards which it was directed to another less dangerous person or object. Projection (option d) is attributing one's own thoughts to another person.
Nursing Process: Analysis   **Client Need:** Psychosocial Integrity

18.   **The correct answer is a.** The question is asking what rash goes with systemic lupus erythematosus (SLE). A scaly, maculopapular rash is seen in a butterfly shape on the face. Many clients who have SLE are also photosensitive and may have a diffuse maculopapular rash on areas that are exposed to the sun, such as the face and arms (option b). Option (c) may be related to childhood diseases such as measles or to an allergic reaction. Option (d) may be related to precancerous or cancerous skin lesions.
Nursing Process: Assessment   **Client Need:** Physiological Integrity

19.   **The correct answer is b.** The question is asking which statement by a bipolar client on carbamazepine (Tegretol) needs to be addressed. While carbomazepine (Tegretol) is associated with an increase of birth defects, it also decreases the effectiveness of oral contraceptives (option b). Therefore, another method of birth control should be used. Driving (option a) is permitted as long as there are no visual disturbances. Carbamazepine (Tegretol) should be taken with food (option c). Dizziness and tremors are often common in initial dosing and do dissipate (option d).
Nursing Process: Analysis   **Client Need:** Physiological Integrity

20.   **The correct answer is b.** The question is asking for the most important factor to help someone with chronic fatigue syndrome. Any long-term, unpredictable disease exerts considerable strain upon the client and the family, thus necessitating a strong support system. All activities should be planned according to energy level (options a & c) but these factors will be more easily followed if support is available. A fat controlled diet (option d) is not necessarily prescribed for these clients.
Nursing Process: Planning   **Client Need:** Health Promotion & Maintenance

21.   **The correct answer is d.** The question is asking for a goal of parents with a child who has Celiac's disease. Celiac's disease is a malabsorption disorder where gluten, a protein, is not tolerated. Gluten is found in grains such as wheat and barley. Management is aimed at avoiding gluten in the diet. The parents must understand the importance of this, particularly in the absence of symptoms. Antacids and antibiotics (option a) may be prescribed for children with peptic ulcer disease. Corrective surgery and transplant (option b) may be true for children with biliary atresia. Infant positioning for feeding (option c) may be an issue in cleft lip and palate.
Nursing Process: Planning   **Client Need:** Physiological Integrity

356

22.   **The correct answer is b.** The question is asking what is most important when working with a homeless person who has a behavioral health disorder. The nurse's priority for a homeless person must be first meeting their basic needs. Although obtaining benefits (option a), medication compliance (option c) and mental health support (option d) are all very important, they are all secondary to their basic needs.
Nursing Process: Analysis   **Client Need:** Psychosocial Integrity

23.   **The correct answer is c.** The question is asking what to do for a client who has paroxysmal supraventricular tachycardia (PSVT). Adenosine (Adenocard) is given rapidly by intravenous push. Slow administration renders it useless in converting the rhythm. Verapamil (Calan) may be used to treat PSVT. However, this client is exhibiting symptoms that need immediate attention. A pill will take too long to work (option a). Atropine sulfate (Atropine) is used to treat bradycardia (option b). Synchronized cardioversion (option d) is used if the medication is unsuccessful.
Nursing Process: Implementation   **Client Need:** Physiological Integrity

24.   **The correct answer is a.** The question is asking what the best plan is for a client with schizophrenia. This option conveys the nurse's belief in the client's worth and prevents the client from feeling ignored and devalued. Option (b) does not make any contact with the client nor does it allow for trust building, which is necessary for the therapeutic relationship and treatment. It is not necessary to set limits on the client's behavior at this time as long as she remains in control (option c). There is no evidence to suggest suicidal behavior or thinking at this time (option d).
Nursing Process: Implementation   **Client Need:** Psychosocial Integrity

25.   **The correct answer is a.** The question is asking how to respond when a client is expressing misgivings about her decision to bottle-feed her baby. In order to be the client's advocate, her choice should be supported. Giving one's personal opinion is not being the client's advocate (option b). Providing the client with biased literature would only confuse her at this point (options c & d).
Nursing Process: Analysis   **Client Need:** Health Promotion & Maintenance

26.   **The correct answer is a.** The question is asking what exercises can be performed immediately post-mastectomy. Immediate postoperative mobility of the site is limited to prevent incisional trauma. Clients should be encouraged to start gentle movements like hand to shoulder, which enhance circulation. All other options (b, c & d) would occur after the drains are removed.
Nursing Process: Implementation   **Client Need:** Physiological Integrity

27.   **The correct answer is c.** The question is asking how the nurse should intervene when a client is having a panic attack. When talking with a client experiencing a panic attack the nurse should speak in simple terms and in a calm voice. A client who is experiencing a panic attack cannot pay attention to lengthy detailed explanations (option b). The nurse should not use touch with a highly anxious client (option a) as the client may misinterpret the nurse's touch as threatening. In option (d), the nurse asks the client who is extremely anxious to give up coping mechanisms that are not working. In this situation, the nurse should not expect the client to give up coping mechanisms unless the nurse has offered new coping mechanisms to replace them.
Nursing Process: Implementation   **Client Need:** Psychosocial Integrity

28.   **The correct answer is c.** The question is asking what an 18-month-old child can do. The child is at the sensorimotor stage of development. Interest is exhibited in the environment with curiosity, experimentation, and novelty. The child enjoys pulling toys for play stimulation. Observation of the other activities may not be seen until later development at 30 months (options a, b & d).
Nursing Process: Assessment   **Client Need:** Health Promotion & Maintenance

29.   **The correct answer is c.** The question is asking for teaching related to uveitis. Uveitis is the inflammation of the vascular layer of the eye, which includes the iris, ciliary body and choroid. It can lead to visual loss if it is not treated. Treatment usually includes mydriatics, antibiotics and steroids. Teaching includes avoiding bending or lifting which increases intraocular pressure (IOP). The eye is already inflamed and swollen. The dull pain and blurred vision is the result of

increased IOP. Further increased pressure could result in glaucoma and vision loss. Massaging eyelids promotes drainage in the eye of clients with a sty (option a). Allergic responses often occur with conjunctivitis (option b). Kissing is avoided in people who have herpes simplex (option d).
Nursing Process: Planning   **Client Need:** Physiological Integrity

30.   **The correct answer is d.** The question is asking which of these clients with drug side effects should be seen first. The client on phenelzine (Nardil) is asking for headache medicine. Headache is a sign of hypertensive crisis. This is an emergency and should be treated immediately or the condition can lead to death. Blurred vision (option c) is a side effect of paroxetine (Paxil) and usually subsides after a few weeks of treatment. Stiff muscles without fever (option a) is a pseudoparkinson side effect of antipsychotic drugs such as haloperidol (Haldol). Inability to sit still (option b) is a sign of akathesia in a client on olanzapine (Zyprexia). Both stiff muscles and akathesia can be treated with medication but are not life threatening.
Nursing Process: Analysis   **Client Need:** Safe, Effective Care Environment

31.   **The correct answer is d.** The question is asking what response would help the graduate nurse decide to give one or two tablets of pain medication. The client is the person feeling the pain and, therefore, would best be able to judge the intensity. With this information, the nurse would then be able to determine if one or two tablets is necessary. The amount of medication the client received earlier is not relevant to the amount of pain he feels now (option a). Giving the client two tablets without first assessing the intensity would also be inappropriate, as this may cause the client to be unnecessarily drowsy (option b). Not all clients demonstrate observable signs of pain and, therefore, need to be asked the intensity of the pain (option c).
Nursing Process: Planning   **Client Need:** Physiological Integrity

32.   **The correct answer is b.** The question is asking the reason for the leg cramps in a pregnant client. Leg cramps may be attributed to an imbalance in the calcium/phosphorous ratio. Of the options (a, c & d), dairy products have the highest concentration of calcium.
Nursing Process: Assessment   **Client Need:** Health Promotion & Maintenance

33.   **The correct answer is c.** The question is asking what drug would be prescribed for a client who is experiencing symptoms of disseminated intravascular coagulopathy (DIC). Heparin sodium (Heparin) is the drug of choice with DIC. Heparin sodium (Heparin) is used to retard the coagulation process, taking place during DIC and permit normalization of clotting tests and a decrease in hemorrhage. Vitamin K (option a) is used to control moderate to severe bleeding caused by warfarin sodium (Coumadin). Menadiol sodium diphosphate (Synkavite) (option b) is used to prevent and/or treat hypoprothrombinemia, which is usually related to a vitamin K deficiency. The substance does not counteract the effects of heparin sodium (Heparin). Albumin is a volume expander and used to treat ascites in clients with liver dysfunction (option d).
Nursing Process: Analysis   **Client Need:** Physiological Integrity

34.   **The correct answer is b.** The question is asking what to do when a nephrostomy tube comes out of the client. Cover the site with a sterile dressing in order to protect the client from sources of infection during the time it takes to notify the physician (option a). While the tube will need to be replaced immediately in order to prevent hydronephrosis, this is not an independent nursing action (option c). While it would not be harmful to obtain the client's vital signs, there is no reason to expect a change (option d).
Nursing Process: Implementation   **Client Need:** Physiological Integrity

35.   **The correct answer is c.** The question is asking how to avoid contracting Lyme disease. Lyme disease is spread through the bite of affected ticks usually found in wooded areas. Biting can be avoided by covering the areas where ticks might bite. Wearing long pants and long sleeves helps. Long pants should be placed inside boots or socks so that ticks cannot gain access to the legs. The body, including the scalp, should be inspected for ticks and the whole tick removed if found. Also check pets that were outside. Antibiotics are given when Lyme disease is discovered (option a). Sunscreen will not prevent tick bites, but insect repellents with diethyltoluamide (DEET) will

(option b). Antibacterial soap will not prevent Lyme disease infection because the bite causes an internal introduction of the spirochete (option d), which shows itself both internally and externally.
Nursing Process: Implementation   **Client Need:** Health Promotion & Maintenance

36.   **The correct answer is d.** The question is asking how the nurse should respond to the client's request to wash after an alleged sexual assault. Washing may discard or change evidence. Even though the client prefers to wash now, physical evidence must be preserved for possible court trial (options a & c). Afterwards, the client should be given privacy and a place to wash. The client's clothes must be kept and are placed in a paper bag (option b).
Nursing Process: Implementation   **Client Need:** Physiological Integrity

37.   **The correct answer is c.** The question is asking what would be best to meet the developmental needs in a 5-week-old infant who just had a ventriculoperitoneal (VP) shunt. The VP shunt is used to treat hydrocephalus. Excessive CSF causes increased intracranial pressure (ICP). Measures to prevent further increased ICP should be implemented. Crying increases the ICP; therefore, the nurse should implement comfort measures to keep the child from crying. Keeping the infant heavily sedated, and lying in her crib at all times (options a & d) would not meet her developmental needs. A 5-week-old infant does not have the developmental ability to play with toys and they could injure the operative site if the infant would bump into them (option b).
Nursing Process: Implementation   **Client Need:** Health Promotion & Maintenance

38.   **The correct answer is a.** The question is asking what would be the best way to teach someone about how to prevent a sexually transmitted disease from recurring. Using as many senses as possible helps the client absorb the information more readily. Visual diagrams often help the client understand more of the verbal discussion. Giving the client a pamphlet to read and then asking questions (option d) does not show active participation in learning. The client may or may not read the pamphlet or feel comfortable asking questions if there has been no previous discussion with the nurse. There is no reason the nurse should not do the teaching in the care. The client does not need to be referred to the physician (option b). Asking about the tests for gonorrhea (option c) is inappropriate in this case since the teaching deals with prevention. The nurse should ask if the client knows about methods to prevent gonorrhea and other sexually transmitted diseases.
Nursing Process: Implementation   **Client Need:** Health Promotion & Maintenance

39.   **The correct answer is a.** The question is asking for the symptoms a client would exhibit if his chest tube disconnected. The client would become restless and complain of shortness of breath because air is collecting in the intrapleural space and creating pressure against the lung wall. Tachypnea and numbness (option b) are signs of anxiety-related chest pain. Dysphagia and gastric reflux (option c) are symptoms of gastroesophageal chest pain. Precordial friction rub and fever (option d) are signs of pericarditis.
Nursing Process: Assessment   **Client Need:** Safe, Effective Care Environment

40.   **The correct answer is d.** The question is asking why a proximal vagotomy is done for a client who has peptic ulcer disease. A proximal vagotomy cuts the nerve impulses that stimulate the parietal cells. The vagotomy also preserves the antrum's ability to function. Small meals would decrease food transit in the stomach (option a). A vagotomy is unrelated to regeneration of gastric mucosa (option b). Antibiotics would be prescribed to reduce Helicobacter pylori (option c).
Nursing Process: Implementation   **Client Need:** Physiological Integrity

41.   **The correct answer is c.** The question is asking the most essential nursing action while large amounts of fluid are being infused into a severely burned client. The nurse should evaluate urine output because the amount of fluid infused is determined by urine output. Urine specific gravity is also checked to determine renal status. Assessing vital signs and auscultating lungs (options a & b) are also important, but are later signs of fluid problems. The most important sign is urine output. Level of consciousness (option d) would be unrelated to fluid infusion.
Nursing Process: Implementation   **Client Need:** Physiological Integrity

42. **The correct answer is d.** The question is asking why cerebral palsy was not detected earlier. In early stages, it is difficult to judge the severity of cerebral palsy. An infant does not usually develop cortical control of movement until the second six months of life. Cerebral palsy does not start at a specific time or with a change in lesions (options a & c). Parents are generally notified of their child's health care conditions immediately upon confirmation (option b).
Nursing Process: Implementation   **Client Need:** Physiological Integrity

43. **The correct answer is b.** The question is asking which factor was not related to peptic ulcer disease. Thiazide diuretics are generally absorbed rapidly from the gastrointestinal tract and without irritation. Caffeine and alcohol stimulate acid production (options a & c) and aspirin suppresses mucous secretion and causes mucosal damage (option d).
Nursing Process: Analysis   **Client Need:** Physiological Integrity

44. **The correct answer is a.** The question is asking which information would be most important for the nurse to know. A client with a ruptured cerebral aneurysm is at risk for rebleeding. The nurse's priority is to prevent constipation and straining. Use of the Valsalva maneuver can increase intracranial pressure and cause rebleeding. Photophobia, blood in the CSF and headache are expected findings in a client who had a ruptured cerebral aneurysm (options b, c & d).
Nursing Process: Analysis   **Client Need:** Physiological Integrity

45. **The correct answer is c.** The question is asking for the initial drug treatment of tuberculosis. Isoniazid (INH) is the primary choice of therapy for the tubercle bacillus. Cycloserine (Seramycin) and ethionamide (Treactor-SC) are second line drugs used in the treatment of tuberculosis (options b & d). Nystatin (Mycostatin) is an antifungal agent used for topical therapy (option a).
Nursing Process: Planning   **Client Need:** Physiological Integrity

46. **The correct answer is 60.** The question is asking how many drops per minute the intravenous infusion should be regulated. When the drop factor is 60-drops/ml then ml/hr equal drops/minute.

$$\frac{60gtts}{ml} \times \frac{60ml}{hr} \times \frac{1hr}{60min} = \frac{60gtts}{min}$$

Nursing Process: Planning   **Client Need:** Safe, Effective Care Environment

47. **The correct answer is c.** The question is asking what can best meet the developmental needs of a 5-month-old infant with rumination. Rumination occurs when infants voluntarily return swallowed food into the mouth. The primary cause of this problem is a lack of attachment between the infant and the parent. It is necessary to maintain a face-to-face posture with the child. Eye contact helps develop the trust necessary for attachment. Bottle propping is discouraged because it can lead to aspiration, attachment difficulties, middle ear infections and dental caries (option b). For the 5-month-old infant, active experimentation with objects serves the important cognitive work of play. Although a musical mobile (option a) provides visual and auditory stimulation, the baby will be distracted from eating. Weight should be monitored, but it is more important to teach the parent how to feed the child so weight is gained, not lost (option d).
Nursing Process: Implementation   **Client Need:** Health Promotion & Maintenance

48. **The correct answer is a.** The question is asking what contraceptive method has the most risk of preventing future pregnancies. An intrauterine device (IUD) is the only contraceptive method listed that may cause infertility. This infertility is due to pelvic inflammatory disease (PID). If the client would like to delay childbearing, the other methods do not alter chances of fertility (options b, c & d).
Nursing Process: Planning   **Client Need:** Health Promotion & Maintenance

49. **The correct answer is c.** The question is asking which is a correct statement for a client post-herniorrhaphy. The client should be instructed to report any drainage from the incision to the physician. Straining and lifting are usually restricted for two weeks (option a). Normal activities are not resumed for some time (option a). The client should be instructed to report pain or

difficulty with urination (option b). The client should be taught to splint the incision for sneezing and coughing (option d).
Nursing Process: Evaluation   **Client Need:** Health Promotion & Maintenance

50.   **The correct answer is b.** The question is asking what the discharge criteria are for a paranoid (suspicious) client. Communicating in a clear manner when relating to others is correct because disrupted relationships are a major problem with the paranoid client. Relating to others when rewarded (option a) is usually a manipulation of the relationship. It is also unlikely that a person will always be rewarded for relating to others and, therefore, is an unrealistic goal. Often the problem is not speaking to others (option c) but clarity of the message. Just because someone does not report paranoid ideation (option d) does not mean they are delusion free.
Nursing Process: Analysis   **Client Need:** Psychosocial Integrity

51.   **The correct answer is d.** The question is asking how to respond to the client's comments of wishing to be dead. The highest priority nursing activity with the self-destructive person is to protect him from inflicting further harm on himself and this message is conveyed verbally and nonverbally. Option (a) is incorrect because it is not the least restrictive. Clients may need to be watched, but seclusion is unwarranted. Option (b) is incorrect because, by ignoring the client, the nurse demonstrates lack of caring. In option (c) the nurse is reinforcing that what the client says is not important, therefore, decreasing self-esteem.
Nursing Process: Implementation   **Client Need:** Safe, Effective Care Environment

52.   **The correct answers are a, d, e and f.** The question is asking what care is necessary for a client with tuberculosis. HEPA-filtered respirators are required for anyone who comes into contact with a client who has tuberculosis. These devices are able to filter bacteria, that is less than 1micron in size (option a). Clients with tuberculosis should wear masks over their face and nose any time they leave the room and unit. This will decrease the risk of infecting visitors and other personnel (option d). Covering a cough with tissues also minimizes the spread of the disease (option e). A negative airflow room prevents air from escaping into the hallway where others can be infected (option f). It is not necessary to wear gloves to take vital signs because the disease is spread by droplets, not contact (option b). Disposable eating utensils are not needed, as inanimate objects do not spread the disease (option c).
Nursing Process: Planning   **Client Need:** Safe, Effective Care Environment

53.   **The correct answer is c.** The question is asking what action the nurse should take if a postpartal woman's uterus is displaced to the left. The most common cause for a deviated uterus is a full bladder. The other options (a, b & d) would be valid if the client had an empty bladder.
Nursing Process: Implementation   **Client Need:** Health Promotion & Maintenance

54.   **The correct answer is b.** The question is asking which option is wrong when performing a wet-to-dry dressing. Plastic cling wrap would be used for an occlusive dressing, not a wet-to-dry dressing. The dressing should be wrung tightly prior to application (option a) so that extra fluid does not escape from the dressing onto other areas of the skin. The dressing should not be moistened if it has become dry (option c) to allow removal of necrotic tissue. This prevents further damage to the wound. Wet-to-dry dressings are considered sterile dressings; therefore, sterile gloves would be used to apply them (option d).
Nursing Process: Evaluation   **Client Need:** Physiological Integrity

55.   **The correct answer is c.** The question is asking the most important nursing diagnosis for a toddler who has vomited six times in four hours. Children dehydrate easily because a higher percentage of their body is water. Vomiting is serious and the child should be monitored closely for signs of dehydration and electrolyte imbalance. Altered nutrition (option b) is also important but will not result in problems as quickly. Altered home health maintenance (option a) can be rectified through teaching after the child is determined to be out of danger. Altered comfort (option d) can be true but is not as dangerous as fluid and electrolyte imbalance.
Nursing Process: Analysis   **Client Need:** Physiological Integrity

56. **The correct answer is b.** The question is asking where to assess a dark skinned client for cyanosis. The best places are areas of lighter color in the client, such as nail beds, soles, palms and conjunctiva. Skin temperature (option a) may show areas of erythema. Gluteal folds (option c) and the inner aspect of forearm (option d) will show petechiae.
Nursing Process: Assessment   **Client Need:** Physiological Integrity

57. **The correct answer is c.** The question is asking what also needs to be assessed about a client diagnosed with cholera. Cholera is a waterborne disease. Contaminated food and water could be contributing to the problem. Cholera should especially be suspected in clients who experience bouts of diarrhea after eating shellfish obtained from the Gulf of Mexico. Farming practices (option a) deal with soil borne diseases such as parasites. Cholera is not a sexually transmitted disease (option b). Flying in a crowded airplane may put the client at risk of developing an airborne disease, not cholera (option d).
Nursing Process: Assessment   **Client Need:** Safe, Effective Care Environment

58. **The correct answer is b.** The question is asking which teaching is correct about a venography. The radiographic dye will be injected into a dorsal foot vein, which will enter the venous system. A diagnosis of thrombosis is made when a segment of a vein becomes unfilled with radiographic dye. There is no arterial site for a venography (option a). The procedure is looking for venous occlusion not arterial occlusion (option c). The client does not have to be NPO since the test does not relate to the abdomen or to receiving anesthesia (option d).
Nursing Process: Implementation   **Client Need:** Physiological Integrity

59. **The correct answer is d.** The question is asking for an essential nursing diagnosis for a client with Cushing's syndrome. The increased steroid production suppresses the inflammatory response and, therefore, the body's ability to fight infection. Clients will contract illness easier and heal more slowly because of the body's inability to use its normal disease fighting mechanisms. Although the other nursing diagnoses are valid (options a, b & d), the most critical is risk for infection because the client could die as a result.
Nursing Process: Analysis   **Client Need:** Physiological Integrity

60. **The correct answer is d.** The question is asking for the dynamics underlying the client's statement. Clients with obsessive-compulsive disorder often understand that their behavior seems ridiculous to others. This embarrasses clients. If the nurse responds with empathy and rewards insight, the client will learn acceptance and the anxiety level will be decreased. Otherwise, the anxiety will increase along with ritualistic behavior. Obsessive thinking (option c) is not present in the client's statement. Actually, the client's statement may represent resistant thinking, which occurs when the person tries to stop recurring thoughts or compulsive behavior. Problem-solving (option b) is not evident, since she is not relating the action to anxiety or proposing alternative actions. Manipulation (option a) is not occurring since there is nothing to be gained or lost by the statement.
Nursing Process: Implementation   **Client Need:** Psychosocial Integrity

61. **The correct answer is c.** The question is asking what role a nurse should take in an abusive situation. Offering information is the most appropriate action a nurse can take. This will help the victim of abuse decrease feelings of powerlessness and promote individual safety. There is not enough evidence to warrant an overnight admission (option a). There is no evidence that the abusing spouse would be interested in couples counseling at this time. It is more important to provide for the safety of the victim (option b). Suggesting that the client leave her spouse is instilling the nurse's values on her (option d).
Nursing Process: Implementation   **Client Need:** Psychosocial Integrity

62. **The correct answer is d.** The question is asking how to respond to a client who is upset about the possibility of being homosexual. An important step in counseling this client is aiding him to identify and examine personal feelings and values about what homosexuality means. Encouraging the client to read factual information about homosexuality is also appropriate but would be

suggested after the client identifies feelings and values (option c). Options (a) and (b) do not encourage the client's expression of feelings and do not address the client's statement specifically.
Nursing Process: Implementation   **Client Need:** Health Promotion & Maintenance

63. **The correct answer is d.** The question is asking how to avoid lung cancer through diet. An increased dietary intake of vitamin A reduces the risk of esophageal, laryngeal and lung cancers although caution must be advised. Megadoses of vitamin A can cause toxicity because it is a fat-soluble vitamin and not as easily excreted from the body. A high-fiber diet (option b) and increased vitamin C (option a) may reduce the risk of developing certain cancers. High-protein diets have not been found to increase the incidence of lung cancer (option c).
Nursing Process: Implementation   **Client Need:** Health Promotion & Maintenance

64. **The correct answer is d.** The question is asking how to intervene with the client's anxiety. Talking with the client about her expectations will demonstrate the willingness of the nurse to stay with the client and support her during the labor experience. The client's anxiety will be decreased, labor will be facilitated and the client will be better able to participate in decisions concerning her children. Social service (option a) intervention is not necessary at this time because the nurse can more easily provide ongoing support in this situation. Giving privacy (option b) would not apply in this situation because it would deny needed support to the client and family and does not address the fears of the client. Bringing the children into the labor room (option c) may be distracting for the client and frightening for children of this age.
Nursing Process: Implementation   **Client Need:** Psychosocial Integrity

65. **The correct answer is a.** The question is asking what to do when a client complains of abdominal pain and rectal bleeding is evident following a colonoscopy. These are signs of bowel perforation. Another accompanying sign might be abdominal distention. Asking the client to stay in bed and obtaining vital signs would also be done, but the physician must be notified immediately as this is an emergency (options b & c). Administering an analgesic would mask symptoms and delay treatment, which places the client in danger (option d).
Nursing Process: Implementation   **Client Need:** Physiological Integrity

66. **The correct answer is b.** The question is asking which measure is appropriate for a client with PMS. Exercise increases the release of endorphins from the brain, thus, decreasing pain and elevating mood. Diuretics are given, not avoided, to relieve fluid retention (option a). Caffeine stimulates the autonomic nervous system, increasing symptoms (option c). Prostaglandin inhibitors, such as ibuprofen (Advil), are given for analgesia and to relieve symptoms. Acetaminophen (Tylenol) has a very weak prostaglandin effect (option d).
Nursing Process: Implementation   **Client Need:** Physiological Integrity

67. **The correct answer is c.** The question is asking how to plan care for a paranoid client. This client lacks trust. His anxiety will increase with more interpersonal contacts (option d), so he must be placed into group activities at a rate that he can handle dealing with the others in the group. The client should have a routine schedule, but it should be individualized to meet his needs (option a). A routine assists the client to predict what his world will be and learn to trust others through consistency. A flexible schedule (option b) does not provide sufficient structure to learn trust.
Nursing Process: Planning   **Client Need:** Psychosocial Integrity

68. **The correct answer is c.** The question is asking what is most important to teach about safer sex to a group of adolescents. The use of latex condoms helps to prevent the spread of sexually transmitted diseases. Natural membrane or skin condoms are not as effective as latex condoms. A woman can increase her own protection by carrying her own condoms. HIV antibodies can take up to 14 months to develop; therefore, a negative HIV test does not necessarily indicate the person has not been infected (option a). Anal intercourse creates the most dangerous potential for infection with AIDS. However, the AIDS virus is found in semen and can be passed to the woman through the vagina during vaginal intercourse or the mouth during oral sex (option b). Water soluble, not petroleum, lubricants should be used to prevent skin tears (option d).
Nursing Process: Evaluation   **Client Need:** Health Promotion & Maintenance

69. **The correct answer is d.** The question is asking how to meet the nutritional needs of an infant prior to surgery for a cleft lip and palate. Before surgery, the infant would still be able to suck and swallow in whatever way she can. This will help enhance development of the muscles used for sucking, swallowing, and speech while, at the same time, help to comfort her. Keeping the infant in a near horizontal position (option a) during feeding would be dangerous because she could choke. Nasogastric tube or gastric tube feedings are not necessary (options b & c).
Nursing Process: Planning   **Client Need:** Physiological Integrity

70. **The correct answer is d.** The question is asking which client would have the highest risk for peripheral vascular disease. The client has two risk factors, which are diabetes and hypertension, even though the hypertension is being controlled through medication. All of the other options (a, b & c) have a single factor being addressed by the individual towards positive health.
Nursing Process: Analysis   **Client Need:** Health Promotion & Maintenance

71. **The correct answer is d.** The question is asking which of the following is most effective in reducing factors that contribute to stress incontinence. Using stool softeners helps to prevent constipation, a major contributing factor to stress incontinence. Clients must maintain a normal fluid intake at 1.5 to 2 Liters per day. Decreasing fluids more than this can cause infections or other problems (option a). Dietary fiber should be increased, not decreased, to prevent constipation (option b). Lack of exercise contributes to constipation and may contribute to heart disease. Clients with stress incontinence should continue to exercise (option c).
Nursing Process: Implementation   **Client Need:** Physiological Integrity

72. **The correct answer is d.** The question is asking how insulin, diet and exercise work together in managing Type 1 diabetes. Normally, glucose will not move into skeletal and muscle cells without insulin. During exercise, glucose does not require insulin to move into cells, so increased glucose is needed for utilization by the insulin present in the system or the insulin dosage prior to exercise must be reduced. Changes should be made only when decreasing dietary intake, increasing exercise activity and increasing insulin will contribute to hypoglycemia (options a & c). Increasing dietary intake and insulin with less exercise will contribute to weight gain (option b).
Nursing Process: Planning   **Client Need:** Physiological Integrity

73. **The correct answer is b.** The question is asking for a sign of concealed (hidden) abruptio placenta. Remember that this is a separation of the placenta from the uterine wall. Bleeding occurs at the separation site. As severity increases, tetanic persistent uterine contractions develop. Uterine tonicity usually increases and the uterus often fails to relax between contractions (options a & c). Uterine atony may occur postpartum (option d).
Nursing Process: Assessment   **Client Need:** Physiological Integrity

74. **The correct answer is c.** The question is asking what parents need to know about a newly diagnosed child diabetic. The diet and insulin regimen will be planned according to the child's normal activities and lifestyle. While the parents need guidance in nutritional planning, the requirements of the diabetic diet are not strict and can be worked into the family's lifestyle (option a). The child should not have to restrict any activities. Hypoglycemia can be prevented through regulation of diet and insulin therapy while maintaining his usual activity schedule (option b). With proper monitoring and control, the child should not experience repeated hospitalization (option d).
Nursing Process: Planning   **Client Need:** Health Promotion & Maintenance

75. **The correct answer is d.** The question is asking which statement would be related to giving sumatriptan (Imitrex). This medicine can cause vasospasm and may increase blood pressure in clients with a history of heart disease or hypertension, so the client should be screened for these problems. General symptoms of migraine include an aura (option a), photophobia (option b) and vomiting (option c). Photophobia and vomiting are usually relieved by the sumatriptan (Imitrex).
Nursing Process: Assessment   **Client Need:** Physiological Integrity

PRACTICE SESSION: 19

> **Instructions:** Allow yourself 90 minutes to complete the following 90 practice questions. Use a timer to notify yourself when 90 minutes are over so that you are not constantly looking at your watch while completing the questions.

1. A client is diagnosed with a 1cm keratotic basal cell carcinoma near the preauricular groove. What information should be included in the health teaching for this client?
   a. It is unlikely that this tumor will metastasize.
   b. This type of tumor is best treated with surgical excision followed by radiation.
   c. The tumor can be removed in the surgeon's office.
   d. The client should not go outside unless the ear is completely covered.

2. A client in labor for eight hours is noted to have a blood pressure of 90/60, pulse 100, respirations 26. Oxytocin (Pitocin) has been infusing for the last hour. There is a small amount of external vaginal bleeding. The fetal heart rate is 180. The nurse should:
   a. stay with the client.
   b. leave to alert the physician.
   c. increase the infusing oxytocin (Pitocin).
   d. recheck the vital signs in half an hour.

3. The nursing staff is notified that a client with viral meningitis is about to be admitted. What would the nurse plan to do? Select all that apply.
   a. Place the client in respiratory isolation.
   b. Elevate the head of bed 45 degrees.
   c. Notify the pharmacy so that antibiotics can be given upon arrival.
   d. Dim the lights in the room.
   e. Observe and notify the physician of a petechial rash.
   f. Determine who has had contact with the client during the last 48 hours.

4. A hospitalized Native American client asks the Native Healer to hold a healing ceremony in the hospital room. The nurse should:
   a. suggest the healing ceremony be held after discharge.
   b. tell the client to ask permission from the physician.
   c. provide privacy and allow the ceremony to be held.
   d. ask that no herbs be in the client's room.

5. The nurse is conducting an in-service on low back pain. An appropriate prevention strategy would be:
   a. placing feet flat on the floor when standing.
   b. twisting while lifting to distribute the pressure.
   c. using a pillow for lumbar support.
   d. lifting objects away from the body.

6. The nurse has been relating to an autistic 4-year-old boy on a limited basis. He has adjusted to a daily schedule and the nurse plans to introduce a new activity to him. How would the nurse expect him to react?
   a. No different than his usual behavior.
   b. Indifferent to the new activity.
   c. Negative and self-destructive.
   d. Positive and accepting.

7. A client scheduled for a right inguinal herniorrhaphy in the morning asks the nurse why he cannot have anything to drink after midnight. The nurse bases her response on the knowledge that:
   a. ingestion of water will cause the bladder to fill during surgery and increase pressure on the hernia.
   b. the goal of withholding food and fluids is to prevent aspiration.
   c. withholding food and fluids preoperatively will prevent nausea and vomiting.
   d. the herniated intestine must be as empty as possible to prevent strangulation.

8. A client, diagnosed with Alzheimer's disease says to the nurse, "I am the president of the largest car manufacturing company in the world." The nurse's most therapeutic response would be:
   a. "You are not the president of a car manufacturing company; you are in a nursing home."
   b. "As president of a large company, you must be very busy."
   c. "Tell me about your visit with your son this morning."
   d. "Believing that you are the president makes you feel very powerful."

9. A home health nurse has four clients on morning rounds. Which client should be seen first?
   a. Post-myocardial infarction client with infrequent PVCs.
   b. Deaf client with an above the knee amputation.
   c. Type 1 diabetic client needing fasting blood work.
   d. Post-hip fracture client complaining of pain.

10. A client is being treated at the clinic for a repetitive stress injury from the computer keyboard. Ligament and tendon damage would be most likely diagnosed through:
    a. visual inspection.
    b. client complaints.
    c. X-rays.
    d. magnetic resonance imagery.

11. A reluctant client with borderline personality disorder tells the nurse that she cannot remember feeling anything but emptiness inside. "I feel so alone, I don't know if I can stand it." The nurse would initially respond to these remarks by stating:
    a. "It sounds as if you are feeling hopeless."
    b. "Are you thinking about harming yourself?"
    c. "You feel sad now, but this is all part of your illness."
    d. "You would feel better if you would participate more in unit activities."

12. A 9-year-old child is climbing a tree in a neighbor's yard when he misses a branch and falls from the tree. The neighbor calls and asks you to check the child. The nurse suspects a possible fractured collarbone. The best action of the nurse would be to:
    a. place the arm in a sling and tell the parent to take the child to the emergency department.
    b. place an ice pack on the shoulder and give the child acetaminophen (Tylenol) for pain.
    c. allow the child to remain lying on the ground and call an ambulance.
    d. cover the child with a blanket and ask the mother to call the physician.

13. A football player is seen in the emergency department for complaints of shortness of breath following a very hard tackle to the chest. A rib fracture is diagnosed. He is to be treated at home. What would be included in his discharge teaching?
    a. Tape the chest to promote splinting of the fracture.
    b. Practice deep breathing but avoid coughing.
    c. Sleep in a high Fowler's position.
    d. Take prescribed analgesics for even mild pain.

14. A client with chronic pain tells the nurse, "I can't take the pain any more. What can I do? I've heard that acupuncture has helped people like me." What is the nurse's best response?
   a. "I don't think the doctor would like it if you tried something like that."
   b. "It may interfere with your current treatment."
   c. "Many people have reported pain relief when it is done by someone who is specially trained."
   d. "As long as you are not afraid of needles, I think it is always wise to try new things that might help you."

15. A female nursing student is giving a male client a bath. During the bath, the client grabs the student's arm and says, "You know, we could have a really good time if you would hop in here with me." The student gets flushed and leaves the room. She tells the nurse what happened. The most appropriate response by the nurse would be:
   a. "Let's talk about why you are so uncomfortable with this."
   b. "I've always found it best just to ignore it; you'll eventually get used to it."
   c. "I'll ask the charge nurse to change your assignment."
   d. "Let's talk about how you could handle this better next time."

16. A college student is brought to the emergency department after being found unconscious outside of his apartment building. The client is difficult to arouse, has slurred speech and alcohol on the breath. Blood alcohol level is 0.6 and the client is diagnosed with alcohol poisoning. A goal to prevent further recurrence would be that the client would:
   a. state the relationship of alcohol to the hospital admission.
   b. attend a meeting of Alcoholics Anonymous within one week.
   c. list five symptoms of alcohol poisoning.
   d. refrain from drinking alcohol when attending parties.

17. A nurse at a pediatric clinic returns from lunch and needs to return phone calls. Place the options in the order in which the families should be called.
   a. A 14-year-old girl that has missed two periods and is afraid she might be pregnant.
   b. A 4-year-old child, who has a ventriculoperitoneal shunt with a slight fever, is alert and complaining of a headache.
   c. A 6-year-old child, who has worsening abdominal pain since this morning, is nauseated and has a fever.
   d. An 8-year-old child who has developed a generalized pruritic vesicular rash on his torso and has a temperature of 103°F.

18. The nurse manager questions which of the charge nurse's assignments for a nurse aide.
   a. An 80-year-old female client who was just admitted and requires assistance with bathing.
   b. A 19-year-old post-surgical client with Von Willebrand's disease and needs frequent vital signs.
   c. A 78-year-old male client who has difficulty transferring from bed to chair.
   d. A 54-year-old client with a spinal cord injury and needs assistance with eating.

19. The nurse understands that a client who experiences a decrease in blood pressure and an increase in pulse in the immediate postoperative period most likely indicates:
   a. hypovolemic shock.
   b. acute infection.
   c. early shock syndrome.
   d. vasogenic shock.

20. The nurse is interviewing a family regarding their daily eating patterns. She assesses that the family members are vegetarians. The nurse would place this under which assessment category?
   a. Roles.
   b. Social support.
   c. Culture.
   d. Family stress.

21. A woman calls the home health nurse stating that her husband was just released from the hospital earlier that day. The husband now has a rash on the trunk of his body, itching and slightly elevated temperature. The nurse ascertains the medications prescribed for the client. The nurse should:

    a. suggest the rash is probably due to hospital linen.
    b. ask the physician to prescribe some diphenhydramine (Benadryl).
    c. suggest that the woman bring her husband to the emergency department.
    d. ask when each of the medications was started.

22. At an organized summer camp, a parent comes to the health station and complains of a bee sting. The area on the arm is rapidly swelling. As prescribed, the nurse administers topical steroid and an ice pack and asks the parent to stay at the station. Pulse and respirations are normal. Fifteen minutes later, the parent states some relief but says that the arm "feels weak." The nurse should:

    a. take off the ice pack to increase circulation.
    b. allow the parent to rejoin the group.
    c. continue to monitor the parent at the station.
    d. call the physician for additional prescriptions.

23. Which statement indicates a need for further teaching from a diabetic client receiving hemodialysis?

    a. "During dialysis, it is common for my blood pressure to go up and I'm worried because I have hypertension."
    b. "I should always weigh myself before I start the dialysis."
    c. "Even though I am on dialysis, I need to monitor my blood sugars in order to keep my diabetes under control."
    d. "I tend to feel somewhat nauseated at times, but find that I feel better if I eat smaller, frequent meals."

24. A primigravida client is diagnosed with placenta previa. The client asks the nurse to explain the condition. The nurse's best response would be:

    a. "Normally the baby is positioned near the cervix; your placenta is positioned near or on the cervical opening."
    b. "Your placenta is producing too many hormones and is causing vaginal bleeding."
    c. "Normally the entire placenta is attached to the uterine wall; part of the placenta has pulled away from this wall."
    d. "Normally your placenta is attached at or near the cervix; your placenta is attached at the fundus."

25. An 18-month-old child has just been diagnosed with Hirschprung's disease. The child's parents ask the nurse what Hirschprung's disease is. The nurse explains that the disease is:

    a. stool, which is hard and passed with difficulty.
    b. an abdominal herniation through the diaphragm.
    c. an absence of nerve impulses to the bowel muscle.
    d. an intestinal protrusion through the umbilical ring.

26. A client is admitted with dyspnea, diaphoresis, rash and fever. The client should be placed with which roommate? A client with:

    a. kidney stones.
    b. pneumonia.
    c. Cushing's disease.
    d. peritoneal dialysis.

27. A child comes to the school nurse's office and says, "There's something in my left eye." The nurse notes that a foreign object appears to be imbedded in the eye. The eye is also bleeding from trauma. The nurse plans to:
   a. immobilize the head and call the parents.
   b. irrigate the eye with normal saline.
   c. place pressure to stop the bleeding.
   d. anesthetize the eye then irrigate.

28. An intensive care unit nurse is pulled to a medical-surgical floor. The best assignment would be:
   a. A man who had a myocardial infarction yesterday and a woman who had a cardiac catheterization this morning.
   b. A woman in sickle cell crisis, a woman with tuberculosis and a man who just had an appendectomy.
   c. A woman with urolithiasis, a man with Addison's disease, a woman with pneumonia and a man with cellulitis.
   d. A woman recovering from a total hip replacement, a man with a methicillan resistant staphylococcus aureus (MRSA) infected decubitus ulcer and a woman with pelvic inflammatory disease.

29. The home care nurse visits a client who recently gave birth. The client has a history of cocaine abuse and the infant was diagnosed with cocaine withdrawal. The client says, "This baby is so fussy. I can't stand this crying. Why does she cry like this?" The nurse's best response would be:
   a. "This is just her temperament. I can show you ways to comfort her."
   b. "She is experiencing withdrawal. This is not uncommon when the mother has used drugs such as cocaine."
   c. "This should show you the effects of your drug use on your baby."
   d. "We should probably have her examined by the pediatrician to make sure she is okay."

30. A client who has been in contact isolation for two days has become increasingly irritable and is often tearful. The nurse should:
   a. obtain a physician's prescription for a sedative.
   b. encourage the client to telephone some friends.
   c. provide time to visit with the client more frequently.
   d. allow the client more privacy to vent feelings.

31. The nurse is assisting with a community blood bank collection. The proper procedure for collecting blood for hematocrit would be:
   a. placing the hand in an upright position when collecting the specimen.
   b. after puncturing the site, wipe it with 70% alcohol.
   c. fill the capillary tube with blood.
   d. place pressure on the puncture site using gauze.

32. The nurse enters the day room and hears a client loudly accuse another client of conspiring to help the CIA put a transmitter in her head. The best action of the nurse is to:
   a. attempt to assure the client this is not true.
   b. ignore the conversation and approach the client later.
   c. invite the client to take a walk with the nurse.
   d. inform the client that this behavior will not be tolerated.

33. What would be included in the plan of care for a client who was diagnosed with amyotrophic lateral sclerosis (ALS) three years ago?
   a. Increased monitoring for mental deterioration.
   b. Meticulous skin care due to increased incontinence.
   c. Effective use of narcotic analgesics for management of muscle spasticity.
   d. Teach the client how to use eye movements to signal for different needs.

34. After one week of taking an antidepressant, a client talks to the nurse about discontinuing the medication because he does not feel any better. The nurse's response should be based on what information?
    a. The client should be evaluated for a different medication.
    b. Antidepressant medication may take two to three weeks to have therapeutic effects.
    c. Negative thinking is preventing therapeutic effects of the medication.
    d. The client may not be taking his medication and should be watched.

35. A client with a hip fracture develops a fat embolism. The goal of treatment is to:
    a. promote oxygenation.
    b. prevent infection.
    c. maintain fracture union.
    d. prevent deformity.

36. The nurse notifies the physician when a client who is in the diuretic phase of acute renal failure develops fatigue, abdominal cramping and confusion. The nurse called the physician because she is concerned that the client is experiencing:
    a. hyponatremia.
    b. hyperkalemia.
    c. hypocalcemia.
    d. acidosis.

37. A client is admitted with cirrhosis of the liver secondary to alcohol abuse. The client is noted to be anemic. Anemia is probably related to:
    a. endocrine imbalance.
    b. splenomegaly.
    c. poor vitamin synthesis.
    d. decreased bilirubin metabolism.

38. A client with bladder cancer has had an ileal conduit performed. What best indicates that she is able to care for the stoma? She:
    a. discusses the steps involved in care of the appliance.
    b. demonstrates the proper method to change the bag.
    c. verbalizes pertinent complications of the procedure.
    d. relates the importance of hand washing in care of the stoma.

39. The best measure of quality of care is:
    a. client satisfaction.
    b. employee satisfaction.
    c. documentation.
    d. employee evaluations.

40. A client in cardiogenic shock is placed on counterpulsation with an intra-aortic balloon pump. The purpose of this is to:
    a. assist with rhythm defects.
    b. decrease plaque buildup.
    c. increase oxygen use.
    d. improve cardiac output.

41. A client is brought to the emergency department after a drive-by shooting. The nurse would expect what to be prescribed to confirm bladder trauma?
    a. Blood urea nitrogen.
    b. Computed tomography.
    c. Urine specific gravity.
    d. White blood cell count.

42. A woman has just found out that her mother was diagnosed with gonorrhea. She is shocked to find out it is only transmitted sexually. She says to the nurse, "How could this happen, my mother is 73." What would be the best reply by the nurse?
   a. "Yes, I know what you mean, I was surprised too."
   b. "You're concerned that your mother is sexually active?"
   c. "Older people are also sexually active."
   d. "How do you think your mother got this disease?"

43. The lab reports that a client in acute renal failure has a serum phosphate of 6.0mg/dL. The nurse assesses the client, who reports a tingling sensation around his mouth. He demonstrates a positive Trousseau's sign. What should the nurse do next?
   a. Call the physician and request a prescription for potassium phosphate (Neutraphos).
   b. Give the client a p.r.n. dose of calcium carbonate (TUMS).
   c. Encourage the client to increase the amount of dairy products he eats.
   d. Place the client on seizure precautions.

44. What risk factors contribute to the development of osteoporosis? Select all that apply.
   a. High caffeine intake.
   b. Regular weight-bearing exercise.
   c. Smoking.
   d. Hereditary predisposition.
   e. Sedentary lifestyle.
   f. High-calcium diet.

45. What principle should the community health nurse use when screening the population for a specific disease?
   a. Clients ask for information.
   b. Public officials ask for it.
   c. Special interest groups lobby for it.
   d. How much it affects the public.

46. At a college football game, a player is injured. The nurse would look for what signs that denote spinal cord injury?
   a. Stated feelings of weakness of both arms.
   b. Complaints of pain in the right arm and shoulder.
   c. Saying, "I got the wind knocked out of me."
   d. Asking for something for pain in the knee.

47. A person who is human immunodeficiency virus (HIV) positive asks about getting a cat for company. The nurse would suggest:
   a. getting a fish tank instead.
   b. having a cat, but asking someone else to feed it.
   c. training the cat to relieve itself outside.
   d. washing hands after cleaning the litter box.

48. The nurse receives daily lab reports. Which client requires immediate attention? A client:
   a. with a DVT, receiving heparin therapy, who has a PT of 14 seconds and a PTT of 60 seconds.
   b. who had a thyroidectomy and a serum calcium level of 8.5mg/dL and a potassium of 4.
   c. who had a renal biopsy and hemoglobin of 10g/dL and a hematocrit of 32%.
   d. admitted with leukemia and has a WBC of 14,000 and a platelet count of 100,000.

49. After returning from lunch who would the nurse call back first?
   a. A 52-year-old with atrial fibrillation who was cardioverted two days ago and is having trouble seeing out of his left eye.
   b. A 60-year-old with COPD who has a large amount of thick green sputum.
   c. A 39-year-old who is being treated for tuberculosis and reports that his urine has suddenly turned red.
   d. A 66-year-old who has developed a painful vesicular rash on the right side of his chest.

50. A client with newly diagnosed glaucoma is placed on pilocarpine (Ocusert) eye drops. The purpose of the drops is to decrease intraocular pressure by:
   a. decreasing inflammation.
   b. constricting pupils.
   c. decreasing aqueous humor.
   d. dilating tear ducts.

51. The nurse is monitoring a client's peritoneal dialysis exchanges. After the first several exchanges, the nurse notes the fluid return is clear and pale yellow. The nurse should:
   a. assess the client's vital signs.
   b. obtain a fluid sample for culture.
   c. stop the exchange and notify the physician.
   d. document the occurrence as a normal finding.

52. A client is resting five days after cardiac surgery for mitral valve replacement. The client is being monitored for complete heart block. The nurse should be alert for signs and symptoms including:
   a. hypertension and syncope.
   b. skipped beats and fever.
   c. ventricular standstill.
   d. fatigue and hypotension.

53. A client with breast cancer is being treated with tamoxifen (Novaldex). The client complains of bone pain in the area of the lesion. The nurse evaluates this as:
   a. an adverse reaction needing immediate attention.
   b. pain related to the original cancer.
   c. pain related to cancer metastasis.
   d. an adverse reaction showing the medicine is working.

54. A nursing student has been assigned to care for a 34-year-old man in the terminal stage of Huntington's disease. He is visiting with his wife and children. While reviewing the client's care with the nurse preceptor, the student says, "I don't understand why he decided to have children when we know that this is a genetic disorder." What is the preceptor's best response?
   a. "Try not to be so judgmental; he may not have known that he could pass on the gene."
   b. "Although Huntington's disease is hereditary, it is very rarely passed to the next generation."
   c. "Most people are not diagnosed until they are 30-years-old and have already had children."
   d. "It is unlikely that his children will get the disease since both parents must be carriers."

55. The nurse has been working with a 58-year-old man who has Alzheimer's disease. The man's wife tells the nurse, "I just don't know how I'm going to manage everything. How will I know what to do?" The nurse's response would be to:
   a. tell her about the support group for families of clients with Alzheimer's disease.
   b. suggest she hospitalize her husband until she feels more organized.
   c. refer her to a psychologist for crisis counseling.
   d. suggest that she consider a residential care facility.

56. A 47-year-old woman fell while washing second story windows. Although no serious injuries are evident, the woman fell into the bushes and has multiple scratches. She has had no immunizations or treatments since childhood. She is not allergic to any medications or substances. The nurse would expect which prescription from the physician?
   a. Prophylactic antibiotics.
   b. Pneumococcal vaccine.
   c. Tetanus vaccine.
   d. Steroid cream.

57. A client with primary hypertension is prescribed propanalol (Inderal). The nurse should teach the client to be alert for which side effects?
   a. Nausea, constipation, tachycardia.
   b. Nausea, blurred vision, bradycardia.
   c. Sexual impotence, bradycardia, hypokalemia.
   d. Sexual impotence, diarrhea, tachycardia.

58. The nurse is unable to auscultate the blood pressure of a client in shock. The initial action by the nurse at this time would be to:
   a. immediately inform the physician.
   b. attempt to palpate a blood pressure.
   c. initiate chest compressions.
   d. tilt the head back and thrust the jaw forward.

59. Who should the nurse care for first? A client:
   a. with an abdominal aortic aneurysm that reports that the mass is pulsating.
   b. who just returned from a bronchoscopy and does not have a gag reflex.
   c. who had a thyroidectomy and has a temperature of 38.5°C (102°F).
   d. who returned from surgery four hours ago and has not voided.

60. The nurse is running a diabetic support group. The nurse teaches that the best way to lower the risk of diabetic atherosclerosis is:
   a. glucose control.
   b. protein ingestion.
   c. carbohydrate intake.
   d. exercise.

61. A client with obsessive-compulsive disorder (OCD) is admitted to the psychiatric unit. What would the nurse anticipate the client's level of anxiety to be immediately after admission to the hospital? Anxiety would be:
   a. higher because of her new status as client.
   b. lower because she is in a hospital environment.
   c. the same because her condition is unchanged.
   d. lower because she expects to get help.

62. A female client undergoes a radical vulvectomy. The client understands discharge instructions when she states she:
   a. will report any temperature over 100°F (37.7°C).
   b. will take walks every day for exercise.
   c. can drive a car in two weeks.
   d. will take tub baths twice a day to relieve incisional pain.

63. A client with gouty arthritis is prescribed a purine-restricted diet. The nurse should recommend:
   a. carrots.
   b. whole grain cereal.
   c. asparagus.
   d. liver.

64. A 64-year-old obese man was admitted this morning following a transurethral resection of the prostate (TURP). Upon assessment he is noted to have a slightly elevated temperature, diaphoresis and dyspnea on exertion. He states this is normal for him due to his size. His oxygen saturaton is 81% on 2L nasal cannula. He has a small amount of blood-tinged sputum and is complaining of minor chest pain. What should the nurse do? Select all that apply.
   a. Perform oral suctioning.
   b. Administer intravenous morphine, as prescribed.
   c. Notify the physician immediately.
   d. Page the respiratory therapist.
   e. Request a prescription for intravenous furosemide (Lasix).
   f. Elevate the head of bed and increase the oxygen, as prescribed.

65. A client comes to the clinic complaining of hearing loss. Otosclerosis is diagnosed. Laser stapedectomy is performed. The client:
   a. will continue to have the hearing loss, but it will not get any worse.
   b. may have a slight hearing loss from the procedure.
   c. may gain some hearing, but will lose it later.
   d. should have hearing improvement.

66. A client with a history of emphysema and cough is diagnosed with lung cancer. The tumor is local and the client has a pneumonectomy performed with removal of adjacent materials. Chest tubes were inserted and the client is brought to the unit. Postoperative care should include:
   a. monitoring chest tube drainage for over 200ml/hr.
   b. discouraging early ambulation to prevent dyspnea.
   c. minimizing coughing so the chest area is less disrupted.
   d. exercising only lower extremities at first.

67. The nurse calls a post-partum mother to check how she and the baby are doing. The mother asks when she can immerse the baby in a baby tub. The nurse replies:
   a. "Any time after you go home."
   b. "Once the cord has fallen off."
   c. "After a bath demonstration by the nurse."
   d. "When a second person is with you."

68. A 24-year-old client has just had an abortion due to a hydatiform mole (molar pregnancy). She is to be discharged on oral contraceptives. The client asks why she is being given contraceptives when she wants to get pregnant again. The nurse's response is based on the fact that:
   a. since the client is 24, she is more likely to have a second hydatiform mole.
   b. pregnancy is not advised for at least three years after HCG titers are normal.
   c. oral contraceptives prevent a false reading of the HCG titer.
   d. oral contraceptives will prevent metastasis of the condition.

69. After checking the cardiac monitor, the nurse has confirmed that a pulseless, unresponsive client is in ventricular fibrillation. While awaiting the arrival of the defibrillator, the nurse's next priority is to:
   a. begin cardiopulmonary resuscitation (CPR).
   b. intubate the client.
   c. administer 1mg of epinephrine IV push.
   d. start an IV.

70. A client is about to undergo electroconvulsive therapy (ECT) for depression. What would the nurse expect to be used as a muscle relaxant for this procedure?
   a. Succinylcholine (Anectine).
   b. Dimenhydrinate (Dramamine).
   c. Methohexital sodium (Brevital).
   d. Glycopyrrolate (Robinul).

71. A client is brought to the unit after a cervical laminectomy with spinal fusion. The care plan would include:
    a. deep breathing, but no coughing.
    b. removing the cervical collar every two hours.
    c. pillow under head while side-lying.
    d. log rolling onto a regular bedpan.

72. After being told that his son is autistic, the parent tells the nurse, "I don't think the doctor knows what he is doing." An appropriate response by the nurse would be:
    a. "It is very difficult to believe your son is ill."
    b. "The doctor is very knowledgeable and can help your son."
    c. "Being angry will not change the situation."
    d. "It's not your fault that your son has autism."

73. A 296-pound woman is admitted to the hospital with a fasting blood sugar of 550. The nurse enters the room to find the client crying, "The doctor told me I'm obese. He says if I don't control my eating, my diabetes is going to kill me. I just can't do it." The therapeutic response by the nurse at this time would be:
    a. "Let me help you plan out a diet that is nutritionally sound."
    b. "You feel you can't control your eating."
    c. "It is hard to lose weight, maybe a support group would help."
    d. "I'm sure the doctor didn't mean to scare you."

74. What would the nurse teach a client who is learning how to care for a new ureterostomy?
    a. Use a soap-containing moisturizer to protect the skin around the stoma.
    b. A baby aspirin placed inside the pouch will help minimize the odor.
    c. The pouch should be emptied as soon as there is urine in it.
    d. Apply some cornstarch to the skin that comes in contact with the pouch.

75. A woman with endometriosis is prescribed danazol (Danocrine) to shrink the endometrial tissue. The nursing care plan should include teaching the client about side effects because danazol (Danocrine):
    a. is generally safe to use during pregnancy.
    b. may also be used to suppress ovulation.
    c. is a type of progesterone.
    d. is a synthetic androgen.

76. A client is brought to the hospital by the police on a psychiatric emergency commitment. During the admission process, the nurse should first:
    a. make sure the client has no dangerous objects.
    b. take the client's vital signs.
    c. introduce yourself and explain what you do.
    d. explain to the client her legal rights.

77. A client is undergoing external radiation therapy. The nurse should instruct the client to:
    a. use talcum powder to decrease itching.
    b. avoid cool wet applications to the area.
    c. use fat-soluble lotions for lubrication.
    d. use mild soap and pat dry for cleaning.

78. A client needs further teaching when she tells the nurse that her intrauterine device (IUD) can cause:
    a. ectopic pregnancy.
    b. pelvic inflammatory disease.
    c. increased menstrual bleeding.
    d. carcinoma of the cervix.

79. A client with trigeminal neuralgia is to be discharged following a percutaneous rhizotomy. Which statement would indicate that the client needs further teaching.
   a. "My carbamazapine (Tegretol) makes me so sleepy; hopefully, I won't have to take it much longer."
   b. "I will use the artificial tears three to four times each day."
   c. "I am going to place a warm moist heat pack over my jaw to help decrease the pain."
   d. "I should call the doctor if I'm having trouble tasting salty foods."

80. A client with fever of unknown origin is admitted to the medical unit. Ultrasound shows a perinephric abscess. Which assessment data relates to this problem?
   a. Chronic urinary tract infections.
   b. Sexually transmitted herpes.
   c. Recent episode of pneumonia.
   d. Type 2 diabetes mellitus.

81. When the nurse on a psychiatric unit attempts to contract for daily one-to-one sessions with a client, he says, "I know you want me to talk about my problems but wouldn't it be easier if we could be friends?" The nurse should respond by stating:
   a. "It's my job to listen to what is bothering you."
   b. "We don't need to discuss problems today, if you don't want to."
   c. "I know it's not easy to talk about problems, but if you try I'm sure you'll feel better."
   d. "It sounds like you are telling me that it is not easy for you to discuss problems."

82. A nurse develops a rash from a new cleaning solution used on the unit. The best place to obtain information on chemicals, their reactions and treatment is the:
   a. distributor of the chemical.
   b. container of the chemical.
   c. maintenance department.
   d. employee health office.

83. The nurse is caring for a 4-year-old with diabetic ketoacidosis. Which finding would be of most concern to the nurse?
   a. Kussmaul respirations of 18 breaths per minute.
   b. Complaint of a headache and a blood pressure of 128/52.
   c. Acetone breath and flushed cheeks.
   d. Serum glucose of 300mg/dL.

84. Who should the nurse care for first?
   a. A client admitted today with pancreatitis that has crackles throughout the lungs.
   b. A woman who had a tubal ligation this morning and is complaining of shoulder pain.
   c. A client admitted with sickle cell crisis and is coughing frequently.
   d. A man with a basilar skull fracture who has bruising behind his ear.

85. The priority nursing action for someone with a pneumothorax is:
   a. monitoring fluid volume.
   b. relief of pressure in the chest.
   c. prevention of intrathoracic infection.
   d. assessment for shock from hemorrhage.

86. A physician writes a medication prescription on a client's chart and leaves the hospital. Although the prescription is difficult to read, the nurse believes it can be deciphered. The nurse should:
   a. ask the supervisor to confirm the prescription.
   b. try to call the physician to clarify the prescription .
   c. ask the pharmacy to confirm the prescription.
   d. check the hospital formulary to clarify the prescription.

87. A client with Alzheimer's disease has become incontinent even though he is up and walking around. The client is usually found in or near the bathroom crying. The client can point out which door is the bathroom. What else should the nurse assess?
    a.   Can the client flush the toilet?
    b.   How well can the client deal with clothes?
    c.   Is the client aware of when the bladder is full?
    d.   Will the client use an incontinence pad?

88. A client has an outpatient skin biopsy. Home care should include:
    a.   take the bandage off in four hours.
    b.   avoid ointment and creams until healed.
    c.   expect some drainage to occur.
    d.   avoid getting the area wet.

89. The mother of a hospitalized toddler tells the nurse that her child "cries, screams and throws himself" whenever she leaves to eat. The nurse should:
    a.   explain that his behavior is a normal response to hospitalization.
    b.   explain that this behavior will diminish in a few days.
    c.   encourage the mother not to leave the child's room.
    d.   encourage the mother to leave when the child is asleep.

90. A client with a brain neoplasm is being prepared for intracranial surgery. Phenytoin (Dilantin) is prescribed preoperatively. The nurse teaches that this is being given to:
    a.   reduce inflammation.
    b.   decrease cortical irritation.
    c.   prevent cerebral edema.
    d.   reduce intracranial pressure.

STOP. You have now completed Practice Session: 19. Now take a few minutes and correct your answers. Calculate your accuracy rate by dividing the number of questions you completed correctly by the total number of questions you completed (90).

Correct answers ÷ total number of questions completed = accuracy rate.

_____ ÷ _____ = _____

ANSWERS AND RATIONALES
Practice Session 19

1. **The correct answer is c.** The question is asking what the nurse would teach a client who has a basal cell carcinoma. A basal cell carcinoma of up to 1cm in diameter can safely be removed via curettage and electrodessication in the physician's office. This technique preserves normal tissue. Keratotic basal cell carcinomas have been known to metastasize if left untreated (option a). Radiation is usually indicated for a basal cell carcinoma only when the size is between 1cm and 8cm or the location presents a surgical difficulty, such as the eyelid (option b). Sunscreen with an SPF of greater than 15 should be used; however, the ear does not need to be covered (option d).
    Nursing Process: Implementation   **Client Need:** Health Promotion & Maintenance

2. **The correct answer is a.** The question is asking what to do when the nurse assesses the presented data. The fetal heart rate of 180 and the mother's vital signs demonstrate both maternal and fetal distress. This is a potentially dangerous situation and the nurse's role is to remain with the client. The nurse will need to take immediate action (option d) rather than to just monitor progress. Since this presents an emergency, the nurse should send others to alert the physician and obtain equipment (option b). During fetal distress, oxytocin (Pitocin) is decreased (option c).
    Nursing Process: Implementation   **Client Need:** Physiological Integrity

3. **The correct answers are b and d.** The question is asking for the appropriate care for a client with viral meningitis. Viral meningitis is caused by a variety of viruses including herpes, Epstein–Barr and cytomegalovirus. The course of the disease is much less severe than bacterial meningitis and treated supportively. Bacterial meningitis is contagious, respiratory isolation is required until the client has received antibiotics for 24 hours. This is not the case for viral meningitis (option a). The head of bed is usually elevated 45° to decrease intracranial pressure and subsequent headaches (option b). Antibiotics are ineffective when treating viral infections (option c). The client may complain of photophobia and dimmed lighting is preferred (option d). Petechial rash may be present when a client is diagnosed with meningococcal meningitis (option e). Determining with whom the client came in contact is unnecessary as viral meningitis is not contagious (option f).
    Nursing Process: Planning   **Client Need:** Physiological Integrity

4. **The correct answer is c.** The question is asking what the nurse should do when a client wants to have the Native Healer come and perform a healing ceremony. The Native Healing Ceremony is a part of the client's religious beliefs and practice. Enhancing a client's spirituality tends to help speed recovery. The nurse should not interfere unless there is some type of problem. Therefore, the healing ceremony does not have to be postponed until after discharge (option a). The client should not need to ask permission from the physician for practicing religion (option c). Herbs may be used, and generally do not interfere with treatment (option d).
    Nursing Process: Implementation   **Client Need:** Health Promotion & Maintenance

5. **The correct answer is c.** The question is asking how to prevent low back pain. A pillow supports the muscles and proper position when placed in the lumbar area. When standing, one foot should be placed higher than the other, such as on a step (option a). Twisting while lifting (option b) places more pressure on the back. Objects should be lifted close to the body (option d).
    Nursing Process: Implementation   **Client Need:** Health Promotion & Maintenance

6. **The correct answer is c.** The question is asking what would happen if you changed an autistic child's usual activities. When a routine is changed, usually an autistic child will become upset, react negatively and may become self-destructive in some way (e.g., head banging, rubbing face on wall). Options (a) and (b) would be true if the activity was parallel and the child did not have to participate. Option (d) is opposite to a change in schedule.
    Nursing Process: Analysis   **Client Need:** Psychosocial Integrity

7. **The correct answer is b.** The question is asking why someone must be without food and fluid prior to surgery. The goal of withholding food and fluids before any surgical procedure during which general anesthesia may be used is to prevent vomiting and aspiration while unconscious.

The client will void just prior to surgery to decrease the chance of additional pressure in the area (option a). Also, during surgery a urinary catheter may be introduced if any problems occur. Nausea and vomiting will be prevented (option c) but aspiration is more of a life-threatening problem and the true reason for the action. Hernia strangulation is unrelated to food and fluid intake (option d). Strangulation occurs when the intestine no longer is receiving any blood supply.

Nursing Process: Analysis　　　　　　**Client Need:** Safe, Effective Care Environment

8.　　**The correct answer is c.** The question is asking the nurse to use therapeutic communication principles to respond to a client with dementia. Option (c) is the correct answer because it allows the client to decrease the focus on her delusional beliefs. Reality orientation (option a) could possibly irritate the client and cause agitation. Option (b) feeds the client's delusion and will eventually increase confusion. Option (d) responds to the theme of the delusion and expects the client to ponder the nurse's comment and gain insight into herself. This would be extremely difficult for a client with dementia.

Nursing Process: Implementation　　　　　　**Client Need:** Psychosocial Integrity

9.　　**The correct answer is c.** The question is asking which client needs to be seen before the others. Ask if anyone will be harmed if not seen early in the morning. The diabetic client needs to stay on a fairly consistent schedule of food and insulin intake. Waiting for fasting blood work means that the client could become hypoglycemic, which could place the client in danger. A post-myocardial infarction client should be safe after discharge as long as the client knows limitations and when to call the physician or nurse. Infrequent premature ventricular contractions are normal. They become abnormal when more than five or six occur in a minute (option a). A client with hearing loss and an above-the-knee amputation would not necessarily be in danger with the data given (option b). Pain is normal after hip fracture (option d). This would need to be investigated but would not be as urgent as fasting in a diabetic client.

Nursing Process: Analysis　　　　　　**Client Need:** Physiological Integrity

10.　　**The correct answer is d.** The question is asking how ligament and tendon damage is usually diagnosed. It is usually diagnosed through magnetic resonance imagery (MRI), which shows the damage. Treatment is often surgery. Visual inspection (option a) and client complaints (option b) lead to prescribing the MRI. A MRI is more diagnostic than an X-ray (option c).

Nursing Process: Assessment　　　　　　**Client Need:** Physiological Integrity

11.　　**The correct answer is b.** The question is asking how the nurse should respond to the client's statement. First, consider that the statement points toward self-harm or suicide. In clients with borderline personality disorder, suicidal ideation and gestures may be manipulative; however, they must always be taken seriously and a suicidal assessment must be conducted. In this situation, the client expresses feelings of never ending "depression and emptiness" and also relates a decreased capacity to tolerate this stress; therefore, suicidal assessment is the priority action for the nurse. Hopelessness (option a) is the identified feeling, which means even more so that the priority at this time is assessment of suicide potential. Explaining feelings rather than exploring them (option c) does not assist the client to cope with them nor keep the client safe. Giving advice (option d) is nontherapeutic because there is no guarantee the client will feel better when participating.

Nursing Process: Implementation　　　　　　**Client Need:** Psychosocial Integrity

12.　　**The correct answer is c.** The question is asking how to deal with a child who has fallen from a tree. The nurse has assessed an injury; other injuries may not be as evident. If possible, the child should not be moved so that injuries will not be worsened. A blanket over the child helps ward off shock. Emergency personnel should be summoned to take proper precautions when transporting and initiating treatment. Often children are brought to the emergency department by parents (option a), but it is in the best interest of the child to prevent further injury and treat the child as soon as possible by calling an ambulance. The child should not have anything for pain (option b) as this masks symptoms, not only of the fractured shoulder, but possibly other less apparent injuries. Calling the physician (option d) may delay emergency treatment.

Nursing Process: Implementation　　　　　　**Client Need:** Physiological Integrity

13. **The correct answer is d.** The question is asking what to teach a client who has just suffered a rib fracture. When the rib has been fractured any pain may prevent the client from taking deep breaths and coughing. This can lead to atelectasis (option b). If the client is treated with analgesics, he is more likely to fully expand his lungs, thus decreasing the opportunity of developing atelectasis. Taping the chest is contraindicated because this also prevents full lung expansion (option a). The client may sleep in whichever position is most comfortable (option c).
Nursing Process: Implementation   **Client Need:** Physiological Integrity

14. **The correct answer is b.** The question is asking how to respond when a client asks about alternative therapy. Exploring the issue with the client is the best communication principle to use. The client is upset and concerned that the pain is still present. There is no indication the client believes the situation is hopeless (option d). Option (a) is advising or telling the client what to do almost in a threatening manner. Option (c) is also advising or giving a personal opinion rather than allowing the client to make the decision.
Nursing Process: Implementation   **Client Need:** Physiological Integrity

15. **The correct answer is d.** The question is asking what the nurse should say to a student who has just been sexually approached by a client. It is not uncommon for hospitalized clients to act seductively towards nurses. Nurses need to be understanding of client's behavior, but this does not mean the nurse's rights should be in any way violated. When this happens, the nurse must set limits in a matter of fact way. In this situation, the student is asking for consultation from the nurse. Sitting down with the student and reviewing the situation will help the student react more appropriately in the future. Option (a) belittles the student's feelings and does not address how to deal with the client's inappropriate behavior. Ignoring the behavior or changing the student's assignment will not make it go away. The student needs to learn how to address the problem, not get use to it (options b & c).
Nursing Process: Evaluation   **Client Need:** Psychosocial Integrity

16. **The correct answer is a.** The question is asking for a goal to prevent another alcohol poisoning episode. A crisis, such as, a hospital admission may help the client understand the seriousness of the episode. This leads to a discussion of how the alcohol poisoning occurred and how to prevent it in the future. At this point, attending an Alcoholics Anonymous meeting would be premature (option b). There is not enough evidence to suggest alcoholism but, hopefully, intervention at this point could prevent the disease from occurring. Listing symptoms of alcohol poisoning (option c) would help the client identify when it was occurring, not necessarily prevent it from occurring. Also, judgment is impaired when symptoms are occurring. Asking the client to refrain from drinking alcohol (option d) may be unrealistic and judgmental. The client may be able to drink more sensibly and responsibly.
Nursing Process: Planning   **Client Need:** Health Promotion & Maintenance

17. **The correct order of answers is c, b, d, a.** The question is asking the order in which the children and/or their families should be called. Worsening abdominal pain, nausea and fever are indicative of possible appendicitis. Any delay in diagnosis can lead to perforation and peritonitis (option c). A low-grade fever and a headache are symptoms of a shunt infection. Although this is not an emergency, this child needs to be evaluated for treatment with antibiotics (option b). A generalized pruritic vesicular rash is diagnostic of varicella zoster (chicken pox). It is usually managed at home. The nurse needs to teach the family how to care for the child. Treatment would include acetaminophen (Tylenol) for a fever, skin care and how to keep the child from scratching (option d). The 14-year-old girl who may be pregnant needs to be called, but this is not a priority. There is nothing to suggest that she is having any current complications. An appointment should be scheduled at her earliest convenience to test for pregnancy.
Nursing Process: Analysis   **Client Need:** Safe, Effective Care Environment

18. **The correct answer is b.** The question is asking about the delegation of a client to a nurse's aide. The client with Von Willebrand's disease is prone to hemorrhage and needs to be assessed and evaluated by the nurse. The aide should not be assigned to an unstable post-surgical client who is prone to hemorrhage due to a bleeding disorder. The nurse must perform the assessment per the

scope of practice. The aide is in an ideal position to assist with routine functions like bathing, transferring, and assisting those with mobility challenges. Option (a) is incorrect as this item is asking for questionable assignments through delegation. An elderly client who requires assistance with bathing is an appropriate assignment for an aide. Option (c) is incorrect as the aide can assist this client to transfer from bed to the chair. Option (d) is incorrect as the aide can assist this client with eating.

Nursing Process: Implementation   **Client Need:** Physiological Integrity

19.   **The correct answer is a.** The question is asking what is wrong when a postoperative client's blood pressure drops and the pulse increases. Hypovolemic shock occurs when there is a loss of fluid from the blood vessels (intravascular space). The fluid lost can be either whole blood, which is often a complication of surgery, or from a loss of water and electrolytes. The loss of fluid causes a decrease in the blood returned to the heart and eventually a decrease in tissue perfusion. Acute infection (option b) would likely manifest later, and would not be the most likely cause. In early shock syndrome (option c) fluid is being lost, but there is no significant change in the vital signs. Vasogenic shock (option d) occurs when the blood vessels are unable to constrict to increase the blood pressure.

Nursing Process: Analysis   **Client Need:** Physiological Integrity

20.   **The correct answer is c.** The question is asking for the appropriate assessment category. Dietary patterns are often placed under culture, particularly with generational patterns, which relate to ethnicity. Other cultural assessment parameters include religion, ethnic health care beliefs and health promotion practices. Roles (option a) include a discussion of expectations within the family. Social support (option b) addresses the people or institutions that may assist the family in times of stress. Stress (option d) deals with possible threats to the social environment.

Nursing Process: Assessment   **Client Need:** Health Promotion & Maintenance

21.   **The correct answer is d.** The question is asking what to do when a client calls with rash, fever and itching post-discharge. Further assessment data are needed to consider a course of action. There is not enough evidence to suggest the problem is related to hospital linen (option a) and may also open the hospital to liability. Prescribing diphenhydramine (Benadryl) would help with an allergic response, if this was the problem (option b), otherwise it may mask symptoms. The woman may need to bring her husband to the emergency department (option c), but additional assessment data should be gathered to determine further action.

Nursing Process: Assessment   **Client Need:** Physiological Integrity

22.   **The correct answer is d.** The question is asking what action to take when the area of a bee sting is "weak." Weakness is a sign of a possible anaphylactic reaction. The nurse should call the physician and obtain prescriptions to further address the problem. Then the parent should be taken to the emergency department for treatment (options b & c). Otherwise, the parent could eventually suffer from shock and possibly die. Taking off the ice pack will increase circulation to the area, which could allow the reaction to progress (option a).

Nursing Process: Implementation   **Client Need:** Safe, Effective Care Environment

23.   **The correct answer is a.** The question is asking to evaluate statements made by a new dialysis client to ascertain the need for further education. The client on hemodialysis normally experiences hypotension during the "run." The client appears to be quite knowledgeable about his weight, diabetes connection, and dietary restrictions. Option (b) is incorrect because weighing himself before dialysis will help ascertain if he has lost too much fluid during the actual dialysis and indicates no need for education. Option (c) is incorrect because this statement about the diabetes, blood sugars, and control is correct and indicates no need for education. Option (d) is incorrect because eating small frequent meals is necessary for people with diabetes.

Nursing Process: Implementation   **Client Need:** Physiological Integrity

24.   **The correct answer is a.** The question is asking the definition of placenta previa. Growth of the placenta normally takes place in the upper body of the uterus. In placenta previa, the placenta implants and grows in the lower uterine segment and may cover the cervical os (option d). If the

placenta has separated, it would be an abruptio placenta (option c). Hormones do not play a role in the etiology of placenta previa (option b).
Nursing Process: Implementation   **Client Need:** Physiological Integrity

25.   **The correct answer is c.** The question is asking for the definition of Hirschprung's disease. This disease is the absence of ganglionic innervation to the muscle section of the bowel. The absent nerve cells means there are no peristaltic waves at this section to aid the passage of fecal materials through that segment of the intestine. Stool that is hard and passed with difficulty (option a) is constipation. Diaphragmatic hernia is an abdominal herniation through the diaphragm (option b). An intestinal protrusion through the umbilical ring (option d) is an umbilical hernia.
Nursing Process: Implementation   **Client Need:** Physiological Integrity

26.   **The correct answer is a.** The question is asking for the best roommate for a newly admitted client with dyspnea, diaphoresis, rash and fever. A client with kidney stones is healthy overall. Fever is a sign of infection, so the client should not be placed with clients who are immunodeficient or at risk for further infection. A client with pneumonia is already infected and may pass that infection along since it is airborne (option b). Clients with Cushing's disease (option c) are more prone to infection due to increased amounts of steroids, which suppress immune response. Clients undergoing peritoneal dialysis (option d) are prone to infection due to the port to the outside and decreased immune response. Infection would usually be a urinary tract infection coming from internal irritation, not outward.
Nursing Process: Analysis   **Client Need:** Safe, Effective Care Environment

27.   **The correct answer is a.** The question is asking what to do when an object is imbedded in the eye. When an object is imbedded in the eye, an ophthalmologist must remove it to prevent further eye damage. The head should be immobilized and the child transported to the emergency department or physician's office. If the object is imbedded in the eye, irrigation will probably not remove it (options b & d) and the eye should be examined for corneal damage. Placing pressure on the eye will cause further damage (option c).
Nursing Process: Planning   **Client Need:** Physiological Integrity

28.   **The correct answer is a.** The question is asking what the best assignment would be for an ICU nurse who is pulled to a medical-surgical floor. The ICU nurse may be familiar with clients just transferred out of her unit to the medical-surgical floor. These clients are also likely to be the higher acuity clients on the unit. This will utilize her skills best and also address the unit care needs. A client who had a myocardial infarction and a client who had a cardiac catheterization would be familiar to the ICU nurse. Option (b) is incorrect since clients with sickle cell crisis and appendectomies are rarely admitted to the ICU. Option (c) is incorrect as urolithiasis is usually treated on a medical-surgical unit, not the ICU. The ICU nurse is not accustomed to caring for a large number of clients. Option (d) is incorrect, as these clients are not usually treated in the ICU.
Nursing Process: Implementation   **Client Need:** Physiological Integrity

29.   **The correct answer is b.** The question is asking how to respond to a mother who asks why a baby in cocaine withdrawal is fussy. The mother should know that her infant is experiencing the effects of her drug use. This information should be given in a straightforward non-judgmental manner. Option (c) is an example of belittling the client and options (a) and (d) avoids the nurse's responsibility to answer the client's questions.
Nursing Process: Implementation   **Client Need:** Psychosocial Integrity

30.   **The correct answer is c.** The question is asking how to help someone with depression while in isolation. Rejection, loneliness and sensory deprivation are common reactions seen in clients who must be isolated. This client needs more personal contact and sensory stimulation. Extra time with the nurse may help to do this. Telephoning friends may help; however, it is not known whether this is possible (option b). Option (a) is not indicated and option (d) is contraindicated in this situation, as the client needs stimulation, not quiet.
Nursing Process: Implementation   **Client Need:** Psychosocial Integrity

31. **The correct answer is d.** The question is asking which option is a correct action for collecting a sample of blood. The procedure for blood collection for hematocrit is as follows: choose a site, such as the side of a finger, heel or ear lobe. Then place the site in a dependent position to help blood flow to the area (option a). Clean the chosen area with 70% alcohol and wait for it to dry. Pierce the skin of the site with a quick motion then wipe the initial blood letting off with gauze. Wiping with alcohol causes the area to burn (option b). Collect the specimen in a capillary tube so that it is about two-thirds full (option c). Then place pressure on the site with gauze (option d). If necessary, place a bandage on the site for additional pressure to prevent bleeding and bruising.
Nursing Process: Implementation   **Client Need:** Physiological Integrity

32. **The correct answer is c.** The question is asking what the nurse should do when a delusional client is threatening others. The nurse should reinforce reality through the use of concrete "here and now" activities such as physical activities. Attempting to argue the client out of a delusion usually results in strengthening the delusional system (option a). Ignoring the conversation (option b) does not respond to the client's immediate need and may impair the nurse-client relationship. Telling the client that the behavior will not be tolerated (option d) is a nontherapeutic response and devalues the nurse-client relationship. Often clients are confused by the delusion and need assistance to know what to do.
Nursing Process: Implementation   **Client Need:** Psychosocial Integrity

33. **The correct answer is d.** The question is asking how the nurse would plan care for a client diagnosed with amyotrophic lateral sclerosis (ALS). This is a progressive, degenerative, neurological disease that occurs because there is demyelination of the motor neurons. This causes atrophy of the muscles. The client eventually loses the ability to communicate verbally because the tongue is also involved. It is important to teach the client eye signals, as eye muscles are not usually affected. In this way, the client can continue to communicate with family, friends and healthcare workers. This disease affects the motor neurons and does not cause mental deterioration (option a). Even in the final stages, clients with ALS do not usually lose sphincter action in the bladder and bowel. However, even if the client does become incontinent, sensory function remains intact and the client can signal others to help him (option b). The muscles become weak and flaccid, not spastic (option d).
Nursing Process: Planning   **Client Need:** Physiological Integrity

34. **The correct answer is b.** The question is asking which information is probably true about this client and the antidepressant medication. Therapeutic responses to antidepressant medications, especially the emotional response, may not be evident for two to three weeks. It is too early to evaluate whether the medication is working and needs to be changed (option a). Negative thinking would not prevent the medication from being effective (option c). There is no evidence to suggest that he is not taking the medication (option d).
Nursing Process: Analysis   **Client Need:** Psychosocial Integrity

35. **The correct answer is a.** The question is asking the most important goal when a client has a fat embolism. Since the embolism often is caught in the respiratory system, promoting oxygenation is the most essential goal. This is accomplished through deep breathing and coughing or even ventilation with positive end expiratory pressure, if needed. Infection (option b), fracture union (option c), and deformity (option d) are all considerations after a hip fracture but fat embolism with consequent oxygen problems is life threatening.
Nursing Process: Planning   **Client Need:** Safe, Effective Care Environment

36. **The correct answer is a.** The question is asking what these symptoms indicate in the diuretic phase of acute renal failure. During this phase, the client loses large amounts of fluid and electrolytes. Fatigue, abdominal cramping and confusion are symptoms of hyponatremia. Hyperkalemia (option b) includes diarrhea, irritability, and irregular heartbeat. In the diuretic phase, the client would have hypokalemia, not hyperkalemia. Hypocalcemia (option c) includes muscle spasms, tetany, tingling and convulsions. Acidosis (option d) includes malaise, a fast deep breathing pattern, disorientation and hyperkalemia.
Nursing Process: Analysis   **Client Need:** Physiological Integrity

37. **The correct answer is b.** The question is asking why a client with alcohol related cirrhosis of the liver would have anemia. Portal hypertension causes a backup of blood into the spleen. This results in splenomegaly. The increased activity in the spleen results in a greater amount of red blood cells being removed from circulation. Endocrine imbalance (option a) relates to aldosterone and antidiuretic hormone production, which is altered. There is poor vitamin synthesis of fat-soluble vitamins (option c). A decreased bilirubin metabolism (option d) results in jaundice.
Nursing Process: Analysis   **Client Need:** Physiological Integrity

38. **The correct answer is b.** The question is asking which behavior best indicates that a client is able to care for the stoma. Return demonstration of new techniques allows the nurse to evaluate the client's skill in performing the procedure. Proper technique indicates ability to perform the procedure. The client may discuss the steps involved, ask appropriate questions, list pertinent complications, and state that she understands what she is to do without being able to actually perform the skill correctly (options a & c). While hand washing is essential, it is only one part of the procedure (option d).
Nursing Process: Evaluation   **Client Need:** Physiological Integrity

39. **The correct answer is a.** The question is asking what the best way to decide if interventions for clients worked. Since the service is going to the clients, client satisfaction is the best way to decide if the job is being done correctly. This would be true from almost every perspective. Employee satisfaction (option b) deals with how good the employees feel about the situation. If the employees have done a good job but the client does not think so, the clients may go elsewhere for care. Documentation (option c) is not explicit enough. What is the documentation about? The outcome may be positive and measurable, but the client may not like what happened, so the client may again go elsewhere for care. Employee evaluations (option d) check to see how well the employees are doing their jobs, not how well the clients believe the people are doing their jobs.
Nursing Process: Evaluation   **Client Need:** Safe, Effective Care Environment

40. **The correct answer is d.** The question is asking the purpose of intra-aortic balloon counter pulsation in a client with cardiogenic shock. The balloon inflates during diastole and deflates during systole, decreasing preload and afterload in the heart. This improves cardiac output, which decreases oxygen consumption (option c). Decreasing plaque buildup is not the purpose during cardiogenic shock (option b). It is unrelated to rhythm defects (option a).
Nursing Process: Planning   **Client Need:** Physiological Integrity

41. **The correct answer is b.** The question is asking what test would be prescribed by the physician to confirm bladder trauma from a bullet. A computed tomography (CT) scan would show the direct damage done to the area and what repairs are needed or able to be performed. An elevated blood urea nitrogen (option a) and altered urine specific gravity (option c) show problems with the kidney. White blood cell count (option d) may be elevated in infection, which might occur later.
Nursing Process: Analysis   **Client Need:** Physiological Integrity

42. **The correct answer is b.** The question is asking how to reply to a daughter who is shocked to find that her mother has been diagnosed with a sexually transmitted disease. Saying, "You're concerned that your mother is sexually active?" encourages expression of feelings and opens communication so the nurse can reinforce that most healthy people remain sexually active throughout their lives. Option (a) is judgmental and closed ended. Option (c) is a true statement but does not encourage the woman to talk about how she feels. The woman has been told that gonorrhea is transmitted only through intimate contact, so asking her how she thinks her mother got it (option d) would be inappropriate. It also belittles the woman for being shocked.
Nursing Process: Implementation   **Client Need:** Health Promotion & Maintenance

43. **The correct answer is b.** The question is asking what the nurse should do when a client has an elevated phosphate level (normal phosphate: 2.5 to 4.5mg/dL) and is exhibiting signs of hypocalcemia. Calcium containing antacids such as calcium carbonate (TUMS) will bind to the phosphate in the GI tract. This will decrease the phosphate level and increase the calcium level. Giving the client potassium phosphate (Neutraphos) will elevate the phosphate level. It is already

elevated (option a). Dairy products contain phosphate, which will also increase the serum levels (option c). Seizures occur in hypophosphatemia, not hyperphosphatemia (option d).
Nursing Process: Implementation   **Client Need:** Physiological Integrity

44.   **The correct answers are a, c, d and e.** The question is asking what would increase the risk of developing osteoporosis. The risk factors for osteoporosis are: female gender; increasing age, thin small frame, family history of osteoporosis (option d), white (European descent) or Asian race, anorexia, diet low in calcium, excessive use of alcohol, cigarette smoking (option c), inactive lifestyle (option e), and being postmenopausal. Ways to prevent osteoporosis include: regular weight bearing exercise (option b), intake of high-protein, high-calcium diet (option f); avoidance of alcohol, caffeine (option a), and tobacco; and finally, taking calcium with vitamin supplements.
Nursing Process: Assessment   **Client Need:** Health Promotion & Maintenance

45.   **The correct answer is d.** The question is asking how the nurse decides what disease to screen for in the community. The significance of the disease to the community is the most important factor. This means how much impact it has on the community in terms of how many people it affects and to what degree it pulls resources from the community. Public officials, special interest groups and client inquiries are all factors that enter into the choice, but the most essential is the significance to the community (options a, b & c).
Nursing Process: Assessment   **Client Need:** Health Promotion & Maintenance

46.   **The correct answer is a.** The question is asking which sign shows possible spinal cord injury. Signs include motor weakness or paralysis, lack of sensation, pain along the spine, and deformities of the spinal areas. Weakness of both arms may be a sign of spinal injury. Pain in the shoulder, arm (option b) and knee (option d) would show feeling is still present and signals are still getting through. "Getting the wind knocked out" (option c) is not a problem since the client can talk.
Nursing Process: Analysis   **Client Need:** Physiological Integrity

47.   **The correct answer is d.** The question is asking about cats and human immunodeficiency virus (HIV) positive persons. Good hygiene is essential when dealing with pets. Someone who is HIV negative, if possible, should handle the litter box. Otherwise, thorough hand washing is necessary when cleaning the litter box. The cat should be kept indoors (option c). The client may have and feed the cat (option a), but should not allow it to lick open areas on the skin. If the client gets a fish tank, gloves should be worn when cleaning it (option a).
Nursing Process: Implementation   **Client Need:** Physiological Integrity

48.   **The correct answer is c.** The question is asking the nurse to prioritize care. A client who just had a renal biopsy is at risk of hemorrhaging due to the invasive procedure. A normal hematocrit is 37 to 54% and normal hemoglobin is 12 to 18g/dL. A hematocrit of 32% and hemoglobin of 10g/dL indicates a possible hemorrhage. Normal PTT is 20 to 30 seconds. A client who is receiving heparin to help with anticoagulation would be expected to have a PTT of 60 seconds since the heparin should double the normal value. A PT of 14 seconds is normal (option a). Normal calcium is 8.4 to 10.6mg/dL and potassium is 3.5 to 5mEq/L (option b). A client with leukemia would be expected to have an elevated WBC and low platelet level (option d).
Nursing Process: Analysis   **Client Need:** Safe, Effective Care Environment

49.   **The correct answer is a.** The question is asking which client requires the nurse's immediate attention. A client with a history of atrial fibrillation is at risk of developing clots. Difficulty seeing out of his left eye may be an indication that a clot has traveled to his brain causing a cerebrovascular accident (CVA). If a CVA is diagnosed early enough, a tissue plasminogen activator (TPA) can be prescribed to decrease the effects of the CVA. Thick green sputum in a client with COPD is indicative of an infection. Although this needs to be confirmed via sputum culture and then treated, it is not the priority (option b) since there is no evidence that it is life threatening at this time. Rifampin (Rifadin) is a drug used to treat tuberculosis and causes the urine to be red (option c). The client in option (d) is experiencing symptoms associated with herpes zoster (shingles). Although this is painful and this client may require medications for pain and itching, it is not life threatening.

50.   **The correct answer is b.** The question is asking how pilocarpine (Ocusert) eye drops decrease intraocular pressure in glaucoma. This medicine decreases the pressure by constricting pupils. Beta blocking agents decrease pressure by blocking production of aqueous humor (option c). Decreasing inflammation (option a) and dilating tear ducts (option d) are unrelated.
Nursing Process: Analysis   **Client Need:** Physiological Integrity

51.   **The correct answer is d.** The question is asking what to do when the fluid comes back clear and pale. After the first several exchanges, the dialysate should be clear and straw colored. Therefore, the findings are normal and should be documented as such. Assessing vital signs (option a) would be unnecessary at this point unless other symptoms presented, such as, dizziness or signs of dehydration. A fluid sample for culture (option b) would be taken if the fluid were blood streaked or foul smelling. The physician does not need to be notified (option c) since nothing abnormal is occurring.
Nursing Process: Implementation   **Client Need:** Physiological Integrity

52.   **The correct answer is d.** The question is asking which option shows signs of complete heart block, which may occur after mitral valve replacement. Atrial impulses are blocked and ventricles may initiate the beat. This means the atria and ventricles act independently. Cardiac failure ensues and symptoms relate to decreased cardiac output; these symptoms include: hypotension (option a), syncope and skipped beats. There should not be fever (option b) since no infection is present. The atria do not function, but the ventricles still attempt to beat (option c).
Nursing Process: Implementation   **Client Need:** Physiological Integrity

53.   **The correct answer is d.** The question is asking what bone pain near the cancer lesion indicates in a client who just started taking tamoxifen (Novaldex). One initial reaction after the drug starts is sudden flashes of pain in the bone marrow, which is believed to be a positive sign of the drug working (options b & c). Another sign is redness around the lesion site. The drug does not have to be discontinued (option a).
Nursing Process: Evaluation   **Client Need:** Physiological Integrity

54.   **The correct answer is c.** The question is asking how the preceptor should respond when a new nurse asks about Huntington's disease. This is a progressive hereditary degenerative disease that does not usually manifest until the client is 30 to 40 years old and has already passed the gene to his children (option a). Huntington's disease causes involuntary movements, speech difficulties and dementia. Huntington's disease frequently occurs in several family members (option b). This disease is autosomal dominant; therefore, only one parent must have the abnormal gene. A person with the abnormal gene, found on chromosome 4 has a 50% chance of producing a child with Huntington's disease with each pregnancy (option d).
Nursing Process: Implementation   **Client Need:** Physiological Integrity

55.   **The correct answer is a.** The question is asking how to assist the caregiver when the person feels overwhelmed. The Alzheimer's Disease and Related Disorders Association (ADRDA) has many local chapters, which support self-help groups and provide the latest information about degenerative disorders. Suggesting hospitalization (option b) is not within the nurse generalist's scope of practice and may be unnecessary at the present time. Referral to a psychologist (option c) for crisis counseling is not necessary since the nurse is capable of supporting the client. Telling the wife that she cannot care for her husband (option d) at the present time is untrue. His condition permits him to be at home under supervision and institutionalization is unwarranted unless the wife chooses to do that right now.
Nursing Process: Implementation   **Client Need:** Health Promotion & Maintenance

56.   **The correct answer is c.** The question is asking what treatment a client would receive for scratches from a bush. Good cleansing and a tetanus booster can prevent infection from clostridium tetani. Most adults are not protected against tetanus. Adults should have the tetanus vaccine every 10 years. Since the client did not have any vaccinations since childhood, she is not

adequately protected. Antibiotics (option a) would not be given unless signs of infection are present. Thorough cleansing should prevent infection. Pneumococcal vaccine (option b) is unrelated to the fall, but the client may receive it during the winter months to prevent pneumonia. Steroid cream (option d) is not necessary unless other problems develop.
Nursing Process: Planning   **Client Need:** Health Promotion & Maintenance

57.   **The correct answer is b.** The question is asking for the side effects of propanolol (Inderal). Nausea, blurred vision and bradycardia (option a) are common side effects of beta-blockers. Beta-blockers lower sympathetic stimulation to the heart and slow the heart rate. Although sexual impotence (options c & d) does occur with beta-blockers, it is rare. Hypokalemia does not result from beta-blockers but from diuretics (option c).
Nursing Process: Evaluation   **Client Need:** Physiological Integrity

58.   **The correct answer is b.** The question is asking what to do when a client's blood pressure is absent. An attempt to palpate a blood pressure is made. Cuff pressures may be inaccurate or difficult to hear during shock because of vasoconstriction. Palpating a blood pressure can be done until doppler or intra-arterial monitoring is available. This is done in the same way as a blood pressure reading, but instead of placing a stethoscope over the brachial artery, the pulse is felt. (This only provides a systolic reading.) The physician should be informed (option a), but it is more important at this moment to ascertain whether there is a blood pressure at all. Chest compressions (option c) are begun when a pulse is absent. The head should be tilted back (option d) to open the airway, but there is no evidence of airway obstruction at this time.
Nursing Process: Implementation   **Client Need:** Physiological Integrity

59.   **The correct answer is c.** The question is asking which client is most in need of the nurse's care at this time. A client who just had a thyroidectomy is at risk of developing thyroid storm after surgery. Excessive amounts of thyroid hormone may be released when the thyroid gland is manipulated during surgery. This can lead to a rapid rise in the metabolic rate which can be life threatening. The temperature rises, the client becomes tachycardic and hypertensive. Treatment with antithyroid drugs, such as propylthiouracil (PTU), should be started as soon as the physician confirms the diagnosis. A pulsating mass is an expected finding in a client with an abdominal aortic aneurysm (option a). The throat is anesthetized in order for the bronchoscope to be inserted. It is not unusual for the client to have an absent gag reflex upon returning to the unit (option b). Bladder distention should be evaluated in a client who has not voided seven to eight hours after surgery (option d).
Nursing Process: Planning   **Client Need:** Safe, Effective Care Environment

60.   **The correct answer is a.** The question is asking how to prevent diabetic atherosclerosis in a client. Glucose control maintenance decreases the risk of plaque agglutination. The client should monitor lipids, as well. Protein and carbohydrate ingestion plus exercise all play a part, but glucose control is the most essential factor (options b, c & d).
Nursing Process: Analysis   **Client Need:** Health Promotion & Maintenance

61.   **The correct answer is a.** The question is asking what would be the client's level of anxiety when coming to a new place. The client is being removed from her normal environment, where she maintains control, and is placed in an environment, which she does not control (option b). This will increase her anxiety level since need for control is part of the dynamics of the illness. The anxiety level usually rises when change occurs (option c) even though there is hope to receive help (option d). It is difficult to give up control to gain help since lack of control increases anxiety and her emotional state and present behavior elicits secondary gains from others.
Nursing Process: Analysis   **Client Need:** Psychosocial Integrity

62.   **The correct answer is b.** The question is asking what discharge instructions are true for a post-vulvectomy client. Exercise, such as walking, helps decrease edema and thrombophlebitis although rest periods are encouraged. Temperatures over 100°F (37.7°C) should be reported as a possible sign of infection (option a). It is too early to drive a car as this leads to venous stasis and thromboembolism (option c). Showers, not baths, are recommended to decrease infection from

contaminated water (option d).).
Nursing Process: Evaluation   **Client Need:** Physiological Integrity

63. **The correct answer is a.** The question is asking which food is not high in purine. Carrots have very low amounts of purine and do not need to be restricted. However, some other vegetables such as mushrooms, asparagus and spinach are higher in purine and should be limited (option c). Whole-grain cereals contain moderate amounts of purine and need to be limited (option b). Liver (option d) is high in purine and should be avoided on a purine-restricted diet.
Nursing Process: Implementation   **Client Need:** Physiological Integrity

64. **The correct answers are b, c, d and f.** The question is asking about the course of action that the nurse needs to take in this emergent situation since the client may be having a myocardial infarction. The nurse would need to give morphine sulfate (Morphine) to decrease the pain and stress on the heart (option b), thus decreasing the cardiac workload. The physician should be notified so the client can be further evaluated and prescribed appropriate care (option c). The respiratory therapist should be notified since the oxygen saturation is only 81% and the client is showing no signs of improvement and ventilatory support may be needed (option d). Since the client's oxygen saturation is low, elevating the head of bed and providing oxygen should help improve the client's respiratory status (option f). There is no need to administer furosemide (Lasix) (option e) since there is no evidence of fluid overload at this time. Suctioning is also not indicated, as there is no evidence of increased secretions (option a).
Nursing Process: Planning   **Client Need:** Physiological Integrity

65. **The correct answer is d.** The question is asking what the hearing status would be after a laser stapedectomy. Hearing should be improved after the procedure. The sclerotic areas are lasered and the stapes replaced by a prosthesis (options a, b & c).
Nursing Process: Evaluation   **Client Need:** Physiological Integrity

66. **The correct answer is a.** The question is asking what the postoperative care would be for a client who had a pneumonectomy. Chest tube drainage should not exceed 200ml per hour for more than two to three hours or hemorrhage is a possibility. Any excessive drainage should be reported to the physician. Early ambulation (option b) is necessary to prevent complications. Coughing and deep breathing (option c) are needed to lessen the chance of pneumonia. Both upper and lower extremities are exercised (option d) so that muscles cut during surgery begin to strengthen.
Nursing Process: Planning   **Client Need:** Physiological Integrity

67. **The correct answer is b.** The question is asking when the mother can place the infant in a tub to bathe. The cord must be kept dry so it eventually falls off. This happens by about two weeks (option a). If the bath demonstration occurs soon after birth, the mother should wait to immerse the infant (option c). Sometimes it is helpful to have a second person home to get items that may be needed since the mother should never leave the child unattended during the bath, but a second person is not a requirement (option d).
Nursing Process: Implementation   **Client Need:** Health Promotion & Maintenance

68. **The correct answer is c.** The question is asking why a woman would not be permitted to conceive following evacuation of a molar pregnancy. Oral contraceptives prevent pregnancy and suppress luteinizing hormone, which distorts human chorionic gonadotropin (HCG) titers. Pregnancy is not advised for a year after HCG titers are negative, but is safe if the woman is under age 40 (options a & b). Metastasis is usually related to choriocarcinoma and not hydatiform mole. Oral contraceptives are used during this time (option d).
Nursing Process: Analysis   **Client Need:** Physiological Integrity

69. **The correct answer is a.** The question is asking what the nurse should do when a client is in ventricular fibrillation and has no pulse. The nurse's first priority is to administer CPR as soon as ventricular fibrillation is confirmed while waiting for the defibrillator. Electrical defibrillation is the definitive treatment for ventricular fibrillation. Once an IV is established (option d),

epinephrine 1mg IV push is given (option c). Endotracheal intubation is performed by the nurse anesthetists or the physicians (option b) if the client has no spontaneous respirations.
Nursing Process: Implementation   **Client Need:** Physiological Integrity

70.   **The correct answer is a.** The question is asking which drug is the muscle relaxant given prior to electroconvulsive therapy. Succinylcholine (Anectine) is the muscle relaxant. However, all of these drugs may be given prior to the treatment. Dimenhydrate (Dramamine) is an antiemetic used to prevent nausea and vomiting (option b). Methohexital sodium (Brevital) is used to induce anesthesia (option c). Glycopyrrolate (Robinul) is used preoperatively to decrease secretions (option d).
Nursing Process: Analysis   **Client Need:** Physiological Integrity

71.   **The correct answer is a.** The question is asking proper care of a client post-cervical laminectomy. The client is usually kept on bed rest and deep breathing is done to reduce the chance of pneumonia. However, coughing may disrupt the surgery. The cervical collar should be kept on to maintain proper alignment and support while healing takes place (option b). A pillow under the head may be too thick (option c). Often a pad is sufficient. A fracture pan should be used (option d) for elimination. This and logrolling help maintain proper alignment.
Nursing Process: Planning   **Client Need:** Safe, Effective Care Environment

72.   **The correct answer is a.** The question is asking how to respond to a parent who expresses anger after being told his child has autism. The nurse is verbalizing the implied shock and disbelief that usually accompanies the diagnosis of childhood autistic disease. Option (b) is defending the doctor and does not allow for outward expression of feelings. Option (c) is belittling the client's emotions as though they are invalid. Allowing the client to express anger and listening will assist the client to work through the problem. Option (d) is false reassurance. The parents may be worried that they caused the disorder, but they have not verbalized this concern. Some research indicates there is a toxin during pregnancy that may precipitate autism. It is best to allow the clients to express their true concerns so that their questions can then be answered, rather than making assumptions.
Nursing Process: Implementation   **Client Need:** Psychosocial Integrity

73.   **The correct answer is b.** The question is asking how to respond when an overweight client states an inability to follow a diet. The nurse has responded by using the technique of restating the main thought that the client expressed. Options (a) and (c) offer the client advice before fully exploring feelings and thoughts, plus prescribing a diet is in the scope of the physician. Option (d) is an attempt by the nurse to defend the physician's comments, which would not be therapeutic.
Nursing Process: Implementation   **Client Need:** Psychosocial Integrity

74.   **The correct answer is d.** The question is asking for the appropriate care of an ureterostomy. Cornstarch is used to absorb perspiration and avoid skin irritation. Moisturizer is avoided near the stoma as it keeps the appliance from adhering to the area around the stoma (option a). Aspirin should not be used to minimize odor as it can cause stomal ulceration (option b). The pouch should be emptied when it is 1/3 full, not as soon as there is urine in it. If the client waits until it is half filled, the weight of the urine can lead to detachment and spillage of urine (option c).
Nursing Process: Planning   **Client Need:** Health Promotion & Maintenance

75.   **The correct answer is d.** The question is asking what the nurse needs to tell the client about this drug. Danazol (Danocrine) is a synthetic androgen and, therefore, may cause male traits, such as hirsutism, decreased breast size, decreased libido and deepening voice. Other side effects include: weight gain, mood changes, vaginitis, dizziness, tiredness, vasomotor disturbances and migraine headaches. It is not a progesterone (option c). The drug does not suppress ovulation (option b) and the client should be cautioned that some type of birth control may be necessary, especially since the drug may cause fetal defects (option a).
Nursing Process: Planning   **Client Need:** Physiological Integrity

76.   **The correct answer is c.** The question is asking how a nurse should conduct an admission

interview for a client newly committed to the psychiatric unit. The nurse should always first try to establish a therapeutic relationship by giving information about whom she is and what her job is in order to promote trust between the nurse and the client. Making sure the client has no dangerous objects (option a), taking the client's vital signs (option b), and explaining the client's legal rights (option d) are all necessary interventions, but the nurse should first provide identification of the nurse's role.

Nursing Process: Implementation   **Client Need:** Psychosocial Integrity

77.   **The correct answer is d.** The question is asking which option is true for client who has external radiation treatments. Mild soap and patting dry help to keep the area clean without causing damage to the skin. Powders should be avoided as they cause drying of the skin (option a). Cool wet compresses and water-soluble lotions may be used for itching (options b & c). Heat and cold extremes should be avoided.

Nursing Process: Implementation   **Client Need:** Physiological Integrity

78.   **The correct answer is d.** The question is asking which is not a side effect of an intrauterine device (IUD). Carcinoma of the cervix is not a known result of using an IUD. However, there is an increased incidence of ectopic pregnancy, pelvic inflammatory disease and increased menstrual bleeding (options a, b & c) associated with the use of IUDs.

Nursing Process: Analysis   **Client Need:** Health Promotion & Maintenance

79.   **The correct answer is c.** The question is asking which statement by the client would be wrong. People with trigeminal neuralgia have severe pain of the face. A percutaneous rhizotomy is a procedure in which glycerol is injected into the trigeminal nerve to sever the nerve root. The client may experience some facial numbness; however, there usually is no paralysis. The involved side of the face becomes insensitive to pain. Ice packs, not heat, are used to decrease bleeding and swelling. Carbamazapine (Tegretol) is the drug of choice to decrease pain, however, surgery should decrease or eliminate the need for any pain medications (option a). A percutaneous rhizotomy may damage the corneal reflex, thus it would be important for the client to protect the eyes by using artificial tears (option b). A percutaneous rhizotomy may damage the trigeminal nerve, which is responsible for taste. This should be reported to the physician (option d).

Nursing Process: Evaluation   **Client Need:** Physiological Integrity

80.   **The correct answer is a.** The question is asking which data would relate to perinephric abscess. This is a pocket of infection in the area of the kidneys, usually relating to chronic urinary tract infections when the bacteria are not totally obliterated. The other options (b, c & d) do not directly relate to the abscess.

Nursing Process: Assessment   **Client Need:** Physiological Integrity

81.   **The correct answer is d.** The question is asking how to reply when the client tries to change the subject. This option verbalizes what the client has implied in the statement and allows the client an opening to respond. Option (a) is an example of defending, which is a nontherapeutic communication technique. Option (b) allows the client to avoid the therapeutic relationship. Option (c) is an example of the nontherapeutic technique of reassuring.

Nursing Process: Implementation   **Client Need:** Psychosocial Integrity

82.   **The correct answer is d.** The question is asking the best place to obtain information about a chemical substance. According to the Occupational Safety and Health Administration (OSHA), all hospitals must have on site a list of all chemicals, their reactions and the treatment. The distributor (option a) just hands out the chemical substance and may not know how to counteract reactions. The chemical's container (option b) may have the composition but not necessarily tell how to treat problems. The maintenance department (option c) may know how to use the substance but not how to treat reactions.

Nursing Process: Implementation   **Client Need:** Health Promotion & Maintenance

83.   **The correct answer is b.** The question is asking which assessment would indicate the child is experiencing a severe complication of diabetic ketoacidosis (DKA). The nurse should be alert for

one the most serious complications of DKA which is cerebral edema. Cerebral edema occurs because the hyperosmolality of the blood causes a fluid shift from the intracellular spaces via osmosis. If left untreated, depression of the central nervous system can lead to coma and eventually death. A headache, elevated blood pressure and widening pulse pressure are indicative of cerebral edema. Kussmaul respirations are expected when someone has DKA. The body is trying to compensate by blowing off the excess acid (option a). Acetone breath and flushed cheeks are also expected with DKA (option c). The acetone breath results from the metabolic acidosis and the flushed cheeks are indicative of dehydration. This is also expected in DKA because the hyperosmolality of the blood causes a fluid shift. This causes the kidneys to excrete the excess fluid leading to polyuria and dehydration. While a glucose level of 300mg/dL is elevated, this would also be expected if the child were admitted with DKA. It can be treated with IV insulin.

Nursing Process: Analysis   **Client Need:** Physiological Integrity

84.   **The correct answer is c.** The question is asking which client is most in need of the nurse's attention. A client in sickle cell crisis must be continually monitored for symptoms of chest syndrome, a life-threatening complication that is caused by vasocclusion of the coronary and pulmonary systems. The symptoms that indicate possible chest syndrome are fever, cough, dyspnea and chest pain. Acute pancreatitis often causes fluid to collect in the lungs. Crackles would be an expected finding (option a). It is not uncommon for a client to complain of referred pain in the shoulder after undergoing a tubal ligation (option b). An ecchymotic area above the mastoid bone (also known as Battle's sign) is an expected finding in a client with a basilar skull fracture (option d).

Nursing Process: Analysis   **Client Need:** Safe, Effective Care Environment

85.   **The correct answer is b.** The question is asking the most essential nursing intervention for a client with a pneumothorax. Relief of the positive pressure within the chest through re-expansion of the lung is considered to be an emergency measure. If this is not accomplished, respiratory and circulatory compromise results, since increased intrathoracic pressure interferes with venous return and cardiac output, which may lead to cardiac arrest. Monitoring fluid volume (option a) is not essential in a tension pneumothorax, unless further problems arise after lung re-expansion occurs. Prevention of intrathoracic infection (option c) is secondary to lung expansion especially with a spontaneous pneumothorax. Shock due to hemorrhage (option d) is unlikely for a spontaneous pneumothorax, but may be a concern for hemothorax or penetrating chest wounds.

Nursing Process: Implementation   **Client Need:** Physiological Integrity

86.   **The correct answer is b.** The question is asking what the nurse should do if the physician's order is too difficult to read. If a prescription is unclear or ambiguous, the nurse should call the physician who wrote the prescription to clarify it. Consulting other personnel (options a & c) does not help the nurse know exactly what the written prescription is and breaks part of the check and balance system necessary for client safety. Any clarification should be with the person who originally wrote the prescription. Checking the prescription against the hospital formulary (option d) involves guessing. The nurse should not carry out a prescription that is unclear or ambiguous.

Nursing Process: Implementation   **Client Need:** Safe, Effective Care Environment

87.   **The correct answer is b.** The question is asking what needs to be assessed when the client is incontinent and found near the bathroom but, also, can point out the correct door. The client may not be able to undo clothing to use the bathroom properly. Clothing can be simplified by using elastic waists or Velcro fasteners. Flushing the toilet (option a) would not be related to incontinence. The client knows when the bladder is full (option c) because the client is found near the bathroom door. Use of an incontinence pad (option d) does not necessarily help the person be continent.

Nursing Process: Assessment   **Client Need:** Physiological Integrity

88.   **The correct answer is c.** The question is asking how to care for a skin biopsy site at home. Some drainage is expected, but excessive drainage should be reported to the physician. The bandage should be kept on for eight hours (option a). Antibiotic creams or ointments may be prescribed to

prevent infection (option b). The area should be cleaned daily with water, saline or hydrogen peroxide (option d).

Nursing Process: Implementation   **Client Need:** Physiological Integrity

89.   **The correct answer is a.** The question is asking how to respond to a child who throws temper tantrums when a parent leaves to eat. This is a normal response to hospitalization. Protest, the initial phase of separation, is a time when children make strenuous efforts to recapture their parents. This is an adaptive behavior that implies presence of trust and autonomy. The mother has to leave the room occasionally to eat, sleep and revive herself (option c) and if she leaves when he is sleeping (option d), his trust level will decrease if he awakens and finds her gone. He may try anything not to sleep. Hopefully, although this behavior is unpleasant for the parent, it will not diminish because this would mean a decrease in the child's trust level (option b).

Nursing Process: Implementation   **Client Need:** Health Promotion & Maintenance

90.   **The correct answer is b.** The question is asking why an anticonvulsant is given to a client prior to a craniotomy for tumor removal. Anticonvulsants raise the seizure threshold and decrease cortical irritation. Dexamethasone (Cortisone) is given to reduce inflammation (option a) and prevent cerebral edema (option c), thus reducing intracranial pressure (option d).

Nursing Process: Analysis   **Client Need:** Safe, Effective Care Environment

Instructions: Allow yourself 90 minutes to complete the following 90 practice questions. Use a timer to notify yourself when 90 minutes are over so that you are not constantly looking at your watch while completing the questions.

1. During an initial assessment, a new client tells the community health nurse, "I just really don't see how talking can help." The most appropriate response at this time would be:
   a. "What do you think you need at this time?"
   b. "Tell me about your problems that you are having right now."
   c. "You are concerned that nothing will help you?"
   d. "It sounds like you are not sure about talking with me."

2. A 13-month-old is admitted with a closed head injury. The parents report that the child hit the side of his head on a coffee table while learning how to walk unassisted. A report of suspected child abuse should be filed with the authorities if which was noted?
   a. Bilateral retinal hemorrhage.
   b. Bulging anterior fontanelle.
   c. Frequent vomiting and decreased appetite.
   d. Decreased level of consciousness.

3. A medical-surgical nurse is pulled to the pediatric unit. What is the best assignment for this nurse?
   a. A 5-year-old with sickle cell anemia, a 10-year-old with asthma and a 15-year-old with a fractured femur.
   b. An 18-month-old with respiratory syncytial virus (RSV), a 16-year-old with cystic fibrosis and a 7-year-old with cellulitis.
   c. A 15-year-old female with anorexia, an infant with pyloric stenosis and a 7-year-old who just had a temporary colostomy created.
   d. A 14-year-old with spina bifida who had a shunt revision, a toddler with epiglottitis and a 14-year-old with cerebral palsy who has a urinary tract infection.

4. A client is brought to the emergency department with a knife wound to the upper right chest. As he begins to develop tachycardia, rapid respirations and air hunger, the nurse knows that he is at risk for a:
   a. closed pneumothorax.
   b. tension pneumothorax.
   c. chylothorax.
   d. cardiac tamponade.

5. A client with a spinal cord tumor at C_7 is being given high doses of dexamethasone (Decadron) to help control spinal edema. The nurse would assess for possible side effects of drug therapy by:
   a. observing for episodes of diarrhea.
   b. testing the stool for blood.
   c. asking the client if he is experiencing pain and tenderness.
   d. monitoring for hypertension and tachycardia.

6. After being NPO for one week, a client is placed on tube feedings. The nurse performs an assessment. Which finding would contraindicate the initial feeding?
   a. Increased flatus.
   b. Esophageal injury.
   c. Absent bowel sounds.
   d. Dysphagia.

7. A 16-year-old is admitted with complaints of sudden onset fatigue, anorexia, facial edema and rust colored urine. The client is febrile and has an admission blood pressure of 162/96. The physician prescribes bed rest. The nurse should assess the client for a recent history of:
   a. urinary tract infection.
   b. an upper respiratory tract infection.
   c. heart disease.
   d. trauma to the flank area.

8. Which would be the nurse's priority in working with a client with dementia who has wandering behaviors?
   a. Consult with family members regarding the onset of the wandering.
   b. Attempt to identify situations that may contribute to the wandering.
   c. Provide lighted areas where the client can move about safely.
   d. Decrease the client's environmental stimulation in the evening.

9. A client is diagnosed with polycystic kidney disease (PKD). The nurse would question which prescription?
   a. Ducosate (Colace) 50mg once a day.
   b. Acetaminophen (Tylenol) 650mg p.r.n.
   c. Furosemide (Lasix) 20mg BID.
   d. Aspirin (Ecotrin) 325mg p.r.n.

10. A hospice nurse is planning care for a client with terminal cancer. One of the goals for this client is to conserve energy. The nurse will accomplish this by:
    a. providing opportunities for rest periods between times of stimulation.
    b. protecting the client from injury by removing safety hazards.
    c. encouraging the client to be as independent as possible.
    d. involving family and friends in the client's care.

11. A client is being screened for Type 2 diabetes. Which data indicates a high risk for Type 2 diabetes?
    a. Glucosuria and ketonuria.
    b. History of recent viral infection.
    c. Recent increase in activity level.
    d. Obesity.

12. A client with pancreatitis is admitted to the hospital. Which lab report would indicate that the nurse must incorporate pain management into the plan of care?
    a. Amylase: 300u/L.
    b. BUN: 30mg/dL.
    c. Calcium: 8mg/dL.
    d. SGOT: 40u/L.

13. Which client behavior indicates that a client has had successful crisis intervention? The client:
    a. frequently seeks advice from her colleagues at work and friends.
    b. finds new friends and changes how she relates to others.
    c. can discuss her feelings about past concerns.
    d. returns to her job and functions successfully.

14. The nurse is assigned the following clients for the 7:00AM to 3:00PM shift. Which client should be cared for first?

    a. A client who is one day postoperative from an open reduction internal fixation (ORIF) of the right hip. She has an IV infusing of 5% Dextrose and 0.45% normal saline solution at 100ml/hour. Vital signs: temperature 99.2°F, pulse 108, respirations 24, and blood pressure 100/64. Laboratory results reveal: hemoglobin 9.1g/dL and hematocrit 26.4%.

    b. A client admitted with chronic obstructive pulmonary disease (COPD) and anemia. He is receiving oxygen at 3L/minute via nasal cannula. The pulse oximeter reading is 92% and respirations 28. Breath sounds decreased bilaterally.

    c. A client admitted with deep vein thrombosis (DVT) receiving IV heparin therapy. Partial thromboplastin time at 6:30AM: control 25 seconds, client 60 seconds.

    d. A client admitted with congestive heart failure (CHF). Scattered rales noted bilaterally in all lung fields. Received IV furosemide (Lasix) last evening. Urinary output on 11:00PM to 7:00AM shift: 975ml clear yellow urine. Laboratory results reveal sodium 132mEq/L and potassium 2.5mEq/L.

15. The nurse would determine that effectiveness of phenytoin (Dilantin) therapy for a client with a seizure disorder most likely has been achieved when what finding is noted in a postoperative craniotomy client?

    a. Sodium and potassium levels are in normal range.

    b. Level of consciousness increases.

    c. Vital signs are within normal range.

    d. Blood levels are within 10 to 20mcg/ml.

16. A client has just been admitted with a Salem sump nasogastric tube. The nurse notes that the color of the drainage is dark brown. The initial intervention would be to:

    a. do nothing, as this is the normal color of tube drainage.

    b. notify the physician as this might indicate bleeding from the stomach.

    c. irrigate the tube with 30ml of NSS to see if it clears.

    d. flush the tube with a 30ml bolus of air to check proper placement.

17. A client is prescribed a 24-hour urine creatinine clearance and a serum creatinine level. If the 24-hour urine collection is started at 8:00AM on Wednesday, when should the nurse draw the blood for the serum level?

    a. 8:00AM on Wednesday.

    b. 12:00PM on Wednesday.

    c. 8:00PM on Wednesday.

    d. 8:00AM on Thursday.

18. A client with schizophrenia is experiencing looseness of association. The nurse cannot understand the client's speech and is becoming frustrated. What is the best response for the nurse?

    a. Pretend to understand the client because the nurse does not want to aggravate the client.

    b. Address the client by saying, "You are not making sense."

    c. Ask the client if he would like to play a game of pool.

    d. Have the client lie down and rest.

19. A client is admitted to the emergency department after complaining of a right facial droop and right hemiparesis. Place the nursing interventions in the order that they should be performed.

    a. Administer a tissue plasminogen activator as prescribed.

    b. Start an IV and infuse normal saline as prescribed.

    c. Escort the client to radiology for a CT scan.

    d. Elevate the head of bed.

20. A nurse is teaching a new mother about her son's temporary gastrostomy tube. The nurse would include:
   a. that the mother will not need to learn gastrostomy tube care because, as the suture line heals, oral feedings will be started and soon the gastrostomy tube will be removed.
   b. explaining gastrostomy tube care to the mother exhibiting various tube sizes to be used as the child grows.
   c. explaining current care, identifying the temporary use of the gastrostomy tube until formula is taken and retained orally.
   d. that the mother's time is better spent holding and cuddling her child and that the nurse will care for the temporary tube.

21. A newborn with repair of a tracheoesophageal fistula (TEF) has had a temporary gastrostomy tube placed. The infant has an increase in respiratory secretions. The nurse should plan to suction:
   a. deep to stimulate a gag reflex.
   b. only oral secretions.
   c. only with a bulb syringe to the nares.
   d. only to the point of the suture.

22. A 27-year-old with pronounced myopia is having her annual physical. During the history, the client tells the nurse that when she went to her optometrist for her yearly exam, her vision had worsened by five diopters in each eye. Which test would the nurse expect the physician to prescribe?
   a. Tonometry.
   b. Fasting blood glucose.
   c. Visual field testing.
   d. Serum T_3 and T_4 level.

23. A school-age child has been brought to the emergency department several evenings in the last two weeks for a worsening respiratory condition. Each time, the nurse has made a referral to a neighborhood clinic. In this case, the nurse would need to assess whether the referral was:
   a. related to the child's respiratory problem.
   b. appropriate for the parent and child.
   c. actually necessary since treatment was started.
   d. a waste of the parent's time.

24. A client comes to the clinic for a post-mastectomy appointment. She complains that her hand and wrist are swollen. Nonpitting edema is present. Lymphedema secondary to the mastectomy is diagnosed. The care plan would include:
   a. avoiding use of diuretics.
   b. bunching clothes at elbow.
   c. observing for signs of infection.
   d. teaching for surgery.

25. The physician recommends an acid ash diet for a client with chronic urinary tract infections and renal calculi. The nurse evaluates that the client understands the diet when he states he will eat:
   a. oranges, grapefruits, and apples.
   b. green leafy vegetables and salads.
   c. beans, rice and cereal products.
   d. red meats and organ meats.

26. A child is prescribed 75mg of phenytoin (Dilantin) IV push. The child weighs 55 lbs. Phenytoin can be given at a rate of 1mg/kg/minute. Over how many minutes would you give this medication?

_____

27. After receiving results from the laboratory, which client should be seen first? A client:
    a. in congestive heart failure (CHF), with a digoxin level of 1.5ng/ml.
    b. on warfarin sodium (Coumadin), with an international normalized ration (INR) of 2.5.
    c. with peptic ulcer disease, with a hemoglobin level of 9.8g/dL and a hematocrit level of 34%.
    d. on heparin sodium (Heparin) therapy, with partial thromboplastin time (PTT): control 25 seconds, client 68 seconds.

28. Three days after a school shooting the school requests a mental health nurse be brought in to a kindergarten class to observe children for posttraumatic stress disorder. What would most alert the nurse to a possible problem?
    a. Two students playing together crashing cars.
    b. A student sleeping at his desk.
    c. A child coloring by herself.
    d. A student frequently asking to use the restroom.

29. A client diagnosed with diverticulitis has been hospitalized for three days. In planning care for this client, an expected outcome would be that he would:
    a. limit fluid intake to 1,200ml per day.
    b. demonstrate techniques of colostomy care.
    c. add fiber or bran to foods.
    d. report an increase in the frequency of watery stools.

30. Due to a call-off from one of the staff members on the psychiatric unit, the scheduled walk outside of the hospital has been postponed until another staff member can be called into work. A client with borderline personality disorder yells at the nurse, "It's not fair, why should we be punished for your mistakes?" The nurse intervenes and later the client apologizes for her remark but repeatedly asks the nurse, "Are you still angry with me?" An appropriate short-term goal for this client would be that she would:
    a. verbalize willingness to avoid rescuing behavior.
    b. verbalize her fears of being alone.
    c. hold herself accountable for the consequences of her behavior.
    d. discriminate between her own projected anger and the anger of others.

31. A 30-year-old client was admitted with a ventriculoperitoneal shunt infection. The shunt was revised a week ago after three infections in less than a month. The abdominal incision is cultured and is positive for Escherichia Coli. The nurse should suspect:
    a. somatoform disorder.
    b. a compromised immune system.
    c. factitious disorder.
    d. suicidal ideation.

32. Which nursing interventions should be included on the care plan of a client receiving hemodialysis?
    a. Assess for a thrill and bruit every shift.
    b. Include green leafy vegetables and potatoes with each evening meal.
    c. Assess for abdominal pain, distention, fever, nausea and change in bowel habits every shift.
    d. Schedule four exchange cycles in each 24-hour period.

33. After providing discharge teaching to a client with a new ileal conduit, the nurse notes the need for further teaching when the client states:
    a. "I will have to be fitted for a permanent appliance once my stoma shrinks."
    b. "It is normal for pieces of stool to be present in my urine."
    c. "I need to increase the amount of fluids that I consume."
    d. "I should include cranberries, plums and prunes in my diet."

34. The father of a child with a brain stem glioma begins to swear and make sarcastic remarks about his child's care to the nurse. When the nurse comes in to give the child his medication, the father screams at the nurse to leave the room. The nurse understands that the father is behaving this way because he:
    a.   is dissatisfied with the care his child is receiving.
    b.   is beginning to understand the reality of the situation.
    c.   is experiencing sensory alteration.
    d.   may prefer another nurse care for his child.

35. A newly diagnosed diabetic client is learning how to plan her meals and snacks. She asks the nurse, "What happens if I change my times for giving the insulin and decide to give it earlier in the morning? Do I still eat at the times we planned today?" The appropriate response by the nurse would be:
    a.   "It really does not matter what time you eat; just make sure you have some insulin in your body at the time."
    b.   "You should always plan your initial meal prior to giving your insulin to insure that glucose will be present in the body."
    c.   "Your meals and snacks should be planned according to the onset, peak and duration of each insulin."
    d.   "Do not deviate from the scheduled eating times planned; it is more important to maintain a set eating time than to adjust it to insulin administration times."

36. A client admitted for dehydration, electrolyte imbalance and wandering behavior was subsequently diagnosed with Alzheimer's disease. The client is being discharged to live with her daughter. The nurse should set what priority in the discharge plan?
    a.   Referral for home care assessment.
    b.   Education on handling wandering behavior.
    c.   Purchasing a medic alert bracelet.
    d.   Handling food and fluid needs.

37. The nurse is assessing a female client with fibromyalgia. What assessment findings would the nurse expect to find in this client?
    a.   Diffuse musculoskeletal aching and pain, fatigue, morning stiffness.
    b.   Asymmetric joint pain on movement, inflamed synovium, limited motion.
    c.   Bilateral joint pain, swelling, warmth, lack of function, morning stiffness.
    d.   Butterfly rash, arthralgias, joint swelling and tenderness.

38. The Parent Teacher Organization has voted to build a new playground at the school. They ask the nurse what safety precautions they should take. The nurse replies that the best way to promote safety would be to:
    a.   cover the ground with loose stone gravel.
    b.   place loose sand at areas where children may fall.
    c.   never place swings or a sliding board on the playground.
    d.   require restraints on the seesaws.

39. The nurse on a 3pm-11pm shift has just received report. Which client should be cared for first? A client:
    a.   with Cushing's disease who has a glucose level of 240.
    b.   with Rheumatic fever who is complaining of severe knee pain and cannot walk to the bathroom.
    c.   who is suspected of having a spinal cord tumor and has not voided since 8am.
    d.   with an intermaxillary fixation who is complaining of nausea.

40. The nurse should teach a client with systemic lupus erythematosus to:
   a. include vitamins A and D in the diet.
   b. include sufficient fluid intake.
   c. avoid sun exposure.
   d. avoid excessively fatty diets.

41. A 7-year-old male with Tourette's syndrome comes to the clinic for a routine physical. His father states that he has been having difficulty concentrating in class and is falling behind. Further exploration reveals that the father has been too embarrassed to tell the teacher his son has Tourette's syndrome. What should the nurse suggest the father do?
   a. Place the child in a school for children with special needs.
   b. Meet with the teacher to plan brief learning tasks for the child.
   c. Meet with the teacher to enhance socialization with peers.
   d. Ask if the school has a special education program.

42. A client with stomach cancer has just undergone a partial gastrectomy with placement of a gastrostomy tube. What would be included in this client's plan of care?
   a. Maintain bed rest for the first two days following surgery.
   b. Cut 4x4 gauze pads to fit snuggly around the gastrostomy tube.
   c. Auscultate after injecting air in the gastrostomy tube to check placement.
   d. Irrigate the gastrostomy tube with 30ml of water.

43. A college student complains of a sore throat, swollen glands and fever. Mononucleosis with streptococcal pharyngitis is diagnosed and treatment with antibiotics begins. The teaching plan by the nurse includes:
   a. steroids to hasten the disease course.
   b. decreased fluids to prevent splenic overload.
   c. bed rest until the fever resolves.
   d. cool throat gargles to relieve the throat pain.

44. During a diet-teaching session, the nurse gives a group of clients a hypothetical restaurant menu. A client demonstrates understanding of a sodium-restricted diet when choosing:
   a. chicken, bread stuffing, salad with oil and vinegar dressing.
   b. fish, plain baked potato, salad with oil and vinegar dressing.
   c. steak, plain baked potato, cooked vegetables.
   d. turkey with gravy, plain baked potato, roll and salad with low calorie dressing.

45. The nurse is catheterizing a male client with a recent spinal cord injury at T_4. During the catheterization, the client has an erection. The nurse would interpret this finding as:
   a. a voluntary motor response.
   b. an indication that spinal shock is decreasing.
   c. an indication to stop the procedure.
   d. a need to set limits on the client's behavior.

46. A client with hydronephrosis has had a nephrostomy tube inserted into the renal pelvis to drain urine and to relieve pressure. In order to care for the tube appropriately, the nurse should plan to:
   a. irrigate the tube with 15ml of sterile saline as needed.
   b. keep the urine collection container at the level of the kidney.
   c. clamp the tube for 20 minutes to obtain urine for culture.
   d. report leakage around the catheter or change in urine output.

47. When evaluating the lab results of a male client on warfarin sodium (Coumadin) therapy for deep vein thrombosis (DVT), the nurse would call the physician about which result?
   a. International normalized ratio (INR) of 4.5 seconds.
   b. Hemoglobin of 14g/dL and hematocrit of 42%.
   c. Partial thromboplastin time (PTT) of 30 seconds.
   d. Prothrombin time (PT) of 10 seconds.

48. A client with cirrhosis is admitted for treatment of worsening ascites. The nursing diagnosis is fluid volume excess. The best way to determine progress would be:
   a. pulse oximetry.
   b. daily weight.
   c. skin inspection.
   d. intake and output.

49. During a one-to-one session with the nurse a psychiatric client says, "I wish my wife understood me like you do, nurse." The nurse should respond by saying:
   a. "What causes you to believe that your wife doesn't understand you?"
   b. "It is hard to believe that your wife does not try to understand you."
   c. "It might be difficult to compare the two relationships."
   d. "I'm glad you feel that I understand you."

50. The physician prescribes two units of packed red blood cells (PRBC) to be given to a client. The nurse hangs one unit and then attends to an emergency admission. The nurse goes back to hang the second unit at the appointed time, but the first unit still has half of the amount to finish. The nurse should:
   a. allow the first unit to finish infusing before hanging the second unit.
   b. discard the contents of the first unit and hang the second unit now.
   c. discontinue the first unit, hang the second unit and call for replacement blood for the first unit.
   d. refrigerate the first unit, transfuse the second unit then re-hang the first unit.

51. In planning care for a group of clients, which client would be most appropriate to assign to a certified nursing assistant (CNA)? A client:
   a. who requires dressing changes on a stage II pressure ulcer.
   b. with a tracheostomy.
   c. in isolation for vancomycin-resistant enterococci (VRE).
   d. who is scheduled for a cardiac catheterization.

52. At 8:30AM the nurse is planning care. Which need should be addressed first?
   a. Morning care.
   b. Assistance with menu completion.
   c. Out of bed to wheelchair for 9:00AM physical therapy.
   d. 9:00AM medications.

53. When analyzing the assessment data for a client with cardiac tamponade, the nurse would expect to observe the following:
   a. tachycardia, paradoxic pulse, narrowed pulse pressure.
   b. bradycardia, bounding atrial pulse, narrowed pulse pressure.
   c. normal cardiac rate, diminished heart sounds, paradoxic pulse.
   d. tachycardia, widened pulse pressure, and distended neck veins.

54. The charge nurse on an orthopedic floor is notified that a client with a pelvic fracture is to be admitted. The unit is full. What is the best solution for the charge nurse to make?
   a. Request that a client who is in the operating room for a hip replacement be sent to a general medical-surgical floor following surgery.
   b. Call the physician and suggest that a client who had an uncomplicated arthroscopic meniscectomy yesterday be discharged early.
   c. Call the maintenance and housekeeping departments to convert the family waiting room into an additional client room.
   d. Make arrangements to transfer a client who had an above the knee amputation yesterday to a medical unit.

55. During labor, the client tells the nurse, "I can't do this anymore." The nurse notes that she is tired, arms and legs are shaky and she complains of nausea. The next action of the nurse should be to:
   a. ask the physician to prescribe an antiemetic medication.
   b. prepare the client for the delivery room.
   c. take the client's vital signs for possible infection.
   d. provide continual assessment data.

56. A nursing student completes a neurological assessment on a client who had a head injury. Which finding would be of most concern to the nurse working with the student?
   a. Redness and warmth at the IV site.
   b. Ipsilateral pupil dilation.
   c. Clear drainage from the ears.
   d. Weak hand grasps on the left side.

57. The physician prescribes glargine (Lantus) therapy for a diabetic client. The nurse:
   a. plans to utilize Lantus for intensive insulin therapy administering multiple doses daily.
   b. is aware that Lantus is released steadily and continuously and does not have a peak of action.
   c. is aware that Lantus is the type of insulin that best mimics natural insulin secretion in response to a meal.
   d. plans to assess for shakiness, clammy skin and disorientation 8 to 12 hours after administration of Lantus.

58. A client having treatment for leukemia has neutropenia. The client should be cautioned against:
   a. raw fruits and vegetables.
   b. daily bathing.
   c. oral hygiene.
   d. venipuncture.

59. Shortly after admission to a psychiatric unit, the client is approached by the nurse. The client stands up and yells, "Stay away from me, you can't help me with my problems." The nurse should reply:
   a. "You seem upset; I'll come back when you are feeling better."
   b. "You are feeling alone with your problems."
   c. "I'll come back later when you can speak more appropriately."
   d. "Avoiding your problems won't help you."

60. A client with fatigue, bradycardia and yellowish skin is diagnosed with hypothyroidism. Which assessment data would predispose the client to this problem?
   a. Car accident three years ago.
   b. Allergic reaction to strawberries.
   c. History of iron deficiency anemia.
   d. Bipolar illness treated with lithium carbonate (Lithium).

61. A pediatric nurse is pulled to a medical-surgical unit. Which assignment would be most appropriate? Clients with:
   a. a femur fracture, cervical cancer and hepatitis.
   b. diabetic ketoacidosis, cellulitis and an ovarian cyst.
   c. an infected decubitus, thallasemia and benign prostatic hypertrophy.
   d. chronic glomerulonephritis, cocaine overdose and a myocardial infarction.

62. The nurse is planning primary prevention strategies for the client with sickle cell anemia. The plan of care, focused on preventing sickle cell crisis, would include:
   a. administering the influenza vaccine.
   b. maintaining daily oxygen therapy.
   c. restricting fluids to two liters per day.
   d. taking aspirin prophylactically.

63. Following delivery of her first child, a woman informs the nurse that she would like to diet and exercise to regain her original shape and weight prior to pregnancy. The nurse should inform the client that, if she plans to breastfeed, she should add how many calories to her diet?
   a.   150 calories.
   b.   450 calories.
   c.   800 calories.
   d.   1,000 calories.

64. A client tells the nurse that her boss suggests she come to the mental health clinic because she has had several major losses in her life in the past two years. Although the client admits that she has experienced much trauma, she thinks she is pretty sure that she is over it. During the interview, the client jumps out of her chair when a door in a near by office slams shut. The nurse would expect to assess which symptoms. Select all that apply.
   a.   Lack of guilt and remorse.
   b.   Lack of expectations regarding the future.
   c.   Absence or numbing of emotion.
   d.   Self-mutilating behaviors.
   e.   Decreased participation in activities.

65. A nurse from a medical-surgical unit is pulled to the pediatric unit. Which assignment would be most appropriate for the pulled nurse?
   a.   A 4-year-old with new onset Type 1 diabetes, a 7-year-old with a seizure disorder and an infant with a cleft palate repair.
   b.   A 16-year-old with pelvic inflammatory disease, a 10-year-old with an appendectomy and a 13-year-old with a tonsil and adenoidectomy.
   c.   An infant with a hypospadias repair, a 2-year-old with tetralogy of Fallot and a 12-year-old with hemophilia.
   d.   A 10-year-old with injuries that indicate a strong possibility of abuse, a 16-year-old in sickle cell crisis and a 7-year-old with asthma.

66. In the event of a bioterrorist attack, it is essential that the nurse initiate isolation measures when dealing with a client who is suspected of having:
   a.   anthrax.
   b.   botulism.
   c.   smallpox.
   d.   tullaremia.

67. A female client presents to the physician's office with complaints of urinary incontinence. The nurse recognizes the need to reinforce teaching when the client states, "I should:
   a.   perform Kegel exercises for five minutes two times a day."
   b.   limit the amount of fluids that I drink."
   c.   avoid caffeine and alcohol."
   d.   try to urinate every two to three hours."

68. The home health nurse has been assigned a client diagnosed with Alzheimer's disease. When conducting interviews of potential family caregivers, the most important assessment data, gathered by the nurse, would be to:
   a.   determine their need for instruction about symptom presentation.
   b.   provide information about respite care in their community.
   c.   determine their understanding of the progression of the illness.
   d.   determine the family members' ability to problem solve.

69. A client with tenacious sputum is having problems bringing up sputum for a specimen. The nurse should:
   a. ask the client to drink fluids one hour before bringing up the specimen.
   b. administer a dose of medication to loosen secretions.
   c. take the specimen in the evening when coughing occurs.
   d. request that a nebulizer treatment be done to help bring up the sputum.

70. A client comes to the clinic with complaints of swelling legs during the day, fatigue and decreased energy. There is no history of heart disease. The most likely cause is related to:
   a. untreated emphysema.
   b. recent abdominal surgery.
   c. impending liver failure.
   d. idiopathic renal disease.

71. A woman has come to the clinic to receive her second injection of depot medroxyprogesterone acetate (Depo-Provera). What would be a potential contraindication to receiving the injection? She reports:
   a. heavy menstrual bleeding.
   b. mood changes.
   c. pain in her right calf.
   d. weight gain.

72. In order to conserve energy and decrease cardiac demands in the client with activity intolerance due to valvular heart disease, the nurse must:
   a. assess vital signs.
   b. administer oxygen by nasal cannula.
   c. monitor cardiac rhythm.
   d. plan rest periods.

73. A client, admitted with metastatic cancer, is scheduled for palliative surgery. The client tearfully says, "I know that the surgery will not cure me, but it is all I have left. It might make me feel better." Which response by the nurse would be most therapeutic?
   a. "You sound so depressed. Please don't give up hope."
   b. "Immediately after surgery you will still feel badly."
   c. "Dealing with death is always so difficult."
   d. "You are discouraged by the probable outcome."

74. The nurse is conducting a group for adult children of alcoholics (ACOA). One member stays silent and just observes the group process. The nurse should:
   a. refer the client for therapy.
   b. see the client separately after the group.
   c. ask the client's opinion about something.
   d. allow the client to speak when ready.

75. A client from another state is in a car accident and admitted to a local hospital. A relative indicates that the client has advanced directives. The nurse would plan to:
   a. honor the intent of the directives until they are faxed to the hospital.
   b. follow the directives if they were filed in this state.
   c. follow the directives because they cross state lines.
   d. determine the client's competency to consent to advanced directives at this hospital.

76. A client, who is just started on lithium carbonate (Lithium), asks the nurse, "Why do I have to have my blood drawn all the time?" The nurse would include what information when teaching the client? Select all that apply.
   a. Lithium can adversely affect thyroid function.
   b. There is a narrow range between therapeutic and toxic levels of the drug.
   c. High doses of the drug can cause hypersexual behaviors.
   d. Blood lithium levels assure that the client is not taking any other drug.
   e. Lithium levels can prove that client has been compliant with dietary restrictions.

77. A woman, who has endometriosis, has opted to start therapy with danazol (Danocrine). The nurse would teach the client side effects of this medication which include:
   a. the formation of blood clots.
   b. a steady loss in bone density.
   c. the inability to ever become fertile again.
   d. an inverse proportion of progesterone related to estrogen.

78. A woman is brought to the hospital by her husband. He found her roaming the neighborhood at 4:00AM, asking people to sample her recipes. He tells the nurse that his wife has become increasingly agitated and energetic over the past two weeks. After admission to the psychiatric unit, the client shouts, "I am the greatest chef in the world. If you peasants are lucky, I may cook for you." The most appropriate room assignment the nurse could make for this client is a:
   a. room without windows and soothing colors.
   b. room near the nurse's station for easy supervision by the staff.
   c. semiprivate room with a client with similar symptoms.
   d. room with a television and stereo for therapeutic distraction.

79. An agency nurse is sent to your unit. Which clients should the charge nurse assign to the agency nurse? Clients with:
   a. tuberculosis, cirrhosis and a laminectomy of yesterday.
   b. uncomplicated laproscopic cholecystectomy of this morning, sickle cell crisis, and hyperosmolar hyperglycemic nonketotic coma.
   c. subdural hematoma evacuation, COPD and cellulitis.
   d. hip replacement of yesterday, cardiac catheterization of this afternoon and congestive heart failure.

80. A man is admitted to the psychiatric unit. He believes that his coworkers are plotting to remove him from the job and they may be poisoning his food. He agreed to the admission because he would be safe from those people who are trying to hurt him. In interacting with the client, the nurse should:
   a. reassure him of his safety on the unit.
   b. plan to meet several times for assessment.
   c. assist him to become involved in a group activity.
   d. orient him to the unit and introduce him to other clients.

81. The evening charge nurse is notified that a client is to be admitted. The nursing unit is full. Which client would the charge nurse suggest be discharged to make room?
   a. A client who had lithotripsy yesterday for renal calculi. He is passing stone particles and has hematuria. His temperature is 37.2°C (99°F).
   b. A client admitted with acute pancreatitis that has a serum amylase of 200. He is NPO and complaining of nausea.
   c. A man who was admitted yesterday morning for a very mild myocardial infarction. He has denied any chest pain for 24 hours and his cardiac enzymes are normal.
   d. A client who had a laminectomy two days ago. The patient controlled analgesia pump was discontinued. The client denies any parasthesias.

82. A client post-liposuction makes the following comments to the recovery room nurse. Which comment indicates the client needs clarification of her expectations?
    a. "I can't wait to get these bandages off to see the results!"
    b. "I know I'll have a lot of bruising postoperatively."
    c. "I have to keep these bandages smooth and tight to help contour my skin."
    d. "I'm not allowed any strenuous exercise for four to six weeks."

83. A couple comes to the fertility clinic because they have not had any success in conceiving a child. After the nurse meets with the couple which statement would indicates a need for further teaching?
    a. "I am going to switch from briefs to boxer shorts", states the male partner.
    b. "We are going to plan a weekend getaway with champagne and a bubble bath to help us relax."
    c. "I am going to monitor and track my temperature twice a day", states the female partner.
    d. "We are going to meet with an adoption agency before we schedule another appointment here."

84. A client is admitted with stage III ovarian cancer. She asks the nurse how she would have known that she had the cancer before it progressed to this stage. The nurse's best response would be:
    a. "Yearly pap tests screen for ovarian cancer."
    b. "Ovarian cancer is usually asymptomatic in its early stages."
    c. "Vaginal spotting is an early symptom of ovarian cancer."
    d. "Lower abdominal pain is an early symptom of ovarian cancer."

85. A client with tinnitus, vertigo and hearing loss in the right ear is diagnosed with Meniere's disease. The nurse would teach which facts to the client?
    a. A low-salt diet will help manage symptoms.
    b. The hearing loss will reverse with treatment.
    c. The tinnitus is relieved through proper sleep.
    d. Make sure to take all of the antibiotics.

86. A client with a history of diverticulitis is admitted with complaints of persistent left lower-quadrant abdominal pain, nausea, and vomiting. Upon assessment, the nurse notes a temperature of 102°F, tenderness upon palpation of the abdomen and a WBC count of 17,000/mm^3. Which prescription would the nurse question?
    a. Clear liquid diet.
    b. Barium enema.
    c. IV fluids: 5% dextrose and 0.45% normal saline solution at 100ml/hour.
    d. Cefoxitin (Mefoxin) 1g IV every six hours.

87. The nurse is caring for a client with acute respiratory distress syndrome (ARDS) secondary to gram-negative sepsis. What initial finding would the nurse expect this client to exhibit?
    a. Respiratory alkalosis.
    b. Increased pulmonary artery wedge pressure (PAWP).
    c. Hypoxemia that responds to an increase in FIO$_2$.
    d. Leukopenia.

88. An elderly client develops herpes zoster and is to be treated at home. What would the nurse teach the client? Select all that apply.
    a. "Clean the sores with soap and water."
    b. "Do not share towels with your spouse."
    c. "Do no let your pregnant granddaughter visit you."
    d. "Keep the room temperature warm."
    e. "Trim your fingernails."

89.   A client, who recently returned from the war zone, tells the nurse, "You cannot possibly understand what I have been through. How can you help?" What would be the most therapeutic response by the nurse?

    a.   "You sound angry; can you tell me more about this?"
    b.   "The more you tell me about your experiences, the more I can understand them."
    c.   "It must have been just horrible for you. You are right, I don't know what it was like."
    d.   "I have had many clients experience traumatic events."

90.   A client is prescribed hormone replacement therapy (HRT). The client asks the nurse if HRT is safe for all women. The nurse knows that HRT is contraindicated in women with:

    a.   peptic ulcer disease.
    b.   active liver disease.
    c.   chlamydia.
    d.   osteoporosis.

STOP. You have now completed Practice Session: 20. Now take a few minutes and correct your answers. Calculate your accuracy rate by dividing the number of questions you completed correctly by the total number of questions you completed (90).

Correct answers ÷ total number of questions completed = accuracy rate.

_____ ÷ _____ = _____

ANSWERS AND RATIONALES
Practice Session 20

1. **The correct answer is d.** The question is asking the nurse what she should say when a client questions the value of the therapeutic relationship. In option (d) the nurse uses the therapeutic technique of reflection. The nurse validates that she understands what the client is saying to her and demonstrates the nurse's sincere concern and respect for the client's feelings. Options (a) and (b) avoid the therapeutic issue and option (c) misinterprets the client's statement. The client is not saying that nothing will help although he does not believe that talking will help.
Nursing Process: Implementation   **Client Need:** Physiological Integrity

2. **The correct answer is a.** The question is asking what finding would indicate that this child was a victim of abuse. Bilateral retinal hemorrhage is diagnostic of shaken baby syndrome. This occurs when the baby is vigorously shaken. The repeated coup-contracoup injury to the brain results in multiple retinal hemorrhages. A single blow to the side of the head may cause a variety of neurological symptoms including increased intracranial pressure, but would not typically create bilateral retinal hemorrhage. Bulging fontanelles, nausea and vomiting and decreased level of consciousness are symptoms of increased intracranial pressure (options b, c & d). These would be expected if the child sustained a head injury after falling and hitting his head on the coffee table.
Nursing Process: Analysis   **Client Need:** Psychosocial Integrity

3. **The correct answer is a.** The question is asking which assignment would be most appropriate for a medical-surgical nurse who is pulled to the pediatric unit. It is necessary that the pulled nurse is able to provide competent, safe care to the client. Some specialized care is not transferable to all client care areas. A medical-surgical nurse would have experience caring for clients with sickle cell anemia, asthma and femur fracture, as these are all found in the adult population. An infant with respiratory syncytial virus (RSV) would need to be cared for by a pediatric nurse, as this disease is rarely seen in people over two years of age. In addition, it can lead to airway obstruction and this client would need the specialized care of a pediatric nurse (option b). Pyloric stenosis is an obstructive disorder found in newborns. A medical-surgical nurse would be unlikely to have the competencies required to care for this infant (option c). Epiglottitis can be life threatening as it can suddenly lead to respiratory obstruction. An experienced pediatric nurse should care for the child (option d).
Nursing Process: Planning   **Client Need:** Safe, Effective Care Environment

4. **The correct answer is b.** The question is asking what the symptoms listed would indicate in a client with a knife wound to the chest. A closed pneumothorax (option a) has no associated external wound. In this case, the tension pneumothorax is an "open pneumothorax" (because of the knife wound) with rapid accumulation of air in the pleural space causing the lung to collapse and the mediastinum to shift towards the heart. The client will experience inadequate cardiac output and marked hypoxemia. Chylothorax (option c) is lymphatic fluid in the pleural space. Cardiac tamponade (option d) occurs when blood rapidly collects in the pericardial sac and compresses the myocardium. This would be a consideration if the knife wound had been on the left side of the chest, rather than the right.
Nursing Process: Analysis   **Client Need:** Physiological Integrity

5. **The correct answer is b.** The question is asking how to tell if the client is experiencing side effects of the medication. Steroid therapy may cause gastrointestinal irritation and bleeding. The client may not experience pain or tenderness (option c) because of the level of his injury. The client's blood pressure will probably be low (option d) because of the loss of sympathetic innervation causing vasodilation leading to decreased venous return and reduced cardiac output. Vital signs cannot be used to monitor for gastrointestinal bleeding. Diarrhea (option a) is not a common side effect of steroid therapy.
Nursing Process: Evaluation   **Client Need:** Physiological Integrity

6. **The correct answer is c.** The question is asking what data would keep the client from having a tube feeding. The absence of bowel sounds means the client cannot tolerate any food in the intestines because they are not functioning properly. Dysphagia and esophageal injury are valid reasons to initiate tube feeding to maintain proper nutrition (options d & b). Excessive flatus or bloating (option a) could be a side effect or due to air swallowing, but would not prevent feeding.
Nursing Process: Analysis   **Client Need:** Physiological Integrity

7. **The correct answer is b.** The question is asking which condition predisposes a client to glomerulonephritis. Acute post-streptococcal glomerulonephritis (APSON) develops 5 to 21 days after an infection of the pharynx or skin (i.e. streptococcal sore throat or impetigo). Urinary tract infection (option a), heart disease (option c) and trauma (option d) are not predisposing conditions for glomerulonephritis.
Nursing Process: Assessment   **Client Need:** Physiological Integrity

8. **The correct answer is b.** The question is asking what the priority is when a client with dementia begins to wander. Identifying what precipitates the wandering behavior will help the nurse plan appropriate interventions to prevent and or minimize it. Consulting with family members of a client with dementia is important, however, it would not take precedence over understanding the contributing factors to the wandering (option a). The nurse can minimize the opportunities for injury, but providing safe areas is an unrealistic goal (option c). There is no evidence that the client is wandering more at night (option d).
Nursing Process: Implementation   **Client Need:** Psychosocial Integrity

9. **The correct answer is d.** The question is asking which drug has adverse reactions with polycystic kidney disease (PKD). Aspirin-containing drugs are discouraged to prevent increased chance of bleeding in client with PKD. Stool softeners, such as ducosate (Colace) (option a), are usually encouraged in PKD to promote healthy bowel activity. Acetaminophen (Tylenol) (option b) is usually encouraged if needed because non-steroidal, anti-inflammatory drugs (NSAIDS) affect renal function and aspirin (Ecotrin) can promote bleeding. Diuretics, such as furosemide (Lasix) (option c) are sometimes prescribed to help control hypertension related to PKD.
Nursing Process: Analysis   **Client Need:** Physiological Integrity

10. **The correct answer is a.** The question is asking how to assist a dying client to get rest. Times of stimulation, such as physical treatment, mealtimes and visitors may deplete the client's physical and emotional energy. The client's functioning ability can be enhanced by rest periods, which replenish needed energy. Protection from injury is important, but does not affect energy levels directly (option b). Encouraging independence decreases powerlessness, but does nothing to conserve energy (option c). Involving friends and family assists the person socially and with support, but may also deplete energy (option d).
Nursing Process: Implementation   **Client Need:** Health Promotion & Maintenance

11. **The correct answer is d.** The question is asking what condition may predispose a client to Type 2 diabetes. Obesity stresses the pancreatic system in that demands for insulin exceed the normal or diminish production of insulin by the islets of Langerhans. Glucosuria is common in Type 2 diabetes, but ketonuria is seldom observed. The islets of Langerhans are producing sufficient amounts of insulin to prevent breakdown of fats into fatty acids (option a). A history of viral infection is important in diagnosing Type 1 diabetes, but has no relationship to the diagnosis of Type 2 diabetes (option b). An increase in exercise will enable the individual to utilize glucose without insulin and would be a factor contributing to prevention of the disorder (option c).
Nursing Process: Evaluation   **Client Need:** Health Promotion & Maintenance

12. **The correct answer is a.** The question is asking which lab report would indicate that a client with pancreatitis is experiencing pain. Pancreatitis occurs when the pancreatic enzymes are activated in the pancreas instead of the intestine. This causes auto digestion of the pancreas, which is very painful. Normal amylase (a pancreatic enzyme) levels are usually 0 to 130u/L. A BUN of 30 mg/dL is on the high side of normal (10 to 30mg/dL). This may be an early sign of renal impairment but would not indicate pain at this time (option b). In pancreatitis, clients often have

hypocalcemia (normal Ca++ is 9 to 11mg/dL), however, this would cause muscle twitching not pain (option c). A normal SGOT is 7 to 40u/L (option d). A level of 40u/L may be an early indication of liver involvement but would not cause pain.
Nursing Process: Planning   **Client Need:** Physiological Integrity

13.   **The correct answer is d.** The question is asking the nurse to identify a successful outcome of crisis intervention. The role of the nurse is to support the client through the crisis and help the client return to a pre-crisis functioning level. If the client can return to his job and function, it indicates successful crisis intervention. The focus of crisis intervention is on the client's immediate problem presented as a crisis, not past problems (option c). Usually the crisis has occurred within the previous two weeks. Options (a) and (b) do not necessarily indicate successful behavioral change and would usually be issues that would be addressed in traditional therapy.
Nursing Process: Planning   **Client Need:** Psychosocial Integrity

14.   **The correct answer is d.** The question is asking which of four clients should be cared for first. Hypokalemia is a common side effect of furosemide (Lasix); a potassium level of 2.5mEq/L is considered a critical value, which needs to be addressed immediately. The incidence of potentially lethal ventricular arrhythmias is increased with hypokalemia. Blood loss is expected during an ORIF of the hip (option a). Decreased hemoglobin and hematocrit levels, tachycardia and tachypnea are symptoms of loss of blood volume. This client is receiving replacement fluids and is stable at present. Hypoxemia (oxygen saturation levels less than 94%) is typical in obstructive pulmonary diseases (option b). Additionally, this client has anemia; therefore, the oxygen-carrying component of the blood is decreased. The pulse oximeter reading may be falsely decreased. A prolonged partial thromboplastin time of 1.5 to 2.5 times the control is the expected response to IV heparin therapy (option c).
Nursing Process: Planning   **Client Need:** Physiological Integrity

15.   **The correct answer is d.** The question is asking what would indicate the medication would probably be effective. The blood level must remain within this range. If the level drops, the client is susceptible to seizure activity. If the level is above the therapeutic range, the client is susceptible to toxic effects. Phenytoin (Dilantin) does not alter sodium or potassium values and will not improve the level of consciousness (options a & b). Blood pressure and pulse should be monitored when intravenous phenytoin (Dilantin) is administered but, since the drug was not being given for the cardiovascular effects, the normal range vital signs would not indicate the desired effect of absence of tonic-clonic seizures (option c).
Nursing Process: Evaluation   **Client Need:** Physiological Integrity

16.   **The correct answer is b.** The question is asking what action to take if the nasogastric drainage is dark brown. Blood that has come in contact with gastric juices becomes "coffee ground" in appearance. The physician should be notified and treatment initiated before further bleeding occurs. The normal color of gastric drainage is light green (option a). Irrigating the NG tube with 30ml of NSS to see if it clears (option c) is incorrect because it is frequently routine to irrigate NG tubes every two hours with 30ml of NSS to maintain patency of the tube. Flushing with a 30ml air bolus to check placement (option d) is a method of checking placement, but would have no effect on the type of drainage being obtained from the tube.
Nursing Process: Implementation   **Client Need:** Physiological Integrity

17.   **The correct answer is c.** The question is asking when the blood should be drawn on a client who is prescribed a 24-hour urine creatinine clearance level. These tests are used to measure the glomerular filtration rate (GFR). This measure is an indication of how well the kidneys can clear solutes from the plasma. For accurate results, the serum creatinine is collected halfway through the urine collection (options a, b & d). Creatinine clearance is determined using the following formula: amount of urine (ml/min) x urine creatinine (mg/dL)
                              serum creatinine (mg/dL)
Nursing Process: Planning   **Client Need:** Physiological Integrity

18.   **The correct answer is c.** The question is asking what the nurse should do when a client is

experiencing looseness of association. Trying to reacclimatize the client to the "here and now" with a game of pool can help the client focus better on thoughts. Pretending to understand the client (option a) can only confuse and prolong the client's disorientation. Addressing the client by saying, "You are not making sense" (option b) puts blame solely on the client. Having the client lie down and rest (option d) does not address the problem.

Nursing Process: Implementation   **Client Need:** Psychosocial Integrity

19.   **The correct answer is d, b, c, a.** The question is asking the order in which the interventions should be completed when a client is admitted with a cerebrovascular accident (CVA). The head of bed should be elevated immediately to help decrease the intracranial pressure (option d). An IV is then started and an isotonic solution (normal saline) is infused. This way if the client later needs IV drugs, they can be given immediately (option b). The client is then taken to radiology for a CT scan to determine the type and extent of the CVA (option c). Once it has been determined that the client does not have a hemorrhagic CVA, a tissue plasminogen activator can be given to break any cerebral clots and increase cerebral blood flow (option a).

Nursing Process: Planning   **Client Need:** Physiological Integrity

20.   **The correct answer is d.** The question is asking what to tell a new mother who asks questions about taking care of her son's temporary gastrostomy tube. The tube is temporarily present to provide calories and nutrients (options a, b & c). When the gastrostomy tube is only a temporary measure, parental time is better spent attaching to the infant by holding, cuddling and rocking to meet developmental needs. Getting to know the infant is important to the attachment process.

Nursing Process: Implementation   **Client Need:** Health Promotion & Maintenance

21.   **The correct answer is d.** The question is asking how to suction an infant with tracheoesophageal fistula (TEF). This infant needs to be closely observed for respiratory distress. It is necessary to suction frequently as mucous tends to accumulate in the pharynx from surgical trauma. Perform suctioning shallowly with care not to penetrate the suture line (options a, b & c). Generally, the surgeon will provide a pre-measured catheter to alert caretakers to the point of the anastomosis.

Nursing Process: Planning   **Client Need:** Safe, Effective Care Environment

22.   **The correct answer is b.** The question is asking what should be prescribed for an adult who has had a significant visual change in one year. This may be an early sign of diabetes. Hyperglycemia may cause the lens of the eye to swell and alter visual acuity. Tonometry, a test to measure intraocular pressure and visual field testing would be indicated if the client were suspected of having glaucoma (options a & c). Serum T_3 and T_4 levels would be drawn if a thyroid problem were suspected. Exophthalmus (bulging eyes) is a symptom of hyperthyroidism, but it does not change visual acuity (option d).

Nursing Process: Analysis   **Client Need:** Physiological Integrity

23.   **The correct answer is b.** The question is asking how to assess why the referral was not appropriate. Several principles should be kept in mind when making a referral. The referral should be individualized to the client and family. Since this parent has not complied with previous referrals, the nurse should assess why follow through was not accomplished. It is possible that the parent and clinic's schedules are not compatible or the client has no transportation to the clinic site. Those are all factors taken into consideration when making the referral. A neighborhood clinic for follow-up would be an appropriate referral for this parent and would probably keep the respiratory problem from becoming worse (option a). Although treatment has been rendered for the emergency condition, follow-up related to ongoing treatment and evaluation effectiveness would be more appropriate in a clinic setting (option c). This referral would not be a waste of the parent's time (option d) since it probably would have kept the parent from making so many visits to the emergency department.

Nursing Process: Assessment   **Client Need:** Physiological Integrity

24.   **The correct answer is c.** The question is asking how to care for a client who is unable to drain excess fluid from the area because the lymph glands have been removed. Clients with lymphedema are at greater risk for infection because the lymph system cannot transport excess

fluid and infection away from the hand and wrist. Care is taken to protect the area from injury. Bunching clothes at the elbow (option b) may cause further edema and constrict circulation. Diuretics (option a) may be used to rid the body of excess fluids. Surgery (option d) is not the first line of treatment and will not be used unless other avenues are explored, such as physical therapy and compression devices.

Nursing Process: Planning   **Client Need:** Health Promotion & Maintenance

25.   **The correct answer is c.** The question is asking what foods are on an acid ash diet. All protein sources are metabolized with an acid ash and result in acid urine but some meat products, e.g. red meat, organ meat and fish have high purine levels which should be avoided by people with a history of renal stones (option d). Most fruits and vegetables produce alkaline ash (options a & b).

Nursing Process: Evaluation   **Client Need:** Health Promotion & Maintenance

26.   **The correct answer is 3.** The question is asking how fast the nurse would give phenytoin (Dilantin) IV push to this child. First you need to convert the child's weight to kilograms.

$$\frac{55 \text{ lbs}}{1} \times \frac{1 \text{kg}}{2.2 \text{ lbs}} = 25 \text{kg}$$

According to the information contained in the question, the child can be given 1mg of phenytoin (Dilantin) for every kg he weighs in a one minute time frame. Therefore, if he weighs 25kg, he can be given 25mg of phenytoin (Dilantin) per minute. Now calculate how many minutes it would take to give him the 75mg he was prescribed.

$$\frac{75 \text{mg}}{25 \text{mg}} = 3 \text{ minutes}$$

Nursing Process: Implementation   **Client Need:** Safe, Effective Care Environment

27.   **The correct answer is c.** The question is asking which client should be seen first regarding laboratory results. A client with peptic ulcer disease is at risk for bleeding. A decrease in hemoglobin (normal: 11.7 to 17.4 g/dL) and hematocrit (normal: 38 to 49%) may suggest bleeding. The therapeutic range for a client receiving digoxin for CHF is 0.8 to 1.5ng/mL (option a). Therapeutic INR levels are 2 to 3 (option b). A prolonged partial thromboplastin time of 1.5 to 2.5 times the control is the expected response to IV heparin therapy (option d).

Nursing Process: Analysis   **Client Need:** Physiological Integrity

28.   **The correct answer is b.** The question is asking which answer is the strongest indication of a possible posttraumatic stress disorder. A student falling asleep in class may indicate sleeping difficulties due to anxiety or depression and needs to be addressed. Playing with cars and crashing them (option a), coloring alone (option c) and frequent trips to the restroom (option d) are all more common behaviors for this age group. Although they may be further evaluated, they would not be as important as a sign the child is sleeping.

Nursing Process: Assessment   **Client Need:** Psychosocial Integrity

29.   **The correct answer is c.** The question is asking what would be an appropriate goal for a client with diverticulitis. Increased fiber is suggested in preventing flare-ups of diverticulitis because it increases the bulk of the stool to facilitate peristalsis, thereby promoting defecation. Option (a) does not allow for enough fluid intake, which should equal 2L/day. The passage of soft, formed stool is the goal rather than diarrhea (option c). Option (b) does not apply here because there is no indication that a colostomy was performed on this client, although clients with acute diverticulitis may require a temporary colostomy.

Nursing Process: Planning   **Client Need:** Physiological Integrity

30.   **The correct answer is d.** The question is asking what dynamic is happening with this client. Clients with this disorder frequently project their own anger onto others. In this case, the client is angry with the nurse and projects those feelings onto her, believing that the nurse is angry with her. Therefore, the client repeatedly asks the nurse about anger. Option (b) is also an appropriate goal, but could not occur until the client recognizes her own feelings of anger. Option (c) is a long-term goal for this client. Option (a) does not apply to the client's behavior in this situation.

Nursing Process: Planning   **Client Need:** Psychosocial Integrity

31. **The correct answer is c.** The question is asking what to suspect when a client has multiple admissions for infection and the incision culture is positive for Escherichia coli (E-coli). E-coli is part of the normal flora of the bowel. However, it is not normally found anywhere else in the body. Factitious disorder is diagnosed when clients deliberately produce physical/psychological symptoms, such as rubbing a small amount of feces on a wound to cause an infection. This is done to gain attention. Somataform disorders occur when there are physical problems without a reason for them to occur. They are not caused by a conscious act of the client (option a). There is no evidence to suggest a compromised immune system or suicidal ideation (options b & d).
Nursing Process: Analysis   **Client Need:** Psychosocial Integrity

32. **The correct answer is a.** The question is asking which intervention would be appropriate for a client receiving hemodialysis. Vascular access for hemodialysis should be assessed on a regular basis. A thrill can be felt by palpating the fistula or graft and a bruit can be heard with a stethoscope. Hyperkalemia is an indication for dialysis; foods high in potassium (option b) should be avoided. Assessing for symptoms of peritonitis (option c) and performing cycle exchanges (option d) are interventions for peritoneal dialysis.
Nursing Process: Planning   **Client Need:** Physiological Integrity

33. **The correct answer is b.** The question is asking which statement made by the client would indicate a need for further teaching. The segment of bowel utilized to create the stoma is completely isolated from the intestinal tract. The irritating effect of the urine on the segment of intestine causes mucous to be present in the urine; however, there would not be stool present. Option (a) is an accurate statement because the stoma continues to shrink within the first few weeks of surgery. A properly fitting appliance is essential to prevent skin problems. Option (c) is an accurate statement because a high fluid intake is necessary to flush the ileal conduit. Option (d) is an accurate statement because urine is kept acidic to prevent alkaline encrustations. Cranberries, prunes and plums contain acids that are excreted in the urine influencing the acidity of the urine.
Nursing Process: Evaluation   **Client Need:** Health Promotion & Maintenance

34. **The correct answer is b.** The question is asking why the father is acting this way. After denial begins to fail as a defense and the reality of the situation begins to be understood by the client, it is not unusual for the client to become angry about why this has happened. The client cannot express his anger physically, but must use words. This anger is a means of dealing with reality and is not personal (options a & d). The client is not demonstrating sensory alteration (option c).
Nursing Process: Analysis   **Client Need:** Psychosocial Integrity

35. **The correct answer is c.** The question is asking the relationship between diet and insulin times. Option (c) insures that adequate glucose is available at appropriate times for maximum utilization. Meals and snacks must be planned around onset, peak and duration effects of insulin (option a). The initial meal should be planned following the injection to insure that insulin will be available to utilize glucose (option b). It is best to have planned time for administering insulin and taking meals; but if an adjustment must be made in one, it must also be made in the other (option d).
Nursing Process: Implementation   **Client Need:** Physiological Integrity

36. **The correct answer is a.** The question is asking what should occur when a client is to be discharged to her daughter's home for the first time. Home care nurses will make an assessment of the home and suggest safety measures. They can also assist with education on all aspects of care (options b, c & d) but the primary concern would be safety.
Nursing Process: Planning   **Client Need:** Health Promotion & Maintenance

37. **The correct answer is a.** The question is asking what symptoms are indicative of fibromyalgia. Fibromyalgia is a chronic disorder characterized by a widespread, nonarticular musculoskeletal pain and fatigue with multiple tender points. Although many clients complain of joint pain and tenderness, there is no evidence of joint swelling or an inflammatory or degenerative process. Option (b) lists symptoms of osteoarthritis, a degenerative disease. Option (c) provides data

consistent with rheumatoid arthritis. The symptoms in option (d) are found in systemic lupus erythematosus.
Nursing Process: Assessment   **Client Need:** Physiological Integrity

38.   **The correct answer is b.** The question is asking how to promote safety on the playground. Federal guidelines suggest cushioning play areas where children may fall to lessen the impact. Stone gravel (option a) could cause more injury. Swings and sliding boards can be placed on the playground if proper precautions are taken for sharp edges and falls (option c). Restraints on the seesaw may cause a choking hazard if the child slides into the restraint (option d).
Nursing Process: Implementation   **Client Need:** Health Promotion & Maintenance

39.   **The correct answer is c.** The question is asking which of four clients should be cared for first. The client with a suspected spinal cord tumor has not voided in over 6 hours. This may be indicative of spinal cord compression; a medical emergency. If the compression is not relieved ischemia may occur. Corticosteroids are given to decrease edema. Hyperglycemia (option a) is an expected finding in clients with excessive adrenocortical activity. Insulin may be prescribed, however this is not as important as caring for the client with a possible cord compression. . Polyarthritis, the most common finding in people with rheumatic fever, does not cause permanent disability (option b). The client with an intermaxillary fixation (option d) should be given an antiemetic however the client with a possible spinal cord compression is more emergent.
Nursing Process: Planning   **Client Need:** Safe, Effective Care Environment

40.   **The correct answer is c.** The question is asking which option is true about systemic lupus erythematosus (SLE). Clients with SLE are photosensitive, causing exacerbations of symptoms with exposure. While vitamins A and D are useful for skin health (option a), they are not as important as avoiding the sun. Fatty foods and increased fluids are not particularly relevant (options b & d).
Nursing Process: Planning   **Client Need:** Health Promotion & Maintenance

41.   **The correct answer is b.** The question is asking what the father should do to help his son perform better in school. Children with Tourette's syndrome often have difficulty concentrating because they are distracted by obsessional thoughts or compulsive behavior. They also may be trying to concentrate on controlling their thoughts and behavior and do not pay attention to the instructions being given in class. Meeting with the teacher, explaining Tourette's syndrome and devising an individualized plan to help him stay on task will enhance the student's learning. There is no evidence to suggest the child needs to go to a special school or class at this time (options a & d). There is also no evidence to suggest that he is having difficulty socializing (option c).
Nursing Process: Planning   **Client Need:** Health Promotion & Maintenance

42.   **The correct answer is d.** The question is asking how the nurse would care for a client who just had a partial gastrectomy. The gastrostomy tube needs to be irrigated with 30 to 50ml of water to maintain patency. It can easily become occluded with tube feeding formula. There is no need to keep the client on bed rest for two days. Ambulation will help prevent a paralytic ileus (option a). Gauze pads should not be cut as the threads can enter the wound. This would cause irritation and, possibly, inflammation (option b). There is no need to inject air to check placement as the tube is surgically placed in the stomach. If placement is to be checked, it can more easily be done by aspirating gastric contents. Listening for a "pop" of air would not guarantee that the tube is in the stomach as the nurse would hear the same sound if the tube were in the peritoneum (option c).
Nursing Process: Planning   **Client Need:** Physiological Integrity

43.   **The correct answer is c.** The question is asking the appropriate instructions for a client who has mononucleosis with streptococcal pharyngitis. Mononucleosis is caused by a virus that must generally run its course. The febrile period generally lasts two to four weeks and the person should remain on bed rest while the fever is present. An increased fluid intake (option b) helps control the fever. Spleen enlargement may occur due to lymphocytosis. Steroids will not alter the disease itself (option a), but may make the client feel better. A warm saline throat gargle is often prescribed to relieve throat pain (option d).

44.   **The correct answer is b.** The question is asking which foods are lowest in sodium when selecting from a hypothetical restaurant menu. These foods are expected to be free of added sodium in restaurants. Foods such as bread products, cooked vegetables and gravies will probably contain substantial amounts of added sodium (options a, c & d).
    Nursing Process: Evaluation   **Client Need:** Health Promotion & Maintenance

45.   **The correct answer is b.** The question is asking what the erection means in a man who has a T_4 spinal injury. Sacral segments 2, 3 and 4 are responsible for a part of sexual functioning including erection. These segments are not isolated from higher cerebral control. With the resolution of spinal shock, the reflex erection will occur, as there has been no damage to the sacral segments. The erection is not a voluntary response (options a & d). In fact, the client is probably unaware that he is having an erection, as there is no sensation associated with this because of his injury. Catheterization does not have to be stopped (option c).
    Nursing Process: Analysis   **Client Need:** Physiological Integrity

46.   **The correct answer is d.** The question is asking how to care for a nephrostomy tube. Leakage around the catheter or a change in urine output may be a sign that the catheter is dislodged. A nephrostomy tube should never be clamped (option c) or irrigated without a specific prescription from the physician. When a prescription to irrigate has been received, no more than 5ml should be used due to the small capacity of the renal pelvis (option a). Urine collection containers should always be placed in a dependent position, in order to decrease reflux into the bladder and consequent infection (option b).
    Nursing Process: Planning   **Client Need:** Physiological Integrity

47.   **The correct answer is a.** The question is asking which result should be reported to the physician. The therapeutic range for INR is 2 to 3 seconds to achieve the appropriate anticoagulant effect in preventing further development of a DVT. The hemoglobin and hematocrit (option b) are within normal limits. The PTT (option c) is used as an indicator in heparin sodium (Heparin) therapy. The PT (option d) is used for oral anticoagulant therapy but this is also within the normal range. INR is considered more accurate than PT.
    Nursing Process: Analysis   **Client Need:** Physiological Integrity

48.   **The correct answer is b.** The question is asking how to evaluate if a client is meeting goals related to decreasing fluid. The nursing diagnosis is fluid volume excess. Daily weights in the morning before eating and after voiding show fluid loss since about one kilogram of body weight is equal to one liter of fluid. Pulse oximetry reflects oxygen in the blood (option a). Oxygen level may be compromised because the distended abdomen limits lung expansion. Elevating the head of the bed can pull fluid away from the diaphragm through gravity. Lung expansion is increased but fluid level is unchanged. Skin inspection shows that skin does not have open areas (option c) but is not directly related to excess fluid measurement. Monitoring intake and output is useful in determining fluid volume deficit, but is not the best (option d).
    Nursing Process: Evaluation   **Client Need:** Physiological Integrity

49.   **The correct answer is c.** The question is asking how the nurse should respond to this socially motivated statement. The client has confused the purpose of the professional therapeutic relationship with the nurse with the purpose of a social relationship. Requesting an explanation is a hindrance to communication (option a). Option (b) is an example of disagreeing with the client and option (d) allows the client to avoid the issue and keep the focus on the nurse.
    Nursing Process: Implementation   **Client Need:** Psychosocial Integrity

50.   **The correct answer is b.** The question is asking what to do when the first unit of packed red blood cells (PRBC) is only halfway finished when it is time to hang the second unit. The PRBC should be in normal room temperatures for a limited amount of time or they will become contaminated and grow bacteria, which could infect the client. The second unit should be started and this one discarded in the method approved by the hospital. The physician should also be

notified in case more PRBC or fluid needs to be prescribed. Allowing the first unit to finish places the client in danger of septic infection (option a). More PRBC cannot be prescribed unless the physician has given permission (option c). Refrigerating the first unit will not rid the unit of bacteria already growing in it (option d).
Nursing Process: Implementation   **Client Need:** Safe, Effective Care Environment

51.   **The correct answer is c.** The question is asking which of four clients would be best to assign to a CNA. Clients in isolation for VRE infections require standard precautions for contact with blood and body fluids and for all direct contact with the client and the immediate environment of the client. Hands are to be washed after contact with the client or the immediate environment. Standard precautions and handwashing are included in CNA training. The nurse is expected to provide guidance or direction for accomplishment of a nursing task delegated to unlicensed personnel. Guidance in isolation requirements would be appropriate. Activities, which require nursing assessment, are not within the scope of sound nursing judgment to delegate. Assessment of a wound as described in option (a) and post-cardiac catheterization assessment in option (d) would, therefore, not be care to be delegated. Tracheostomy care is not included in CNA training making option (b) incorrect.
Nursing Process: Planning   **Client Need:** Safe, Effective Care Environment

52.   **The correct answer is d.** The question is asking which client need should be addressed first. Of the four needs listed, the medications are the most important. Medications given within 30 minutes before or after the scheduled time are considered to meet the right time standard. Morning care (option a) and menu completion (option b) can be performed at any time. The nurse has 30 minutes until the client needs to be in the physical therapy department (option c).
Nursing Process: Implementation   **Client Need:** Physiological Integrity

53.   **The correct answer is a.** The question is asking about assessment data for a client with cardiac tamponade. This is a classic assessment question to test the knowledge base of cardiac tamponade. Reviewing the pathophysiology related to cardiac tamponade will assist the learner in understanding why tachycardia, paradoxic pulse, narrowed pulse pressure are correct. Option (b) is incorrect as the pulse does not slow, nor is the atrial pulse bounding with cardiac tamponade. There is, however, a narrowed pulse pressure. Option (c) is incorrect as the heart rate is not normal, however, heart sounds may be diminished and there may be a paradoxic pulse with cardiac tamponade. Option (d) is incorrect as there is not a widened pulse pressure (but a narrowed pulse pressure), however, there are distended neck veins with cardiac tamponade.
Nursing Process: Assessment   **Client Need:** Physiological Integrity

54.   **The correct answer is b.** The question is asking what is the best action to make room for a new admission. A client undergoing an arthroscopic meniscectomy, a procedure to remove damaged cartilage, is usually able to resume activities in 24 to 48 hours. Since this procedure was done 24-hours previously and was uncomplicated, this client is the healthiest. A new postoperative hip replacement client would be best cared for by an orthopedic nurse (option a). A family waiting room would not have the emergency equipment found at the head of the bed in a client room, such as a call light, suction and oxygen (option c). This would create an unsafe environment. A client who had an above the knee amputation yesterday would need the specialized care of an orthopedic surgical nurse (option d).
Nursing Process: Planning   **Client Need:** Safe, Effective Care Environment

55.   **The correct answer is d.** The question is asking what the nurse should do based on the client's symptoms. These symptoms indicate that the client is in the second stage of labor. Additional signs include upper lip perspiration, vomiting, bloody show, and a feeling she needs to bear down. The true sign of second stage labor is when the physician determines that the cervix cannot be felt when a vaginal examination is performed. Continual assessment of the mother and fetus are necessary at this time. It is too early to transfer the client to the delivery room (option b). An antiemetic medication would not be indicated initially (option a). The symptoms are not indicative of infection but labor progression (option c).
Nursing Process: Implementation   **Client Need:** Health Promotion & Maintenance

56.   **The correct answer is b.** The question is asking what finding would alert the nurse that the client is having a problem that needs to be addressed immediately. Ipsilateral pupil dilation is an early sign of brain herniation. This occurs when the intracranial pressure (ICP) increases to the point that it is pushing down on the brain stem. Redness and warmth at the IV site may indicate thrombophlebitis. Although the IV may need to be removed, this should not take precedence over the worsening neurological status (option a). Clear drainage from the ears may indicate a cerebrospinal fluid leak. Although it is concerning, the increased ICP at the brainstem can cause respiratory depression, a more important finding (option c). Unilateral weakness is a symptom of increased ICP, however, it does not indicate that the client's breathing would be affected (option d).
        Nursing Process: Analysis   **Client Need:** Physiological Integrity

57.   **The correct answer is b.** The question is asking which statement is accurate regarding the use of glargine (Lantus). Insulin glargine (Lantus) is long-acting insulin that is released steadily and continuously and does not have a peak of action so the risk of hypoglycemia is greatly reduced. Therefore, option (d) is incorrect, as these are signs of hypoglycemia. Intensive insulin therapy utilizes multiple doses of rapid-acting insulin (option a). Rapid-acting insulin is considered to be the type of insulin that best mimics natural insulin secretion in response to a meal (option b).
        Nursing Process: Implementation   **Client Need:** Physiological Integrity

58.   **The correct answer is a.** The question is asking what a client prone to infection should avoid. Raw fruits and vegetables may introduce bacteria and infection. The client should bathe daily using an antibacterial soap (option b). Oral hygiene should be performed several times per day (option c). Venipuncture may be done as long as proper cleaning takes place (option d).
        Nursing Process: Implementation   **Client Need:** Safe, Effective Care Environment

59.   **The correct answer is b.** The question is asking how to address the client's outburst. Option (b) addresses the client's feelings of loneliness and attempts at distancing from the nurse. Options (a) and (c) promote the client's distancing behavior which delays the promotion of the therapeutic relationship. Option (d) is nontherapeutic and belittling and, therefore, does not support the development of a healthy ego structure.
        Nursing Process: Implementation   **Client Need:** Psychosocial Integrity

60.   **The correct answer is d.** The question is asking what condition may have helped cause the hypothyroidism. A possible side effect of lithium carbonate (Lithium) treatment is hypothyroidism. It is used to stabilize moods of a bipolar client. History of a car accident would be unrelated (option a). Overindulgence of foods, such as strawberries, peaches, peanuts and cabbage, may induce hypothyroidism. An absence of the foods, as avoidance due to allergy, would not be a factor (option b). Anemia is a consequence of hypothyroidism in some clients, not a cause of it (option c).
        Nursing Process: Analysis   **Client Need:** Physiological Integrity

61.   **The correct answer is b.** The question is asking for the best assignment for a pediatric nurse who has been temporarily reassigned to an adult medical-surgical unit. The pediatric nurse would know how to care for clients in diabetic ketoacidosis, as Type 1 diabetes is usually diagnosed in childhood. Cellulitis occurs in both children and adults. Ovarian cysts are found in adolescents as well as in adult women. The pediatric nurse would not have specific knowledge to care for clients with ovarian cancer (option a), benign prostatic hypertrophy (option c) and a myocardial infarction (option d).
        Nursing Process: Planning   **Client Need:** Safe, Effective Care Environment

62.   **The correct answer is a.** The question is asking which of the following helps prevent sickle cell crisis. Influenza vaccine prevents acquiring an infection, the most common trigger for crisis. Oxygen therapy may be used during a crisis, but does not prevent one (option b). Fluids should be increased, not restricted, to promote adequate circulation (option c). Aspirin affects platelet function and is not usually given to prevent sickle cell crisis (option d).
        Nursing Process: Implementation   **Client Need:** Physiological Integrity

63. **The correct answer is b.** The question is asking the number of calories for a breastfeeding mother. Approximately 200 to 500 calories are added to the breastfeeding mother's diet to ensure that the mother and child have sufficient food intake to promote health (options a, b & d).
Nursing Process: Analysis   **Client Need:** Health Promotion & Maintenance

64. **The correct answers are b, c and e.** The question is asking the nurse to recognize the clinical presentation of post-traumatic stress disorder (PTSD). This disorder occurs after exposure to a clearly identifiable event that threatens the client's sense of control over her life and overwhelms her usual coping abilities. Clinical symptoms of PTSD occur one month or more after the traumatic event or events, such as natural disaster, being held hostage, terrorist attack, gross injury, sudden losses, etc. The clinical presentation of PTSD can include: changes in perceptions or hopelessness regarding the future (option b), restricted affect or numbing of responsiveness (option c), outbursts of anger, decreased participation and interest in activities (option e), hypervigilance, flashbacks and feelings of being detached or estranged from loved ones. Lack of remorse (option a) is a symptom of antisocial personality disorder. Clients with PTSD can experience survivor guilt. Self-mutilating behaviors (option d) are seen in clients with borderline personality disorder.
Nursing Process: Assessment   **Client Need:** Psychosocial Integrity

65. **The correct answer is b.** The question is asking for the most appropriate assignment for a nurse who is unfamiliar with pediatric clients. When making the assignment, the nurse would want to provide the safest care for the clients while keeping in mind the "pulled" nurse's knowledge and skill level. Providing safe care and the knowledge and skill level of the nurse are the two most important factors to consider when making an assignment. The "pulled" nurse could care for the clients in option (b) because they are problems that a medical-surgical nurse would be familiar with. Appendectomies and pelvic inflammatory disease are seen in the adult population as well as in children. Tonsil and adenoidectomies are more common in children, but the postoperative care is the same as for adults. The child with a new onset Type 1 diabetes (option a) should be assigned to a pediatric nurse, as this is a potentially fatal situation. Also, rarely are adults diagnosed with new onset Type 1 diabetes. Tetralogy of Fallot (option c) is a potentially fatal cyanotic heart defect that is corrected early in childhood. A medical-surgical nurse would not be familiar with this problem. The child who is suspected of being abused (option d) should also be taken care of by a pediatric nurse. The pediatric nurse is more familiar with the signs that indicate abuse and interventions appropriate for the child and family.
Nursing Process: Planning   **Client Need:** Safe, Effective Care Environment

66. **The correct answer is c.** The question is asking which clients need to be isolated to prevent spread of the disease. Smallpox is the only disease that is transmitted from person-to-person contact. Anthrax (option a) is contracted by direct contact with the bacteria and the spores. Botulism (option b) is transmitted through the air or in food. Tullaremia (option d) is spread by rabbits, ticks, contaminated food, air, and water.
Nursing Process: Implementation   **Client Need:** Safe, Effective Care Environment

67. **The correct answer is b.** The question is asking which statement, made by the client, indicates a need for further patient teaching. Fluid intake should not be limited because an adequate fluid intake and adequate urine production are necessary to stimulate the micturition reflex. A daily fluid intake of one-half ounce of fluid for every pound of body weight is suggested. Kegel exercises (option a) help to strengthen the pelvic floor muscles. These exercises are an effective treatment for mild to moderate urinary incontinence. Caffeine and alcohol are bladder irritants and should be avoided (option c). Bladder training (option d), by voiding every two to three hours, enhances bladder capacity and reduces the frequency and volume of urine loss.
Nursing Process: Implementation   **Client Need:** Health Promotion & Maintenance

68. **The correct answer is d.** The question is asking what family information would be most important for the nurse to know when caring for a client with Alzheimer's disease. When the nurse is able to enhance the family's problem-solving skills, they often can be given the power to help the client. Understanding symptom presentation (option a) and illness progression (option c)

are important; however, these will not help the family assist the client. Providing information about respite care is also important, but it would not take precedence over problem solving (option b).

Nursing Process: Planning   **Client Need:** Psychosocial Integrity

69.   **The correct answer is d.** The question is asking how to assist a client to raise a sputum specimen. A nebulizer treatment using distilled water helps loosen the sputum and makes it easier to bring up the specimen. Drinking fluids one-hour prior is not sufficient time for the fluid to reach the lungs to moisten secretions (option a). One dose of medication would also not have sufficient time to work (option b). The best time to take specimens is in the morning (option c).

Nursing Process: Planning   **Client Need:** Physiological Integrity

70.   **The correct answer is a.** The question is asking what these symptoms mean if unrelated to present heart disease. Dependent edema, fatigue and energy loss are all signs of right-sided heart failure related to hypoxemia. When oxygen levels are down in the blood for extended periods of time, the heart tries to compensate by beating strongly enough to get more blood and oxygen into the system. This results in cor pulmonale, or right ventricular failure, when it occurs over an extended time. Then the heart cannot pump effectively on the overworked right side and failure results in systemic symptoms. Abdominal surgery, liver failure and idiopathic renal disease are unrelated to these symptoms (options b, c & d).

Nursing Process: Analysis   **Client Need:** Physiological Integrity

71.   **The correct answer is c.** The question is asking which reported symptom is a contraindication to administering a progestin-only birth control medication. Contraindications to receiving this medication are similar to combined oral contraceptives and include thrombophlebitis. Pain in the right calf may be a symptom of thrombophlebitis. Heavy menstrual bleeding (option a) may occur when the medication is first initiated and is not a contraindication at this time. Mood changes and weight gain (options b & d) are side effects that can occur while taking this medication. They are not contraindications.

Nursing Process: Implementation   **Client Need:** Physiological Integrity

72.   **The correct answer is d.** The question is asking which measure conserves energy and decreases cardiac demands. Cardiac demands are reduced during rest periods. Less oxygen is needed and the client is able to conserve energy. Assessing vital signs (option a) and monitoring cardiac rhythm (option c) may detect problems, but do not decrease cardiac demands nor do they conserve energy. They are both assessment measures. Administering oxygen (option b) provides necessary oxygen to meet cardiac demands, but does not conserve energy.

Nursing Process: Implementation   **Client Need:** Physiological Integrity

73.   **The correct answer is d.** The question is asking what statement is therapeutic in response to the client. Option (d) voices the feeling level of the client or verbalizes the implied meaning of the statement. Option (b) is negative. Option (c) is an incorrect interpretation. Option (a) is false reassurance that surgery outcome would be different.

Nursing Process: Implementation   **Client Need:** Psychosocial Integrity

74.   **The correct answer is c.** The question is asking how the nurse should intervene when a client stays silent in an adult-children of alcoholics group. This client is acting in the role played in the family i.e., the lost child. Children of alcoholics learn to be in control and not to express feelings or needs in order to keep the family functioning and balanced. The group experience assists members to change the roles for more constructive ones. Encouraging the client through asking the client's opinion assists the client with that change process. Allowing the client to stay silent and speak when ready (option d) helps preserve that lost child role. If the client does not respond in the group, the nurse could talk separately about the behavior (option b). If this does not work, then the client may need to be referred for therapy if the role interferes with daily functioning abilities or is personally uncomfortable (option a).

Nursing Process: Implementation   **Client Need:** Health Promotion & Maintenance

75. **The correct answer is b.** The question is asking if the nurse should honor advanced directives from another state. Each state legislates rules about advanced directives and the rules may not be the same from one state to the next (option c). However, if the person has filed them in this state, they are legally binding. The nurse should have the documents on hand before following them legally (option a) because they may not actually say what the relative thinks they say. It is not the nurse's job to determine competency (option d).
Nursing Process: Planning   **Client Need:** Safe, Effective Care Environment

76. **The correct answers are a and b.** The question is asking what the nurse would include in her teaching the client about the need for lithium blood levels to be drawn on a regular basis. The nurse must explain to the client that it is very important to make sure that the lithium blood level reaches a therapeutic level but does not reach a toxic level. There is a narrow index between the therapeutic and toxic range (option b). A client's lithium level can quickly become toxic and even fatal. Therefore, it is necessary for ongoing blood lithium levels to be drawn. Lithium is excreted by the kidneys and can also have an adverse reaction on the thyroid gland (option a). Hypersexual behavior is a symptom of mania (option c) not caused by the drug lithium. Lithium should decrease the behavior. Blood lithium levels will measure only the amount of lithium in the bloodstream not other drugs that the client may be taking (option d), nor will it monitor any specific dietary intake (option e).
Nursing Process: Planning   **Client Need:** Physiological Integrity

77. **The correct answer is b.** The question is asking about the detrimental side effect of GnRH agonists in the treatment of a client with endometriosis. The key here is that the mediation is hypoestrogenic and that is an indicator that there is the potential for steady bone loss. Reversal of the condition and terminating the medication will increase the individual's ability to become fertile again (option c). Progesterone does not play a significant role and is not in an inverse proportion to estrogen in these situations (option d). Administration of hormones is sometimes linked to a higher predisposition to blood clots, but here a hypoestrogenic state is being addressed (option a).
Nursing Process: Analysis   **Client Need:** Physiological Integrity

78. **The correct answer is b.** The question is asking for the best room for a client with mania. When a client is in an agitated manic state, direct supervision by staff is appropriate for her well-being and safety as well as that of other clients. A room without windows (option a) may feel too confining to the client and increase, rather than decrease, agitation. A semiprivate room of any kind is inappropriate for this client while she is in an agitated state because these two clients will escalate each others' symptoms. Even if the other client does not have similar symptoms, the client will be unable to control her actions well enough to allow the other client to have necessary rest and privacy (option c). A room with a television and stereo will serve to increase agitation, rather than decrease it, by distraction (option d).
Nursing Process: Planning   **Client Need:** Safe, Effective Care Environment

79. **The correct answer is a.** The question is asking what the most appropriate assignment for the agency nurse is. The agency nurse should be assigned clients who have expected responses. Treatment for tuberculosis includes respiratory isolation, drug therapy and diagnostic exams. The primary care necessary for a client with cirrhosis is to promote rest so the liver tissue can regenerate. After undergoing a laminectomy, the client will need pain medication, neurologic assessment and proper body alignment. An agency nurse would be equipped to care for all of these clients. Sickle cell crisis can lead to further complications, such as chest syndrome and multi-organ failure due to lack of oxygen. Hyperosmolar hyperglycemic nonketotic coma is a potentially life threatening condition that may occur in clients with Type 2 diabetes. Since these clients may have unexpected responses to treatment, they should not be cared for by the agency nurse (option b). A subdural hematoma evacuation requires a craniotomy to remove the blood. This client needs to be closely monitored postoperatively for signs of increased ICP, meningitis and any reaccumulation of the blood; therefore, this client should not be cared for by the agency nurse (option c). A client who had a cardiac catheterization needs to be closely monitored for hemorrhage from the insertion site; therefore, this would not be a client who would have expected

responses and should not be cared for by the agency nurse (option d).
Nursing Process: Planning   **Client Need:** Safe, Effective Care Environment

80.   **The correct answer is b.** The question is asking how to have a therapeutic relationship with a suspicious client. Brief meetings allow the client to feel that he is in control, feel secure and build trust. Reassuring the client that he will be safe on the unit (option a) is really false reassurance. The paranoid client tends to misinterpret events in the environment and will probably repeat that pattern of thinking while hospitalized. Involvement in group activities (option c) and introducing him to other clients (option d) would prove overwhelming at this point. The environment should be quiet with fewer stimuli to misinterpret.
Nursing Process: Assessment   **Client Need:** Physiological Integrity

81.   **The correct answer is a.** The question is asking which client can be sent home to make room for a more critically ill client. The purpose of lithotripsy is to break up the stone. Hematuria is expected and the client has no signs of infection. Therefore, he demonstrates that the therapy was effective and has no obvious complications. A client with acute pancreatitis, who has an amylase of 200, is still experiencing problems and is not ready for discharge. An amylase level of 200 or higher is indicative of pancreatic cell injury (option b). When a client has a myocardial infarction, he is usually admitted for three to five days. The client is at risk of having a second myocardial infarction within 24 to 48 hours after having the first (option c). Although the client who had the laminectomy is showing signs of improvement, he is not ready for discharge. The client needs to be monitored for a paralytic ileus and complete bladder emptying as well as other neurosensory problems (option d).
Nursing Process: Analysis   **Client Need:** Safe, Effective Care Environment

82.   **The correct answer is a.** The question is asking which statement, made by the client, would indicate a need for further teaching. Many clients expect the results of liposuction to be immediate. Usually up to six months is required for final results to be apparent after edema subsides and subcutaneous tissue heals. Bruising (option b) is common after liposuction and may take weeks to disappear. Dressings must remain smooth, uniform and compressing; otherwise contour irregularities can result. Normal activity may gradually be resumed, except for strenuous activity. Resuming activity too rapidly may result in soreness and swelling (option d).
Nursing Process: Analysis   **Client Need:** Physiological Integrity

83.   **The correct answer is b.** The question is asking what would be inappropriate for a couple that is trying to conceive. Since there is no known safe level of alcoholic beverage, it should be avoided. Alcohol is most dangerous to the fetus during the first trimester. Many women do not realize they have conceived until they have missed their menstrual period and are often at least 4 to 6 weeks pregnant. Therefore, it is important to avoid alcohol while trying to conceive. Tight fitting underwear, such as briefs may increase the temperature of the testicles, which decreases sperm production (option a). Tracking basal body temperature will help determine ovulation (option c). When a couple is having difficulty conceiving, adoption is an option many potential parents want to consider (option d).
Nursing Process: Evaluation   **Client Need:** Health Promotion & Maintenance

84.   **The correct answer is b.** The question is asking which response made by the nurse is an accurate statement regarding early detection of ovarian cancer. In its early stages, ovarian cancer is usually asymptomatic. No screening test exists for ovarian cancer. Pap smears are used to detect cervical cancer (option a). Vaginal spotting (option c) is a symptom of cervical cancer, not ovarian cancer. Pain (option d) is not an early symptom of ovarian cancer.
Nursing Process: Implementation   **Client Need:** Physiological Integrity

85.   **The correct answer is a.** The question is asking what to teach a client with Meniere's disease. The symptoms are related to too much fluid, which swells a small area of the ear and disturbs the balance and hearing of the individual. A low-salt diet helps to decrease the amount of fluid pulled into the system and prevents added pressure to the inner ear. Hearing loss may fluctuate during the acute attack, but is permanent after the client goes into remission (option b). Sleep does not

affect the tinnitus (option c). The condition is not an infection and antibiotics are not used (option d).

Nursing Process: Implementation   **Client Need:** Physiological Integrity

86.   **The correct answer is b.** The question is asking which prescription would be questioned for a client admitted with symptoms of an acute phase of diverticulitis. The client with diverticulitis usually does not undergo a barium enema examination in the acute phase of the illness, because of the risk of rupture of the inflamed diverticulum. During the acute phase of the illness, the client's diet is restricted to clear liquids (option a). IV fluids (option c) are administered for hydration. IV antibiotics (option d) are administered to treat the inflammation of the diverticula.

     Nursing Process: Implementation   **Client Need:** Physiological Integrity

87.   **The correct answer is a.** The question is asking what finding would be consistent with a diagnosis of acute respiratory distress syndrome (ARDS). A client with ARDS will often experience tachypnea in an attempt to compensate for low oxygen levels. The tachypnea will then cause respiratory alkalosis. As ARDS progresses, there is increased fluid accumulation in the alveoli and decreased lung compliance. The chest X-ray is often termed "whiteout" because consolidation and infiltrates are seen throughout the lungs, leaving few recognizable air spaces. Pulmonary artery wedge pressure (option b) does not increase in ARDS because the cause is noncardiogenic. Hypoxemia (option c), despite increased FIO_2 by mask, cannula, or endotracheal tube, is a hallmark of ARDS. You would expect this client to have an elevated white blood cell count due to the sepsis, rather than leukopenia (option d), which is a decreased count.

     Nursing Process: Assessment   **Client Need:** Physiological Integrity

88.   **The correct answers are a, b, c and e.** The question is asking what the client should be taught about how to care for his herpes zoster. Herpes Zoster is an infection in which there is a reactivation of the varicella virus. It usually occurs when the client is immunosuppressed. The sores should be cleansed to assist in drying and healing (option a). Towels should not be shared to decrease the chance of spreading the infection (option b). Viruses cross the placenta and may cause teratogenic effect to the fetus (option c). The lesions may create severe pruritus, however, the client should be taught not to scratch. In the event that he does scratch, fingernails should be trimmed (option e) so that bleeding is less likely and the chance of spreading the infection is diminished. A warm temperature promotes itching and the desire to scratch (option d).

     Nursing Process: Planning   **Client Need:** Health Promotion & Maintenance

89.   **The correct answer is b.** The question is asking how the nurse should respond. The client is experiencing trauma from his war experience and believes that his experience is so unique that it is impossible for anyone to understand what he has experienced and, therefore, cannot help him. The client needs to know that the nurse is interested in him and genuinely wants to understand his experiences. If she is able to understand what the client experienced, she is more likely able to help. Clients who experience extremely traumatic events, like war, often believe that no one can help them who have not had the exact same experience. It is important for the nurse to be honest and sincere. The nurse explains to the client that he must help her understand by sharing his experience with her. If she is able to understand what the client has been through, she can better develop interventions to help. Option (a) is too vague and general and does not specifically address the client's concerns. Option (c) increases the client's feelings of isolation. Option (d) is a defensive response by the nurse and could easily increase the client's feeling of isolation.

     Nursing Process: Implementation   **Client Need:** Psychosocial Integrity

90.   **The correct answer is b.** The question is asking what women should not receive hormone replacement therapy (HRT). This therapy is contraindicated in women with active liver disease, uterine cancer, vascular thrombosis, undiagnosed vaginal bleeding and women with estrogen-response-positive breast tumors. Peptic ulcer disease and chlamydia (options a & c) are not affected by HRT. HRT is used to reduce the risk of osteoporosis (option d).

     Nursing Process: Analysis   **Client Need:** Health Promotion & Maintenance

REFERENCES

Adamson, E. (2002). The everything stress management book: Practical ways to relax, be healthy and maintain your sanity. Avon, MA: Adams Media.

Allender, J. A. & Spradley, B. W. (2001). Community health nursing: Concepts and practice (5th ed.). Philadelphia: Lippincott.

Altman, G.B. (2004). Delmar's fundamental and advanced nursing skills (2nd ed.). Clifton Park, NY: Delmar.

Applegate, M.D., Quinn, D.B. & Applegate, A.J. (1994). Using metacognitive strategies to enhance achievement for at risk liberal arts college students. Journal of Reading, 38 (1) 32-40.

Beck, A. T. (1976). Cognitive therapy and the emotional disorders. New York: International Universities Press.

Beitz, J.M. (1995). Metacognition: State of the art learning theory strategies for nurse educators. PLN Visions 2-5.

Beitz, J.M. (1997). Unleashing the power of memory: The mighty mnemonic. Nurse Educator, 22 (2) 25-29.

Bernstein, D A., Borkovec,T.D. & Hazlett-Smith, H. (2000). New Directions in Progressive Relaxation Training:A guide for helping professionals. New York: Praeger.

Black, J. M., Hawks, J. H. & Keene, A. M. (2001). Medical-surgical nursing: Clinical management for positive outcomes (6th ed.). Philadelphia, PA: W. B. Saunders.

Bourne,E.J., Brownstein,A. & Garano,L. (2004). Natural relief for anxiety: Complementary Strategies for easing fear, panic and worry. Oakland, CA:New Harbinger.

Bourne, E. & Garano, L. (2003). Coping with anxiety: Ten simple ways to relieve anxiety, fear and worry. Oakland, CA: New Harbinger

Bourne, E. J. (2005). The anxiety and phobia workbook (4th ed.). Oakland, CA: New Harbinger.

Boyd, M.A. (2005). Psychiatric nursing: Contemporary practice (3rd ed.). Philadelphia: Lippincott Williams & Wilkins.

Broyles, B. E. (2002). Pharmacological aspects of nursing care (6th ed.). Albany, NY: Delmar.

Burns, D. (2006). When Panic attacks: The new drug free, anxiety therapy that can change your life. New York: Morgan Roads Books.

Cangelosi, P. R. & Whitt, K. J. (2006). Teaching through storytelling: An exemplar. International Journal of Nursing Scholarship, 3 (1)1-7.

Carson, V. B. (2000). Mental health nursing: The nurse-patient journey (2nd ed.). Philadelphia: Saunders.

Casbarro, J. (2003). Test anxiety and what you can do about it: A practical guide for teachers, parents and kids. Port Chester, NY: Dude Publishing.

Catalano, J. (2003). <u>Nursing now! Today's issues, tomorrow's trends. (3rd ed.)</u> Philadelphia: F.A. Davis Company.

Cavanaugh, B. (2003). <u>Nurse's manual of laboratory and diagnostic tests.</u> Philadelphia: F.A. Davis.

Chernecky, C., Alichnie, M.C., Garrett, K., George-Gay, B., Hodges, R. K. & Terry, C.. (2002). <u>ECGs and the heart.</u> Philadelphia: W.B. Saunders Co.

Cowen, K.J & Tesh, A.S. (2002) Effects of gaming on nursing students' knowledge of pediatric cardiovascular dysfunction. <u>Journal of Nursing Education, 41</u>(11) 507-509.

Daniels, R. (2004). <u>Nursing fundamentals: Caring and clinical decision making.</u> Clifton Park, NY: Delmar.

Daniels, R. (2003). <u>Delmar's manual of laboratory and diagnostic tests.</u> Clifton Park, NY: Delmar.

Davis M, Eshelman, M.R. & McKay, M. (2000). <u>The relaxation and stress reduction workbook</u> (5th ed.). Oakland CA: New Harbinger.

Deglin, J. H. & Vallerand, A. H. (2005). <u>Davis's drug guide for nurses</u> (9th ed.). Philadelphia, PA: F. A. Davis.

Eilers, L. H. & Pinkley, C. (2006).Metacognitive strategies to help students comprehend all text. <u>Reading Improvement, 43</u> (1) 13-17.

Fontaine, K.L. (2003). <u>Mental health nursing</u> (5th ed.). Upper Saddle River, NJ: Prentice Hall.

Fortinash, K.M. & Holoday-Worret, P.A. (2000<u>). Psychiatric mental health nursing</u> (2nd ed.). St. Louis: Mosby.

Gaglione, T., Zerwekh, J., Claborn, J.C. & Miller, C.J. ((2005). <u>Memory notebook of nursing: Pharmacology and diagnostics.</u> Ingram, TX: Nursing Education Consultants.

Goodwin, V. T. (2003). <u>Disaster nursing and emergency preparedness for chemical, biological, and radiological terrorism and other hazards.</u> New York: Springer.

Gorman, L. M., Raines, M.L. & Sultan, D. F. (2002). <u>Psychosocial nursing for general patient care</u> (2nd ed). Philadelphia: F.A. Davis.

Hansten, R.I. & Jackson, M. (2004). <u>Clinical delegation skills: A handbook for professional practice</u> (3rd ed). Sudbury, MA: Jones and Bartlett.

Harkreader, H. & Hogan, M. A. (2004). <u>Fundamental of nursing: Caring and clinical judgment</u> (2nd ed.). Philadelphia, PA: W. B. Saunders.

Henderson, D. (2005). Games: making nursing fun. In: M.H. Oermann, and K.T. Heinrich (Eds). <u>Annual Review of Nursing Education</u> Vol.3. New York: NY. Springer.

Hockenberry, M.J., Wilson, D., Winkefstein, M.L., and Kline, N.E. (2003). <u>Wong's nursing care of infants and children, (7th ed)</u>. Mosby: St. Louis.

Huber, D. (2000). <u>Leadership and nursing care management</u> (2nd ed.). Philadelphia: W. B. Saunders.

Ignatavicius, D. D. & Workman, M. L. (2002). <u>Medical-surgical nursing: Critical thinking for collaborative care</u> (4th ed.). Philadelphia, PA: W. B. Saunders.

Jacobowitz, T. (1990). AIM: A metacognitive strategy for constructing the main idea of a text. Journal of Reading, 33 (8) 620-624.

Jensen, E. (2003). Students' success secrets (5th ed.) Hauppauge, NY: Barron.

Johnson, S. (2000). Taking the anxiety out of taking tests: A step by step guide. New York: Barnes and Noble.

Karch, A. M. (2002). Lippincott's nursing drug guide. Philadephia: Lippincott.

Kelly-Heidenthal, P. (2003). Nursing leadership and management. Delmar: New York.

Kniesl, C. R., Wilson, H.S. & Trigoboff, E. (2004). Contemporary psychiatric – mental health nursing . Upper Saddle River, NJ: Prentice Hall.

Kozier, B., Erb, G., Berman, A., & Snyder, S. (2004). Fundamentals of nursing: Concepts, process, and practice (7th ed.). Upper Saddle River, NJ: Prentice Hall.

Kuhn, M.A. (1995). Gaming: A technique that adds spice to learning. Journal of Continuing Education in Nursing, 26 (1) 35-39.

Kuiper, R.A. & Pesut, D. J. (2004). Promoting cognitive and metacognitive reflective reasoning skills in nursing practice: Self regulated learning theory. Journal of Advanced Nursing, 45 (4) 381-391.

Ladewig, P. W., London, M. L., Moberly, S., & Olds, S. B. (2002). Contemporary maternal-newborn care (5th ed.). Upper Saddle River, NJ: Prentice Hall.

Lam, D. C. K. (2005). A brief overview of CBT techniques. In S. M. Freeman and A. Freeman (Eds.), Cognitive Behavior Therapy in Nursing Practice (pp. 29-47). New York: Springer.

Lemone, P. & Burke, K. (2004). Medical-Surgical Nursing: Critical Thinking in Client Care (3rd ed). Upper Saddle River, NJ: Prentice Hall.

Lewis, S, M., Heitkemper, M. M., & Dirksen, S. R. (2004). Medical-surgical nursing: Assessment and management of clinical problems (6th ed.). St. Louis: Mosby.

Littleton, L.Y., Engebretson, J.C. (2005). Maternity Nursing Care. Delmar: New York.

Livingston, J.A. (2003). Metacognition: An overview (Report No. TM-034-808). Buffalo, NY: State university of New York at Buffalo. (ERIC Document Reproduction Service No. 474273).

Lowdermilk, D. L. & Perry, S. E. (2003). Maternity nursing (6th ed.). St. Louis: Mosby.

Lutz, C. & Przytulski, K. (2001). Nutrition and diet therapy (3rd ed.). Philadelphia: F.A. Davis.

Mahan, L. K. & Escott-Stump, S. (2000). Krause's food, nutrition, & diet therapy (10th ed.). Philadelphia, PA: W. B. Saunders.

Malarkey, L.M. & McMoroow, M.E. (2000). Nurse's manual of laboratory tests and diagnostic procedures (2nd ed.). Philadelphia: Saunders.

Marquis, B.L. & Huston, C.J. (2003). Leadership roles and management functions in nursing: Theory and application (4th ed). Philadelphia: Lippincott Williams & Wilkins.

Martinez, M. (2006). What is Metacognition? Phi Delta Kappan, 87 (9) 696-705.

Mayer, D. P. (2005). The everything health guide to controlling anxiety: Professional advice to get you through any situation. Avon, MA: Adams Media.

Nettina, S.M. (2001). The Lippinicott manual of nursing practice (7th ed). Philadelphia: Lippincott.

Nies, M.A. & McEwen, M. (2001). Community health nursing: Promoting the health of populations (3rd ed.). Philadelphia: W. B. Saunders.

Nolan, T.E. (1991). Self-questioning and prediction: Combining metacognitive strategies. Journal of Reading, 35 (2) 132-138.

O'Toole, M. T. (Ed.). (2003). Encyclopedia and dictionary of medicine, nursing and allied health (7th ed.). Philadelphia, PA: W. B. Saunders.

Peden, A.R., Rayens, M.K. Hall, L.A. & Grant, E. (2005). Testing an intervention to reduce negative thinking, depressive symptoms and chronic stressors in low- income single mothers. Journal of Nursing Scholarship, 37 (3) 268-273.

Peden, A.R., Rayens, M.K. Hall, L.A. (2005). A community-based prevention intervention with low-income single mothers. American Psychiatric Nurses' Association, 11 (1) 18-25.

Phipps, W. J., Monahan, F. D., Sands, J. K. Marek, J. F., & Neighbors, M. (2003). Medical Surgical Nursing: Health and Illness Perspective. (2003). St. Louis: Mosby.

Poorman, S.G., Mastorovich, M.L., Webb, C.A. & Molcan, K.L. (2003). Good thinking: Test taking and study skills for nursing students (2nd ed). Pittsburgh: STAT Nursing Consultants.

Potts, N. L. Mandleco, B. L. (2002). Pediatric nursing: Caring for children and their families. Clifton Park, NY: Delmar.

Reeve, R.A. & Brown, A.L. (1985). Metacognition reconsidered: Implications for intervention research. Journal of Abnormal Child Psychology, 13 (3) 343 -356.

Schnell, Z. B., Leeuwen, A. M., & Kranpitz, T. R. (2003). Davis's comprehensive handbook of laboratory and diagnostic tests with nursing implications. Philadelphia: F. A. Davis.

Smeltzer, S. & Bare, B. (2003). Brunner & Suddarth's textbook of medical-surgical nursing (10th ed.). Philadelphia: Lippincott.

Spielberger CD, Vagg PR. (1995). Test anxiety: Theory assessment and treatment. Bristol, PA: Taylor & Francis.

Spratto, G.R. & Woods, A. L. (2004). PDR Nurse's drug handbook. Clifton Park, NY: Delmar.

Springhouse Nurse's Drug Guide 2004 (5th ed). (2004). Philadelphia: Lippincott Williams & Wilkins.

Stuart, G. W. & Lairia (2005). Principles and practice of psychiatric nursing (8th ed.). St. Louis: Elsevier Mosby.

Sullivan, E. J. & Decker, P. J. (2001). Effective leadership and management in nursing (5th ed.). Upper Saddle River, NJ: Prentice Hall.

Tappen, R. M., Weiss, S. A., & Whitehea, D. K. (2001). Essentials of nursing leaership and management (2nd ed.). Philadelphia, PA: F. A. Davis.

Thompson, J.M., McFarland, G.K., Hirsch, J.E. & Tucker, S.M. (2002). Mosby's clinical nursing (5th ed). St. Louis: Mosby.

Townsend, M.C. (2003). Psychiatric mental health nursing: Concepts of care (4th ed.). Philadelphia: F.A. Davis.

Trausch, P. (2003). Student drawing: A clinical learning tool. Nurse Educator, 28 (2) 58-60.

Varcarolis, E. M. (2006). Foundations of psychiatric mental health nursing (6th ed.). Philadelphia: Elsevier Saunders.
Videbeck, S. L. (2001). Psychiatric mental health nursing. Philadelphia: Lippincott.

Yoder-Wise, P. S. (2003). Leading and managing in nursing (3rd ed.). St. Louis: Mosby.

Zerwekh, J., Claborn, J.C. & Miller, C.J. (2004). Memory notebook of nursing (3rd ed., Vol. 1). Dallas: Nursing Education Consultants.

Zerwekh, J. & Claborn, J. C. (2000). Nursing today: Transition and trends (3rd ed.). Philadelphia: W. B. Saunders.